ENGINEERING WORKSHOP DATA

A Book of Reference containing Data,
Formulae, Tables, Hints and Recipes
relating to all Phases of Engineering
Workshop Practice

by

ARTHUR W. JUDGE

Whitworth Scholar, A.R.C.Sc., D.I.C., A.M.I.Mech.E.

THE CAXTON PUBLISHING COMPANY, LIMITED
MORLEY HALL, ST. GEORGE STREET, HANOVER SQUARE
LONDON, W.1

First Published . . *August* 1947
Second Edition . . *February* 1954

CAXTON'S
LIST OF ENGINEERING BOOKS

CENTRE, CAPSTAN AND AUTOMATIC LATHES
ENGINEERING WORKSHOP DATA
ENGINEERING WORKSHOP PRACTICE
GRINDING, LAPPING AND POLISHING
MACHINE TOOLS AND OPERATIONS
MODERN HIGH-SPEED OIL ENGINES
MODERN PRACTICAL RADIO AND TELEVISION
MODERN WELDING PRACTICE
SHEET-METAL WORK
STEAM LOCOMOTION
THE MODERN MOTOR ENGINEER
TOOLROOM PRACTICE

PRINTED AND BOUND IN GREAT BRITAIN BY
HAZELL WATSON AND VINEY LTD
AYLESBURY AND LONDON

PREFACE

There is at present a vast amount of data and information on engineering workshop practice subjects scattered among the very numerous technical periodicals, papers, proceedings, textbooks, etc., issued during the past half-century or so.

Unfortunately, however, the ordinary individual interested in these subjects is seldom able to obtain access to the original sources mentioned, and he is therefore liable to lose some at least of the benefits of the available valuable reference information.

The present handbook represents the results of an endeavour to make a careful selection, from the extremely wide range of original sources, of the more essential technical data, formulæ, information and facts, to meet most of the requirements of those engaged in the engineering workshop and machine shop. In particular it should appeal to designers, draughtsmen, machinists, mechanics, improvers and apprentices.

The material selected has been arranged into fourteen separate sections, each of which is more or less complete in itself. Thus it is possible to refer, quickly, to any particular group of subjects included under one general heading, e.g. Screw Threads, Grinding Practice, Drilling Data, Tool-cutting, Data, etc. By reference to the Index it is possible to pick out any individual item of information sought, in the minimum of time.

In this edition much new information is given, and the opportunity has been taken to make minor corrections and improvements to the previous edition. Whilst it is not possible to detail all of the fresh material that has been introduced, special mention should be made of the following, namely, Unified Thread System agreed upon by Great Britain, Canada and the United States ; British Standard Cycle and Buttress Screw Threads ; Screw Thread Helix Angles ; Standard Thread Depths ; Grinding Cemented Carbides ; Grinding Faults, Causes and Cures ; New Metric Tables ; Standard Vernier Height Gauges, etc.

Another useful addition is the set of Antilogarithm Tables, occupying some twenty pages ; these will be found of much assistance when used in conjunction with the existing Logarithm

Tables. In the course of the present revision no less than sixty-eight pages of new matter have been added.

We take this opportunity of expressing our thanks to certain Institutions and Firms for their assistance in connection with the preparation of some of the text-matter. In particular, mention is made of the British Standards Institution, The Carborundum Company Ltd., and the publication *Mechanics*.

A. W. JUDGE.

CONTENTS

SECTION 1

GENERAL DATA 1–50

SECTION 2

PHYSICAL PROPERTIES AND WEIGHTS OF
MATERIALS 51–69

SECTION 3

PRECISION MEASUREMENTS 70–96

SECTION 4

SCREW THREAD DATA 97–184

SECTION 5

BRITISH STANDARD PRECISION HEXAGON
BOLTS, SCREWS, NUTS AND PLAIN
WASHERS, ETC. 185–223

SECTION 6

MACHINE-CUT GEARS 224–274

SECTION 7

DRILLS AND DRILLING DATA. . . . 275–305

SECTION 8

CUTTING ANGLES OF TOOLS 306–333

CONTENTS

SECTION 9

GRINDING WHEELS 334–382

SECTION 10

PROPERTIES OF MATERIALS 383–427

SECTION 11

WORKSHOP METHODS AND RECIPES . . . 428–450

SECTION 12

MOMENTS OF INERTIA 451–456

SECTION 13

MENSURATION AND TRIGONOMETRY . . . 457–491

SECTION 14

TABLES OF LOGARITHMS AND
ANTILOGARITHMS 492–571

INDEX 573–604

ABBREVIATIONS

The following abbreviations will be found in this book :

c.cm.	.	cubic centimetre	max.	.	maximum
cm.	.	centimetre	min.	.	minimum ; minute(s)
c.mm.	.	cubic millimetre	mm.	.	millimetre(s)
cu.	.	cubic	nom.	.	nominal
cwt.	.	hundredweight(s)	oz.	.	ounce(s)
° C.	.	degrees Centigrade	/	.	per
° F.	.	degrees Fahrenheit	revs.	.	revolutions
ft.	.	foot, feet	r.p.m.	.	revolutions per minute
h.p.	.	horse-power	sec.	.	second(s)
in.	.	inch(es)	sq.	.	square
kg.	.	kilogram(s)	S.W.G.	.	Standard wire gauge
lb.	.	pound(s)	t.p.i.	.	threads per inch
m.	.	metre(s)			

SECTION 1

GENERAL DATA

ENGLISH WEIGHTS AND MEASURES

The English standard yard of 36 inches is the length of a pendulum which vibrates once in $\dfrac{39\cdot1393}{36}$ seconds at 62° F. at sea-level and Greenwich latitude.

LENGTH

12 inches = 1 foot.
3 feet = 1 yard.
6 feet = 1 fathom.
$5\frac{1}{2}$ yards = 1 rod, pole or perch.
66 feet = 22 yards = 100 links = 1 chain = 4 poles.
220 yards = 10 chains = 1 furlong.
8 furlongs = 80 chains = 1 mile.
1 mile = 1,760 yards = 5,280 feet.
1 nautical mile = 6,080 feet.
1 Admiralty knot = 6,080 feet per hour = 1·1515 miles per hour.

Useful linear data : 1 halfpenny = 1 inch ; 10 penny diameters = 1 foot.

SURFACE

1 square foot = 144 square inches.
1 square yard = 9 square feet.
1 square rod, pole or perch = $30\frac{1}{4}$ square yards.
1 rood = 40 square poles.
1 acre = 4,840 square yards = 4 roods.
1 square mile = 640 acres.

VOLUME

1 cubic foot = 1,728 cubic inches.
1 cubic yard = 27 cubic feet.
1 Imperial gallon = 277·420 cubic inches.
1 U.S. gallon = 231·0 cubic inches.
1 gallon = 4 quarts = 8 pints = 32 gills.
1 quart = 69·355 cubic inches.
1 pint = 34·677 cubic inches.

One Imperial gallon of distilled water at 62° F. weighs 10 lb. (avoir.) at barometric height of 30 ins. of mercury.

E.W.D.—I

ENGLISH WEIGHTS
(*Avoirdupois*)
1 pound = 16 ounces.
1 cwt. = 112 pounds.
1 ton = 20 cwt. = 2,240 pounds.
1 ounce = 16 drams.
1 pound = 256 drams.

(*Troy*)
1 pennyweight (dwt.) = 24 grains.
1 ounce = 20 dwt. = 480 grains.
1 pound = 12 ounces = 240 dwt. = 5,760 grains.

(*Apothecaries*)
1 scruple = 20 grains.
1 dram = 3 scruples.
1 ounce = 8 drams = 480 grains.
1 pound = 12 ounces = 5,760 grains.

METRICAL WEIGHTS AND MEASURES
Length
10 millimetres = 1 centimetre.
10 centimetres = 1 decimetre.
10 decimetres = 1 metre.
10 metres = 1 decametre.
10 decametres = 1 hectometre.
10 hectometres = 1 kilometre = 1,000 metres.

The International Standard Metre is the length between two inscribed lines on a platinum-iridium bar at 32° F., the bar being deposited at the International Bureau of Weights and Measures at Sèvres, France.

Surface
1 square centimetre = 100 square millimetres.
1 square decimetre = 100 square centimetres.
1 square metre = 100 square decimetres.
1 square kilometre = 1,000,000 square metres.

Volume
1 cubic centimetre = 1,000 cubic millimetres.
1 cubic metre = 1,000,000 cubic centimetres.
1 litre = 1,000·028 cubic centimetres.

The litre is the volume occupied by 1 kg. of distilled water at 4° C. and 760 mm. of mercury pressure.

ENGLISH AND METRIC EQUIVALENTS

LINEAR MEASURE

1 inch = 2·54 centimetres = 25·4 millimetres.
1 millimetre = 0·03937 inch.
1 centimetre = 0·393701 inch = 0·032808 foot.
1 foot = 30·4799 centimetres.
1 yard = 0·914399 metre.
1 metre = 39·3701 inches = 3·28084 feet = 1·093614 yard.
1 kilometre = 1,093·6143 yards = 0·621374 mile.
1 mile = 1·6093 kilometres.

SURFACE

1 square inch = 6·451367 square centimetres.
1 square centimetre = 0·1550 square inch.
1 square foot = 929·03 square centimetres.
1 square yard = 0·836126 square metre.
1 acre = 0·40468 hectare [1 hectare = 10,000 square metres].
1 square mile = 259 hectares.
1 square kilometre = 0·386103 square mile.
1 hectare = 2·4711 acres.
1 square metre = 10·7639 square feet = 1·1960 square yards.

VOLUME

1 cubic inch = 16·387 cubic centimetres.
1 cubic centimetre = 0·061024 cubic inch.
1 cubic foot = 0·028317 cubic metre = 28·317 litres.
1 cubic yard = 0·763355 cubic metre = 763·553 litres.
1 litre = 1·75980 pints = 0·219975 gallon = 35·1961 fluid ounces.
1 gallon = 4·545963 litres.
1 U.S. gallon = 0·83254 Imperial gallon = 231 cubic inches.
1 cubic metre = 35·3148 cubic feet = 1·307954 cubic yards.

WEIGHT

1 grain (avoirdupois or troy) = 0·0648 gramme.
1 dram (avoirdupois) = 1·772 grammes.
1 gramme = 15·432 grains = weight of 1 cubic centimetre of water at 4° C.
= 0·035 ounce (avoirdupois).

WEIGHT (*contd.*)

1 ounce (avoirdupois) = 28·350 grammes.
1 ounce (troy) = 31·1035 grammes.
1 pound = 16 ounces (avoirdupois) = 0·45359 kilogram.
1 kilogram = 2·20462 pounds = 35·27396 ounces (avoirdupois).
1 cwt. = 112 pounds = 50·8 kilograms.
1 ton = 1,016 kilograms = 1·016 tonnes.
1 tonne = 1,000 kilograms = 0·9842 ton.
1 American ton = 2,000 pounds = 0·908 tonne.
1 quintal = 100 kilograms = 1·968 cwt.
1 milligramme = 0·015 grain = 0·001 gramme.

MISCELLANEOUS USEFUL INFORMATION

1 gallon of distilled water at 62° F. = 10 pounds.
1 cubic foot of distilled water at 60° F. = 62·37 pounds.
1 cubic inch of distilled water at 60° F. = 0·0361 pound.
$$1 \text{ mil} = \tfrac{1}{1000} \text{ inch.}$$
$$1 \text{ micro-inch} = \tfrac{1}{1,000,000} \text{ inch.}$$

ATMOSPHERIC PRESSURE

Standard atmospheric pressure = 14·496 lb. per sq. in.
= 29·5306 inches of mercury at 0° C.
= 760 millimetres of mercury at 0° C.
One pound per square inch = 2·035 inches of mercury at 0° C.
= 51·7 millimetres of mercury at 0° C.
= 2·31 feet of water at 17° C.
One cubic foot of air at 14·7 lb. per sq. in. at 0° C. weighs 0·080728 pound.

WORK AND POWER

One foot-pound = 1·356 joules.
One English horse-power = 33,000 foot-pounds per minute.
= 550 foot-pounds per second.
= 1·014 metric horse-power.
= 746 watts.

WORK AND POWER (*contd.*)

One watt = 1 volt × 1 ampere.

One joule = 1 watt per second.

One Board of Trade unit = 1 kilowatt-hour = 1,000 watt-hours = 1·34 horse-power hour.

One metric horse-power = 736 watts = 0·986 horse-power (English).
(force de cheval)

One kilogrammetre = 7·233 foot-pounds.

One kilowatt = 1·3406 horse-power (English).

HEAT

One British thermal unit (B.T.U.) = heat required to raise 1 lb. of water from 60° F. to 61° F. = 778 foot-pounds.

Heat equivalent of 1 horse-power = 42·4 B.T.U. per minute.

One Centigrade heat unit (C.H.U.) = heat required to raise 1 lb. of water from 14° C. to 15° C. = 1,400 foot-pounds.

If F. denote degrees Fahrenheit and C. degrees Centigrade, then

$$\frac{F - 32}{9} = \frac{C}{5}.$$

One degree Centigrade = 1·8 degree Fahrenheit.

VELOCITY

One mile per hour = 1·467 feet per second = 88 feet per minute. = 44·70 centimetres per second.

15 miles per hour = 22 feet per second.

One metre per minute = 0·0547 feet per second.

PRESSURE

One pound per square inch = 0·0703 kilogram per square centimetre.

One pound per square foot = 4·88 kilograms per square metre.

One kilogram per square centimetre = 14·22 pounds per square inch.

One kilogram per square metre = 0·205 pound per square foot. = 0·635 ton per square inch.

FRACTIONS AND DECIMALS OF INCH AND MILLIMETRES

Fraction (inch)	Decimal (inch)	Millimetre	Fraction (inch)	Decimal (inch)	Millimetre
1/64	·015625	0·3969	33/64	·515625	13·0969
1/32	·03125	0·7937	17/32	·53125	13·4937
3/64	·046875	1·1906	35/64	·546875	13·8906
1/16	·0625	1·5875	9/16	·5625	14·2875
5/64	·078125	1·9844	37/64	·578125	14·6844
3/32	·09375	2·3812	19/32	·59375	15·0812
7/64	·109375	2·7781	39/64	·609375	15·4781
1/8	·125	3·1750	5/8	·625	15·8750
9/64	·140625	3·5719	41/64	·640625	16·2719
5/32	·15625	3·9687	21/32	·65625	16·6687
11/64	·171875	4·3656	43/64	·671875	17·0656
3/16	·1875	4·7625	11/16	·6875	17·4625
13/64	·203125	5·1594	45/64	·703125	17·8594
7/32	·21875	5·5562	23/32	·71875	18·2562
15/64	·234375	5·9531	47/64	·734375	18·6531
1/4	·25	6·3500	3/4	·75	19·0500
17/64	·265625	6·7469	49/64	·765625	19·4469
9/32	·28125	7·1437	25/32	·78125	19·8437
19/64	·296875	7·5406	51/64	·796875	20·2406
5/16	·3125	7·9375	13/16	·8125	20·6375
21/64	·328125	8·3344	53/64	·828125	21·0344
11/32	·34375	8·7312	27/32	·84375	21·4312
23/64	·359375	9·1281	55/64	·859375	21·8281
3/8	·375	9·5250	7/8	·875	22·2250
25/64	·390625	9·9219	57/64	·890625	22·6219
13/32	·40625	10·3187	29/32	·90625	23·0187
27/64	·421875	10·7156	59/64	·921875	23·4156
7/16	·4375	11·1125	15/16	·9375	23·8125
29/64	·453125	11·5094	61/64	·953125	24·2094
15/32	·46875	11·9062	31/32	·96875	24·6062
31/64	·484375	12·3031	63/64	·984375	25·0031
1/2	·5	12·7000	1	1	25·4000

MILLIMETRE–INCH EQUIVALENTS

Millimetres	Inches	Millimetres	Inches	Millimetres	Inches
1	·0394	48	1·8899	96	3·7795
2	·0787	49	1·9291	97	3·8190
3	·1180	50	1·9685	98	3·8583
4	·1575	51	2·0080	99	3·8975
5	·1968	52	2·0472	100	3·9370
6	·2362	53	2·0866	110	4·3307
7	·2755	54	2·1260	120	4·7245
8	·3150	55	2·1653	130	5·1180
9	·3543	56	2·2047	140	5·5118
10	·3937	57	2·2441	150	5·9055
11	·4331	58	2·2835	160	6·2991
12	·4725	59	2·3228	170	6·6929
13	·5118	60	2·3623	180	7·0865
14	·5512	61	2·4016	190	7·4803
15	·5905	62	2·4409	200	7·8740
16	·6299	63	2·4803	210	8·2677
17	·6692	64	2·5197	220	8·6615
18	·7087	65	2·5590	230	9·0551
19	·7480	66	2·5985	240	9·4488
20	·7874	67	2·6378	250	9·8425
21	·8268	68	2·6772	260	10·2362
22	·8661	69	2·7164	270	10·6299
23	·9055	70	2·7559	280	11·0235
24	·9449	71	2·7953	290	11·4173
25	·9842	72	2·8345	300	11·8110
25·4	1·0000	73	2·8740	320	12·5984
26	1·0256	74	2·9134	340	13·3859
27	1·0630	75	2·9527	360	14·1732
28	1·1025	76	2·9921	380	14·9605
29	1·1417	77	3·0314	400	15·7480
30	1·1810	78	3·0709	420	16·5354
31	1·2205	79	3·1102	440	17·3228
32	1·2598	80	3·1495	460	18·1102
33	1·2991	81	3·1890	480	18·8975
34	1·3385	82	3·2283	500	19·6850
35	1·3780	83	3·2677	550	21·6535
36	1·4173	84	3·3071	600	23·6220
37	1·4567	85	3·3465	650	25·5905
38	1·4961	86	3·3858	700	27·5590
39	1·5354	87	3·4252	750	29·5275
40	1·5748	88	3·4645	800	31·4960
41	1·6142	89	3·5040	850	33·4645
42	1·6535	90	3·5433	900	35·4330
43	1·6930	91	3·5827	950	37·4015
44	1·7323	92	3·6221	1000	39·3700
45	1·7716	93	3·6614		
46	1·8111	94	3·7008		
47	1·8504	95	3·7400		

INCH–MILLIMETRE EQUIVALENTS

Inches	Millimetres	Inches	Millimetres	Inches	Millimetres
1	25·4001	4⅛	104·775	7⅛	180·974
1⅛	28·5751	4¼	107·951	7¼	184·150
1¼	31·7501	4⅜	111·125	7⅜	187·325
1⅜	34·9250	4½	114·300	7½	190·500
1½	38·1001	4⅝	117·475	7⅝	193·674
1⅝	41·2751	4¾	120·649	7¾	196·850
1¾	44·4501	4⅞	123·825	7⅞	200·025
1⅞	47·6250	5	127·000	8	203·200
2	50·8001	5⅛	130·175	8⅛	206·374
2⅛	53·9750	5¼	133·350	8¼	209·550
2¼	57·1501	5⅜	136·525	8⅜	212·725
2⅜	60·3251	5½	139·700	8½	215·900
2½	63·5001	5⅝	142·875	8⅝	219·075
2⅝	66·6750	5¾	146·050	8¾	222·250
2¾	69·8501	5⅞	149·225	8⅞	225·425
2⅞	73·0250	6	152·400	9	228·600
3	76·2001	6⅛	155·576	9⅛	231·774
3⅛	79·3751	6¼	158·750	9¼	234·950
3¼	82·5502	6⅜	161·925	9⅜	238·125
3⅜	85·7251	6½	165·100	9½	241·300
3½	88·9002	6⅝	168·275	9⅝	244·475
3⅝	92·0751	6¾	171·450	9¾	247·650
3¾	95·2502	6⅞	174·625	9⅞	250·824
3⅞	98·4251	7	177·800	10	254·001
4	101·6004				

SQUARE FEET-SQUARE METRE EQUIVALENTS

Square Feet	Square Metres	Square Metres	Square Feet
1	0·0929	1	10·76
2	0·1858	2	21·52
3	0·2787	3	32·28
4	0·3716	4	43·04
5	0·4645	5	53·80
6	0·5574	6	64·56
7	0·6503	7	75·32
8	0·7432	8	86·08
9	0·8361	9	96·84
10	0·9290	10	107·60
20	1·8580	20	215·20
25	2·3225	25	269·00
50	4·6450	50	538·00
100	9·2900	100	1076·00

CUBIC INCH–CUBIC CENTIMETRE EQUIVALENTS

Cubic Inches	Cubic Centimetres	Cubic Centimetres	Cubic Inches
1	16·3870	1	0·06102
2	32·774	2	0·1220
3	49·161	3	0·1831
4	65·548	4	0·2441
5	81·934	5	0·3050
6	98·322	6	0·3661
7	114·710	7	0·4272
8	131·097	8	0·4882
9	147·484	9	0·5492
10	163·870	10	0·6102
20	327·740	20	1·2205
25	409·676	25	1·5256
50	819·355	50	3·0512
100	1638·710	100	6·1024

SQUARE INCHES INTO SQUARE CENTIMETRES

1 square inch = 6·451367 square centimetres

Square Inches	·0	·1	·2	·3	·4	·5	·6	·7	·8	·9
1	6·4514	7·0965	7·7416	8·3868	9·0319	9·6770	10·3222	10·9673	11·6125	12·2576
2	12·9027	13·5479	14·1930	14·8381	15·4833	16·1284	16·7736	17·4187	18·0638	18·7090
3	19·3541	19·9992	20·6444	21·2895	21·9346	22·5798	23·2249	23·8701	24·5152	25·1603
4	25·8055	26·4506	27·0957	27·7409	28·3860	29·0312	29·6763	30·3214	30·9666	31·6117
5	32·2568	32·9020	33·5471	34·1922	34·8374	35·4825	36·1277	36·7728	37·4179	38·0631
6	38·7082	39·3533	39·9985	40·6436	41·2887	41·9339	42·5790	43·2242	43·8693	44·5144
7	45·1596	45·8046	46·4498	47·0950	47·7401	48·3853	49·0304	49·6755	50·3207	50·9658
8	51·6109	52·2561	52·9012	53·5463	54·1915	54·8366	55·4818	56·1269	56·7720	57·4172
9	58·0623	58·7074	59·3526	59·9977	60·6428	61·2880	61·9331	62·5783	63·2234	63·8685
10	64·5137	65·1588	65·8039	66·4491	67·0942	67·7394	68·3845	69·0296	69·6748	70·3199

SQUARE CENTIMETRES INTO SQUARE INCHES

One square centimetre = ·1550059 of 1 inch

Square Centimetres	·0	·1	·2	·3	·4	·5	·6	·7	·8	·9
1	·15501	·17051	·18601	·20151	·21701	·23251	·24801	·26351	·27901	·29451
2	·31001	·32551	·34101	·35651	·37201	·38751	·40301	·41852	·43402	·44952
3	·46502	·48052	·49602	·51152	·52702	·54252	·55802	·57352	·58902	·60452
4	·62002	·63552	·65102	·66652	·68203	·69753	·71303	·72853	·74403	·75953
5	·77503	·79053	·80603	·82153	·83703	·85253	·86803	·88353	·89903	·91453
6	·93004	·94554	·96104	·97654	·99204	1·00754	1·02304	1·03854	1·05404	1·06954
7	1·08504	1·10054	1·11604	1·13154	1·14704	1·16254	1·17804	1·19355	1·20905	1·22455
8	1·24005	1·25555	1·27105	1·28655	1·30205	1·31755	1·33305	1·34855	1·36405	1·37955
9	1·39505	1·41055	1·42605	1·44156	1·45706	1·47256	1·48806	1·50356	1·51906	1·53456
10	1·55006	1·56556	1·58106	1·59656	1·61206	1·62756	1·64306	1·65856	1·67406	1·68956

CONVERSION OF FEET INTO METRES

Feet	Metres	Feet	Metres	Feet	Metres
1	0·3048	14	4·2672	35	10·668
2	0·6096	15	4·5720	40	12·192
3	0·9144	16	4·8768	45	13·716
4	1·2192	17	5·1816	50	15·240
5	1·5240	18	5·4864	55	16·764
6	1·8288	19	5·7912	60	18·288
7	2·1336	20	6·0960	65	19·812
8	2·4384	21	6·4008	70	21·336
9	2·7432	22	6·7056	75	22·860
10	3·0480	23	7·0104	80	24·384
11	3·3528	24	7·3152	85	25·908
12	3·6576	25	7·6200	90	27·432
13	3·9624	30	9·1440	100	30·480

CONVERSION OF METRES INTO FEET

Metres	Feet	Metres	Feet	Metres	Feet
1	3·2808	14	45·932	35	114·83
2	6·5617	15	49·213	40	131·23
3	9·8425	16	52·493	45	147·64
4	13·123	17	55·774	50	164·04
5	16·406	18	59·055	55	180·45
6	19·685	19	62·336	60	196·85
7	22·966	20	65·617	65	213·25
8	26·247	21	68·898	70	229·66
9	29·528	22	72·179	75	246·06
10	32·808	23	75·459	80	262·47
11	36·089	24	78·740	85	278·87
12	39·370	25	82·081	90	295·28
13	42·651	30	98·425	100	328·08

CONVERSION OF YARDS INTO METRES

Yards	Metres	Yards	Metres	Yards	Metres
1	0·9144	21	19·2025	41	37·4905
2	1·8288	22	20·1167	42	38·4047
3	2·7432	23	21·0313	43	39·3192
4	3·6575	24	21·9455	44	40·2336
5	4·5720	25	22·8600	45	41·1480
6	5·4865	26	23·7745	46	42·0625
7	6·4008	27	24·6889	47	42·9766
8	7·3151	28	25·6032	48	43·8911
9	8·2295	29	26·5175	49	44·8055
10	9·1440	30	27·4320	50	45·7200
11	10·0585	31	28·3465	55	50·2920
12	10·9727	32	29·2608	60	54·8640
13	11·8871	33	30·1753	65	59·4360
14	12·8015	34	31·0896	70	64·0080
15	13·7160	35	32·0040	75	68·5800
16	14·6305	36	32·9185	80	73·1520
17	15·5447	37	33·8327	85	77·7240
18	16·4592	38	34·7473	90	82·2960
19	17·3735	39	35·6615	95	86·8680
20	18·2880	40	36·5760	100	91·4400

CONVERSION OF METRES INTO YARDS

Metres	Yards	Metres	Yards	Metres	Yards
1	1·0936	21	22·9659	41	44·8380
2	2·1872	22	24·0595	42	45·9316
3	3·2808	23	25·1530	43	47·0255
4	4·3744	24	26·2467	44	48·1190
5	5·4680	25	27·3403	45	49·2125
6	6·5617	26	28·4340	46	50·3063
7	7·6552	27	29·5276	47	51·3998
8	8·7490	28	30·6212	48	52·4934
9	9·8425	29	31·7148	49	53·5870
10	10·9360	30	32·8085	50	54·6806
11	12·0297	31	33·9020	55	60·1487
12	13·1233	32	34·9955	60	65·6167
13	14·2170	33	36·0892	65	71·0849
14	15·3106	34	37·1828	70	76·5530
15	16·4041	35	38·2765	75	82·0210
16	17·4978	36	39·3700	80	87·4890
17	18·5914	37	40·4637	85	92·9570
18	19·6851	38	41·5572	90	98·4251
19	20·7785	39	42·6509	95	103·8933
20	21·8723	40	43·7445	100	109·3614

CONVERSION OF KILOGRAMS TO POUNDS AND POUNDS TO KILOGRAMS

Kilograms	Pounds	Pounds	Kilograms
1	2·2046	1	0·4536
2	4·4092	2	0·9072
3	6·6138	3	1·3608
4	8·8184	4	1·8144
5	11·023	5	2·2680
6	13·228	6	2·7216
7	15·432	7	3·1752
8	17·637	8	3·6287
9	19·842	9	4·0823
10	22·046	10	4·5359
20	44·092	20	9·0718
25	55·116	25	11·3398
50	110·23	50	22·6597
100	220·46	100	45·3593

CONVERSION OF KILOGRAMS PER SQUARE CENTI-METRE TO POUNDS PER SQUARE INCH AND POUNDS PER SQUARE INCH TO KILOGRAMS PER SQUARE CENTIMETRE

Kilograms per sq. cm.	Pounds per sq. in.	Pounds per sq. in.	Kilograms per sq. cm.
1	14·22	1	0·0703
2	28·45	2	0·1406
3	42·67	3	0·2109
4	56·89	4	0·2812
5	71·12	5	0·3515
6	85·34	6	0·4218
7	99·56	7	0·4921
8	113·78	8	0·5625
9	128·01	9	0·6328
10	142·23	10	0·7031
20	284·46	20	1·4062
25	355·58	25	1·7577
50	711·16	50	3·5154
100	1422·32	100	7·0308

CONVERSION OF LITRES TO PINTS AND PINTS TO LITRES

Litres	Pints	Pints	Litres
1	1·760	1	0·568
2	3·520	2	1·136
3	5·279	3	1·705
4	7·039	4	2·273
5	8·799	5	2·841
6	10·599	6	3·409
7	12·319	7	3·978
8	14·078	8	4·546
9	15·838	9	5·114
10	17·598	10	5·682
20	35·196	20	11·364
25	43·995	25	14·206
50	87·990	50	28·412
100	175·980	100	56·824

SOME USEFUL CONVERSION FACTORS

One pound per lineal foot = 1·4882 kilograms per metre.
One pound per lineal yard = 0·496 kilogram per metre.
One ton per lineal mile = 0·63135 tonne per kilometre.
One ton per square inch = 157·494 kilograms per square centimetre.
One pound per cubic inch = 0·02768 kilogram per cubic centimetre.
One pound per cubic foot = 16·019 kilograms per cubic metre.
One pound per cubic yard = 0·5933 kilogram per cubic metre.
One cubic inch per pound = 36·1253 cubic centimetres per kilogram.
One cubic foot per pound = 0·06242 cubic metre per kilogram.
One cubic yard per pound = 1·68546 cubic metres per kilogram.
One kilogram per lineal
metre . . . = 0·67196 pound per foot.
= 2·01587 pounds per yard.
One tonne per lineal metre = 0·8999 ton per yard.
One tonne per lineal kilo-
metre . . . = 1·5839 tons per mile.

EQUIVALENTS OF IMPERIAL GALLONS IN CUBIC FEET

Gallons	0	1	2	3	4	5	6	7	8	9	Gallons
0	—	·16046	·32092	·48138	·64184	·80230	·96276	1·12322	1·28368	1·44414	0
10	1·60460	1·76505	1·92551	2·08597	2·24643	2·40689	2·56735	2·72781	2·88827	3·04873	10
20	3·20919	3·36965	3·53011	3·69057	3·85103	4·01149	4·17195	4·33241	4·49287	4·65333	20
30	4·81379	4·97424	5·13470	5·29516	5·45562	5·61608	5·77654	5·93700	6·09746	6·25792	30
40	6·41838	6·57884	6·73930	6·89976	7·06022	7·22068	7·38114	7·54160	7·70206	7·86252	40
50	8·02298	8·18343	8·34389	8·50435	8·66481	8·82527	8·98573	9·14619	9·30665	9·46711	50
60	9·62757	9·78803	9·94849	10·10895	10·26941	10·42987	10·59033	10·75079	10·91125	11·07171	60
70	11·23216	11·39262	11·55308	11·71354	11·87400	12·03446	12·19492	12·35538	12·51584	12·67630	70
80	12·83676	12·90722	13·15768	13·31814	13·47860	13·63906	13·79952	13·95998	14·12044	14·28090	80
90	14·44136	14·60181	14·76227	14·92273	15·08319	15·24365	15·40411	15·56457	15·72503	15·88549	90
Gallons	0	1	2	3	4	5	6	7	8	9	Gallons

AREAS AND CIRCUMFERENCES OF CIRCLES

Diameter (inch)	Circumference (inch)	Area (square inch)	Diameter (inch)	Circumference (inch)	Area (square inch)
$\frac{1}{32}$	0·0982	0·00077	$1\frac{5}{16}$	4·1233	1·353
$\frac{1}{16}$	0·1964	0·00307	$1\frac{3}{8}$	4·3197	1·4848
$\frac{3}{32}$	0·2945	0·0069	$1\frac{7}{16}$	4·516	1·6229
$\frac{1}{8}$	0·3927	0·01227	$1\frac{1}{2}$	4·7124	1·7671
$\frac{5}{32}$	0·4909	0·0192	$1\frac{9}{16}$	4·9087	1·9175
$\frac{3}{16}$	0·589	0·02761	$1\frac{5}{8}$	5·1051	2·0739
$\frac{7}{32}$	0·6872	0·0376	$1\frac{11}{16}$	5·3014	2·2365
$\frac{1}{4}$	0·7854	0·04909	$1\frac{3}{4}$	5·4978	2·4052
$\frac{9}{32}$	0·8836	0·0621	$1\frac{13}{16}$	5·6941	2·58
$\frac{5}{16}$	0·9817	0·0767	$1\frac{7}{8}$	5·8905	2·7611
$\frac{11}{32}$	1·0799	0·0928	$1\frac{15}{16}$	6·0868	2·9483
$\frac{3}{8}$	1·1781	0·1104	2	6·2832	3·1416
$\frac{13}{32}$	1·2763	0·1296	$2\frac{1}{16}$	6·4795	3·3410
$\frac{7}{16}$	1·3745	0·1503	$2\frac{1}{8}$	6·6759	3·5465
$\frac{15}{32}$	1·4726	0·1725	$2\frac{3}{16}$	6·8722	3·7584
$\frac{1}{2}$	1·5708	0·1963	$2\frac{1}{4}$	7·0686	3·976
$\frac{17}{32}$	1·6690	0·2216	$2\frac{5}{16}$	7·2649	4·2
$\frac{9}{16}$	1·7672	0·2485	$2\frac{3}{8}$	7·4613	4·4302
$\frac{19}{32}$	1·8653	0·2768	$2\frac{7}{16}$	7·6576	4·6664
$\frac{5}{8}$	1·9635	0·3068	$2\frac{1}{2}$	7·854	4·9087
$\frac{21}{32}$	2·0617	0·3382	$2\frac{9}{16}$	8·0503	5·1573
$\frac{11}{16}$	2·1598	0·3712	$2\frac{5}{8}$	8·2467	5·4119
$\frac{23}{32}$	2·258	0·4057	$2\frac{11}{16}$	8·443	5·6723
$\frac{3}{4}$	2·3562	0·4417	$2\frac{3}{4}$	8·6394	5·9395
$\frac{25}{32}$	2·4453	0·4793	$2\frac{13}{16}$	8·8357	6·2126
$\frac{13}{16}$	2·5525	0·5185	$2\frac{7}{8}$	9·0321	6·4918
$\frac{27}{32}$	2·6507	0·5591	$2\frac{15}{16}$	9·2284	6·7772
$\frac{7}{8}$	2·7489	0·6013	3	9·4248	7·0686
$\frac{29}{32}$	2·8471	0·645	$3\frac{1}{16}$	9·6211	7·3662
$\frac{15}{16}$	2·9452	0·6903	$3\frac{1}{8}$	9·8175	7·6699
$\frac{31}{32}$	3·0434	0·737	$3\frac{3}{16}$	10·014	7·9798
1	3·1416	0·7854	$3\frac{1}{4}$	10·21	8·2957
$1\frac{1}{16}$	3·3379	0·8866	$3\frac{5}{16}$	10·406	8·618
$1\frac{1}{8}$	3·5343	0·994	$3\frac{3}{8}$	10·602	8·9462
$1\frac{3}{16}$	3·7306	1·1075	$3\frac{7}{16}$	10·799	9·2807
$1\frac{1}{4}$	3·927	1·2271	$3\frac{1}{2}$	10·995	9·6211

Areas and Circumferences of Circles (*contd.*)

Diameter (inch)	Circumference (inch)	Area (square inch)	Diameter (inch)	Circumference (inch)	Area (square inch)
3 9/16	11·191	9·968	5 13/16	18·261	26·535
3 5/8	11·388	10·32	5 7/8	18·457	27·108
3 11/16	11·584	10·679	5 15/16	18·653	27·688
3 3/4	11·781	11·044	6	18·85	28·27
3 13/16	11·977	11·416	6 1/8	19·24	29·46
3 7/8	12·173	11·793	6 1/4	19·63	30·67
3 15/16	12·369	12·177	6 3/8	20·02	31·91
4	12·566	12·566	6 1/2	20·42	33·18
4 1/16	12·762	12·962	6 5/8	20·81	34·47
4 1/8	12·959	13·364	6 3/4	21·20	35·78
4 3/16	13·155	13·772	6 7/8	21·60	37·12
4 1/4	13·351	14·186	7	21·99	38·48
4 5/16	13·547	14·606	7 1/8	22·38	39·87
4 3/8	13·744	15·033	7 1/4	22·77	41·28
4 7/16	13·94	15·465	7 3/8	23·17	42·71
4 1/2	14·137	15·904	7 1/2	23·56	44·17
4 9/16	14·333	16·394	7 5/8	23·95	45·66
4 5/8	14·529	16·8	7 3/4	24·34	47·17
4 11/16	14·725	17·257	7 7/8	24·74	48·70
4 3/4	14·922	17·72	8	25·13	50·26
4 13/16	15·119	18·19	8 1/8	25·52	51·84
4 7/8	15·315	18·665	8 1/4	25·91	53·45
4 15/16	15·511	19·147	8 3/8	26·31	55·08
5	15·708	19·635	8 1/2	26·70	56·74
5 1/16	15·904	20·129	8 5/8	27·09	58·42
5 1/8	16·1	20·629	8 3/4	27·49	60·13
5 3/16	16·296	21·135	8 7/8	27·88	61·86
5 1/4	16·493	21·647	9	28·27	63·62
5 5/16	16·689	22·166	9 1/8	28·66	65·39
5 3/8	16·886	22·69	9 1/4	29·06	67·20
5 7/16	17·082	23·221	9 3/8	29·45	69·02
5 1/2	17·278	23·758	9 1/2	29·84	70·88
5 9/16	17·474	24·301	9 5/8	30·23	72·75
5 5/8	17·671	24·85	9 3/4	30·63	74·66
5 11/16	17·867	25·406	9 7/8	31·02	76·58
5 3/4	18·064	25·967	10	31·41	78·54

Areas and Circumferences of Circles (*contd.*)

Diameter (inch)	*Circumference (inch)*	*Area (square inch)*	*Diameter (inch)*	*Circumference (inch)*	*Area (square inch)*
10⅛	31·80	80·51	14⅝	45·94	167·98
10¼	32·20	82·51	14¾	46·34	170·87
10⅜	32·59	84·54	14⅞	46·73	173·78
10½	32·98	86·59	15	47·12	176·71
10⅝	33·38	88·66	15⅛	47·51	179·67
10¾	33·77	90·76	15¼	47·91	182·65
10⅞	34·16	92·88	15⅜	48·30	185·66
11	34·56	95·08	15½	48·69	188·69
11⅛	34·95	97·20	15⅝	49·08	191·74
11¼	35·34	99·40	15¾	49·48	194·82
11⅜	35·73	101·62	15⅞	49·87	197·93
11½	36·13	103·87	16	50·26	201·06
11⅝	36·52	106·14	16⅛	50·65	204·21
11¾	36·91	108·43	16¼	51·05	207·40
11⅞	37·30	110·75	16⅜	51·44	210·59
12	37·69	113·09	16½	51·83	213·82
12⅛	38·09	115·46	16⅝	52·23	217·07
12¼	38·48	117·86	16¾	52·62	220·35
12⅜	38·87	120·27	16⅞	53·01	223·65
12½	39·27	122·71	17	53·40	226·98
12⅝	39·66	125·18	17⅛	53·79	230·33
12¾	40·05	127·67	17¼	54·19	233·70
12⅞	40·44	130·19	17⅜	54·58	237·10
13	40·84	132·73	17½	54·97	240·52
13⅛	41·23	135·29	17⅝	55·37	243·97
13¼	41·62	137·88	17¾	55·76	247·45
13⅜	42·01	140·50	17⅞	56·15	250·94
13½	42·41	143·13	18	56·54	254·47
13⅝	42·80	145·80	18⅛	56·94	258·01
13¾	43·19	148·48	18¼	57·33	261·58
13⅞	43·58	151·20	18⅜	57·72	265·18
14	43·98	153·93	18½	58·12	268·80
14⅛	44·37	156·70	18⅝	58·51	272·44
14¼	44·76	159·48	18¾	58·90	276·11
14⅜	45·16	162·30	18⅞	59·29	279·81
14½	45·55	165·13	19	59·69	283·53

Areas and Circumferences of Circles (*contd.*)

Diameter (inch)	Circumference (inch)	Area (square inch)	Diameter (inch)	Circumference (inch)	Area (square inch)
19⅛	60·08	287·27	37	116·24	1075·21
19¼	60·47	291·04	38	119·38	1134·11
19⅜	60·86	294·83	39	122·52	1194·59
19½	61·26	298·64	40	125·66	1256·64
19⅝	61·65	302·49	41	128·80	1320·66
19¾	62·04	306·35	42	131·94	1385·44
19⅞	62·44	310·24	43	135·08	1452·20
20	62·83	314·16	44	138·23	1520·53
21	65·97	346·36	45	141·37	1590·43
22	69·11	380·13	46	144·51	1661·90
23	72·25	415·47	47	147·65	1734·94
24	75·39	452·39	48	150·79	1809·56
25	78·54	490·87	49	153·94	1885·74
26	81·68	530·93	50	157·08	1963·50
27	84·82	572·55	55	172·788	2375·8
28	87·96	615·75	60	188·496	2827·4
29	91·10	660·52	65	204·204	3318·3
30	94·24	706·86	70	219·911	3848·5
31	97·39	754·76	75	235·619	4417·9
32	100·53	804·25	80	251·327	5026·5
33	103·67	855·30	85	267·036	5674·4
34	106·81	907·92	90	282·744	6361·6
35	109·95	962·11	95	298·451	7088·4
36	113·09	1017·87	100	315·160	7854·0

TABLE OF SQUARES, SQUARE ROOTS, CUBES AND CUBE ROOTS

No.	Square	Square Root	Cube	Cube Root
1	1	1·0000	1	1·0000
2	4	1·4142	8	1·2599
3	9	1·7320	27	1·4422
4	16	2·0000	64	1·5874
5	25	2·2361	125	1·7100
6	36	2·4495	216	1·8171
7	49	2·6457	343	1·9129
8	64	2·8284	512	2·0000
9	81	3·0000	729	2·0801
10	100	3·1623	1,000	2·1544
11	121	3·3166	1,331	2·2240
12	144	3·4641	1,728	2·2894
13	169	3·6055	2,197	2·3513
14	196	3·7417	2,744	2·4101
15	225	3·8730	3,375	2·4662
16	256	4·0000	4,096	2·5198
17	289	4·1231	4,913	2·5713
18	324	4·2426	5,832	2·6207
19	361	4·3589	6,859	2·6684
20	400	4·4721	8,000	2·7144
21	441	4·5826	9,261	2·7589
22	484	4·6904	10,648	2·8020
23	529	4·7958	12,167	2·8439
24	576	4·8990	13,824	2·8845
25	625	5·0000	15,625	2·9240
26	676	5·0990	17,576	2·9625
27	729	5·1961	19,683	3·0000
28	784	5·2915	21,952	3·0366
29	841	5·3852	24,389	3·0723
30	900	5·4772	27,000	3·1072
31	961	5·5678	29,791	3·1414
32	1,024	5·6568	32,768	3·1748
33	1,089	5·7446	35,937	3·2075
34	1,156	5·8309	39,304	3·2396
35	1,225	5·9161	42,875	3·2711
36	1,296	6·0000	46,656	3·3019
37	1,369	6·0828	50,653	3·3322
38	1,444	6·1644	54,872	3·3620
39	1,521	6·2450	59,319	3·3912
40	1,600	6·3246	64,000	3·4199
41	1,681	6·4031	68,921	3·4482
42	1,764	6·4807	74,088	3·4760
43	1,849	6·5574	79,507	3·5034
44	1,936	6·6332	85,184	3·5303
45	2,025	6·7082	91,125	3·5569
46	2,116	6·7823	97,336	3·5830
47	2,209	6·8556	103,823	3·6088
48	2,304	6·9282	110,592	3·6342
49	2,401	7·0000	117,649	3·6593
50	2,500	7·0711	125,000	3·6840

Table of Squares, Square Roots, Cubes and Cube Roots
(contd.)

No.	Square	Square Root	Cube	Cube Root
51	2,601	7·1414	132,651	3·7084
52	2,704	7·2111	140,608	3·7325
53	2,809	7·2801	148,877	3·7563
54	2,916	7·3485	157,464	3·7798
55	3,025	7·4162	166,375	3·8029
56	3,136	7·4833	175,616	3·8259
57	3,249	7·5498	185,193	3·8485
58	3,364	7·6158	195,112	3·8709
59	3,481	7·6811	205,379	3·8930
60	3,600	7·7460	216,000	3·9149
61	3,721	7·8102	226,981	3·9365
62	3,844	7·8740	238,328	3·9579
63	3,969	7·9372	250,047	3·9791
64	4,096	8·0000	262,144	4·0000
65	4,225	8·0623	274,625	4·0207
66	4,356	8·1240	287,496	4·0412
67	4,489	8·1853	300,763	4·0615
68	4,624	8·2462	314,432	4·0817
69	4,761	8·3066	328,509	4·1016
70	4,900	8·3666	343,000	4·1213
71	5,041	8·4261	357,911	4·1408
72	5,184	8·4853	373,248	4·1602
73	5,329	8·5440	389,017	4·1793
74	5,476	8·6023	405,224	4·1983
75	5,625	8·6602	421,875	4·2172
76	5,776	8·7178	438,976	4·2358
77	5,929	8·7750	456,533	4·2543
78	6,084	8·8318	474,552	4·2727
79	6,241	8·8882	493,039	4·2908
80	6,400	8·9443	512,000	4·3089
81	6,561	9·0000	531,441	4·3267
82	6,724	9·0554	551,368	4·3445
83	6,889	9·1104	571,787	4·3621
84	7,056	9·1651	592,704	4·3795
85	7,225	9·2195	614,125	4·3968
86	7,396	9·2736	636,056	4·4140
87	7,569	9·3274	658,503	4·4310
88	7,744	9·3808	681,472	4·4480
89	7,921	9·4340	704,969	4·4647
90	8,100	9·4868	729,000	4·4814
91	8,281	9·5394	753,571	4·4979
92	8,464	9·5917	778,688	4·5144
93	8,649	9·6436	804,357	4·5306
94	8,836	9·6954	830,584	4·5468
95	9,025	9·7468	857,375	4·5629
96	9,216	9·7980	884,736	4·5789
97	9,409	9·8489	912,673	4·5947
98	9,604	9·8995	941,192	4·6104
99	9,801	9·9499	970,299	4·6261
100	10,000	10·0000	1,000,000	4·6416

Table of Squares, Square Roots, Cubes and Cube Roots
(contd.)

No.	Square	Square Root	Cube	Cube Root
101	10,201	10·050	1,030,301	4·6570
102	10,404	10·099	1,061,208	4·6723
103	10,609	10·149	1,092,727	4·6875
104	10,816	10·198	1,124,864	4·7027
105	11,025	10·247	1,157,625	4·7177
106	11,236	10·296	1,191,016	4·7326
107	11,449	10·344	1,225,043	4·7475
108	11,664	10·392	1,259,712	4·7622
109	11,881	10·440	1,295,029	4·7769
110	12,100	10·488	1,331,000	4·7914
111	12,321	10·536	1,367,631	4·8059
112	12,544	10·583	1,404,928	4·8203
113	12,769	10·630	1,442,897	4·8346
114	12,996	10·677	1,481,544	4·8488
115	13,225	10·724	1,520,875	4·8629
116	13,456	10·770	1,560,896	4·8770
117	13,689	10·817	1,601,613	4·8910
118	13,924	10·863	1,643,032	4·9049
119	14,161	10·909	1,685,159	4·9187
120	14,400	10·954	1,728,000	4·9324
121	14,641	11·000	1,771,561	4·9461
122	14,884	11·045	1,815,848	4·9597
123	15,129	11·090	1,860,867	4·9732
124	15,376	11·135	1,906,624	4·9866
125	15,625	11·180	1,953,125	5·0000
126	15,876	11·225	2,000,376	5·0133
127	16,129	11·269	2,048,383	5·0265
128	16,384	11·314	2,097,152	5·0397
129	16,641	11·358	2,146,689	5·0528
130	16,900	11·402	2,197,000	5·0658
131	17,161	11·445	2,248,091	5·0787
132	17,414	11·489	2,299,968	5·0916
133	17,689	11·533	2,352,637	5·1045
134	17,956	11·576	2,406,104	5·1172
135	18,225	11·619	2,460,375	5·1299
136	18,496	11·662	2,515,456	5·1426
137	18,769	11·705	2,571,353	5·1551
138	19,044	11·747	2,628,072	5·1676
139	19,321	11·790	2,685,619	5·1801
140	19,600	11·832	2,744,000	5·1925
141	19,881	11·874	2,803,221	5·2048
142	20,164	11·916	2,863,288	5·2171
143	20,449	11·958	2,924,207	5·2293
144	20,736	12·000	2,985,984	5·2415
145	21,025	12·042	3,048,625	5·2536
146	21,316	12·083	3,112,136	5·2656
147	21,609	12·124	3,176,523	5·2776
148	21,904	12·165	3,241,792	5·2896
149	22,201	12·207	3,307,949	5·3015
150	22,500	12·247	3,375,000	5·3132

Table of Squares, Square Roots, Cubes and Cube Roots
(*contd.*)

No.	Square	Square Root	Cube	Cube Root
151	22,801	12·288	3,442,951	5·3250
152	23,104	12·329	3,511,808	5·3368
153	23,409	12·369	3,581,577	5·3485
154	23,716	12·410	3,652,264	5·3601
155	24,025	12·450	3,723,875	5·3717
156	24,336	12·490	3,796,416	5·3832
157	24,649	12·530	3,869,893	5·3947
158	24,964	12·570	3,944,312	5·4061
159	25,281	12·609	4,019,679	5·4175
160	25,600	12·649	4,096,000	5·4288
161	25,921	12·689	4,173,281	5·4401
162	26,244	12·728	4,251,528	5·4513
163	26,569	12·767	4,330,747	5·4626
164	26,896	12·806	4,410,944	5·4737
165	27,225	12·845	4,492,125	5·4848
166	27,556	12·884	4,574,296	5·4959
167	27,889	12·923	4,657,463	5·5069
168	28,224	12·961	4,741,632	5·5178
169	28,561	13·000	4,826,809	5·5288
170	28,900	13·038	4,913,000	5·5397
171	29,241	13·077	5,000,211	5·5505
172	29,584	13·115	5,088,448	5·5613
173	29,929	13·153	5,177,717	5·5720
174	30,276	13·191	5,268,024	5·5828
175	30,625	13·229	5,359,375	5·5934
176	30,976	13·266	5,451,776	5·6041
177	31,329	13·304	5,545,233	5·6147
178	31,684	13·342	5,639,752	5·6252
179	32,041	13·379	5,735,339	5·6357
180	32,400	13·416	5,832,000	5·6462
181	32,761	13·454	5,929,741	5·6566
182	33,124	13·491	6,028,568	5·6670
183	33,489	13·528	6,128,487	5·6774
184	33,856	13·565	6,229,504	5·6877
185	34,225	13·601	6,331,625	5·6980
186	34,596	13·638	6,434,856	5·7083
187	34,969	13·675	6,539,203	5·7185
188	35,344	13·711	6,644,672	5·7286
189	35,721	13·748	6,751,269	5·7388
190	36,100	13·784	6,859,000	5·7489
191	36,481	13·820	6,967,871	5·7590
192	36,864	13·856	7,077,888	5·7690
193	37,249	13·892	7,189,057	5·7790
194	37,636	13·928	7,301,384	5·7890
195	38,025	13·964	7,414,875	5·7989
196	38,416	14·000	7,529,536	5·8088
197	38,809	14·036	7,645,373	5·8186
198	39,204	14·071	7,762,392	5·8285
199	39,601	14·107	7,880,599	5·8383
200	40,000	14·142	8,000,000	5·8480

Table of Squares, Square Roots, Cubes and Cube Roots
(*contd.*)

No.	Square	Square Root	Cube	Cube Root
201	40,401	14·177	8,120,601	5·8578
202	40,804	14·213	8,242,408	5·8675
203	41,209	14·248	8,365,427	5·8771
204	41,616	14·283	8,489,664	5·8868
205	42,025	14·318	8,615,125	5·8964
206	42,436	14·353	8,741,816	5·9059
207	42,849	14·387	8,869,743	5·9155
208	43,264	14·422	8,998,912	5·9250
209	43,681	14·457	9,129,329	5·9345
210	44,100	14·491	9,261,000	5·9439
211	44,521	14·526	9,393,931	5·9533
212	44,944	14·560	9,528,128	5·9627
213	45,369	14·594	9,663,597	5,9721
214	45,796	14·629	9,800,344	5·9814
215	46,225	14·663	9,938,375	5·9907
216	46,656	14·697	10,077,696	6·0000
217	47,089	14·731	10,218,313	6·0092
218	47,524	14·765	10,360,232	6·0185
219	47,961	14·799	10,503,459	6·0276
220	48,400	14·832	10,648,000	6·0368
221	48,841	14·866	10,793,861	6·0459
222	49,284	14·900	10,941,048	6·0550
223	49,729	14·933	11,089,567	6·0641
224	50,176	14·967	11,239,424	6·0732
225	50,625	15·000	11,390,625	6·0822
226	51,076	15·033	11,543,176	6·0912
227	51,529	15·066	11,697,083	6·1002
228	51,984	15·100	11,852,352	6·1091
229	52,441	15·132	12,008,989	6·1180
230	52,900	15·166	12,167,000	6·1269
231	53,361	15·199	12,326,391	6·1358
232	53,824	15·231	12,487,168	6·1446
233	54,289	15·264	12,649,337	6·1534
234	54,756	15·297	12,812,904	6·1622
235	55,225	15·330	12,977,875	6·1710
236	55,696	15·362	13,144,256	6·1797
237	56,169	15·395	13,312,053	6·1885
238	56,644	15·427	13,481,272	6·1971
239	57,121	15,460	13,651,919	6·2058
240	57,600	15·492	13,824,000	6·2145
241	58,081	15·524	13,997,521	6·2231
242	58,564	15·556	14,172,488	6·2317
243	59,049	15·588	14,348,907	6·2402
244	59,536	15·620	14,526,784	6·2488
245	60,025	15·652	14,706,125	6·2573
246	60,516	15·684	14,886,936	6·2658
247	61,009	15·716	15,069,223	6·2743
248	61,504	15·748	15,252,992	6·2828
249	62,001	15·780	15,438,249	6·2912
250	62,500	15·811	15,625,000	6·2996

Table of Squares, Square Roots, Cubes and Cube Roots
(*contd.*)

No.	Square	Square Root	Cube	Cube Root
251	63,001	15·843	15,813,251	6·3080
252	63,504	15·874	16,003,008	6·3164
253	64,009	15·906	16,194,277	6·3247
254	64,516	15·937	16,387,064	6·3330
255	65,025	15·969	16,581,375	6·3413
256	65,536	16·000	16,777,216	6·3496
257	66,049	16·031	16,974,593	6·3579
258	66,564	16·062	17,173,512	6·3661
259	67,081	16·093	17,373,979	6·3743
260	67,600	16·124	17,576,000	6·3825
261	68,121	16·155	17,779,581	6·3907
262	68,644	16·186	17,984,728	6·3988
263	69,169	16·217	18,191,447	6·4070
264	69,696	16·248	18,399,744	6·4151
265	70,225	16·279	18,609,625	6·4232
266	70,756	16·309	18,821,096	6·4312
267	71,289	16·340	19,034,163	6·4393
268	71,824	16·371	19,248,832	6·4473
269	72,361	16·401	19,465,109	6·4553
270	72,900	16·432	19,683,000	6·4633
271	73,441	16·462	19,902,511	6·4713
272	73,984	16·492	20,123,648	6·4792
273	74,529	16·523	20,346,417	6·4871
274	75,076	16·553	20,570,824	6·4951
275	75,625	16·583	20,796,875	6·5030
276	76,176	16·613	21,024,576	6·5108
277	76,729	16·643	21,253,933	6·5187
278	77,284	16·673	21,484,952	6·5265
279	77,841	16·703	21,717,639	6·5343
280	78,400	16·733	21,952,000	6·5421
281	78,961	16·763	22,188,041	6·5499
282	79,524	16·793	22,425,768	6·5577
283	80,089	16·823	22,665,187	6·5654
284	80,656	16·852	22,906,304	6·5731
285	81,225	16·882	23,149,125	6·5808
286	81,796	16·911	23,393,656	6·5885
287	82,369	16·941	23,639,903	6·5962
288	82,944	16·971	23,887,872	6·6038
289	83,521	17·000	24,137,569	6·6115
290	84,100	17·029	24,389,000	6·6191
291	84,681	17·059	24,642,171	6·6267
292	85,264	17·088	24,897,088	6·6343
293	85,849	17·117	25,153,757	6·6418
294	86,436	17·146	25,412,184	6·6494
295	87,025	17·176	25,672,375	6·6569
296	87,616	17·205	25,934,336	6·6644
297	88,209	17·234	26,198,073	6·6719
298	88,804	17·263	26,463,592	6·6794
299	89,401	17·292	26,730,899	6·6869
300	90,000	17·320	27,000,000	6·6943

Table of Squares, Square Roots, Cubes and Cube Roots
(*contd.*)

No.	Square	Square Root	Cube	Cube Root
301	90,601	17·349	27,270,901	6·7018
302	91,204	17·378	27,543,608	6·7092
303	91,809	17·407	27,818,127	6·7166
304	92,416	17·436	28,094,464	6·7239
305	93,025	17·464	28,372,625	6·7313
306	93,636	17·493	28,652,616	6·7387
307	94,249	17·521	28,934,443	6·7460
308	94,864	17·550	29,218,112	6·7533
309	95,481	17·578	29,503,629	6·7606
310	96,100	17·607	29,791,000	6·7679
311	96,721	17·635	30,080,231	6·7752
312	97,344	17·663	30,371,328	6·7824
313	97,969	17·692	30,664,297	6·7897
314	98,596	17·720	30,959,144	6·7969
315	99,225	17·748	31,255,875	6·8041
316	99,856	17·776	31,554,496	6·8113
317	100,489	17·804	31,855,013	6·8185
318	101,124	17·833	32,157,432	6·8256
319	101,761	17·861	32,461,759	6·8328
320	102,400	17·888	32,768,000	6·8399
321	103,041	17·916	33,076,161	6·8470
322	103,684	17·944	33,386,248	6·8541
323	104,329	17·972	33,698,267	6·8612
324	104,976	18·000	34,012,224	6·8683
325	105,625	18·028	34,328,125	6·8753
326	106,276	18·055	34,645,976	6·8824
327	106,929	18·083	34,965,783	6·8894
328	107,584	18·111	35,287,552	6·8964
329	108,241	18·138	35,611,289	6·9034
330	108,900	18·166	35,937,000	6·9104
331	109,561	18·193	36,264,691	6·9174
332	110,224	18·221	36,594,368	6·9244
333	110,889	18·248	36,926,037	6·9313
334	111,566	18·276	37,259,704	6·9382
335	112,225	18·303	37,595,375	6·9451
336	112,896	18·330	37,933,056	6·9520
337	113,569	18·358	38,272,753	6·9589
338	114,244	18·385	38,614,472	6·9658
339	114,921	18·412	38,958,219	6·9727
340	115,600	18·439	39,304,000	6·9795
341	116,281	18·466	39,651,821	6·9864
342	116,964	18·493	40,001,688	6·9932
343	117,649	18·520	40,353,607	7·0000
344	118,336	18·547	40,707,584	7·0068
345	119,025	18·574	41,063,625	7·0136
346	119,716	18·601	41,421,736	7·0203
347	120,409	18·628	41,781,923	7·0271
348	121,104	18·655	42,144,192	7·0338
349	121,801	18·681	42,508,549	7·0406
350	122,500	18·708	42,875,000	7·0473

Table of Squares, Square Roots, Cubes and Cube Roots
(contd.)

No.	Square	Square Root	Cube	Cube Root
351	123,201	18·735	43,243,551	7·0540
352	123,904	18·762	43,614,208	7·0607
353	124,609	18·788	43,986,977	7·0674
354	125,316	18·815	44,361,864	7·0740
355	126,025	18·841	44,738,875	7·0807
356	126,736	18·868	45,118,016	7·0873
357	127,449	18·894	45,499,293	7·0940
358	128,164	18·921	45,882,712	7·1006
359	128,881	18·947	46,268,279	7·1072
360	129,600	18·974	46,656,000	7·1138
361	130,321	19·000	47,045,881	7·1204
362	131,044	19·026	47,437,928	7·1269
363	131,769	19·053	47,832,147	7·1335
364	132,496	19·079	48,228,544	7·1400
365	133,225	19·105	48,627,125	7·1466
366	133,956	19·131	49,027,896	7·1531
367	134,689	19·157	49,430,863	7·1596
368	135,424	19·183	49,836,032	7·1661
369	136,161	19·209	50,243,409	7·1726
370	136,900	19·235	50,653,000	7·1790
371	137,641	19·261	51,064,811	7·1855
372	138,384	19·287	51,478,848	7·1920
373	139,129	19·313	51,895,117	7·1984
374	139,876	19·339	52,313,624	7·2048
375	140,625	19·365	52,734,375	7·2112
376	141,376	19·391	53,157,376	7·2176
377	142,129	19·416	53,582,633	7·2240
378	142,884	19·442	54,010,152	7·2304
379	143,641	19·468	54,439,939	7·2368
380	144,400	19·494	54,872,000	7·2432
381	145,161	19·519	55,306,341	7·2495
382	145,924	19·545	55,742,968	7·2558
383	146,689	19·570	56,181,887	7·2622
384	147,456	19·596	56,623,104	7·2685
385	148,225	19·621	57,066,625	7·2748
386	148,996	19·647	57,512,456	7·2811
387	149,769	19·672	57,960,603	7·2874
388	150,544	19·698	58,411,072	7·2936
389	151,321	19·723	58,863,869	7·2999
390	152,100	19·748	59,319,000	7·3061
391	152,881	19·774	59,776,471	7·3124
392	153,664	19·799	60,236,288	7·3186
393	154,449	19·824	60,698,457	7·3248
394	155,236	19·849	61,162,984	7·3310
395	156,025	19·875	61,629,875	7·3372
396	156,816	19·890	62,099,136	7·3434
397	157,609	19·925	62,570,773	7·3496
398	158,404	19·950	63,044,792	7·3558
399	159,201	19·975	63,521,199	7·3619
400	160,000	20·000	64,000,000	7·3681

Table of Squares, Square Roots, Cubes and Cube Roots
(*contd.*)

No.	Square	Square Root	Cube	Cube Root
401	160,801	20·025	64,481,201	7·3742
402	161,604	20·050	64,964,808	7·3803
403	162,409	20·075	65,450,827	7·3864
404	163,216	20·100	65,939,264	7·3925
405	164,025	20·125	66,430,125	7·3986
406	164,836	20·149	66,923,416	7·4047
407	165,649	20·174	67,419,143	7·4108
408	166,464	20·199	67,917,312	7·4169
409	167,281	20·224	68,417,929	7·4229
410	168,100	20·248	68,921,000	7·4290
411	168,921	20·273	69,426,531	7·4350
412	169,744	20·298	69,934,528	7·4410
413	170,569	20·322	70,444,997	7·4470
414	171,396	20·347	70,957,944	7·4530
415	172,225	20·371	71,473,375	7·4590
416	173,056	20·396	71,991,296	7·4650
417	173,889	20·421	72,511,713	7·4710
418	174,724	20·445	73,034,632	7·4770
419	175,561	20·469	73,560,059	7·4829
420	176,400	20·494	74,088,000	7·4889
421	177,241	20·518	74,618,461	7·4948
422	178,084	20·543	75,151,448	7·5007
423	178,929	20·567	75,686,967	7·5067
424	179,776	20·591	76,225,024	7·5126
425	180,625	20·615	76,765,625	7·5185
426	181,476	20·640	77,308,776	7·5244
427	182,329	20·664	77,854,483	7·5302
428	183,184	20·688	78,402,752	7·5361
429	184,041	20·712	78,953,589	7·5420
430	184,900	20·736	79,507,000	7·5478
431	185,761	20·760	80,062,991	7·5537
432	186,624	20·785	80,621,568	7·5595
433	187,489	20·809	81,182,737	7·5653
434	188,356	20·833	81,746,504	7·5712
435	189,225	20·857	82,312,875	7·5770
436	190,096	20·881	82,881,856	7·5828
437	190,969	20·904	83,453,453	7·5886
438	191,844	20·928	84,027,672	7·5944
439	192,721	20·952	84,604,519	7·6001
440	193,600	20·976	85,184,000	7·6059
441	194,481	21,000	85,766,121	7·6117
442	195,364	21·024	86,350,888	7·6174
443	196,249	21·048	86,938,307	7·6231
444	197,136	21·071	87,528,384	7·6289
445	198,025	21·095	88,121,125	7·6346
446	198,916	21·119	88,716,536	7·6403
447	199,809	21·142	89,314,623	7·6460
448	200,704	21·166	89,915,392	7·6517
449	201,601	21·190	90,518,849	7·6574
450	202,500	21·213	91,125,000	7·6631

Table of Squares, Square Roots, Cubes and Cube Roots
(contd.)

No.	Square	Square Root	Cube	Cube Root
451	203,401	21·237	91,733,851	7·6688
452	204,304	21·260	92,345,408	7·6744
453	205,209	21·284	92,959,677	7·6801
454	206,116	21·307	93,576,664	7·6857
455	207,025	21·330	94,196,375	7·6914
456	207,936	21·354	94,818,816	7·6970
457	208,849	21·378	95,443,993	7·7026
458	209,764	21·401	96,071,912	7·7082
459	210,681	21·424	96,702,579	7·7138
460	211,600	21·448	97,336,000	7·7194
461	212,521	21·471	97,972,181	7·7250
462	213,444	21·494	98,611,128	7·7306
463	214,369	21·517	99,252,847	7·7362
464	215,296	21·541	99,897,344	7·7417
465	216,225	21·564	100,544,625	7·7473
466	217,156	21·587	101,194,696	7·7529
467	218,089	21·610	101,847,563	7·7584
468	219,024	21·633	102,503,232	7·7639
469	219,961	21·656	103,161,709	7·7695
470	220,900	21·679	103,823,000	7·7750
471	221,841	21·702	104,487,111	7·7805
472	222,784	21·726	105,154,048	7·7860
473	223,729	21·749	105,823,817	7·7915
474	224,676	21·771	106,496,424	7·7970
475	225,625	21·794	107,171,875	7·8024
476	226,576	21·817	107,850,176	7·8079
477	227,529	21·840	108,531,333	7·8134
478	228,484	21·863	109,215,352	7·8188
479	229,441	21·886	109,902,239	7·8243
480	230,400	21·909	110,592,000	7·8297
481	231,361	21·932	111,284,641	7·8352
482	232,324	21·954	111,980,168	7·8406
483	233,289	21·977	112,678,587	7·8460
484	234,256	22·000	113,379,904	7·8514
485	235,225	22·023	114,084,125	7·8568
486	236,196	22·045	114,791,256	7·8622
487	237,169	22·068	115,501,303	7·8676
488	238,144	22·091	116,214,272	7·8730
489	239,121	22·113	116,930,169	7·8784
490	240,100	22·136	117,649,000	7·8837
491	241,081	22·158	118,370,771	7·8891
492	242,064	22·181	119,095,488	7·8944
493	243,049	22·204	119,823,157	7·8998
494	244,036	22·226	120,553,784	7·9051
495	245,025	22·249	121,287,375	7·9105
496	246,016	22·271	122,023,936	7·9158
497	247,009	22·293	122,763,473	7·9211
498	248,004	22·316	123,505,992	7·9264
499	249,001	22·338	124,251,499	7·9317
500	250,000	22·361	125,000,000	7·9370

Table of Squares, Square Roots, Cubes and Cube Roots
(contd.)

No.	Square	Square Root	Cube	Cube Root
501	251,001	22·383	125,751,501	7·9423
502	252,004	22·405	126,506,008	7·9476
503	253,009	22·428	127,263,527	7·9528
504	254,016	22·450	128,024,064	7·9581
505	255,025	22·472	128,787,625	7·9634
506	256,036	22·494	129,554,216	7·9686
507	257,049	22·517	130,323,843	7·9739
508	258,064	22·539	131,096,512	7·9791
509	259,081	22·561	131,872,229	7·9843
510	260,100	22·583	132,651,000	7·9896
511	261,121	22·605	133,432,831	7·9948
512	262,144	22·627	134,217,728	8·0000
513	263,169	22·649	135,005,697	8·0052
514	264,196	22·672	135,796,744	8·0104
515	265,225	22·694	136,590,875	8·0156
516	266,256	22·716	137,388,096	8·0208
517	267,289	22·738	138,188,413	8·0260
518	268,324	22·760	138,991,832	8·0311
519	269,361	22·781	139,798,359	8·0363
520	270,400	22·803	140,608,000	8·0414
521	271,441	22·825	141,420,761	8·0466
522	272,484	22·847	142,236,648	8·0517
523	273,529	22·869	143,055,667	8·0569
524	274,576	22·891	143,877,824	8·0620
525	275,625	22·913	144,703,125	8·0671
526	276,676	22·935	145,531,576	8·0723
527	277,729	22·956	146,363,183	8·0774
528	278,784	22·978	147,197,952	8·0825
529	279,841	23·000	148,035,889	8·0876
530	280,900	23·022	148,877,000	8·0927
531	281,961	23·043	149,721,291	8·0978
532	283,024	23·065	150,568,768	8·1028
533	284,089	23·087	151,419,437	8·1079
534	285,156	23·108	152,273,304	8·1130
535	286,225	23·130	153,130,375	8·1180
536	287,296	23·152	153,990,656	8·1231
537	288,369	23·173	154,854,153	8·1281
538	289,444	23·195	155,720,872	8·1332
539	290,521	23·216	156,590,819	8·1382
540	291,600	23·238	157,464,000	8·1432
541	292,681	23·259	158,340,421	8·1483
542	293,764	23·281	159,220,088	8·1533
543	294,849	23·302	160,103,007	8·1583
544	295,936	23·324	160,989,184	8·1633
545	297,025	23·345	161,878,625	8·1683
546	298,116	23·367	162,771,336	8·1733
547	299,209	23·388	163,667,323	8·1783
548	300,304	23·409	164,566,592	8·1833
549	301,401	23·431	165,469,149	8·1882
550	302,500	23·452	166,375,000	8·1932

Table of Squares, Square Roots, Cubes and Cube Roots
(contd.)

No.	Square	Square Root	Cube	Cube Root
551	303,601	23·473	167,284,151	8·1982
552	304,704	23·495	168,196,608	8·2031
553	305,809	23·516	169,112,377	8·2081
554	306,916	23·537	170,031,464	8·2130
555	308,025	23·558	170,953,875	8·2180
556	309,136	23·580	171,879,616	8·2229
557	310,249	23·601	172,808,693	8·2278
558	311,364	23·622	173,741,112	8·2327
559	312,481	23·643	174,676,879	8·2377
560	313,600	23·664	175,616,000	8·2426
561	314,721	23·685	176,558,481	8·2475
562	315,844	23·706	177,504,328	8·2524
563	316,969	23·728	178,453,547	8·2573
564	318,096	23·749	179,406,144	8·2621
565	319,225	23·770	180,362,125	8·2670
566	320,356	23·791	181,321,496	8·2719
567	321,489	23·812	182,284,263	8·2768
568	322,624	23·833	183,250,432	8·2816
569	323,761	23·854	184,220,009	8·2865
570	324,900	23·875	185,193,000	8·2913
571	326,041	23·896	186,169,411	8·2962
572	327,184	23·916	187,149,248	8·3010
573	328,329	23·937	188,132,517	8·3059
574	329,476	23·958	189,119,224	8·3107
575	330,625	23·979	190,109,375	8·3155
576	331,776	24·000	191,102,976	8·3203
577	332,929	24·020	192,100,033	8·3251
578	334,084	24·042	193,100,552	8·3299
579	335,241	24·062	194,104,539	8·3348
580	336,400	24·083	195,112,000	8·3395
581	337,561	24·104	196,122,941	8·3443
582	338,724	24·125	197,137,368	8·3491
583	339,889	24·145	198,155,287	8·3539
584	341,056	24·166	199,176,704	8·3587
585	342,225	24·187	200,201,625	8·3634
586	343,396	24·207	201,230,056	8·3682
587	344,569	24·228	202,262,003	8·3730
588	345,744	24·249	203,297,472	8·3777
589	346,921	24·269	204,336,469	8·3825
590	348,100	24·290	205,379,000	8·3872
591	349,281	24·310	206,425,071	8·3919
592	350,464	24·331	207,474,688	8·3967
593	351,649	24·352	208,527,857	8·4014
594	352,836	24·372	209,584,584	8·4061
595	354,025	24·393	210,644,875	8·4108
596	355,216	24·413	211,708,736	8·4155
597	356,409	24·433	212,776,173	8·4202
598	357,604	24·454	213,847,192	8·4249
599	358,801	24·474	214,921,799	8·4296
600	360,000	24·495	216,000,000	8·4343

Table of Squares, Square Roots, Cubes and Cube Roots
(*contd.*)

No.	Square	Square Root	Cube	Cube Root
601	361,201	24·515	217,081,801	8·4390
602	362,404	24·536	218,167,208	8·4437
603	363,609	24·556	219,256,227	8·4484
604	364,816	24·576	220,348,864	8·4530
605	366,025	24·597	221,445,125	8·4577
606	367,236	24·617	222,545,016	8·4623
607	368,449	24·637	223,648,543	8·4670
608	369,664	24·658	224,755,712	8·4716
609	370,881	24·678	225,866,529	8·4763
610	372,100	24·698	226,981,000	8·4809
611	373,321	24·718	228,099,131	8·4856
612	374,544	24·739	229,220,928	8·4901
613	375,769	24·759	230,346,397	8·4948
614	376,996	24·779	231,475,544	8·4994
615	378,225	24·799	232,608,375	8·5040
616	379,456	24·819	233,744,896	8·5086
617	380,689	24·839	234,885,113	8·5132
618	381,924	24·860	236,029,032	8·5178
619	383,161	24·880	237,176,659	8·5224
620	384,400	24·900	238,328,000	8·5270
621	385,641	24·920	239,483,061	8·5316
622	386,884	24·940	240,641,848	8·5362
623	388,129	24·960	241,804,367	8·5407
624	389,376	24·980	242,970,624	8·5453
625	390,625	25·000	244,140,625	8·5499
626	391,876	25·020	245,314,376	8·5544
627	393,129	25·040	246,491,883	8·5590
628	394,384	25·060	247,673,152	8·5635
629	395,641	25·080	248,858,189	8·5681
630	396,900	25·100	250,047,000	8·5726
631	398,161	25·120	251,239,591	8·5771
632	399,424	25·140	252,435,968	8·5817
633	400,689	25·159	253,636,137	8·5862
634	401,956	25·179	254,840,104	8·5907
635	403,225	25·199	256,047,875	8·5952
636	404,496	25·219	257,259,456	8·5997
637	405,769	25·239	258,474,853	8·6042
638	407,044	25·259	259,694,072	8·6087
639	408,321	25·278	260,917,119	8·6132
640	409,600	25·298	262,144,000	8·6177
641	410,881	25·318	263,374,721	8·6222
642	412,164	25·338	264,609,288	8·6267
643	413,449	25·357	265,847,707	8·6312
644	414,736	25·377	267,089,984	8·6357
645	416,025	25·397	268,336,125	8·6401
646	417,316	25·416	269,586,136	8·6446
647	418,609	25·436	270,840,023	8·6490
648	419,904	25·456	272,097,792	8·6535
649	421,201	25·475	273,359,449	8·6579
650	422,500	25·495	274,625,000	8·6624

Table of Squares, Square Roots, Cubes and Cube Roots
(contd.)

No	Square	Square Root	Cube	Cube Root
651	423,801	25·515	275,894,451	8·6668
652	425,104	25·534	277,167,808	8·6713
653	426,409	25·554	278,445,077	8·6757
654	427,716	25·573	279,726,264	8·6801
655	429,025	25·593	281,011,375	8·6845
656	430,336	25·612	282,300,416	8·6890
657	431,649	25·632	283,593,393	8·6934
658	432,964	25·651	284,890,312	8·6978
659	434,281	25·671	286,191,179	8·7022
660	435,600	25·690	287,496,000	8·7066
661	436,921	25·710	288,804,781	8·7110
662	438,244	25·729	290,117,528	8·7154
663	439,569	25·749	291,434,247	8·7198
664	440,896	25·768	292,754,944	8·7241
665	442,225	25·788	294,079,625	8·7285
666	443,556	25·807	295,408,296	8·7329
667	444,889	25·826	296,740,963	8·7373
668	446,224	25·846	298,077,632	8·7416
669	447,561	25·865	299,418,309	8·7460
670	448,900	25·884	300,763,000	8·7503
671	450,241	25·904	302,111,711	8·7547
672	451,584	25·923	303,464,448	8·7590
673	452,929	25·942	304,821,217	8·7634
674	454,276	25·961	306,182,024	8·7677
675	455,625	25·981	307,546,875	8·7720
676	456,976	26·000	308,915,776	8·7764
677	458,329	26·019	310,288,733	8·7807
678	459,684	26·038	311,665,752	8·7850
679	461,041	26·058	313,046,839	8·7893
680	462,400	26·077	314,432,000	8·7937
681	463,761	26·096	315,821,241	8·7980
682	465,124	26·115	317,214,568	8·8023
683	466,489	26·134	318,611,987	8·8066
684	467,856	26·153	320,013,504	8·8109
685	469,225	26·172	321,419.125	8·8152
686	470,596	26·192	322,828,856	8·8194
687	471,969	26·211	324,242,703	8·8237
688	473,344	26·230	325,660,672	8·8280
689	474,721	26·249	327,082,769	8·8323
690	476,100	26·268	328,509,000	8·8366
691	477,481	26·287	329,939,371	8·8408
692	478,864	26·306	331,373,888	8·8451
693	480,249	26·325	332,812,557	8·8493
694	481,636	26·344	334,255,384	8·8536
695	483,025	26·363	335,702,375	8·8578
696	484,416	26·382	337,153,536	8·8621
697	485,809	26·401	338,608,873	8·8663
698	487,204	26·420	340,068,392	8·8706
699	488,601	26·439	341,532,099	8·8748
700	490,000	26·457	343,000,000	8·8790

Table of Squares, Square Roots, Cubes and Cube Roots
(contd.)

No.	Square	Square Root	Cube	Cube Root
701	491,401	26·476	344,472,101	8·8832
702	492,804	26·495	345,948,408	8·8875
703	494,209	26·514	347,428,927	8·8917
704	495,616	26·533	348,913,664	8·8959
705	497,025	26·552	350,402,625	8·9001
706	498,436	26·571	351,895,816	8·9043
707	499,849	26·589	353,393,243	8·9085
708	501,264	26·608	354,894,912	8·9127
709	502,681	26·627	356,400,829	8·9169
710	504,100	26·646	357,911,000	8·9211
711	505,521	26·665	359,425,431	8·9253
712	506,944	26·683	360,944,128	8·9295
713	508,369	26·702	362,467,097	8·9337
714	509,796	26·721	363,994,344	8·9378
715	511,225	26·739	365,525,875	8·9420
716	512,656	26·758	367,061,696	8·9462
717	514,089	26·777	368,601,813	8·9503
718	515,524	26·795	370,146,232	8·9545
719	516,961	26·814	371,694,959	8·9587
720	518,400	26·833	373,248,000	8·9628
721	519,841	26·851	374,805,361	8·9669
722	521,284	26·870	376,367,048	8·9711
723	522,729	26·889	377,933,067	8·9752
724	524,176	26·907	379,503,424	8·9794
725	525,625	26·925	381,078,125	8·9835
726	527,076	26·944	382,657,176	8·9876
727	528,529	26·963	384,240,583	8·9918
728	529,984	26·981	385,828,352	8·9959
729	531,441	27·000	387,420,489	9·0000
730	532,900	27·018	389,017,000	9·0041
731	534,361	27·037	390,617,891	9·0082
732	535,824	27·055	392,223,168	9·0123
733	537,289	27·074	393,832,837	9·0164
734	538,756	27·092	395,446,904	9·0205
735	540,225	27·111	397,065,375	9·0246
736	541,696	27·129	398,688,256	9·0287
737	543,169	27·148	400,315,553	9·0328
738	544,644	27·166	401,947,272	9·0369
739	546,121	27·185	403,583,419	9·0409
740	547,600	27·202	405,224,000	9·0450
741	549,081	27·221	406,869,021	9·0491
742	550,564	27·240	408,518,488	9·0532
743	552,049	27·258	410,172,407	9·0572
744	553,536	27·276	411,830,784	9·0613
745	555,025	27·295	413,493,625	9·0654
746	556,516	27·313	415,160,936	9·0694
747	558,009	27·331	416,832,723	9·0735
748	559,504	27·350	418,508,992	9·0775
749	561,001	27·368	420,189,749	9·0816
750	562,500	27·386	421,875,000	9·0856

Table of Squares, Square Roots, Cubes and Cube Roots
(*contd.*)

No.	Square	Square Root	Cube	Cube Root
751	564,001	27·404	423,564,751	9·0896
752	565,504	27·423	425,259,008	9·0937
753	567,009	27·440	426,957,777	9·0977
754	568,516	27·459	428,661,064	9·1017
755	570,025	27·477	430,368,875	9·1057
756	571,536	27·495	432,081,216	9·1098
757	573,049	27·514	433,798,093	9·1138
758	574,564	27·532	435,519,512	9·1178
759	576,081	27·550	437,245,479	9·1218
760	577,600	27·568	438,976,000	9·1258
761	579,121	27·586	440,711,081	9·1298
762	580,644	27·604	442,450,728	9·1338
763	582,169	27·622	444,194,947	9·1378
764	583,696	27·640	445,943,744	9·1418
765	585,225	27·659	447,697,125	9·1458
766	586,756	27·677	449,455,096	9·1498
767	588,289	27·695	451,217,663	9·1537
768	589,824	27·713	452,984,832	9·1577
769	591,361	27·731	454,756,609	9·1617
770	592,900	27·749	456,533,000	9·1657
771	594,441	27·767	458,314,011	9·1696
772	595,984	27·785	460,099,648	9·1736
773	597,529	27·803	461,889,917	9·1775
774	599,076	27·821	463,684,824	9·1815
775	600,625	27·839	465,484,375	9·1854
776	602,176	27·857	467,288,576	9·1894
777	603,729	27·875	469,097,433	9·1933
778	605,284	27·893	470,910,952	9·1973
779	606,841	27·911	472,729,139	9·2012
780	608,400	27·928	474,552,000	9·2052
781	609,961	27·946	476,379,541	9·2091
782	611,524	27·964	478,211,768	9·2130
783	613,089	27·982	480,048,687	9·2169
784	614,656	28·000	481,890,304	9·2209
785	616,225	28·018	483,736,625	9·2248
786	617,796	28·036	485,587,656	9·2287
787	619,369	28·053	487,443,403	9·2326
788	620,944	28·071	489,303,872	9·2365
789	622,521	28·089	491,169,069	9·2404
790	624,100	28·107	493,039,000	9·2443
791	625,681	28·125	494,913,671	9·2482
792	627,264	28·142	496,793,088	9·2521
793	628,849	28·160	498,677,257	9·2560
794	630,436	28·178	500,566,184	9·2599
795	632,025	28·196	502,459,875	9·2638
796	633,616	28·213	504,358,336	9·2677
797	635,209	28·231	506,261,573	9·2716
798	636,804	28·249	508,169,592	9·2754
799	638,401	28·267	510,082,399	9·2793
800	640,000	28·284	512,000,000	9·2832

Table of Squares, Square Roots, Cubes and Cube Roots
(*contd.*)

No.	Square	Square Root	Cube	Cube Root
801	641,601	28·302	513,922,401	9·2870
802	643,204	28·320	515,849,608	9·2909
803	644,809	28·337	517,781,627	9·2948
804	646,416	28·355	519,718,464	9·2986
805	648,025	28·372	521,660,125	9·3025
806	649,636	28·390	523,606,616	9·3063
807	651,249	28·408	525,557,943	9·3102
808	652,864	28·425	527,514,112	9·3140
809	654,481	28·443	529,475,129	9·3179
810	656,100	28·460	531,441,000	9·3217
811	657,721	28·478	533,411,731	9·3255
812	659,344	28·496	535,387,328	9·3294
813	660,969	28·513	537,367,797	9·3331
814	662,596	28·531	539,353,144	9·3370
815	664,225	28·548	541,343,375	9·3408
816	665,856	28·566	543,338,496	9·3447
817	667,489	28·583	545,338,513	9·3485
818	669,124	28·601	547,343,432	9·3523
819	670,761	28·618	549,353,259	9·3561
820	672,400	28·636	551,368,000	9·3599
821	674,041	28·653	553,387,661	9·3637
822	675,684	28·670	555,412,248	9·3675
823	677,329	28·688	557,441,767	9·3713
824	678,976	28·705	559,476,224	9·3751
825	680,625	28·723	561,515,625	9·3789
826	682,276	28·740	563,559,976	9·3827
827	683,929	28·758	565,609,283	9·3864
828	685,574	28·775	567,663,552	9·3902
829	687,241	28·792	569,722,789	9·3940
830	688,900	28·810	571,787,000	9·3978
831	690,561	28·827	573,856,191	9·4016
832	692,224	28·844	575,930,368	9·4053
833	693,889	28·862	578,009,537	9·4091
834	695,556	28·879	580,093,704	9·4129
835	697,225	28·896	582,182,875	9·4166
836	698,896	28·914	584,277,056	9·4204
837	700,569	28·931	586,376,253	9·4241
838	702,244	28·948	588,480,472	9·4279
839	703,921	28·965	590,589,719	9·4316
840	705,600	28·983	592,704,000	9·4354
841	707,281	29·000	594,823,321	9·4391
842	708,964	29·017	596,947,688	9·4429
843	710,649	29·034	599,077,107	9·4466
844	712,336	29·052	601,211,584	9·4503
845	714,025	29·069	603,351,125	9·4541
846	715,716	29·086	605,495,736	9·4578
847	717,409	29·103	607,645,423	9·4615
848	719,104	29·120	609,800,192	9·4652
849	720,801	29·138	611,960,049	9·4690
850	722,500	29·155	614,125,000	9·4727

Table of Squares, Square Roots, Cubes and Cube Roots
(*contd.*)

No.	Square	Square Root	Cube	Cube Root
851	724,201	29·172	616,295,051	9·4764
852	725,904	29·189	618,470,208	9·4801
853	727,609	29·206	620,650,477	9·4838
854	729,316	29·223	622,835,864	9·4875
855	731,025	29·240	625,026,375	9·4912
856	732,736	29·257	627,222,016	9·4949
857	734,449	29·275	629,422,793	9·4986
858	736,164	29·292	631,628,712	9·5023
859	737,881	29·309	633,839,779	9·5060
860	739,600	29·326	636,056,000	9·5097
861	741,321	29·343	638,277,381	9·5134
862	743,044	29·360	640,503,928	9·5170
863	744,769	29·377	642,735,647	9·5207
864	746,496	29·394	644,972,544	9·5244
865	748,225	29·411	647,214,625	9·5281
866	749,956	29·428	649,461,896	9·5317
867	751,689	29·445	651,714,363	9·5354
868	753,424	29·462	653,972,032	9·5391
869	755,161	29·479	656,234,909	9·5427
870	756,900	29·496	658,503,000	9·5464
871	758,641	29·513	660,776,311	9·5501
872	760,384	29·530	663,054,848	9·5537
873	762,129	29·547	665,338,617	9·5574
874	763,876	29·563	667,627,624	9·5610
875	765,625	29·580	669,921,875	9·5647
876	767,376	29·597	672,221,376	9·5683
877	769,129	29·614	674,526,133	9·5719
878	770,884	29·631	676,836,152	9·5756
879	772,641	29·648	679,151,439	9·5792
880	774,400	29·665	681,472,000	9·5828
881	776,161	29·682	683,797,841	9·5865
882	777,924	29·698	686,128,968	9·5901
883	779,689	29·715	688,465,387	9·5937
884	781,456	29·732	690,807,104	9·5973
885	783,225	29·749	693,154,125	9·6009
886	784,996	29·766	695,506,456	9·6046
887	786,769	29·782	697,864,103	9·6082
888	788,544	29·799	700,227,072	9·6118
889	790,321	29·816	702,595,369	9·6154
890	792,100	29·833	704,969,000	9·6190
891	793,881	29·850	707,347,971	9·6226
892	795,664	29·866	709,732,288	9·6262
893	797,499	29·883	712,121,957	9·6298
894	799,236	29·900	714,516,984	9·6334
895	801,025	29·917	716,917,375	9·6370
896	802,816	29·933	719,323,136	9·6406
897	804,609	29·950	721,734,273	9·6441
898	806,404	29·967	724,150,792	9·6477
899	808,201	29·983	726,572,699	9·6513
900	810,000	30·000	729,000,000	9·6549

Table of Squares, Square Roots, Cubes and Cube Roots
(*contd.*)

No.	Square	Square Root	Cube	Cube Root
901	811,801	30·017	731,432,701	9·6585
902	813,604	30·033	733,870,808	9·6620
903	815,409	30·050	736,314,327	9·6656
904	817,216	30·067	738,763,264	9·6692
905	819,025	30·083	741,217,625	9·6727
906	820,836	30·100	743,677,416	9·6763
907	822,649	30·116	746,142,643	9·6799
908	824,464	30·133	748,613,312	9·6834
909	826,281	30·150	751,089,429	9·6870
910	828,100	30·166	753,571,000	9·6905
911	829,921	30·183	756,058,031	9·6941
912	831,744	30·199	758,550,528	9·6976
913	833,569	30·216	761,048,497	9·7012
914	835,396	30·232	763,551,944	9·7047
915	837,225	30·249	766,060,875	9·7082
916	839,056	30·265	768,575,296	9·7118
917	840,889	30·282	771,095,213	9·7153
918	842,724	30·298	773,620,632	9·7188
919	844,561	30·315	776,151,559	9·7224
920	846,400	30·331	778,688,000	9·7259
921	848,241	30·348	781,229,961	9·7294
922	850,084	30·364	783,777,448	9·7329
923	851,929	30·381	786,330,467	9·7364
924	853,776	30·397	788,889,024	9·7400
925	855,625	30·414	791,453,125	9·7435
926	857,476	30·430	794,022,776	9·7470
927	859,329	30·447	796,597,983	9·7505
928	861,184	30·463	799,178,752	9·7540
929	863,041	30·479	801,765,089	9·7575
930	864,900	30·496	804,357,000	9·7610
931	866,761	30·512	806,954,491	9·7645
932	868,624	30·529	809,557,568	9·7680
933	870,489	30·545	812,166,237	9·7715
934	872,356	30·561	814,780,504	9·7750
935	874,225	30·578	817,400,375	9·7785
936	876,096	30·594	820,025,856	9·7819
937	877,969	30·610	822,656,953	9·7854
938	879,844	30·627	825,293,672	9·7889
939	881,721	30·643	827,936,019	9·7924
940	883,600	30·659	830,584,000	9·7959
941	885,481	30·676	833,237,621	9·7993
942	887,364	30·692	835,896,888	9·8028
943	889,249	30·708	838,561,807	9·8063
944	891,136	30·725	841,232,384	9·8097
945	893,025	30·741	843,908,625	9·8132
946	894,916	30·757	846,590,536	9·8167
947	896,809	30·773	849,278,123	9·8201
948	898,704	30·799	851,971,392	9·8236
949	900,601	30·806	854,670,349	9·8270
950	902,500	30·822	857,375,000	9·8305

Table of Squares, Square Roots, Cubes and Cube Roots
(*contd.*)

No.	Square	Square Root	Cube	Cube Root
951	904,401	30·838	860,085,351	9·8339
952	906,304	30·854	862,801,408	9·8374
953	908,209	30·871	865,523,177	9·8408
954	910,116	30·887	868,250,664	9·8442
955	912,025	30·903	870,983,875	9·8477
956	913,936	30·919	873,722,816	9·8511
957	915,849	30·935	876,467,493	9·8546
958	917,764	30·951	879,217,912	9·8580
959	919,681	30·968	881,974,079	9·8614
960	921,600	30·984	884,736,000	9·8648
961	923,521	31·000	887,503,681	9·8683
962	925,444	31·016	890,277,128	9·8717
963	927,369	31·032	893,056,347	9·8751
964	929,296	31·048	895,841,344	9·8785
965	931,225	31·064	898,632,125	9·8819
966	933,156	31·080	901,428,696	9·8854
967	935,089	31·097	904,231,063	9·8888
968	937,024	31·112	907,039,232	9·8921
969	938,961	31·129	909,853,209	9·8956
970	940,900	31·144	912,673,000	9·8990
971	942,841	31·160	915,498,611	9·9024
972	944,784	31·177	918,330,048	9·9058
973	946,729	31·192	921,167,317	9·9091
974	948,676	31·209	924,010,424	9·9126
975	950,625	31·225	926,859,375	9·9160
976	952,576	31·241	929,714,176	9·9193
977	954,529	31·257	932,574,833	9·9227
978	956,484	31·273	935,441,352	9·9261
979	958,441	31·289	938,313,739	9·9295
980	960,400	31·305	941,192,000	9·9329
981	962,361	31·321	944,076,141	9·9363
982	964,324	31·337	946,966,168	9·9396
983	966,289	31·353	949,862,087	9·9430
984	968,256	31·369	952,763,904	9·9464
985	970,225	31·385	955,671,625	9·9497
986	972,196	31·401	958,585,256	9·9531
987	974,169	31·417	961,504,803	9·9565
988	976,144	31·432	964,430,272	9·9598
989	978,121	31·448	967,361,669	9·9632
990	980,100	31·464	970,299,000	9·9665
991	982,081	31·480	973,242,271	9·9699
992	984,064	31·496	976,191,488	9·9733
993	986,049	31·512	979,146,657	9·9766
994	988,036	31·528	982,107,784	9·9800
995	990,025	31·544	985,074,875	9·9833
996	992,016	31·559	988,047,936	9·9866
997	994,009	31·575	991,026,973	9·9900
998	996,004	31·591	994,011,992	9·9933
999	998,001	31·607	997,002,999	9·9967
1000	1,000,000	31·623	1,000,000,000	10·0000

WIRE GAUGES USED IN THE UNITED STATES

Number of Wire Gauge	American, or Brown and Sharpe	English, or Birmingham*	Washburn and Moen Manufacturing Co.	Number of Wire Gauge
000000	—	—	·4600	000000
00000	—	—	·4300	00000
0000	·460000	·454	·3930	0000
000	·409640	·425	·3620	000
00	·364800	·380	·3310	00
0	·324860	·340	·3070	0
1	·289300	·300	·2830	1
2	·257630	·284	·2630	2
3	·229420	·259	·2440	3
4	·204310	·238	·2250	4
5	·181940	·220	·2070	5
6	·162020	·203	·1920	6
7	·144280	·180	·1770	7
8	·128490	·165	·1620	8
9	·114430	·148	·1480	9
10	·101890	·134	·1350	10
11	·090742	·120	·1200	11
12	·080808	·109	·1050	12
13	·071961	·095	·0920	13
14	·064084	·083	·0800	14
15	·057068	·072	·0720	15
16	·050820	·065	·0630	16
17	·045257	·058	·0540	17
18	·040303	·049	·0470	18
19	·035890	·042	·0410	19
20	·031961	·035	·0350	20
21	·028462	·032	·0320	21
22	·025347	·028	·0280	22
23	·022571	·025	·0250	23
24	·020100	·022	·0230	24
25	·017900	·020	·0200	25
26	·015940	·018	·0180	26
27	·014195	·016	·0170	27

* B.W.G.

Wire Gauges used in the United States (*contd.*)

Number of Wire Gauge	American, or Brown and Sharpe Diam. (inch)	English, or Birmingham* Diam. (inch)	Washburn and Moen Manufacturing Co. Diam. (inch)	Number of Wire Gauge
28	·012641	·014	·0160	28
29	·011257	·013	·0150	29
30	·010025	·012	·0140	30
31	·008928	·010	·0135	31
32	·007950	·009	·0130	32
33	·007080	·008	·0110	33
34	·006304	·007	·0100	34
35	·005614	·005	·0095	35
36	·005000	·004	·0090	36
37	·004453	—	·0085	37
38	·003965	—	·0080	38
39	·003531	—	·0075	39
40	·003144	—	·0070	40

* B.W.G.

WARRINGTON WIRE GAUGE

Mark	Diameter (inch)	Mark	Diameter (inch)
7/0	$\frac{1}{2}$	9	0·146
6/0	$\frac{15}{32}$	10	0·133
5/0	$\frac{7}{16}$	10½	0·125 or $\frac{1}{8}$
4/0	$\frac{13}{32}$	11	0·117
3/0	$\frac{3}{8}$	12	0·100
2/0	$\frac{11}{32}$	13	0·090
0	0·326	14	0·079
1	0·300	15	0·069
2	0 274	16	0·0625 or $\frac{1}{16}$
3	0·250	17	0·053
4	0·229	18	0·047
5	0·209	19	0·041
6	0·191	20	0·036
7	0·174	21	0·0315 or $\frac{1}{32}$
8	0·159	22	0·028

E.W.D.— 2*

IMPERIAL WIRE GAUGE (S.W.G.)

Size on Standard Wire Gauge	Diameter		Sectional Area in Square Inches	Size on Standard Wire Gauge	Diameter		Sectional Area in Square Inches
	Decimal of an Inch	Milli-metres			Decimal of an Inch	Milli-metres	
7/0	·5000	12·700	·1963500	23	·0240	0·600	·0004500
6/0	·4640	11·800	·1691000	24	·0220	0·550	·0003800
5/0	·4320	11·000	·1465700	25	·0200	0·500	·0003100
4/0	·4000	10·200	·1256800	26	·0180	0·450	·0002500
3/0	·3720	9·400	·1086900	27	·0164	0·400	·0002100
2/0	·3480	8·800	·0951000	28	·0148	0·370	·0001700
1/0	·3240	8·200	·0824400	29	·0136	0·350	·0001400
1	·3000	7·600	·0706900	30	·0124	0·320	·0001200
2	·2760	7·000	·0598200	31	·0116	0·280	·0001000
3	·2520	6·400	·0498700	32	·0108	0·270	·0000910
4	·2320	5·900	·0422700	33	·0100	0·254	·0000780
5	·2120	5·400	·0353000	34	·0092	0·230	·0000660
6	·1920	4·900	·0289600	35	·0084	0·203	·0000550
7	·1760	4·500	·0243200	36	·0076	0·177	·0000450
8	·1600	4·100	·0201100	37	·0068	0·172	·0000360
9	·1440	3·700	·0162800	38	·0060	0·152	·0000280
10	·1280	3·300	·0128700	39	·0052	0·127	·0000210
11	·1160	3·000	·0105700	40	·0048	0·122	·0000180
12	·1040	2·600	·0085000	41	·0044	0·112	·0000150
13	·0920	2·300	·0066500	42	·0040	0·101	·0000120
14	·0800	2·000	·0050300	43	·0036	0·091	·0000100
15	·0720	1·800	·0040700	44	·0032	0·081	·0000080
16	·0640	1·600	·0032200	45	·0028	0·071	·0000060
17	·0560	1·400	·0024600	46	·0024	0·061	·0000040
18	·0480	1·200	·0018100	47	·0020	0·050	·0000030
19	·0400	1·000	·0012600	48	·0016	0·040	·0000020
20	·0360	0·900	·0010200	49	·0012	0·030	·0000010
21	·0320	0·800	·0008000	50	·0010	0·025	·0000007
22	·0280	0·700	·0006200				

STUBS' STEEL WIRE GAUGE

No.	Diameter (inch)	No.	Diameter (inch)	No.	Diameter (inch)
Z	0·413	11	0·188	47	0·077
Y	0·404	12	0·185	48	0·075
X	0·397	13	0·182	49	0·072
W	0·386	14	0·180	50	0·069
V	0·377	15	0·178	51	0·066
U	0·368	16	0·175	52	0·063
T	0·358	17	0·172	53	0·058
S	0·348	18	0·168	54	0·055
R	0·339	19	0·164	55	0·050
Q	0·332	20	0·161	56	0·045
P	0·323	21	0·157	57	0·042
O	0·316	22	0·155	58	0·041
N	0·302	23	0·153	59	0·040
M	0·295	24	0·151	60	0·039
L	0·290	25	0·148	61	0·038
K	0·281	26	0·146	62	0·037
J	0·277	27	0·143	63	0·036
I	0·272	28	0·139	64	0·035
H	0·266	29	0·134	65	0·033
G	0·261	30	0·127	66	0·032
F	0·257	31	0·120	67	0·031
E	0·250	32	0·115	68	0·030
D	0·246	33	0·112	69	0·029
C	0·242	34	0·110	70	0·027
B	0·238	35	0·108	71	0·026
A	0·234	36	0·106	72	0·024
1	0·227	37	0·103	73	0·023
2	0·219	38	0·101	74	0·022
3	0·212	39	0·099	75	0·020
4	0·207	40	0·097	76	0·018
5	0·204	41	0·095	77	0·016
6	0·201	42	0·092	78	0·015
7	0·199	43	0·088	79	0·014
8	0·197	44	0·085	80	0·013
9	0·194	45	0·081		
10	0·191	46	0·079		

BIRMINGHAM WIRE GAUGE (B.W.G.)

B.W.G. No.	Diameter (inch)	B.W.G. No.	Diameter (inch)	B.W.G. No.	Diameter (inch)
0000	0·454	11	0·120	25	0·020
000	0·425	12	0·109	26	0·018
00	0·380	13	0·095	27	0·016
0	0·340	14	0·083	28	0·014
1	0·300	15	0·072	29	0·013
2	0·284	16	0·065	30	0·012
3	0·259	17	0·058	31	0·010
4	0·238	18	0·049	32	0·009
5	0·220	19	0·042	33	0·008
6	0·203	20	0·035	34	0·007
7	0·180	21	0·032	35	0·005
8	0·165	22	0·028	36	0·004
9	0·148	23	0·025		
10	0·134	24	0·022		

WHITWORTH'S WIRE GAUGE

Mark	Size. Inch	Mark	Size. Inch	Mark	Size. Inch	Mark	Size. Inch	Mark	Size. Inch
1	·001	14	·014	34	·034	85	·085	240	·240
2	·002	15	·015	36	·036	90	·090	260	·260
3	·003	16	·016	38	·038	95	·095	280	·280
4	·004	17	·017	40	·040	100	·100	300	·300
5	·005	18	·018	45	·045	110	·110	325	·325
6	·006	19	·019	50	·050	120	·120	350	·350
7	·007	20	·020	55	·055	135	·135	375	·375
8	·008	22	·022	60	·060	150	·150	400	·400
9	·009	24	·024	65	·065	165	·165	425	·425
10	·010	26	·026	70	·070	180	·180	450	·450
11	·011	28	·028	75	·075	200	·200	475	·475
12	·012	30	·030	80	·080	220	·220	500	·500
13	·013	32	·032						

METHODS OF CIRCLE DIVISION

METHOD (1). *By Direct Calculation*

In marking-out practice in the machine shop it is often necessary to mark out the centres of holes on a given pitch circle, so that there will be a given number of holes with equally-spaced centres.

The general solution of this problem is as follows : referring to Fig. 1, it is required to find the length of the chord AB, where A and B are the centres of a pair of consecutive holes on the pitch circle of radius OA = OB = R in.

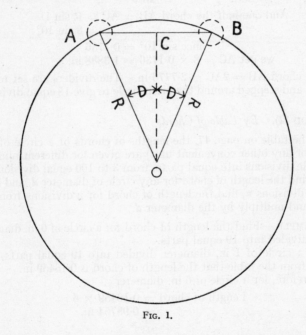

FIG. 1.

First find the value of the angle AOB. This will be equal to $\frac{360°}{n}$, where n is the number of holes. Denote this angle by 2D degrees.

Thus $AOB = 2D = \dfrac{360}{n}$ degrees.

Then, in the right-angled triangle OCA, the angle OCA is a right-angle and the distance AC is given by

$$AC = R \sin D.$$

As we know both R and D, the distance AC can be ascertained, and from this the length of the chord AB, which is equal to twice AC.

EXAMPLE.—It is required to divide a pitch circle of 8 in. radius into 18 equal parts.

In this case the angle $AOB = \dfrac{360}{18} = 20° = 2D$ or $D = 10°$

And one-half the chord $AB = AC = R \sin D$
$$= 8 \sin 10°$$

Since $\sin 10° = 0.1736$
we get $AC = 8 \times 0.1736 = 1.3888$ in.

The chord $AB = 2AC = 2.7776$ in. The dividers are set to this length and stepped around the pitch circle to give 18 equal divisions.

METHOD (2). *By Table of Chords*

In the table on page 47, the lengths of chords of a circle of unit (1 in. or any other convenient unit) are given for different numbers of circle divisions into equal parts, from 3 to 100 equal divisions.

To find the length of chord for any circle of diameter d, and number of divisions n, find the length of chord for n divisions from the table and multiply by the diameter d.

EXAMPLE.—Find the length of chord for a circle of 6 in. diameter to be divided into 19 equal parts.

For a circle of 1 in. diameter divided into 19 equal parts, it is found from the table that the length of chord is 0.16459 in.

Therefore, for a circle of 6 in. diameter :

$$\text{Length of chord} = 0.16459 \times 6$$
$$= 0.98754 \text{ in.}$$

TABLE OF CHORDS FOR CIRCLE DIVISION PURPOSES *

No. of Divisions	Length of Chord	No. of Divisions	Length of Chord	No. of Divisions	Length of Chord	No. of Divisions	Length of Chord
3	0·86602	28	0·11196	53	0·05924	77	0·04079
4	0·70711	29	0·10812	54	0·05814	78	0·04026
5	0·58778	30	0·10453	55	0·05709	79	0·03976
6	0·50000	31	0·10117	56	0·05607	80	0·03926
7	0·43883	32	0·09802	57	0·05509	81	0·03877
8	0·38268	33	0·09506	58	0·05414	82	0·03830
9	0·34202	34	0·09227	59	0·05322	83	0·03784
10	0·30902	35	0·08964	60	0·05234	84	0·03739
11	0·28173	36	0·08715	61	0·05148	85	0·03695
12	0·25882	37	0·08480	62	0·05065	86	0·03652
13	0·23931	38	0·08258	63	0·04984	87	0·03610
14	0·22252	39	0·08047	64	0·04907	88	0·03569
15	0·20791	40	0·07846	65	0·04831	89	0·03529
16	0·19509	41	0·07655	66	0·04758	90	0·03490
17	0·18375	42	0·07473	67	0·04687	91	0·03452
18	0·17365	43	0·07299	68	0·04618	92	0·03414
19	0·16459	44	0·07134	69	0·04551	93	0·03377
20	0·15643	45	0·06976	70	0·04486	94	0·03341
21	0·14904	46	0·06824	71	0·04423	95	0·03306
22	0·14231	47	0·06679	72	0·04362	96	0·03272
23	0·13617	48	0·06540	73	0·04302	97	0·03238
24	0·13053	49	0·06407	74	0·04244	98	0·03205
25	0·12533	50	0·06279	75	0·04187	99	0·03173
26	0·12054	51	0·06156	76	0·04132	100	0·03141
27	0·11609	52	0·06038				

* See explanatory notes on page 42.

PHYSICAL PROPERTIES OF METALS

Metal	Symbol	Atomic Weight O = 16	Atomic Volume	Specific Gravity	Specific Heat	Melting Point °C.	Coefficient of Linear Expansion	Therm. Cond. C.G.S. Units	Elect. Cond. C.G.S. Units
Aluminium . . .	Al	27·1	10·6	2·56	0·218	657	0·0000231	0·502	390,000
Antimony . . .	Sb	120·2	17·9	6·71	0·051	632	0·0000105	0·042	31,471
Arsenic . . .	As	74·96	13·2	5·67	0·081	450 under pressure	0·0000055	—	32,425
Barium . . .	Ba	137·37	36·3	3·78	0·047	850	—	—	—
Bismuth . . .	Bi	208·0	21·2	9·80	0·031	266	0·0000162	0·019	9,091
Cadmium . . .	Cd	112·4	13·2	8·60	0·056	322	0·0000306	0·219	99,800
Caesium . . .	Cs	132·81	71·0	1·87	0·048	26	0·0001316	—	25,400
Calcium . . .	Ca	40·09	25·5	1·57	0·170	780	—	—	150,818
Cerium . . .	Ce	140·25	21·0	6·68	0·045	623	—	—	—
Chromium . . .	Cr	52·0	7·6	6·80	0·120	1,482	—	—	—
Cobalt . . .	Co	58·97	6·9	8·50	0·103	1,464	0·0000123	—	106,140
Columbium . . .	Cb	93·5	13·0	7·2	0·071	1,950	—	—	—
Copper . . .	Cu	63·57	7·1	8·93	0·098	1,084	0·000167	0·924	640,615
Gallium . . .	Ga	69·9	11·8	5·90	0·079	30	—	—	—
Glucinum . . .	Gl	9·1	4·7	1·93	0·621	Below 960	—	—	—
Gold . . .	Au	197·2	10·2	19·32	0·031	1,064	0·0000144	0·700	455,166
Indium . . .	In	114·8	15·5	7·42	0·057	155	0·0000417	—	112,400
Iridium . . .	Ir	193·1	8·6	22·42	0·033	1,950	0·0000070	—	—
Iron . . .	Fe	55·85	7·2	7·86	0·110	1,505	0·0000121	0·147	110,314
Lanthanum . . .	La	139·0	22·7	6·10	0·045	810	0·0000292	—	49,067
Lead . . .	Pb	207·1	18·2	11·37	0·031	327	—	0·084	119,428
Lithium . . .	Li	7·0	13·0	0·54	0·941	186	—	—	—

Element	Symbol								
Magnesium	Mg	24.32	13.9	1.74	0.250	633	0.0000269	0.343	229,616
Manganese	Mn	54.93	7.3	7.50	0.120	1,207	0.0000610	0.015	—
Mercury	Hg	200.0	14.7	13.59	0.032	—39	—	—	10,630
Molybdenum	Mo	96.0	11.2	8.60	0.072	2,500	—	—	—
Nickel	Ni	58.68	6.7	8.80	0.108	1,427	0.0000127	0.141	144,196
Osmium	Os	190.9	8.5	22.48	0.031	2,500	0.0000065	—	105,300
Palladium	Pd	106.7	9.3	11.50	0.059	1,535	0.0000117	0.168	97,857
Platinum	Pt	195.0	9.1	21.50	0.032	1,745	0.0000089	0.166	91,600
Potassium	K	39.1	45.5	0.86	0.170	62	0.0000841	—	141,990
Rhodium	Rh	102.9	8.5	12.10	0.058	1,660	0.0000085	—	—
Rubidium	Rb	85.45	55.8	1.53	0.077	38	—	—	—
Ruthenium	Ru	101.7	8.3	12.26	0.061	1,800	0.0000096	—	—
Scandium	Sc	44.1	17.6	2.5	0.153	1,200	0.0000192	0.993	681,198
Silver	Ag	107.88	10.2	10.53	0.056	962	0.0000710	0.365	253,973
Sodium	Na	23.0	23.8	0.97	0.290	95	—	—	45,708
Strontium	Sr	87.62	34.5	2.54	—	800	—	—	—
Tantalum	Ta	181.0	14.1	12.8	0.033	2,910	0.0000079	—	60,600
Tellurium	Te	127.5	20.4	6.25	0.049	440	0.0000167	—	46,600
Thallium	Tl	204.0	17.2	11.85	0.033	303	0.0000302	—	56,712
Thorium	Th	232.42	20.9	11.10	0.028	1,450	—	0.155	—
Tin	Sn	119.0	16.3	7.29	0.055	232	0.0000232	—	76,640
Titanium	Ti	48.1	13.5	3.54	0.13	2,000 ?	—	—	—
Tungsten	W	184.0	9.6	19.10	0.034	3,100	—	—	11,600
Uranium	U	238.5	12.8	18.7	0.028	—	—	—	—
Vanadium	V	51.2	9.3	5.50	0.125	1,680	—	—	—
Yttrium	Y	89.0	23.4	3.80	—	1,000 ?	—	—	—
Zinc	Zn	65.37	9.1	7.15	0.094	419	0.0000291	0.269	171,381
Zirconium	Zr	90.6	21.8	4.15	0.066	1,500	—	—	—

WEIGHTS OF VARIOUS MATERIALS

(Metals and Timbers)

Material	Specific Gravity	Weight per Cub. Ft. in lb.	Weight per Cub. In. in lb.
Magnesium	1·74	107	0·0626
Magnesium Alloy. Elektron .	1·82	114	0·0656
Beryllium	1·84	115	0·0660
Aluminium Alloy R.R. 56 . .	2·75	172	0·0100
Duralumin	2·800	175·0	0·1015
Aluminium (rolled, sheet) . .	2·670	166·6	0·0960
,, (cast) . . .	2·560	159·6	0·0920
Copper (sheet)	8·780	548·1	0·3160
,, (wire)	8·900	555·0	0·3210
Iron (cast	7·230	451·0	0·2600
,, (wrought)	7·780	486·0	0·2800
Steel (mild)	7·852	489·6	0·2810
,, (cast)	7·848	489·3	0·2810
Brass (cast), average . .	8·280	517·0	0·2980
Gunmetal (10 copper to 1 tin) .	8·464	528·4	0·3060
,, (8 copper to 1 tin) .	8·459	528·0	0·3050
Tin (cast)	7·291	455·0	0·2620
Zinc (cast)	7·000	437·0	0·2520
German silver	8·280	516·0	0·3000
Phosphor bronze (cast) . .	8·600	536·8	0·3100
Aluminium bronze . . .	7·680	475·0	0·2750
Lead	11·37	710·0	0·410
Nickel	8·80	550·0	0·319
Balsa	0·11	6·9	0·0040
Cork	0·24	15·0	0·0087
Oak* (dry)	0·80	50·0	0·029
Ash (dry)	0·69	43·0	0·025
Beech (dry)	0·69	43·0	0·025
Pine, White (dry) . . .	0·43	27·0	0·015
Spruce, Silver (dry) . . .	0·512	32·0	0·018
Walnut, English (dry) . .	0·670	42·0	0·024
Ebony	1·17	73·0	0·042
Lignum Vitae	0·790 to 1·610	49 to 89	0.028 to 0·052
Cedar, American (dry) . .	0·554	35·0	0·020
Elm, English (dry) . . .	0·550	34·0	0·020

* Minimum dry weight.

SECTION 2

PHYSICAL PROPERTIES AND WEIGHTS OF MATERIALS

WEIGHTS OF MISCELLANEOUS MATERIALS

Material	Specific Gravity	Weight per Cub. Ft. in lb.	Weight per Cub. In. in lb.
Alabaster	2·73	171	0·098
Asbestos	3·0	187	0·108
Bakelite (Wood Flour Filler)	1·35	84·4	0·049
Beeswax	0·96	60	0·035
Brickwork	1·5–1·7	94–106	0·054–0·061
Celluloid	1·4	87·5	0·0505
Cement	2·7–3·0	169–187	0·097–0·108
Ebonite	1·15	72	0·0414
Gas Carbon	1·9	119	0·0684
Glass	2·4–2·6	150–163	0·0865–0·093
Granite	2·5–3·0	156–187	0·090–0·108
Gutta-percha	0·95–1·0	59·5–62·5	0·0345–0·0360
India Rubber (Pure)	0·92–0·97	57·5–60·6	0·0330–0·034
India Rubber (Vulcanised)	1·25–1·73	78–108	0·045–0·062
Ivory	1·85	116	0·0665
Leather (Dry)	0·86	53·7	0·0310
Marble	2·70	169	0·097
Mica	2·80	175	0·101
Paper	0·7–1·2	43·8–75	0·025–0·043
Paraffin Wax	0·87–0·93	54·4–58·1	0·031–0·033
Pitch	1·1	69	0·040
Porcelain	2·1–2·5	131–156	0·075–0·090
Resin	1·1	69	0·040
Silica (Fused)	2·15	134	0·0774
Slate	2·65	166	0·095

WEIGHTS AND DIMENSIONS OF METAL SHEETS

Standard Wire Gauge	Thickness		Weight: Pounds per Square Foot				
	Inch	Milli-metres	Alu-minium	Brass	Copper	Steel	Tin
	·375	9·525	5·180	16·70	17·10	15·00	14·40
3/0	·372	9·449	5·140	16·50	17·00	14·90	14·30
2/0	·348	8·839	4·810	15·50	15·90	13·90	13·40
1/0	·324	8·229	4·480	14·40	14·80	13·00	12·50
	·312	7·937	4·310	13·90	14·20	12·50	12·00
1	·300	7·620	4·150	13·30	13·70	12·00	11·50
	·289	7·341	3·990	12·90	13·20	11·60	11·10
	·278	7·061	3·840	12·40	12·70	11·10	10·70
2	·276	7·010	3·810	12·30	12·60	11·00	10·60
	·270	6·858	3·730	12·00	12·30	10·80	10·40
3	·252	6·401	3·480	11·20	11·50	10·10	9·68
	·250	6·350	3·450	11·10	11·40	10·00	9·60
	·238	6·045	3·290	10·60	10·90	9·52	9·14
4	·232	5·893	3·200	10·30	10·60	9·28	8·91
	·216	5·486	2·980	9·61	9·86	8·64	8·31
5	·212	5·385	2·930	9·43	9·68	8·48	8·14
	·200	5·080	2·760	8·90	9·12	8·00	7·68
6	·192	4·877	2·650	8·54	8·76	7·68	7·37
	·187	4·762	2·580	8·32	8·53	7·48	7·18
	·182	4·623	2·520	8·10	8·31	7·28	6·99
7	·176	4·470	2·430	7·83	8·03	7·05	6·70
	·166	4·216	2·290	7·38	7·58	6·64	6·37
8	·160	4·064	2·210	7·12	7·30	6·40	6·15
	·150	3·810	2·070	6·67	6·85	6·00	5·76
9	·144	3·658	1·990	6·41	6·57	5·76	5·53
	·136	3·454	1·880	6·05	6·20	5·44	5·22
10	·128	3·251	1·770	5·69	5·84	5·12	4·92
	125	3·175	1·730	5·56	5·70	5·00	4·80
	·124	3·150	1·710	5·52	5·66	4·96	4·76
11	·116	2·946	1·600	5·16	5·29	4·64	4·46
	·112	2·845	1·550	4·98	5·11	4·48	4·30
12	·104	2·642	1·440	4·63	4·75	4·16	3·99
	·100	2·540	1·380	4·45	4·57	4·00	3·84
13	·092	2·337	1·270	4·09	4·20	3·68	3·53
	·090	2·286	1·240	4·00	4·11	3·60	3·46
	·082	2·082	1·130	3·65	3·75	3·28	3·15
14	·080	2·032	1·110	3·56	3·65	3·20	3·07
	·077	1·956	1·070	3·43	3·52	3·08	2·96
15	·072	1·829	0·995	3·20	3·29	2·88	2·77
	·068	1·727	0·940	3·02	3·11	2·72	2·61
	·065	1·651	0·898	2·89	2·97	2·60	2·50
16	·0640	1·626	0·885	2·85	2·92	2·56	2·46
	·0630	1·600	0·870	2·80	2·88	2·52	2·42
	·0620	1·587	0·857	2·76	2·83	2·48	2·38
	·0600	1·524	0·829	2·67	2·74	2·40	2·30
17	·0560	1·422	0·774	2·49	2·56	2·24	2·15
	·0530	1·397	0·760	2·45	2·51	2·20	2·11
	·0510	1·295	0·705	2·27	2·33	2·04	1·96
18	·0480	1·219	0·663	2·13	2·19	1·92	1·84
	·0470	1·194	0·649	2·09	2·15	1·88	1·81
	·0420	1·067	0·580	1·87	1·92	1·68	1·61

Weights and Dimensions of Metal Sheets (*contd.*)

Standard Wire Gauge	Thickness		Weight : Pounds per Square Foot				
	Inch	Milli-metres	Alu-minium	Brass	Copper	Steel	Tin
19	·0400	1·016	0·552	1·780	1·830	1·600	1·540
	·0380	0·965	0·525	1·690	1·740	1·520	1·460
20	·0360	0·914	0·497	1·600	1·650	1·440	1·380
	·0350	0·889	0·484	1·560	1·600	1·400	1·340
21	·0320	0·813	0·442	1·420	1·460	1·280	1·230
	·0310	0·793	0·429	1·380	1·420	1·240	1·190
22	·0280	0·711	0·387	1·250	1·280	1·120	1·080
	·0270	0·686	0·373	1·200	1·240	1·080	1·040
23	·0240	0·610	0·332	1·070	1·100	0·960	0·921
	·0230	0·584	0·318	1·020	1·050	0·920	0·883
24	·0220	0·559	0·304	0·979	1·010	0·880	0·845
	·0210	0·533	0·290	0·935	0·960	0·840	0·806
25	·0200	0·508	0·276	0·890	0·914	0·800	0·768
	·0190	0·483	0·262	0·846	0·868	0·760	0·730
26	·0180	0·457	0·249	0·801	0·823	0·720	0·691
27	·0164	0·416	0·227	0·730	0·750	0·656	0·630
	·0160	0·406	0·221	0·712	0·731	0·640	0·614
	·0156	0·397	0·215	0·694	0·713	0·624	0·599
28	·0148	0·376	0·204	0·658	0·677	0·592	0·568
	·0140	0·356	0·193	0·623	0·640	0·560	0·537
29	·0136	0·345	0·188	0·605	0·622	0·544	0·522
30	·0124	0·315	0·171	0·552	0·566	0·496	0·476
	·0120	0·305	0·166	0·534	0·548	0·480	0·461
	·0105	0·267	0·145	0·467	0·480	0·420	0·403
	·0090	0·229	5·125	0·400	0·412	0·360	0·360
	·0080	0·203	0·111	0·356	0·366	0·320	0·307
Specific gravity . . .			2·670	8·620	8·820	7·740	7·400
Ratio of weights . . .			1	3·230	3·300	2·900	2·780

WEIGHT OF ANGLE AND TEE STEEL BARS
(PER FOOT LENGTH)

Breadth (flanges added)	Thickness in Fractions of an Inch											
	$\frac{3}{16}$	$\frac{1}{4}$	$\frac{5}{16}$	$\frac{3}{8}$	$\frac{7}{16}$	$\frac{1}{2}$	$\frac{9}{16}$	$\frac{5}{8}$	$\frac{11}{16}$	$\frac{3}{4}$	$\frac{13}{16}$	$\frac{7}{8}$
In.	Lb.	Lb.	Lb.	Lb.	Lb.	Lb.	Lb.	Lb.	Lb.	Lb.	Lb.	Lb.
2	1·16	1·49	1·79	2·07	—	—	—	—	—	—	—	—
2¼	1·32	1·70	2·06	2·39	—	—	—	—	—	—	—	—
2½	1·47	1·91	2·32	2·71	3·07	—	—	—	—	—	—	—
2¾	1·63	2·13	2·59	3·03	3·44	—	—	—	—	—	—	—
3	1·79	2·34	2·86	3·35	3·81	4·25	—	—	—	—	—	—
3¼	1·95	2·55	3·12	3·67	4·18	4·68	—	—	—	—	—	—
3½	2·11	2·76	3·39	3·98	4·56	5·10	5·62	—	—	—	—	—
3¾	2·27	2·98	3·65	4·30	4·93	5·53	6·10	—	—	—	—	—
4	2·43	3·19	3·92	4·62	5·30	5·95	6·57	7·17	—	—	—	—
4¼	2·59	3·40	4·18	4·94	5·67	6·38	7·05	7·70	—	—	—	—
4½	2·75	3·61	4·45	5·26	6·04	6·80	7·53	8·23	8·91	—	—	—
4¾	2·91	3·83	4·72	5·58	6·42	7·23	8·01	8·77	9·50	—	—	—
5	3·07	4·04	4·98	5·90	6·79	7·65	8·49	9·30	10·08	10·84	—	—
5¼	3·23	4·25	5·25	6·22	7·16	8·08	8·97	9·83	10·67	11·48	—	—
5½	3·39	4·46	5·51	6·53	7·53	8·50	9·44	10·36	11·25	12·11	12·95	—
5¾	3·55	4·68	5·78	6·85	7·90	8·93	9·92	10·89	11·83	12·75	13·64	—
6	3·71	4·89	6·04	7·17	8·27	9·35	10·40	11·42	12·42	13·39	14·33	15·25
6¼	3·87	5·10	6·31	7·49	8·65	9·78	10·88	11·95	13·00	14·03	15·02	15·99
6½	4·02	5·31	6·57	7·81	9·02	10·20	11·36	12·48	13·59	14·66	15·71	16·73
6¾	4·18	5·53	6·84	8·13	9·39	10·63	11·83	13·02	14·17	15·30	16·40	17·48
7	4·34	5·74	7·11	8·45	9·76	11·05	12·31	13·55	14·76	15·94	17·09	18·22
7¼	4·50	5·95	7·37	8·77	10·13	11·48	12·79	14·08	15·34	16·58	17·78	18·97
7½	4·66	6·16	7·64	9·08	10·51	11·90	13·27	14·61	15·92	17·21	18·47	19·71
7¾	4·82	6·38	7·90	9·40	10·88	12·33	13·75	15·14	16·51	17·85	19·17	20·45
8	4·98	6·59	8·17	9·72	11·25	12·75	14·22	15·67	17·09	18·49	19·86	21·20
8¼	5·14	6·80	8·43	10·04	11·62	13·18	14·70	16·20	17·68	19·13	20·55	21·94
8½	5·30	7·01	8·70	10·36	11·99	13·60	15·18	16·73	18·26	19·76	21·24	22·68
8¾	5·46	7·23	8·97	10·68	12·37	14·03	15·66	17·27	18·85	20·40	21·93	23·43
9	5·62	7·44	9·23	11·00	12·74	14·45	16·14	17·80	19·43	21·04	22·62	24·17
9¼	5·78	7·65	9·50	11·32	13·11	14·88	16·62	18·33	20·02	21·68	23·31	24·92
9½	5·94	7·86	9·76	11·63	13·48	15·30	17·09	18·86	20·60	22·31	24·00	25·66
9¾	6·10	8·08	10·03	11·95	13·85	15·73	17·57	19·39	21·18	22·95	24·69	26·40
10	6·26	8·29	10·29	12·27	14·22	16·15	18·05	19·92	21·77	23·59	25·38	27·15
10¼	6·42	8·50	10·56	12·59	14·60	16·58	18·53	20·45	22·35	24·23	26·07	27·89
10½	6·57	8·71	10·82	12·91	14·97	17·00	19·01	20·98	22·94	24·86	26·76	28·63
10¾	6·73	8·93	11·09	13·23	15·34	17·43	19·48	21·52	23·52	25·50	27·45	29·38
11	6·89	9·14	11·36	13·55	15·71	17·85	19·96	22·05	24·11	26·14	28·14	30·12
11¼	—	9·35	11·62	13·87	16·08	18·38	20·44	22·58	24·69	26·78	28·83	30·87
11½	—	9·56	11·89	14·18	16·46	18·70	20·92	23·11	25·27	27·41	29·52	31·61
11¾	—	—	12·15	14·50	16·83	19·13	21·40	23·64	25·86	28·05	30·22	32·35
12	—	—	12 42	14·82	17·20	19·55	21·87	24·17	26·44	28·69	30·91	33·10

(Henderson & Glass.)

WEIGHT OF WROUGHT MAGNESIUM ALLOY (ELEKTRON)

(Sheet and Strip)

Thickness S.W.G.	Decimal Equivalent (inch)	Weight in Lb. per Sq. Ft.
0	0·324	2·99
1	0·300	2·88
2	0·276	2·63
3	0·252	2·40
4	0·232	2·22
5	0·212	2·02
6	0·192	1·83
7	0·176	1·69
8	0·160	1·53
9	0·144	1·37
10	0·128	1·22
11	0·116	1·11
12	0·104	1·00
13	0·092	0·88
14	0·080	0·76
15	0·072	0·69
16	0·064	0·61
17	0·056	0·54
18	0·048	0·46
19	0·040	0·38
20	0·036	0·34
21	0·032	0·31
22	0·028	0·26
23	0·024	0·23
24	0·022	0·21
25	0·020	0·19
26	0·018	0·17
27	0·016	0·15
28	0·014	0·14
29	0·013	0·13
30	0·012	0·12

WEIGHTS AND DIMENSIONS OF HARD STEEL WIRE

Standard Wire Gauge	Diameter		Sectional Area in Square Inches	Approximate Weight of—		
	Decimal of an Inch	Milli-metres		100 Feet	Mile	Kilometre
				Lb.	Lb.	Lb.
7/0	·5000	12·700	·1963500	66·700000	3,552	2,188
6/0	·4640	11·800	·1691000	57·440000	3,033	1,885
5/0	·4320	11·000	·1465700	49·790000	2,629	1,634
4/0	·4000	10·200	·1256800	42·690000	2,254	1,400
3/0	·3720	9·400	·1086900	36·930000	1,950	1,211
2/0	·3480	8·800	·0951000	32·310000	1,706	1,060
1/0	·3240	8·200	·0824400	28·010000	1,479	919
1	·3000	7·600	·0706900	24·010000	1,268	788
2	·2760	7·000	·0598200	20·320000	1,073	667
3	·2520	6·400	·0498700	16·850000	895	556
4	·2320	5·900	·0422700	14·360000	758	471
5	·2120	5·400	·0353000	12·000000	633	393
6	·1920	4·900	·0289600	9·810000	518	323
7	·1760	4·500	·0243200	8·260000	436	271
8	·1600	4·100	·0201100	6·820000	360	224
9	·1440	3·700	·0162800	5·530000	292	182
10	·1280	3·300	·0128700	4·370000	231	143
11	·1160	3·000	·0105700	3·600000	190	118
12	·1040	2·600	·0085000	2·880000	152	95
13	·0920	2·300	·0066500	2·250000	119	74
14	·0800	2·000	·0050300	1·700000	90	56
15	·0720	1·800	·0040700	1·380000	73	45
16	·0640	1·600	·0032200	1·100000	58	36
17	·0560	1·400	·0024600	·830000	44	27·5000
18	·0480	1·200	·0018100	·610000	32·500	20·2000
19	·0400	1·000	·0012600	·420000	22·540	14·0000
20	·0360	·900	·0010200	·340000	18·250	11·3400
21	·0320	·800	·0008000	·273000	14·420	8·9600
22	·0280	·700	·0006200	·209000	11·040	6·8600
23	·0240	·600	·0004500	·154000	8·110	5·0400
24	·0220	·550	·0003800	·129000	6·820	4·2400
25	·0200	·500	·0003100	·107000	5·630	3·5000

Weights and Dimensions of Hard Steel Wire (*contd.*)

Size on Standard Wire Gauge	Diameter		Sectional Area in Square Inches	Approximate Weight of—		
	Decimal of an Inch	Milli-metres		100 *Feet*	Mile	Kilometre
				Lb.	Lb.	Lb.
26	·0180	·450	·0002500	·086000	4·560	2·8400
27	·0164	·400	·0002100	·072000	3·790	2·3500
28	·0148	·370	·0001700	·058000	3·090	1·9200
29	·0136	·350	·0001400	·050000	2·610	1·6200
30	·0124	·320	·0001200	·041000	2·170	1·3500
31	·0116	·280	·0001000	·036000	1·890	1·1600
32	·0108	·270	·0000910	·031000	1·640	1·0200
33	·0100	·254	·0000780	·026000	1·400	·8750
34	·0092	·230	·0000660	·022000	1·190	·7440
35	·0084	·203	·0000550	·019000	·901	·5630
36	·0076	·177	·0000450	·015000	·813	·5080
37	·0068	·172	·0000360	·012000	·651	·4070
38	·0060	·152	·0000280	·009600	·507	·3170
39	·0052	·127	·0000210	·007200	·380	·2380
40	·0048	·122	·0000180	·006100	·324	·2020
41	·0044	·112	·0000150	·005100	·272	·1700
42	·0040	·101	·0000120	·004200	·225	·1400
43	·0036	·091	·0000100	·003400	·182	·1140
44	·0032	·081	·0000080	·002700	·144	·0900
45	·0028	·071	·0000060	·002100	·110	·0700
46	·0024	·061	·0000040	·001500	·081	·0500
47	·0020	·050	·0000030	·001060	·056	·0350
48	·0016	·040	·0000020	·000700	·036	·0250
49	·0012	·030	·0000010	·000350	·020	·0125
50	·0010	·025	·0000007	·000245	·014	·0087

WEIGHTS OF ROUND AND SQUARE SECTION BARS

[Aluminium Alloy (R.R.56), Brass and Steel]

Diam. or Distance across Flats in Inches		Round Rod, Pounds per Foot			Square Bar, Pounds per Foot		
Fraction	Decimal	R.R.56	Brass	Steel	R.R.56	Brass	Steel
1/16	·062	·003	·011	·010	·004	·014	·013
3/32	·093	·008	·025	·023	·010	·032	·029
1/8	·125	·014	·045	·041	·018	·057	·053
5/32	·156	·023	·070	·065	·029	·090	·083
3/16	·187	·030	·101	·094	·041	·129	·119
7/32	·218	·042	·138	·127	·056	·176	·162
1/4	·250	·057	·181	·167	·074	·230	·212
9/32	·281	·073	·229	·211	·093	·291	·269
5/16	·312	090	·282	·261	·115	·360	·332
11/32	·343	·110	·342	·316	·139	·435	·402
3/8	·375	·130	·407	·375	·166	·518	·478
13/32	·406	·153	·477	·441	·194	·608	·561
7/16	·437	·178	·554	·511	·226	·705	·651
15/32	·468	·205	·636	·587	·260	·809	·747
1/2	·500	·232	·723	·668	·296	·922	·851
9/16	·562	·294	·916	·845	·374	1·166	1·077
5/8	·625	·362	1·130	1·044	·461	1·439	1·329
11/16	·687	·445	1·368	1·263	·565	1·742	1·609
3/4	·750	·521	1·628	1·503	·663	2·073	1·914
13/16	·812	·611	1·911	1·765	·775	2·433	2·247
7/8	·875	·710	2·216	2·047	·902	2·822	2·606
15/16	·937	·815	2·544	2·349	1·042	3·240	2·991
1	1·00	·925	2·89	2·67	1·18	3·68	3·40
1 1/16	1·06	1·04	3·26	3·01	1·33	4·16	3·84
1 1/8	1·12	1·17	3·66	3·38	1·48	4·66	4·31

[Reynolds Tube Co. Ltd.]

Note.—For aluminium multiply R.R.56 weight values by 0·980.

Weights of Round and Square Section Bars (*contd.*)

Diam. or Distance across Flats in Inches.		Round Rod, Pounds per Foot			Square Bar, Pounds per Foot		
Fraction	Decimal	R.R.56	Brass	Steel	R.R.56	Brass	Steel
1 3/16	1·18	1·30	4·08	3·76	1·67	5·19	4·79
1 1/4	1·25	1·45	4·52	4·17	1·85	5·76	5·32
1 5/16	1·31	1·60	4·98	4·60	2·02	6·35	5·86
1 3/8	1·37	1·75	5·47	5·05	2·25	6·97	6·43
1 7/16	1·43	1·92	5·98	5·52	2·45	7·61	7·03
1 1/2	1·50	2·08	6·51	6·01	2·65	·8·29	7·65
1 9/16	1·56	2·26	7·06	6·52	2·86	8·99	8·30
1 5/8	1·62	2·44	7·64	7·06	3·10	9·73	8·99
1 11/16	1·68	2·65	8·24	7·61	3·34	10·49	9·69
1 3/4	1·75	2·85	8·86	8·18	3·62	11·29	10·42
1 13/16	1·81	3·02	9·51	8·78	3·86	12·11	11·18
1 7/8	1·87	3·24	10·18	9·40	4·11	12·96	11·96
1 15/16	1·93	3·49	10·86	10·03	4·40	13·83	12·77
2	2·00	3·72	11·58	10·69	4·71	14·74	13·61
2 1/8	2·12	4·17	13·07	12·07	5·30	16·64	15·37
2 1/4	2·25	4·67	14·65	13·53	5·96	18·66	17·23
2 3/8	2·37	5·22	16·33	15·08	6·62	20·79	19·20
2 1/2	2·50	5·80	18·09	16·70	7·36	23·04	21·27
2 5/8	2·62	6·40	19·95	18·42	8·10	25·40	23·45
2 3/4	2·75	6·97	21·89	20·22	8·90	27·88	25·74
2 7/8	2·87	7·65	23·93	22·10	9·70	30·47	28·13
3	3·00	8·33	26·05	24·06	10·61	33·17	30·63

Note.—For aluminium multiply R.R.56 weight values by 0·980

WEIGHT OF GAS AND STEAM PIPE

Gas Pipe Size. Inch	Weight in Lb. per Foot Length	
	Gas Pipe	Steam Pipe
⅛	. ·27	·32
¼	·40	·49
⅜	·56	·68
½	·84	1·01
¾	1·20	1·43
1	1·67	2·01
1¼	2·34	2·80
1½	3·10	3·76
1¾	3·64	4·36
2	4·21	5·07
2¼	4·614	5·49
2½	5·349	6·33
2¾	5·874	6·95
3	6·347	7·52
3½	7·213	8·55
4	8·097	9·60

[J. Russell & Co. Ltd.]

WEIGHT OF FLEXIBLE METALLIC TUBING

Diameter in Inches (External)	Weight in Lb. and Oz.			
	Steel Fireproof		Steel No. 2	
	lb.	oz.	lb.	oz.
5/32		1·25		—
3/16		1·25		—
¼		1·25		—
5/16		2·0		3·0
⅜		2·25		4·0
½		2·75		5·5
⅝		3·75		7·5
¾		6·5		9·5
1		—		12·5
1¼		—		14·75
1½		—	1	4·50
2		—	1	12·75
2½		—	2	11·00
3		—	3	12·25
3½		—	4	3·25
4		—	5	10·50

[United Flexible Metallic Tubing Co.]

ALUMINIUM TUBES. SIZES AND WEIGHTS *

Weight in Lb. per Linear Foot

S.W.G.	Thickness In.	Thickness Mm.	3/16 (4·76)	1/4 (6·35)	5/16 (7·94)	3/8 (9·52)	7/16 (11·1)	1/2 (12·7)	9/16 (14·3)	5/8 (15·9)
								Outside Diameter		
6	·192	4·87								·306
7	·176	4·46								·291
8	·160	4·06								·274
9	·144	3·66						·189	·222	·255
10	·128	3·25					·146	·175	·205	·234
11	·116	2·94				·111	·137	·164	·191	·217
12	·104	2·64				·104	·128	·152	·176	·200
13	·092	2·34			·0747	·0959	·117	·138	·159	·181
14	·080	2·03		·0501	·0685	·0869	·105	·124	·142	·161
15	·072	1·83		·0472	·0638	·0803	·0969	·113	·130	·147
16	·064	1·62	·0291	·0438	·0586	·0733	·0880	·103	·117	·132
17	·056	1·42	·0271	·0400	·0529	·0658	·0787	·0915	·104	·117
18	·048	1·22	·0247	·0357	·0467	·0578	·0688	·0799	·0909	·102
19	·040	1·02	·0217	·0309	·0401	·0493	·0585	·0677	·0770	·0862
20	·036	0·914	·0201	·0284	·0367	·0449	·0532	·0615	·0698	·0781
21	·032	0·812	·0183	·0257	·0330	·0404	·0478	·0551	·0625	·0699
22	·028	0·711	·0164	·0229	·0293	·0358	·0422	·0487	·0551	·0615
23	·024	0·610	·0144	·0200	·0255	·0310	·0365	·0421	·0476	·0531
24	·022	0·559	·0134	·0185	·0235	·0286	·0337	·0387	·0438	·0488

* *British Aluminium Company Ltd., London.*

Aluminium Tubes. Sizes and Weights (contd.)

Weight in Lb. per Linear Foot

S.W.G.	Thickness In.	Thickness Mm.	11/16 · 17·5	¾ · 19·0	13/16 · 20·6	⅞ · 22·2	15/16 · 23·8	1 · 25·4	1⅛ · 28·6	1¼ · 31·8
1	·300	7·62	—	—	—	—	—	·773	·911	1·049
2	·276	7·00	—	—	—	—	—	·736	·863	·990
3	·252	6·40	—	—	—	·578	·636	·694	·810	·926
4	·232	5·89	—	—	—	·549	·603	·656	·763	·870
5	·212	5·38	—	·420	·469	·518	·566	·615	·713	·810
6	·192	4·87	·350	·394	·439	·483	·527	·571	·660	·748
7	·176	4·46	·331	·372	·412	·453	·493	·534	·615	·696
8	·160	4·06	·311	·348	·384	·421	·458	·495	·569	·642
9	·144	3·66	·288	·321	·354	·388	·421	·454	·520	·586
10	·128	3·25	·264	·293	·323	·352	·381	·411	·470	·529
11	·116	2·94	·244	·271	·297	·324	·351	·378	·431	·484
12	·104	2·64	·223	·247	·271	·295	·319	·343	·391	·439
13	·092	2·34	·202	·223	·244	·265	·286	·308	·350	·392
14	·080	2·03	·179	·197	·216	·234	·253	·271	·308	·345
15	·072	1·83	·163	·180	·196	·213	·229	·246	·279	·312
16	·064	1·62	·147	·162	·176	·191	·206	·221	·250	·279
17	·056	1·42	·130	·143	·156	·169	·182	·195	·220	·248
18	·048	1·22	·113	·124	·135	·146	·157	·168	·190	·212
19	·040	1·02	·0954	·105	·114	·123	·132	·141	·160	·178
20	·036	0·914	·0864	·0946	·103	·111	·119	·128	·144	·161
21	·032	0·812	·0772	·0846	·0920	·0993	·107	·114	·129	·143
22	·028	0·711	·0680	·0744	·0809	·0863	·0938	·100	·113	·126
23	·024	0·610	·0586	·0642	·0697	·0752	·0807	·0862	·0973	·108
24	·022	0·559	·0539	·0590	·0640	·0691	·0742	·0792	·0893	·0995

Aluminium Tubes. Sizes and Weights (*contd.*)

Weight in Lb. per Linear Foot

S.W.G.	Thickness In.	Mm.	1⅜ 34·9	1½ 38·1	1⅝ 41·3	1¾ 44·5	1⅞ 47·6	2 50·8	2⅛ 53·9
1	·300	7·62	1·187	1·326	1·464	1·602	1·740	1·878	2·016
2	·276	7·00	1·117	1·244	1·371	1·498	1·625	1·752	1·879
3	·252	6·40	1·042	1·158	1·274	1·390	1·506	1·622	1·738
4	·232	5·89	·976	1·083	1·190	1·297	1·403	1·510	1·617
5	·212	5·38	·908	1·005	1·103	1·200	1·298	1·396	1·493
6	·192	4·87	·836	·925	1·013	1·101	1·190	1·278	1·368
7	·176	4·46	·777	·858	·939	1·020	1·101	1·182	1·263
8	·160	4·06	·716	·789	·863	·937	1·010	1·084	1·158
9	·144	3·66	·653	·719	·785	·852	·918	·984	1·050
10	·128	3·25	·588	·647	·705	·764	·823	·882	·941
11	·116	2·94	·538	·591	·625	·698	·751	·805	·858
12	·104	2·64	·487	·535	·582	·630	·678	·726	·774
13	·092	2·34	·435	·477	·519	·562	·604	·646	·689
14	·080	2·03	·381	·418	·455	·492	·529	·566	·602
15	·072	1·83	·345	·379	·412	·445	·478	·511	·544
16	·064	1·62	·309	·338	·368	·397	·427	·456	·486
17	·056	1·42	·272	·298	·324	·349	·375	·401	·427
18	·048	1·22	·235	·257	·279	·301	·323	·345	·367
19	·040	1·02	·197	·215	·233	·252	·270	·289	·307
20	·036	·914	·177	·194	·211	·227	·244	·266	·277
21	·032	·812	·158	·173	·188	·202	·217	·232	·247
22	·028	·711	·139	·152	·165	·178	·190	·203	·216

Aluminium Tubes. Sizes and Weights (contd.)

Outside Diameter	In.		2¼	2⅜	2½	2⅝	2¾	2⅞	3
	Mm.		57·1	60·3	63·5	66·6	69·8	73·0	76·2
	Thickness					Weight in Lb. per Linear Foot			
S.W.G.	In.	Mm.							
1	·300	7·62	2·154	2·292	2·430	2·568	2·706	2·844	2·982
2	·276	7·00	2·006	2·133	2·260	2·387	2·514	2·641	2·768
3	·252	6·40	1·854	1·970	2·086	2·202	2·318	2·434	2·550
4	·232	5·89	1·724	1·831	1·937	2·044	2·151	2·258	2·364
5	·212	5·38	1·591	1·688	1·786	1·883	1·981	2·078	2·176
6	·192	4·87	1·455	1·543	1·631	1·720	1·808	1·896	1·985
7	·176	4·46	1·344	1·425	1·506	1·587	1·668	1·749	1·830
8	·160	4·06	1·231	1·305	1·378	1·452	1·526	1·599	1·673
9	·144	3·66	1·117	1·183	1·249	1·315	1·382	1·448	1·514
10	·128	3·25	1·000	1·059	1·118	1·177	1·236	1·295	1·354
11	·116	2·94	·911	·965	1·018	1·072	1·125	1·178	1·232
12	·104	2·64	·822	·870	·918	·965	1·013	1·061	1·109
13	·092	2·34	·731	·773	·816	·858	·900	·943	·985
14	·080	2·03	·639	·676	·713	·750	·787	·823	·860
15	·072	1·83	·577	·611	·644	·677	·710	·743	·776
16	·064	1·62	·515	·545	·574	·603	·633	·662	·692
17	·056	1·42	·452	·478	·504	·530	·555	·581	·607
18	·048	1·22	·389	·411	·433	·455	·478	·500	·522

Aluminium Tubes. Sizes and Weights (contd.)

	Outside Diameter In.	Mm.	3⅛ 79·4	3¼ 82·6	3⅜ 85·7	3½ 88·9	3⅝ 92·0	3¾ 95·2	3⅞ 98·4
S.W.G.	Thickness In.	Mm.			Weight in Lb. per Linear Foot				
1	·300	7·62	3·120	3·258	3·397	3·534	3·673	3·811	3·949
2	·276	7·00	2·895	3·022	3·149	3·276	3·403	3·530	3·658
3	·252	6·40	2·666	2·782	2·898	3·013	3·129	3·246	3·362
4	·232	5·89	2·471	2·578	2·685	2·791	2·898	3·005	3·112
5	·212	5·38	2·274	2·371	2·469	2·566	2·664	2·762	2·859
6	·192	4·87	2·073	2·162	2·250	2·338	2·427	2·515	2·603
7	·176	4·46	1·911	1·992	2·073	2·154	2·235	2·316	2·397
8	·160	4·06	1·747	1·820	1·894	1·968	2·041	2·115	2·188
9	·144	3·66	1·581	1·647	1·713	1·779	1·846	1·912	1·978
10	·128	3·25	1·412	1·471	1·530	1·589	1·648	1·707	1·766
11	·116	2·94	1·285	1·339	1·392	1·445	1·499	1·552	1·606
12	·104	2·64	1·157	1·205	1·253	1·300	1·348	1·396	1·444
13	·092	2·34	1·027	1·070	1·112	1·155	1·197	1·239	1·282
14	·080	2·03	·897	·934	·971	1·007	1·044	1·081	1·118
15	·072	1·83	·809	·842	·876	·909	·942	·975	1·008
16	·064	1·62	·721	·751	·780	·810	·839	·869	·898

Aluminium Tubes. Sizes and Weights (contd.)

Outside Diameter } In.	Mm.	Thickness S.W.G.	In.	Mm.	4 / 102	4⅛ / 105	4¼ / 108	4⅜ / 111	4½ / 114	4⅝ / 117	4¾ / 121
					Weight in Lb. per Linear Foot						
		1	·300	7·62	4·087	4·225	4·363	4·501	4·639	4·777	4·915
		2	·276	7·00	3·784	3·911	4·038	4·165	4·292	4·419	4·546
		3	·252	6·40	3·478	3·594	3·710	3·826	3·942	4·058	4·174
		4	·232	5·89	3·219	3·325	3·432	3·539	3·646	3·752	3·859
		5	·212	5·38	2·957	3·054	3·152	3·249	3·347	3·444	3·542
		6	·192	4·87	2·692	2·780	2·869	2·957	3·045	3·134	3·222
		7	·176	4·46	2·478	2·559	2·640	2·721	2·802	2·883	2·964
		8	·160	4·06	2·263	2·336	2·410	2·483	2·557	2·631	2·704
		9	·144	3·66	2·045	2·111	2·177	2·243	2·310	2·376	2·442
		10	·128	3·25	1·824	1·883	1·942	2·001	2·059	2·118	2·177
		11	·116	2·94	1·659	1·712	1·766	1·819	1·872	1·926	1·979
		12	·104	2·64	1·492	1·540	1·588	1·635	1·683	1·731	1·779
		13	·092	2·34	1·324	1·366	1·408	1·451	1·493	1·536	1·578
		14	·080	2·03	1·155	1·191	1·228	1·265	1·302	1·339	1·376
		15	·072	1·83	1·041	1·074	1·108	1·141	1·174	1·207	1·240
		16	·064	1·62	·928	·957	·986	1·016	1·045	1·075	1·104

Aluminium Tubes. Sizes and Weights (*contd.*)

Outside Diameter	Thickness S.W.G.	In.	Mm.	4⅞ / 124	5 / 127	5⅛ / 130	5¼ / 133	5⅜ / 136	5½ / 140	5⅝ / 143
		In.	Mm.	*Weight in Lb. per Linear Foot*						
	1	·300	7·62	5·054	5·192	5·330	5·468	5·606	5·774	5·882
	2	·276	7·00	4·673	4·801	4·928	5·055	5·182	5·309	5·436
	3	·252	6·40	4·289	4·405	4·521	4·637	4·753	4·869	4·985
	4	·232	5·89	3·966	4·073	4·180	4·286	4·393	4·500	4·607
	5	·212	5·38	3·641	3·738	3·836	3·933	4·031	4·128	4·226
	6	·192	4·87	3·311	3·399	3·487	3·576	3·664	3·753	3·841
	7	·176	4·46	3·045	3·126	3·207	3·288	3·369	3·450	3·531
	8	·160	4·06	2·778	2·851	2·925	2·999	3·072	3·146	3·219
	9	·144	3·66	2·509	2·575	2·641	2·707	2·773	2·840	2·906
	10	·128	3·25	2·237	2·296	2·355	2·414	2·473	2·532	2·591

Aluminium Tubes. Sizes and Weights (*contd.*)

Outside Diameter (In. / Mm.)			5¾ / 146	6 / 152	6¼ / 159	6½ / 165	6¾ / 171	7 / 177	7¼ / 184	7½ / 191	7¾ / 197
Thickness						*Weight in Lb. per Linear Foot*					
	Inches	Mm.									
½	·500	12·7	9·666	10·13	10·59	11·05	11·51	11·97	12·43	12·89	13·35
15/32	·469	11·9	9·121	9·552	9·985	10·42	10·85	11·28	11·71	12·14	12·58
7/16	·438	11·1	8·549	8·951	9·353	9·756	10·16	10·56	10·96	11·36	11·77
13/32	·406	10·3	7·989	8·363	8·736	9·110	9·484	9·858	10·23	10·61	10·98
3/8	·375	9·52	7·422	7·767	8·112	8·457	8·802	9·148	9·493	9·838	10·18
11/32	·344	8·74	6·847	7·164	7·480	7·797	8·114	8·430	8·746	9·064	9·380
5/16	·313	7·92	6·247	6·534	6·822	7·108	7·396	7·683	7·970	8·258	8·544
9/32	·281	7·14	5·659	5·917	6·176	6·434	6·693	6·952	7·210	7·470	7·728
¼	·250	6·35	5·063	5·293	5·523	5·753	5·983	6·213	6·444	6·674	6·904
7/32	·219	5·54	4·441	4·641	4·842	5·059	5·261	5·462	5·663	5·865	6·066
3/16	·188	4·75	3·831	4·003	4·175	4·347	4·519	4·691	4·863	5·036	5·208
5/32	·156	3·96	3·213	3·356	3·500	3·643	3·787	3·931	4·074	4·218	4·361
⅛	·125	3·18	2·589	2·704	2·819	2·934	3·049	3·164	3·279	3·394	3·509

Aluminium Tubes. Sizes and Weights (*contd.*)

Weight in Lb. per Linear Foot

Outside Diameter — In.	Mm.	8	8¼	8½	8¾	9	9¼	9½	9¾	10
		203	210	216	222	228	234	241	248	254

Thickness — Inches	In.	Mm.	8 / 203	8¼ / 210	8½ / 216	8¾ / 222	9 / 228	9¼ / 234	9½ / 241	9¾ / 248	10 / 254
½	·500	12·7	13·81	14·27	14·73	15·19	15·65	16·11	16·57	17·03	17·49
15/32	·469	11·9	13·00	13·44	13·87	14·30	14·73	15·16	15·60	16·03	16·46
7/16	·438	11·1	12·17	12·57	12·97	13·38	13·78	14·18	14·58	14·99	15·39
13/32	·406	10·3	11·35	11·73	12·10	12·47	12·85	13·22	13·60	13·97	14·34
3/8	·375	9·52	10·53	10·87	11·22	11·56	11·91	12·25	12·60	12·95	13·29
11/32	·344	8·74	9·697	10·01	10·33	10·65	10·96	11·28	11·60	11·91	12·23
5/16	·313	7·92	8·832	9·119	9·406	9·694	9·980	10·27	10·56	10·84	11·13
9/32	·281	7·14	7·993	8·252	8·511	8·770	9·029	9·288	9·547	9·805	10·06
¼	·250	6·35	7·134	7·364	7·594	7·824	8·055	8·285	8·515	8·745	8·975
7/32	·219	5·54	6·246	6·448	6·648	6·848	7·049	7·250	7·451	7·651	7·852
3/16	·188	4·75	5·379	5·552	5·723	5·896	6·068	6·240	6·412	6·584	6·756
5/32	·156	3·96	4·505	4·649	4·793	4·936	5·080	5·223	5·367	5·511	5·654
⅛	·125	3·18	3·624	3·760	3·855	3·970	4·085	4·200	4·315	4·430	4·545

SECTION 3

PRECISION MEASUREMENTS

READING MICROMETER CALIPERS

The usual terms employed in connection with micrometers are illustrated in Fig. 1. The spindle C is attached to the thimble E on the inside. The nut or thread for the spindle screw is in the frame A.

The screw on spindle and its nut has 40 threads per inch.

One revolution of spindle moves it axially by $\frac{1}{40} = \frac{25}{1000}$ in.

The thimble E is graduated in 25 divisions, so that 1 division $= \frac{1}{1000}$ in.

The sleeve D is graduated in $\frac{1}{10}$ in., and each $\frac{1}{10}$ in. subdivided into 4 equal parts.

1 subdivision on D $= \frac{1}{40} = \frac{25}{1000}$ in.

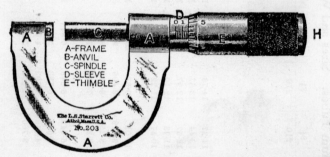

FIG. 1.—THE MICROMETER CALIPER.

To read the micrometer

   (1) Read off number of whole $\frac{1}{10}$ths on D.

   (2) Add number of $\frac{1}{40}$ths on D.

   (3) Add number of $\frac{1}{1000}$ths on E.

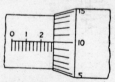

FIG. 2.—READING MICRO-METER CALIPER.

EXAMPLE.—(Fig. 2)

   (1) Number of whole $\frac{1}{10}$ths $= 2 = 0 \cdot 200$ in.

   (2) Number of $\frac{1}{40}$ths $\quad= 3 = 0 \cdot 075$ in.

   (3) Number of $\frac{1}{1000}$ths $= 10 = 0 \cdot 010$ in.

      Complete reading $\quad\quad = \underline{0 \cdot 285}$ in.

Reading Ten-thousandth Micrometer

In this micrometer, in addition to the graduations of the simple $\frac{1}{1000}$ths micrometer (Fig. 1), there is a vernier scale on the sleeve (Fig. 3). The difference between the width of one of the 10 divisions on the sleeve and one of the 9 divisions on the thimble is $\frac{1}{10}$th of a space on the thimble. In diagram B (Fig. 3), the third line from 0

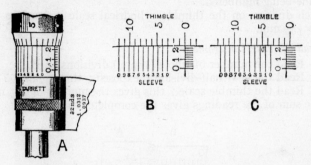

Fig. 3.—Reading the Ten-thousandth Micrometer.

on thimble coincides with the first line on sleeve. The next two lines do not coincide by $\frac{1}{10}$th of a space on thimble. The next two, marked 5 and 2, are $\frac{2}{10}$ths apart ; and so on.

The coincidence of the third line from 0 and first line on sleeve indicates that nothing must be added to the micrometer reading as obtained in the manner described above. In diagram A the correct micrometer reading is :

$$
\begin{array}{r}
0{\cdot}200 \\
0{\cdot}025 \\
0{\cdot}000 \\
0{\cdot}0001 \\
\hline
\end{array}
$$

Complete reading $= \underline{0{\cdot}2251}$ in.

In diagram C (Fig. 3) the line 10 on thimble coincides with the 7 on sleeve, so that $\frac{7}{10000}$ or 0·0007 in. must be added to the ordinary micrometer reading. The complete reading shown is 0·2507 in. In diagram B (Fig. 3) the complete reading shown is 0·2500 in.

Reading a Metric Micrometer

In the metric micrometer, with which readings can be made to within $\frac{1}{100}$ or 0·01 mm., the pitch of the screw is 0·5 mm. One revolution of the spindle advances it through 0·5 mm. The sleeve B (Fig. 4) is here graduated in 25 millimetre divisions, so that each revolution of the thimble moves the spindle through $\frac{1}{2}$ of 25 $= \frac{1}{50}$ mm.

The thimble is graduated from 0 to 50 in 50 equal divisions, each 5th line being numbered.

Each division on the thimble cylindrical scale is equal to $\frac{1}{50} \times 0·5 = \frac{1}{100}$ mm.

To read the metric micrometer

  (1) Read the number of whole (1 mm.) divisions on B.

  (2) Read the next half-division if exposed ; this equals 0·5 mm.

  (3) Read the thimble scale ; this gives the number of $\frac{1}{100}$ mm.

The sum of the readings gives the complete reading.

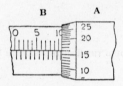

FIG. 4.—READING THE METRIC MICROMETER.

EXAMPLE.—(Fig. 4)

  (1) Number of whole mm. divisions on B = 10·00 mm.

  (2) Half-division exposed   = 0·50 mm.

  (3) Reading on thimble A (16 divisions) = 0·16 mm.

        Complete reading   = 10·66 mm.

THE VERNIER CALIPER

The vernier caliper enables caliper readings, both inside and out, to be made to within $\frac{1}{1000}$ in.

Referring to Fig. 5, this shows the British Standard terms for the various components. In the specification (B.S. No. 887—1940), it is laid down that the material used should be tool or stainless steel, and that the measuring faces shall be hardened to a diamond pyramid hardness of not less than 800 (or equivalent Rockwell C scale number, 62). The standard sizes and projection of the jaws are given in the following table :

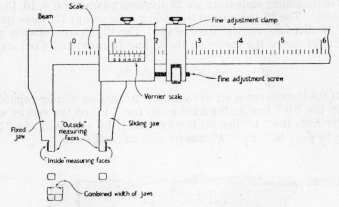

FIG. 5.—THE VERNIER CALIPER.

B.S. STANDARD SIZES AND PROJECTION OF JAWS

1	2	3
To Measure Externally up to		*Projection of Jaws (approximate)*
In.	*Mm.*	*In.*
6	150	1¼
9	225	1¾
12	300	2
24	600	2¼
36	900	2½
—	1,000	2½
48	—	3

The maximum permissible error of reading is ± 0·001 in. for calipers up to 12 in. ; ± 0·0015 for calipers from 12 to 24 in. and ± 0·002 for 24 to 48 in.

Reading the Vernier Caliper

Referring to Fig. 6 * the sliding jaw is shown in front of the fixed beam scale. The latter is graduated in $\frac{1}{40}$th parts of an inch, i.e. 0·025 in. divisions. Every 4th division is numbered, each space between numbered divisions being $\frac{1}{10}$th in.

* Starrett vernier caliper.

On the sliding scale there are 25 divisions numbered 0, 5, 10, 15, 20 and 25. The 25 divisions on the sliding scale occupy the same space as 24 divisions on the fixed scale. The difference between the width of one of the spaces on the sliding (vernier) and fixed scales is :

$$\tfrac{1}{25} \times \tfrac{1}{40} = \tfrac{1}{1000} \text{ in.}$$

If the instrument is set so that the " 0 " line on vernier coincides with the " 0 " line on the fixed scale, the " 1 " on the vernier will differ from the " 1 " line on the fixed scale by $\tfrac{1}{1000}$ in. ; the " 2 " line by $\tfrac{2}{1000}$ in. ; the " 3 " line by $\tfrac{3}{1000}$ in., and so on.

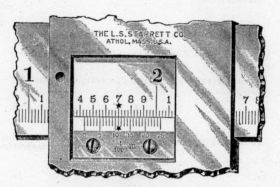

FIG. 6.—READING THE VERNIER CALIPER.

To read the vernier caliper, note how many whole inches, tenths (0·1 in.) and $\tfrac{1}{40}$ths (0·025 in.) the mark " 0 " on the vernier is from the " 0 " mark on the fixed scale. Then note which division on the vernier coincides with a division on the fixed scale. The coincident vernier number gives the number of $\tfrac{1}{1000}$ in. (0·001 in.) that have to be added to the fixed-scale reading to give the complete reading.

In Fig. 6 the reading is as follows :

Fixed scale whole inches	= 1·000 in.
Fixed scale tenths	= 0·400 in.
Fixed scale $\tfrac{1}{40}$ths (one)	= 0·025 in.
Vernier scale coincident division (11)	= 0·011 in.
Complete reading	= 1·436 in.

Reading the $\frac{1}{128}$-in. Vernier Caliper

In this less-expensive type vernier caliper the multiples of $\frac{1}{16}$ in., viz. $\frac{1}{64}$ and $\frac{1}{128}$ in., are used and readings can be made to within $\frac{1}{128}$ in.

The fixed scale is graduated in inches, $\frac{1}{4}$- and $\frac{1}{16}$-in. divisions.

The vernier scale is graduated in 8 divisions; the total length, i.e. 8 divisions, equals 7 divisions on the fixed scale. The difference between one division on fixed scale and one on vernier scale is $\frac{8}{128} - \frac{7}{128} = \frac{1}{128}$ in.

To read the vernier caliper note the whole inch and sixteenth readings on fixed scale and add coincident vernier scale number of $\frac{1}{128}$ in.

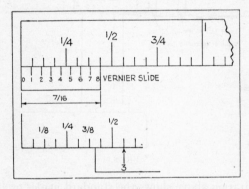

FIG. 7.—THE $\frac{1}{128}$-IN. VERNIER CALIPER.

EXAMPLE.—(Fig. 7, lower diagram).

$$\begin{aligned}
\text{Fixed scale reading} &= \tfrac{3}{8}\text{ in.} = \tfrac{48}{128}\text{ in.}\\
\text{Vernier scale reading} &= \tfrac{3}{128}\text{ in.}\\
\text{Complete reading} &= \tfrac{51}{128}\text{ in.}
\end{aligned}$$

The $\frac{1}{64}$-in. Vernier Caliper

In this instrument the fixed scale is divided into inches and $\frac{1}{8}$-in. divisions. The vernier scale measures $\frac{7}{8}$ in. and is divided into 8 divisions. The difference between the divisions on the fixed and vernier scales is $\frac{1}{64}$ in. The coincident vernier line number, on its scale, represents the number of $\frac{1}{64}$ in. that must be added to the full-scale reading to give the complete reading.

VERNIER HEIGHT GAUGE

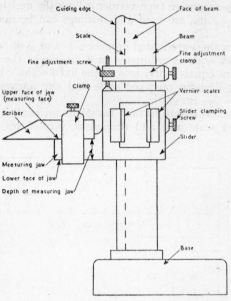

FIG. 8.

The illustration above shows the standard names of all the component parts, as laid down in British Standards Specification B.S. 1643 : 1950. This specifies also the three types of scales, viz. (a) Inch units up to as much as 48 in. to read with the vernier to 0·001 inch. (b) Metric units up to 1 metre, to read with the vernier to 0·02 mm. (c) Combination of (a) and (b) on the one instrument. The gauge is to be of good-quality steel, heat-treated to remove any cold-working stresses. The underside of the base and faces of the jaw and scriber must be hardened to a diamond pyramid hardness of not less than 700. For stainless steel it should be not less than 650. The design of the base and beam are specified in some detail, and a table of permissible errors on the beam is included. The graduations must be clearly engraved, and the thickness of these must not be less than 0·0025 in. nor more than 0·0035 in. The permissible errors in the inch and metric scale readings are specified and a number of alternative graduations of beams and verniers, with illustrations of each, are tabulated.

THE PROTRACTOR VERNIER

The fitting of a vernier scale to a protractor scale enables angular readings to be made to within $\frac{1}{12}$ degree, or 5 minutes of arc.

The disc of protractor is graduated in degrees and the vernier plate is graduated so that 12 divisions on its scale occupy the same space as 23° on the fixed disc. The difference between the widths of the divisions on the fixed and vernier scales is $\frac{1}{12}$ degree.

Note that the vernier scale is divided similarly from 0 to 60 on either side of the central zero reading ; this enables readings to be taken in either direction.

To read the vernier protractor note the disc number of whole degrees between " 0 " on the disc and " 0 " on the vernier. Then count or read in the same direction the number of spaces on the vernier to the line on fixed scale with which the vernier line coincides ; this gives the number of $\frac{1}{12}$ degrees to be added to the fixed scale reading.

Fig. 9.—The Protractor Vernier.

In the example (Fig. 9) the whole number of degrees on fixed scale is 52. The number of divisions on vernier scale to the coincident line division is such that the line 45 on vernier coincides with 70 on the fixed scale. The number of spaces from 0 to 45 on vernier is 9, so that $\frac{9}{12}$ degrees must be added to the 52 degrees.

The complete reading is $52° + \frac{9}{12}° = 52$ deg. 45 min.

JOHANSSON OR SLIP GAUGES

These flat and parallel steel block gauges are made with lapped parallel faces accurate to within a few millionths of an inch flat and also parallel.

The English measurement (inch) set of slip gauges consists of 81 blocks or gauges, as follows :

(1) 9 blocks with a range of 0·1001 to 0·1009 in. (steps of 0·0001 in.).

(2) 49 blocks with a range of 0·101 to 0·149 in. (steps of 0·001 in.).

(3) 19 blocks with a range of 0·05   to 0·95 in. (steps of 0·05 in.).

(4) 4 blocks of 1 in., 2 in., 3 in., and 4 in.

With combinations of these blocks wrung together measurements from 0·1001 in. to more than 10 in. can be made.

The metric set of slip gauges consists of 103 blocks, as follows :

(1) 49 blocks with a range of 1·01 to 1·49 mm. (steps of 0·01 mm.).

(2) 49 blocks with a range of 0·50 to 24·50 mm. (steps of 0·50 mm.).

(3) 4 blocks of 25 mm., 50 mm., 75 mm., and 100 mm.

(4) 1 extra block of 1·005 mm.

GRADES OF ACCURACY FOR SLIP BLOCKS

Three grades of accuracy are provided in commercial slip block sets, viz. (1) *Reference Grade*, (2) *Inspection Grade* and (3) *Workshop Grade.*

(1) *Reference Grade.*—The accuracy is within 2-millionths in. below 1 in. thickness and 2-millionths in. per in. above 1 in. thickness.

(2) *Inspection Grade.*—The accuracy is within 5-millionths in. below 1 in. thickness and 5-millionths in. per in. above 1 in. thickness.

(3) *Workshop Grade.*—The accuracy is within 10-millionths in. below 1 in. thickness and 10-millionths in. per in. above 1 in. thickness.

BRITISH STANDARD SLIP (OR BLOCK) GAUGES

The British Standard Specification No. 888—1940 specifies slip (or block) gauges and their accessories, e.g. measuring jaws, scribing and centre point, holder (or slides), in three grades, viz. Calibration, Inspection and Workshop grades. The gauges are to be made in high-grade steel hardened and stabilised, to give a diamond pyramid hardness of not less than 800 (Rockwell C Scale, 62). The finish, accuracy, case for housing the gauges, packing and markings are specified. In regard to the accuracy, *the flatness and parallelism* of the measuring faces is specified according to the following tabular values.

B.S. Maximum Permissible Errors in Flatness and Parallelism of
Measuring Faces

Unit = 1 Millionth of an Inch

Size of Gauge	Workshop Grade		Inspection Grade		Calibration Grade	
	Flatness	Parallel-ism	Flatness	Parallel-ism	Flatness	Parallel-ism
Up to and including 1 in. (25 mm.) .	10	10	5	5	2	2
2 in. (50 mm.) .	10	10	5	5	3	4
3 in. (75 mm.) .	10	15	7	7	4	7
4 in. (100 mm.).	10	15	7	7	4	7

Note.—When testing the flatness and parallelism of gauge surfaces the last $\frac{1}{32}$ in. round their edges is to be ignored.

The lengths of the gauges are specified as follows :

B.S. Maximum Permissible Errors in Length

Unit = 1 Millionth of an Inch

Size of Gauge	Workshop Grade	Inspection Grade	Calibration Grade
Up to and including 1 in. (25 mm.) . .	+ 10 − 5	+ 7 − 3	± 5
2 in. (50 mm.) . .	+ 20 − 10	+ 10 − 5	± 10
3 in. (75 mm.) . .	+ 30 − 15	+ 15 − 8	± 15
4 in. (100 mm.) . .	+ 40 − 20	+ 20 − 10	± 20

Note.—Slip gauges, in common with other engineers' precision gauges, are checked at a standard temperature of 68° F. (20° C.).

LIMITS AND FITS IN ENGINEERING

There are various kinds of fits in engineering practice between mating members, such as shafts and holes, ranging from loose running fits to hydraulic, thermal, force, or shrinkage fits. These may be grouped broadly into the following three classes, viz. :

(1) *Interference Fits.*—These include force fits, shrinkage fits, heavy driving fits and light driving fits. In these instances the diameters of the shaft members are actually greater than those of the holes in which the shafts fit.

(2) *Running Fits.*—These include the usual shaft bearing fits, ranging from close running, easy running and slack running, down to clearance fits.

(3) *Transition Fits.*—These cover other types of engineering fits between mating parts and range from heavy keying, medium keying and light keying, to easy push or sliding fits.

The various kinds of engineering fits have been standardised in the much-used Newall Standards and in the British Specification for Limits and Fits.

The British Standards Limits and Fits*

In 1906 the British Engineering Standards Association issued their Report No. 27, entitled " British Standard System for Limit Gauges." In this Report a " shaft basis " was recommended, but as this was not generally adopted by the engineering industry a committee was appointed in 1917 to revise it, and the Report B.S. 164 was the result of its deliberations ; this was issued in 1924. The latter specification is compiled on a " hole basis," as in the case of the Newall Standard System of limits and fits. In addition to placing the British Standard Limit System on a hole basis the committee also recommended the use of a unilateral system of tolerances. Although a unilateral system is recommended, bilateral tolerances are given in the B.S. No. 164 specifications for the benefit of those firms who find it convenient to work to this system.

As the standing type of the B.S. No. 164—1924 edition was destroyed by enemy action during the Second World War, the earlier edition was revised and the text was simplified. The new issue (B.S. 164—1924, war-time issue 1941) is the one to which the information here given refers.

DEFINITIONS

Dimension.—A dimension is a feature of any piece of work, such as a length or a diameter, of which the size is specified.

Nominal Size.—The nominal size of a dimension or part is the size by which it is conveniently referred to.

---

* See also Reference to B.S. 1916, Part I, 1953, on page 90.

Basic Size.—The basic size of a dimension or part is the size in relation to which all limits of variation are assigned.

Limits.—The limits of size for a dimension or part are the two permissible extreme sizes for that dimension.

Tolerance.—The tolerance of a dimension is the difference between the high and low limits of size for that dimension. It is the variation tolerated in the size of that dimension to cover allowable imperfections in workmanship.

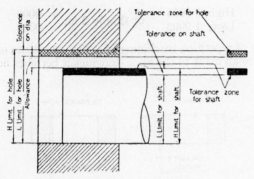

Fig. 10.—Limits and Tolerances.

The limits and tolerances are illustrated diagrammatically in Fig. 10 for a hole and its mating shaft. For convenience the hole and shaft are shown in contact below so that the whole of their tolerances are illustrated at the top. The tolerance for the shaft is shown in black and that for the hole in cross-hatched shading. The difference between the low-limit dimension of the hole and the high-limit one of the shaft is termed the *allowance*. This is defined as a presented difference between the high limit of the shaft and the low limit of the hole in order to provide for a certain class of engineering fit. This allowance *for force fits is negative* and *for running fits is positive.*

Unilateral and Bilateral Systems

There are two systems for expressing the allowable limits within which the dimensions of a shaft or hole should fall, namely, the *Unilateral* and the *Bilateral* ones. In the former method, as illustrated at A in Fig. 11, the lower limit of the hole is equal to the nominal diameter of the hole, whilst in the latter case, as shown at

B, the nominal diameter lies between the higher and lower limits of the dimensions given.

An example of the unilateral method may be quoted in the case of a 2-in. hole with a difference in limiting dimensions of 0·0016 in. In this instance the dimensions would be as follows :

$$\text{High, } 2{\cdot}0016 \text{ in.}$$
$$\text{Low, } 2{\cdot}0000 \text{ in.}$$ or simply 2 in. $\begin{array}{l} + \cdot 0016 \\ - \cdot 0000 \end{array}$

In the bilateral method the dimensions would be :

$$\text{High, } 2{\cdot}0008$$
$$\text{Low, } 1{\cdot}9992$$ or simply 2 in. $\begin{array}{l} + \cdot 0008 \\ - \cdot 0008 \end{array}$

In the case of repetition machining in which quantities of engineering parts are all made to the same drawings it becomes necessary to

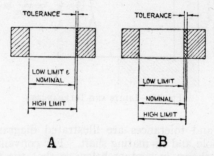

FIG. 11.—UNILATERAL (A) AND BILATERAL (B) FITS.

ensure that these parts shall be interchangeable and that they should not be made more accurate than the nature of the fit and type of work indicates ; otherwise unnecessary time and cost would be expended in the manufacture.

By the adoption of a system of limiting dimensions, such as the bilateral or unilateral ones mentioned previously, it is possible to ensure that parts made on different machines or by different machinists will always give the desired degree of fit.

In the British Standard System which, as previously stated, is now on the " hole basis," two classes of holes are provided for in the tables, namely, U (unilateral) and X (bilateral). The finer tolerances B and K would only be used on high-precision work.

The tables cover no less than fourteen different shafts which may be used with either unilateral or bilateral holes, providing for any kind of fit from a *heavy drive* to a *coarse clearance*.

The tolerances for shafts F to M remain unchanged, but the *allowance* varies progressively from F to M to ensure the desired type of fit. From Q to TT the tolerances and allowances are both increased to provide for lower grades of workmanship and increased clearances.

B.S. Unilateral Fits

Designation	Description of Fit	Class of Fit
UF	Heavy drive	Interference
UE	Light drive	
UD	Heavy keying	
UC	Medium keying	Transition
UB	Light keying	
UK	Push	
UL	Slide or Easy push	
UP	Easy slide or Close running	
UM	Close running (1)	
UQ	Close running (2)	
UR	Normal running	Clearance
US	Slack running	
UT	Extra-slack running	
UTT	Coarse clearance	

B.S. Bilateral Fits

Designation	Description of Fit	Class of Fit
XF	Force	
XE	Heavy drive	Interference
XD	Light drive	
XC	Extra-light drive	
XB	Heavy keying	
XK	Medium keying	Transition
XL	Light keying	
XP	Push	
XM	Slide or Easy push	
XQ	Easy slide or Close running	
XR	Normal running	
XS	Slack running	Clearance
XT	Extra-slack running	
XTT	Coarse clearance	

The chart reproduced in Fig. 12 shows the tolerances for the various British Standard fits, and the Tables A, B, C and D, of the following pages, give the British Standard limits for unilateral and bilateral holes, and shafts for use in these holes in both English and metric measurements.

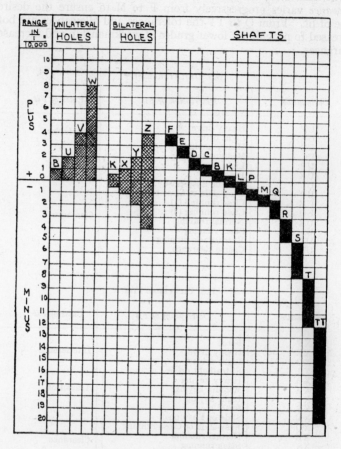

Fig. 12.—British Standards System of Fits.

The chart shown in Fig. 12 can be used with the following table of multipliers for B.S. tolerances to enable the tolerances to be calculated readily for shafts up to 80 in. diameter.

MULTIPLIERS FOR B.S. TOLERANCES

Nominal Sizes	Size Multiplier " m "	Nominal Sizes	Size Multiplier " m "
In.		*In.*	
0 to 0·29	3	21·0 to 23·09	22
0·3 ,, 0·59	4	23·1 ,, 25·29	23
0·6 ,, 0·99	5	25·3 ,, 27·59	24
1·0 ,, 1·49	6	27·6 ,, 29·99	25
1·5 ,, 2·09	7	30·0 ,, 32·49	26
2·1 ,, 2·79	8	32·5 ,, 35·09	27
2·8 ,, 3·59	9	35·1 ,, 37·79	28
3·6 ,, 4·49	10	37·8 ,, 40·59	29
4·5 ,, 5·49	11	40·6 ,, 43·49	30
5·5 ,, 6·59	12	43·5 ,, 46·49	31
6·6 ,, 7·79	13	46·5 ,, 49·59	32
7·8 ,, 9·09	14	49·6 ,, 52·79	33
9·1 ,, 10·49	15	52·8 ,, 56·09	34
10·5 ,, 11·99	16	56·1 ,, 59·49	35
12·0 ,, 13·59	17	59·5 ,, 62·99	36
13·6 ,, 15·29	18	63·0 ,, 66·59	37
15·3 ,, 17·09	19	66·6 ,, 70·29	38
17·1 ,, 18·99	20	70·3 ,, 74·09	39
19·0 ,, 20·99	21	74·1 ,, 77·99	40

In order to illustrate the use of the chart (Fig. 12) and the table of multipliers for B.S. tolerances the following examples are given :

Example 1.—3·0-in. *U* hole. Multiplier, 9 ; low limit, 3·0 in. ; high limit, 3·0018 in.

Example 2.—4·0 in. *Z* hole. Multiplier, 10 ; low limit, 3·996 in. ; high limit, 4·004 in.

Example 3.—1·5-in. *R* shaft. Multiplier, 7 ; low limit, 1·5 − 0·0035 = 1·4965 in. ; high limit, 1·5 − 0·0021 = 1·4979 in.

Example 4.—4-in. *F* shaft. Multiplier, 10 ; low limit, 4·003 in. ; high limit, 4·004 in.

Formula for B Tolerances

The progressive increase in the range of nominal sizes as well as the constant increase in the tolerance for the successive ranges indicates a square-root relationship between the nominal size and tolerance. If the tolerance, for B holes, is associated with the mean of each corresponding range of sizes, the following formula holds good :

B tolerance = $0.000466 \sqrt{d} + 0.0001$ in. where d = nominal size in inches.

TABLE A. BRITISH STANDARD LIMITS FOR UNILATERAL, BILATERAL AND OVERSIZE HOLES*

Nominal Sizes (Inches)	UNILATERAL HOLES (In which the Low Limit of the Hole is Nominal Size.)								BILATERAL HOLES (In which the Nominal Size of the Hole lies between the High and Low Limits.)								OVERSIZE HOLES (In which the Low Limit of the Hole is larger than the Nominal Size.)						Non-Mating Holes and Shafts.	
	B		U		V		W		K		X		Y		Z		A		G		H		J	
	H	L	H	L	H	L	H	L	H	L	H	L	H	L	H	L	H	L	H	L	H	L	H	L
0 to 0.29	+0.3	0	+06	0	+12	0	+24	0	+01	−02	+03	−03	+06	−06	+12	−12	+12	+06	+18	+12	+24	+18	+30	−30
0.3 :: 0.59	+0.4	0	+08	0	+16	0	+32	0	+02	−02	+04	−04	+08	−08	+16	−16	+16	+08	+24	+16	+32	+24	+40	−40
0.6 :: 0.99	+0.5	0	+10	0	+20	0	+40	0	+02	−03	+05	−05	+10	−10	+20	−20	+20	+10	+30	+20	+40	+30	+50	−50
1.0 :: 1.49	+0.6	0	+12	0	+24	0	+48	0	+03	−03	+06	−06	+12	−12	+24	−24	+24	+12	+36	+24	+48	+36	+60	−60
1.5 :: 2.09	+0.7	0	+14	0	+28	0	+56	0	+03	−04	+07	−07	+14	−14	+28	−28	+28	+14	+42	+28	+56	+42	+70	−70
2.1 :: 2.79	+0.8	0	+16	0	+32	0	+64	0	+04	−04	+08	−08	+16	−16	+32	−32	+32	+16	+48	+32	+64	+48	+80	−80
2.8 :: 3.59	+0.9	0	+18	0	+36	0	+72	0	+04	−05	+09	−09	+18	−18	+36	−36	+36	+18	+54	+36	+72	+54	+90	−90
3.6 :: 4.49	+1.0	0	+20	0	+40	0	+80	0	+05	−05	+10	−10	+20	−20	+40	−40	+40	+20	+60	+40	+80	+60	+100	−100
4.5 :: 5.49	+1.1	0	+22	0	+44	0	+88	0	+05	−06	+11	−11	+22	−22	+44	−44	+44	+22	+66	+44	+88	+66	+110	−110
5.5 :: 6.59	+1.2	0	+24	0	+48	0	+96	0	+06	−06	+12	−12	+24	−24	+48	−48	+48	+24	+72	+48	+96	+72	+120	−120
6.6 :: 7.79	+1.3	0	+26	0	+52	0	+104	0	+06	−07	+13	−13	+26	−26	+52	−52	+52	+26	+78	+52	+104	+78	+130	−130
7.8 :: 9.09	+1.4	0	+28	0	+56	0	+112	0	+07	−07	+14	−14	+28	−28	+56	−56	+56	+28	+84	+56	+112	+84	+140	−140
9.1 :: 10.49	+1.5	0	+30	0	+60	0	+120	0	+07	−08	+15	−15	+30	−30	+60	−60	+60	+30	+90	+60	+120	+90	+150	−150
10.5 :: 11.99	+1.6	0	+32	0	+64	0	+128	0	+08	−08	+16	−16	+32	−32	+64	−64	+64	+32	+96	+64	+128	+96	+160	−160
12.0 :: 13.59	+1.7	0	+34	0	+68	0	+136	0	+08	−09	+17	−17	+34	−34	+68	−68	+68	+34	+102	+68	+136	+102	+170	−170
13.6 :: 15.29	+1.8	0	+36	0	+72	0	+144	0	+09	−09	+18	−18	+36	−36	+72	−72	+72	+36	+108	+72	+144	+108	+180	−180
15.3 :: 17.09	+1.9	0	+38	0	+76	0	+152	0	+09	−10	+19	−19	+38	−38	+76	−76	+76	+38	+114	+76	+152	+114	+190	−190
17.1 :: 18.99	+2.0	0	+40	0	+80	0	+160	0	+10	−10	+20	−20	+40	−40	+80	−80	+80	+40	+120	+80	+160	+120	+200	−200
19.0 :: 20.99	+2.1	0	+42	0	+84	0	+168	0	+10	−11	+21	−21	+42	−42	+84	−84	+84	+42	+126	+84	+168	+126	+210	−210
21.0 :: 23.09	+2.2	0	+44	0	+88	0	+176	0	+11	−11	+22	−22	+44	−44	+88	−88	+88	+44	+132	+88	+176	+132	+220	−220
23.1 :: 25.29	+2.3	0	+46	0	+92	0	+184	0	+11	−12	+23	−23	+46	−46	+92	−92	+92	+46	+138	+92	+184	+138	+230	−230

H = High Limit.   L = Low Limit.   Tolerance Unit = 0.001 Inch.

* B.S. 164–1924 (War-time issue 1941).

TABLE B. BRITISH STANDARD LIMITS FOR SHAFTS*

(For use with either Unilateral, Bilateral or Oversize Holes.)

Nominal Sizes	F		E		D		C		B		K		L		P		M		Q		R		S		T		TT	
Inches	H	L	H	L	H	L	H	L	H	L	H	L	H	L	H	L	H	L	H	L	H	L	H	L	H	L	H	L
0 to 0·29	+12	+09	+09	+06	+06	+03	+04	+01	+03	0	+01	-02	0	-03	-02	-05	-03	-06	-05	-09	-09	-15	-15	-24	-24	-36	-36	-60
0·3 " 0·59	+16	+12	+12	+08	+08	+04	+06	+02	+04	0	+02	-02	0	-04	-02	-06	-04	-08	-06	-12	-12	-20	-20	-32	-32	-48	-48	-80
0·6 " 0·99	+20	+15	+15	+10	+10	+05	+07	+02	+05	0	+02	-03	0	-05	-03	-08	-05	-10	-08	-15	-15	-25	-25	-40	-40	-60	-60	-100
1·0 " 1·49	+24	+18	+18	+12	+12	+06	+09	+03	+06	0	+03	-03	0	-06	-03	-09	-06	-12	-09	-18	-18	-30	-30	-48	-48	-72	-72	-120
1·5 " 2·09	+28	+21	+21	+14	+14	+07	+10	+03	+07	0	+03	-04	0	-07	-04	-11	-07	-14	-11	-21	-21	-35	-35	-56	-56	-84	-84	-140
2·1 " 2·79	+32	+24	+24	+16	+16	+08	+12	+04	+08	0	+04	-04	0	-08	-04	-12	-08	-16	-12	-24	-24	-40	-40	-64	-64	-96	-96	-160
2·8 " 3·59	+36	+27	+27	+18	+18	+09	+13	+04	+09	0	+04	-05	0	-09	-05	-14	-09	-18	-14	-27	-27	-45	-45	-72	-72	-108	-108	-180
3·6 " 4·49	+40	+30	+30	+20	+20	+10	+15	+05	+10	0	+05	-05	0	-10	-05	-15	-10	-20	-15	-30	-30	-50	-50	-80	-80	-120	-120	-200
4·5 " 5·49	+44	+33	+33	+22	+22	+11	+16	+05	+11	0	+05	-06	0	-11	-06	-17	-11	-22	-17	-33	-33	-55	-55	-88	-88	-132	-132	-220
5·5 " 6·59	+46	+36	+36	+24	+24	+12	+18	+06	+12	0	+06	-06	0	-12	-06	-18	-12	-24	-18	-36	-36	-60	-60	-96	-96	-144	-144	-240
6·6 " 7·79	+52	+39	+39	+26	+26	+13	+19	+06	+13	0	+06	-07	0	-13	-07	-20	-13	-26	-20	-39	-39	-65	-65	-104	-104	-156	-156	-260
7·8 " 9·09	+56	+42	+42	+28	+28	+14	+21	+07	+14	0	+07	-07	0	-14	-07	-21	-14	-28	-21	-42	-42	-70	-70	-112	-112	-168	-168	-280
9·1 " 10·49	+60	+45	+45	+30	+30	+15	+22	+07	+15	0	+07	-08	0	-15	-08	-23	-15	-30	-23	-45	-45	-75	-75	-120	-120	-180	-180	-300
10·5 " 11·99	+64	+48	+48	+32	+32	+16	+24	+08	+16	0	+08	-08	0	-16	-08	-24	-16	-32	-24	-48	-48	-80	-80	-128	-128	-192	-192	-320
12·0 " 13·59	+68	+51	+51	+34	+34	+17	+25	+08	+17	0	+08	-09	0	-17	-09	-26	-17	-34	-26	-51	-51	-85	-85	-136	-136	-204	-204	-340
13·6 " 15·29	+72	+54	+54	+36	+36	+18	+27	+09	+18	0	+09	-09	0	-18	-09	-27	-18	-36	-27	-54	-54	-90	-90	-144	-144	-216	-216	-360
15·3 " 17·00	+76	+57	+57	+38	+38	+19	+28	+09	+19	0	+09	-10	0	-19	-10	-29	-19	-38	-29	-57	-57	-95	-95	-152	-152	-228	-228	-380
17·1 " 18·99	+80	+60	+60	+40	+40	+20	+30	+10	+20	0	+10	-10	0	-20	-10	-30	-20	-40	-30	-60	-60	-100	-100	-160	-160	-240	-240	-400
19·0 " 20·99	+84	+63	+63	+42	+42	+21	+31	+10	+21	0	+10	-11	0	-21	-11	-32	-21	-42	-32	-63	-63	-105	-105	-168	-168	-252	-252	-420
21·0 " 23·09	+88	+66	+66	+44	+44	+22	+33	+11	+22	0	+11	-11	0	-22	-11	-33	-22	-44	-33	-66	-66	-110	-110	-176	-176	-264	-264	-440
23·1 " 25·29	+92	+69	+69	+46	+46	+23	+34	+11	+23	0	+11	-12	0	-23	-12	-35	-23	-46	-35	-69	-69	-115	-115	-184	-184	-276	-276	-460

H = HIGH LIMIT.   L = LOW LIMIT.   TOLERANCE UNIT = 0·001 INCH.

* B.S. (164-1924 War-time issue 1941).

TABLE C. BRITISH STANDARD LIMITS FOR UNILATERAL, BILATERAL AND OVERSIZE HOLES (Metric Units)

Nominal Sizes.	UNILATERAL HOLES. (In which the Low Limit of the Hole is Nominal Size.)								BILATERAL HOLES. (In which the Nominal Size of the Hole lies between the High and Low Limits.)								OVERSIZE HOLES. (In which the Low Limit of the Hole is larger than the Nominal Size.)						Holes and Shafts for Non-Mating Fits.	
	B		U		V		W		K		X		Y		Z		A		G		H		J	
mm	H	L	H	L	H	L	H	L	H	L	H	L	H	L	H	L	H	L	H	L	H	L	H	L
0 to 7·49	+ ¾	0	+ 1½	0	+ 3	0	+ 6	0	+ ¼	− ½	+ ¾	− ¾	+ 1½	− 1½	+ 3	− 3	+ 3	+ 1½	+ 4½	+ 3	+ 6	+ 4½	+ 6	− 6
7·5 „ 14·99	+1	0	+ 2	0	+ 4	0	+ 8	0	+ ½	− ½	+1	−1	+ 2	− 2	+ 4	− 4	+ 4	+ 2	+ 6	+ 4	+ 8	+ 6	+ 8	− 8
15·0 „ 24·99	+1¼	0	+ 2½	0	+ 5	0	+10	0	+ ½	− ¾	+1¼	−1¼	+ 2½	− 2½	+ 5	− 5	+ 5	+ 2½	+ 7½	+ 5	+10	+ 7½	+10	−10
25·0 „ 37·49	+1½	0	+ 3	0	+ 6	0	+12	0	+ ¾	− ¾	+1½	−1½	+ 3	− 3	+ 6	− 6	+ 6	+ 3	+ 9	+ 6	+12	+ 9	+12	−12
37·5 „ 52·49	+1¾	0	+ 3½	0	+ 7	0	+14	0	+ ¾	−1	+1¾	−1¾	+ 3½	− 3½	+ 7	− 7	+ 7	+ 3½	+10½	+ 7	+14	+10½	+14	−14
52·5 „ 69·99	+2	0	+ 4	0	+ 8	0	+16	0	+1	−1	+2	−2	+ 4	− 4	+ 8	− 8	+ 8	+ 4	+12	+ 8	+16	+12	+16	−16
70·0 „ 89·99	+2¼	0	+ 4½	0	+ 9	0	+18	0	+1	−1¼	+2¼	−2¼	+ 4½	− 4½	+ 9	− 9	+ 9	+ 4½	+13½	+ 9	+18	+13½	+18	−18
90·0 „ 112·49	+2½	0	+ 5	0	+10	0	+20	0	+1¼	−1¼	+2½	−2½	+ 5	− 5	+10	−10	+10	+ 5	+15	+10	+20	+15	+20	−20
112·5 „ 137·49	+2¾	0	+ 5½	0	+11	0	+22	0	+1¼	−1½	+2¾	−2¾	+ 5½	− 5½	+11	−11	+11	+ 5½	+16½	+11	+22	+16½	+22	−22
137·5 „ 164·99	+3	0	+ 6	0	+12	0	+24	0	+1½	−1½	+3	−3	+ 6	− 6	+12	−12	+12	+ 6	+18	+12	+24	+18	+24	−24
165·0 „ 194·99	+3¼	0	+ 6½	0	+13	0	+26	0	+1½	−1¾	+3¼	−3¼	+ 6½	− 6½	+13	−13	+13	+ 6½	+19½	+13	+26	+19½	+26	−26
195·0 „ 227·49	+3½	0	+ 7	0	+14	0	+28	0	+1¾	−1¾	+3½	−3½	+ 7	− 7	+14	−14	+14	+ 7	+21	+14	+28	+21	+28	−28
227·5 „ 262·49	+3¾	0	+ 7½	0	+15	0	+30	0	+1¾	−2	+3¾	−3¾	+ 7½	− 7½	+15	−15	+15	+ 7½	+22½	+15	+30	+22½	+30	−30
262·5 „ 299·99	+4	0	+ 8	0	+16	0	+32	0	+2	−2	+4	−4	+ 8	− 8	+16	−16	+16	+ 8	+24	+16	+32	+24	+32	−32
300·0 „ 339·99	+4¼	0	+ 8½	0	+17	0	+34	0	+2	−2¼	+4¼	−4¼	+ 8½	− 8½	+17	−17	+17	+ 8½	+25½	+17	+34	+25½	+34	−34
340·0 „ 382·49	+4½	0	+ 9	0	+18	0	+36	0	+2¼	−2¼	+4½	−4½	+ 9	− 9	+18	−18	+18	+ 9	+27	+18	+36	+27	+36	−36
382·5 „ 427·49	+4¾	0	+ 9½	0	+19	0	+38	0	+2¼	−2½	+4¾	−4¾	+ 9½	− 9½	+19	−19	+19	+ 9½	+28½	+19	+38	+28½	+38	−38
427·5 „ 474·99	+5	0	+10	0	+20	0	+40	0	+2½	−2½	+5	−5	+10	−10	+20	−20	+20	+10	+30	+20	+40	+30	+40	−40
475·0 „ 524·99	+5¼	0	+10½	0	+21	0	+42	0	+2½	−2¾	+5¼	−5¼	+10½	−10½	+21	−21	+21	+10½	+31½	+21	+42	+31½	+42	−42
525·0 „ 577·49	+5½	0	+11	0	+22	0	+44	0	+2¾	−2¾	+5½	−5½	+11	−11	+22	−22	+22	+11	+33	+22	+44	+33	+44	−44
577·5 „ 632·49	+5¾	0	+11½	0	+23	0	+46	0	+2¾	−3	+5¾	−5¾	+11½	−11½	+23	−23	+23	+11½	+34½	+23	+46	+34½	+46	−46

H = High Limit. L = Low Limit. Tolerance Unit = 0·01 Millimetre.

* B.S. 164–1924 (War-time issue. Supplement 1941).

TABLE D. BRITISH STANDARD LIMITS FOR SHAFTS (Metric Units)

(For use with either Unilateral, Bilateral or Oversize Holes.)

Nominal Sizes.	F		E		D		C		B		K		L		P		M		Q		R		S		T		TT	
mm.	H	L	H	L	H	L	H	L	H	L	H	L	H	L	H	L	H	L	H	L	H	L	H	L	H	L	H	L
0 to 7·49	+3	+2¼	+2¼	+1½	+1½	+¾	+1	+¼	+¾	0	+¼	—½	0	—¾	—½	—1¼	—¾	—1½	—1¼	—2¼	—2¼	—3¾	—3¾	—6	—6	—9	—9	—15
7·5 „ 14·99	+4	+3	+3	+2	+2	+1	+1½	+½	+1	0	+½	—½	0	—1	—½	—1½	—1	—2	—1¼	—3	—3	—5	—5	—8	—8	—12	—12	—20
15·0 „ 24·99	+5	+3¾	+3¾	+2½	+2½	+1¼	+1¾	+½	+1¼	0	+½	—¾	0	—1¼	—¾	—2	—1¼	—2½	—2	—3¾	—3¾	—6¼	—6¼	—10	—10	—15	—15	—25
25·0 „ 37·49	+6	+4½	+4½	+3	+3	+1½	+2¼	+¾	+1½	0	+¾	—¾	0	—1½	—¾	—2¼	—1½	—3	—2¼	—4½	—4½	—7½	—7½	—12	—12	—18	—18	—30
37·5 „ 52·49	+7	+5¼	+5¼	+3½	+3½	+1¾	+2½	+¾	+1¾	0	+¾	—1	0	—1¾	—1	—2¾	—1¾	—3½	—2¾	—5¼	—5¼	—8¾	—8¾	—14	—14	—21	—21	—35
52·5 „ 69·99	+8	+6	+6	+4	+4	+2	+3	+1	+2	0	+1	—1	0	—2	—1	—3	—2	—4	—3	—6	—6	—10	—10	—16	—16	—24	—24	—40
70·0 „ 89·99	+9	+6¾	+6¾	+4½	+4½	+2¼	+3¼	+1	+2¼	0	+1	—1¼	0	—2¼	—1¼	—3½	—2¼	—4½	—3½	—6¾	—6¾	—11¼	—11¼	—18	—18	—27	—27	—45
90·0 „ 112·49	+10	+7½	+7½	+5	+5	+2½	+3¾	+1¼	+2½	0	+1¼	—1¼	0	—2½	—1¼	—3¾	—2½	—5	—3¾	—7½	—7½	—12½	—12½	—20	—20	—30	—30	—50
112·5 „ 137·49	+11	+8¼	+8¼	+5½	+5½	+2¾	+4	+1¼	+2¾	0	+1¼	—1½	0	—2¾	—1½	—4¼	—2¾	—5½	—4¼	—8¼	—8¼	—13¾	—13¾	—22	—22	—33	—33	—55
137·5 „ 164·99	+12	+9	+9	+6	+6	+3	+4½	+1½	+3	0	+1½	—1½	0	—3	—1½	—4½	—3	—6	—4½	—9	—9	—15	—15	—24	—24	—36	—36	—60
165·0 „ 194·99	+13	+9¾	+9¾	+6½	+6½	+3¼	+4¾	+1½	+3¼	0	+1½	—1¾	0	—3¼	—1¾	—5	—3¼	—6½	—5	—9¾	—9¾	—16¼	—16¼	—26	—26	—39	—39	—65
195·0 „ 227·49	+14	+10½	+10½	+7	+7	+3½	+5¼	+1¾	+3½	0	+1¾	—1¾	0	—3½	—1¾	—5¼	—3½	—7	—5¼	—10½	—10½	—17½	—17½	—28	—28	—42	—42	—70
227·5 „ 262·49	+15	+11¼	+11¼	+7½	+7½	+3¾	+5½	+1¾	+3¾	0	+1¾	—2	0	—3¾	—2	—5¾	—3¾	—7½	—5¾	—11¼	—11¼	—18¾	—18¾	—30	—30	—45	—45	—75
262·5 „ 299·99	+16	+12	+12	+8	+8	+4	+6	+2	+4	0	+2	—2	0	—4	—2	—6	—4	—8	—6	—12	—12	—20	—20	—32	—32	—48	—48	—80
300·0 „ 339·99	+17	+12¾	+12¾	+8½	+8½	+4¼	+6¼	+2	+4¼	0	+2	—2¼	0	—4¼	—2¼	—6½	—4¼	—8½	—6½	—12¾	—12¾	—21¼	—21¼	—34	—34	—51	—51	—85
340·0 „ 382·49	+18	+13½	+13½	+9	+9	+4½	+6¾	+2¼	+4½	0	+2¼	—2¼	0	—4½	—2¼	—6¾	—4½	—9	—6¾	—13½	—13½	—22½	—22½	—36	—36	—54	—54	—90
382·5 „ 427·49	+19	+14¼	+14¼	+9½	+9½	+4¾	+7	+2¼	+4¾	0	+2¼	—2½	0	—4¾	—2½	—7¼	—4¾	—9½	—7¼	—14¼	—14¼	—23¾	—23¾	—38	—38	—57	—57	—95
427·5 „ 474·99	+20	+15	+15	+10	+10	+5	+7½	+2½	+5	0	+2½	—2½	0	—5	—2½	—7½	—5	—10	—7½	—15	—15	—25	—25	—40	—40	—60	—60	—100
475·0 „ 524·99	+21	+15¾	+15¾	+10½	+10½	+5¼	+7¾	+2½	+5¼	0	+2½	—2¾	0	—5¼	—2¾	—8	—5¼	—10½	—8	—15¾	—15¾	—26¼	—26¼	—42	—42	—63	—63	—105
525·0 „ 577·49	+22	+16½	+16½	+11	+11	+5½	+8¼	+2¾	+5½	0	+2¾	—2¾	0	—5½	—2¾	—8¼	—5½	—11	—8¼	—16½	—16½	—27½	—27½	—44	—44	—66	—66	—110
577·5 „ 632·49	+23	+17¼	+17¼	+11½	+11½	+5¾	+8½	+2¾	+5¾	0	+2¾	—3	0	—5¾	—3	—8¾	—5¾	—11½	—8¾	—17¼	—17¼	—28¾	—28¾	—46	—46	—69	—69	—115

* B.S. 164–1924 (War-time issue. Supplement, 1941).

BRITISH STANDARDS FOR LIMITS AND FITS FOR ENGINEERING (Later Publication, 1953)

In 1953 a revised specification No. 1916, Part I, 1953, was issued, to be followed later by a separate B.S. No. 1916, Part II. The later specification, while following the general lines of the previous B.S. 164—1924, is much more comprehensive, covering the needs from the watchmaker to the heaviest industries.

The new specification has been prepared with the collaboration of the aircraft, electrical, gauge and tool, machine tool, railway and other branches of engineering, as well as the Service Departments.

The first British Standard to be issued on limits and fits for Engineering was B.S. 164—1924 and this was re-issued with some amendments in 1941. Whilst B.S. 164 was widely used in Great Britain it had little acceptance in other countries ; for instance, European countries almost universally used some selection from the old ISA (International Standards Association) system.

Committees of the B.S.I. have been investigating for some years past the possibility of providing a comprehensive system of limits and fits which would both be acceptable to the British industry and would also offer a basis for a universal standard. B.S. 1916, Part I, is the result of this work and it makes available in inch measure the same range of fits, covering almost all the needs of engineering, as the ISA system has long given to the Continental countries. Tables of metric equivalents are also included in this British Standard, for the benefit of those who have to work to metric measure; the same method of designating fits is applicable to both systems of measurement.

B.S. 1916, Part I, supersedes B.S. 164, and it gives a choice of fits so wide that users should be able to make the transition from existing systems without undue difficulty. But to help users in applying the system to their own needs, and at the same time to encourage a greater degree of uniformity and interchangeability in the future than in the past, there is in course of preparation Part II of B.S. 1916 which will give guidance in the use of Part I and offer recommendations and examples of the selection of fits.

THE NEWALL STANDARDS

The standards of engineering fits and tolerances founded by The Newall Engineering Company Ltd. uses the " hole " as a basis of comparison and specifies various classes of force, driving, running and push fits. Two classes of standard holes, designated A and B respectively, are given, and the table that follows gives the tolerances for these holes, the former being the higher accuracy holes, for commercial purposes.

The Newall internal gauges are made to these limits and ensure the accuracy of the holes produced to within the stated tolerances. The high-grade hole reamers used in engineering works will produce holes to within the limits specified.

Allowances for the classes of fits are made on the shaft and the classes F, D, P, X, Y and Z provide suitable allowances ; in addition they allow a permissible margin of error.

Class F shafts require hydraulic, screw pressure, or thermal fitting methods to force them into their holes.

Class D shafts require driving into their holes.

Class P shafts can be pushed in, but are not sufficiently free to rotate.

Class X shafts are suitable for running fits for engines, shafting and similar applications where easy running fits are permissible.

Class Y shafts are suitable for running fits in the case of high speeds, and for good-quality machine bearings.

Class Z shafts are suitable for the running fits employed in fine tool work.

The tolerance in each case is the difference between the high and low limits and represents the working margin.

THE NEWALL STANDARDS OF FIT

Table of Tolerances in Standard Holes (Two Grades) for Various Classes of Engineering Fits

Class *A* (above), and *B* (below)

Nominal Diameters	*Up to ½ in.*	*9/16–1 in.*	1 1/16–2 *in.*	2 1/16–3 *in.*	3 1/16–4 in.	4 1/16–5 *in.*	5 1/16–6 *in.*
High Limit .	+ 0·00025	+ 0·00050	+ 0·00075	+ 0·00100	+ 0·00100	+ 0·00100	+ 0·00150
Low Limit .	− 0·00025	− 0·00025	− 0·00025	− 0·00050	− 0·00050	− 0·00050	− 0·00050
Tolerance .	0·00050	0·00075	0·00100	0·00150	0·00150	0·00150	0·00200
High Limit .	+ 0·00050	+ 0·00075	+ 0·00100	+ 0 00125	+ 0·00150	+ 0·00175	+ 0·00200
Low Limit .	− 0·00050	− 0·00050	− 0·00050	− 0·00075	− 0·00075	− 0·00075	− 0·00100
Tolerance .	0·00100	0·00125	0·00150	0·00200	0·00225	0·00250	0·00300

ALLOWANCES ON SHAFTS FOR VARIOUS FITS

Force Fits (Class *F*)

Nominal Diameters	*Up to ½ in.*	*9/16–1 in.*	1 1/16–2 *in.*	2 1/16–3 *in.*	3 1/16–4 *in.*	4 1/16–5 *in.*	5 1/16–6 *in.*
High Limit .	+ 0·00100	+ 0·00200	+ 0·00400	+ 0·00600	+ 0·00800	+ 0·01000	+ 0·01200
Low Limit .	+ 0·00050	+ 0·00150	+ 0·00300	+ 0·00450	+ 0·00600	+ 0·00800	+ 0·01000
Tolerance .	0·00050	0·00050	0·00100	0·00150	0·00200	0·00200	0·00200

Driving Fits (Class *D*)

Nominal Diameters	*Up to ½ in.*	*9/16–1 in.*	1 1/16–2 *in.*	2 1/16–3 *in.*	3 1/16–4 *in.*	4 1/16–5 *in.*	5 1/16–6 *in.*
High Limit .	+ 0·00050	+ 0·00100	+ 0·00150	+ 0·00250	+ 0·00300	+ 0·00350	+ 0·00400
Low Limit .	+ 0·00025	+ 0·00075	+ 0·00100	+ 0·00150	+ 0·00200	+ 0·00250	+ 0·00300
Tolerance .	0·00025	0·00025	0·00050	0·00100	0·00100	0·00100	0·00100

Push Fits (Class *P*)

Nominal Diameters	*Up to ½ in.*	*9/16–1 in.*	1 1/16–2 *in.*	2 1/16–3 *in.*	3 1/16–4 *in.*	4 1/16–5 *in.*	5 1/16–6 *in.*
High Limit .	− 0·00025	− 0·00025	− 0·00025	− 0·0005	− 0·0005	− 0·0005	− 0·0005
Low Limit .	− 0·00075	− 0·00075	− 0·00075	− 0·0010	− 0·0010	− 0·0010	− 0·0010
Tolerance .	0·0005	0·0005	0·0005	0·0005	0·0005	0·0005	0·0005

Running Fits (3 Grades) (Classes *X*, *Y*, and *Z*)

Nominal Diameters	*Up to ½ in.*	*9/16–1 in.*	1 1/16–2 *in.*	2 1/16–3 *in.*	3 1/16–4 *in.*	4 1/16–5 *in.*	5 1/16–6 *in.*
High Limit .	− 0·00100	− 0·00125	− 0·00175	− 0·00200	− 0·00250	− 0·00300	− 0·00350
Low Limit .	− 0·00200	− 0·00275	− 0·00350	− 0·00425	− 0·00500	− 0·00575	− 0·00650
Tolerance .	0·00100	0·00150	0·00175	0·00225	0·00250	0·00275	0·00300
High Limit .	− 0·00075	− 0·00100	− 0·00125	− 0·00150	− 0·00200	− 0·00225	− 0·00250
Low Limit .	− 0·00125	− 0·00200	− 0·00250	− 0·00300	− 0·00350	− 0·00400	− 0·00450
Tolerance .	0·00050	0·00100	0·00125	0·00150	0·00150	0·00175	0·00200
High Limit .	− 0·00050	− 0·00075	− 0·00075	− 0·00100	− 0·00100	− 0·00125	− 0·00125
Low Limit .	− 0·00075	− 0·00125	− 0·00150	− 0·00200	− 0·00225	− 0·00250	− 0·00275
Tolerance .	0·00025	0·00050	0·00075	0·00100	0·00125	0·00125	0·00150

NEWALL'S STANDARDS

(Metric Measure)

	Metric	Dia. in mm.	0–15	16–25	26–50	51–75	76–100	101–125	126–150	151–175	176–200	201–225	226–250	251–275	276–300
Holes	Class "A" — First Grade	+	·007	·013	·019	·026	·026	·039	·039	·039	·044	·044	·044	·051	·051
		−	·007	·007	·007	·013	·013	·013	·013	·019	·022	·025	·025	·025	·025
	Class "B" — Second Grade	+	·013	·019	·026	·032	·039	·045	·051	·057	·057	·063	·063	·070	·070
		−	·013	·013	·013	·019	·019	·019	·026	·026	·032	·032	·032	·032	·038
Fits	Force Fit	+	·026	·051	·102	·153	·204	·255	·306	·358	·410	·462	·514	·566	·618
		+	·013	·038	·077	·115	·152	·203	·254	·306	·358	·410	·462	·514	·566
	Driving Fit	+	·013	·026	·039	·064	·077	·089	·102	·114	·127	·140	·152	·165	·178
		−	·007	·019	·026	·039	·051	·063	·076	·076	·089	·102	·114	·114	·127
	Push Fit	−	·006	·006	·006	·012	·012	·012	·012	·013	·013	·013	·019	·019	·019
		−	·019	·019	·019	·026	·026	·026	·026	·032	·038	·038	·051	·051	·051
Running Fits	Class "X" — Third Grade	−	·025	·032	·045	·051	·063	·076	·089	·089	·089	·095	·102	·102	·108
		−	·051	·070	·090	·108	·127	·146	·165	·171	·179	·191	·203	·210	·216
	Class "Y" —	−	·019	·025	·032	·038	·051	·057	·063	·070	·070	·076	·083	·083	·089
	Second Grade	−	·032	·051	·064	·076	·089	·101	·114	·121	·127	·140	·147	·152	·158
	Class "Z" —	−	·012	·019	·019	·025	·025	·032	·032	·032	·038	·038	·038	·044	·044
	First Grade	−	·019	·032	·039	·051	·057	·064	·070	·070	·076	·076	·083	·089	·089

GRINDING LIMITS FOR SHAFTS
(Brown & Sharpe)

Type of Fit	Diameter	Lower Limit	Higher Limit	Nature of Limits
Running Fits—ordinary speed	To ½ in. inclusive „ 1 in. „ „ 2 in. „ „ 3½ in. „ „ 6 in. „	*In.* ·00025 ·00075 ·0015 ·0025 ·0035	*In.* ·00075 ·0015 ·0025 ·0035 ·005	Small
Running Fits—high speed, heavy pressure and rocker shafts	To ½ in. inclusive „ 1 in. „ „ 2 in. „ „ 3½ in. „ „ 6 in. „	·0005 ·001 ·002 ·003 ·0045	·001 ·002 ·003 ·0045 ·0065	Small
Sliding Fits	To ½ in. inclusive „ 1 in. „ „ 2 in. „ „ 3½ in. „ „ 6 in. „	·00025 ·0005 ·001 ·002 ·003	·0005 ·001 ·002 ·0035 ·005	Small
Standard Fits	To ½ in. inclusive „ 1 in. „ „ 2 in. „ „ 3½ in. „ „ 6 in. „	Standard „ „ „ „	·00025 ·0005 ·001 ·0015 ·002	Small
Driving Fits	To ½ in. inclusive „ 1 in. „ „ 2 in. „ „ 3½ in. „ „ 6 in. „	·0005 ·001 ·002 ·003 ·004	·001 ·002 ·003 ·004 ·005	Large
Force Fits	To ½ in. inclusive „ 1 in. „ „ 2 in. „ „ 3½ in. „ „ 6 in. „	·00075 ·0015 ·0025 ·004 ·006	·0015 ·0025 ·004 ·006 ·009	Large
Driving Fits—for such pieces as require to be readily taken apart	To ½ in. inclusive „ 1 in. „ „ 2 in. „ „ 3½ in. „ „ 6 in. „	Standard ·00025 ·0005 ·00075 ·001	·00025 ·0005 ·00075 ·001 ·0015	Large

Grinding Limits for Shafts (*contd.*)

Type of Fit	Diameter		Lower Limit	Higher Limit	Nature of Limits
			In.	*In.*	
Shrinking Fits—for hardened shells ⅜ in. thick and less	To	½ in. inclusive	·00025	·0005	
	,,	1 in. ,,	·0005	·001	
	,,	2 in. ,,	·001	·0015	Large
	,,	3½ in. ,,	·0015	·002	
	,,	6 in. ,,	·002	·003	
Shrinking Fits—for shells, etc., having thickness greater than ⅜ in.	To	½ in. inclusive	·0005	·001	
	,,	1 in. ,,	·001	·0025	
	,,	2 in. ,,	·0025	·0035	Large
	,,	3½ in. ,,	·0035	·005	
	,,	6 in. ,,	·005	·007	
Grinding limits for holes	To	½ in. inclusive	Standard	·0005	
	,,	1 in. ,,	,,	·00075	
	,,	2 in. ,,	,,	·001	Large
	,,	3½ in. ,,	,,	·0015	
	,,	6 in. ,,	,,	·002	
	,,	12 in. ,,	,,	·0025	

These limits should be followed under ordinary conditions, but for very special cases it may be necessary to depart slightly from these values.

LIMIT GAUGE DIMENSIONS

(Brown & Sharpe)

(*Specially suitable for Lathe Work*)

Size	Not to go on	To go on	Size	Not to go on	To go on
In.	*In.*	*In.*	*In.*	*In.*	*In.*
⅜	·383	·387	1⅛	1·133	1·137
⁷⁄₁₆	·4455	·4495	1³⁄₁₆	1·1955	1·1995
½	·508	·512	1¼	1·258	1·262
⁹⁄₁₆	·5705	·5745	1⁵⁄₁₆	1·3205	1·3245
⅝	·633	·637	1⅜	1·383	1·387
¹¹⁄₁₆	·6955	·6995	1⁷⁄₁₆	1·4455	1·4495
¾	·758	·762	1½	1·508	1·512
¹³⁄₁₆	·8205	·8245	1⅝	1·633	1·637
⅞	·883	·887	1¾	1·758	1·762
¹⁵⁄₁₆	·9455	·9495	1⅞	1·883	1·887
1	1·008	1·012	2	2·008	2·012
1 ¹⁄₁₆	1·0705	1·0745			

Note.—These sizes, which it will be noticed are oversize, refer to the dimensions of lathe-finished parts intended for final finishing upon the grinding machine. Parts turned to these limits will enable a smooth finished surface to be obtained with the minimum amount of grinding.

B.S.I. TOLERANCE ZONES FOR LIMIT GAUGES *

Two types of " Go " and " Not Go " limit gauges are employed for engineering inspection purposes, namely, *Workshop* and *Inspection* gauges. The former are used for checking dimensions of work during and after machining operations, and the latter for the final or acceptance test. The gauges are of the same general design but have different tolerance zones.

The British Standards Institution has specified the tolerance zones for these two types of limit gauges.

These are arranged in relation to the work in the manner indicated in the diagrams on this page. The latter indicate that the tolerance zones for the inspection gauges border on the outside of the tolerance zone for the corresponding work, the object being to ensure that all inspection gauges made within their appropriate tolerance zones will not reject any piece of work which is within its own tolerance zone.

Further, it is arranged that the tolerance zones for the workshop gauges all lie within

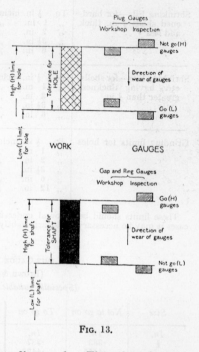

Fig. 13.

the tolerance zone for the corresponding work. Thus the tolerance zones for the " Go " workshop gauges are separated from the low limit L by a margin in the case of a hole or the high limit H in the case of a shaft. This margin is arranged so as to provide some latitude for gauge wear. A similar but smaller margin is often allowed between the tolerance zones for the " Not Go " workshop gauges and those of the corresponding " Not Go " inspection gauges.

* B.S. 164–1924 (Later issue 1941).

SECTION 4

SCREW THREAD DATA

Vee Section Screw Threads

These comprise the Whitworth, British Association, American Sellers, International (Metric) and others.

GENERAL INFORMATION

A single-start screw thread is the ridge produced by forming on a cylinder or tapered circular-section member a continuous helical groove of uniform section such that the distance measured parallel to the axis between two corresponding points on its contour is proportional to their relative angular displacement about the axis (Fig. 1).

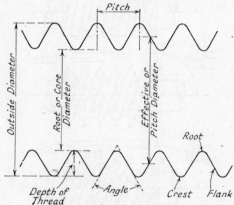

FIG. 1.—SCREW THREAD NOMENCLATURE.

DEFINITIONS *

Full Diameter or outside diameter of a parallel thread is the diameter of the imaginary coaxial cylinder which just touches the crest of an external thread or the root of an internal thread.

Minor Diameter or Core Diameter.—The minor diameter is the diameter of a parallel cylinder which just touches the root of an external thread or the crest of an internal thread.

Effective Diameter.—The effective diameter of a parallel thread is the diameter of the imaginary coaxial cylinder which intersects the

* British Standard Specification, No. 84–1940.

surface of the thread in such a manner that the intercept on a generator of the cylinder, between the points where it meets the opposite flanks of the thread groove (Fig. 1), is equal to half the nominal pitch of the thread.

Pitch.—The pitch of a screw thread is the distance, measured parallel to the axis, between corresponding points on adjacent thread forms in the same axial plane (Fig. 1).

Lead.—The lead of a screw thread is the distance it advances axially for one complete revolution.

Note.—On single-start threads the lead is equal to the pitch. On multiple-start threads the lead is equal to the pitch multiplied by

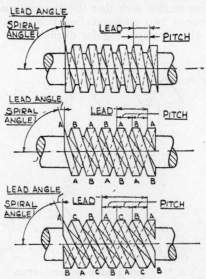

FIG. 2.—SINGLE-, DOUBLE- AND TREBLE-START THREADS.

the number of starts. On double-start threads (Fig. 2) * the lead equals twice the pitch. On treble-start threads the lead equals three times the pitch.

Pitch Line.—The pitch line is one of the two lines of intersection between the effective diameter cylinder and an axial section of the screw.

Crest.—The crest is the prominent part of the thread, whether the thread be external or internal (Fig. 1).

* Courtesy *Mechanics*.

Root of Thread.—The root of a thread is the bottom of the groove between the two flanking surfaces of the thread, whether the thread be external or internal (Fig. 1).

Flanks of Thread.—The flanks of a thread are the straight lines which connect the crest and root.

Depth of Thread.—The depth of a thread is the radial distance between the crest and root.

Form of Thread.—The form of a thread is the shape of one complete contour of the thread between corresponding points on adjacent ridges, as revealed by an axial section.

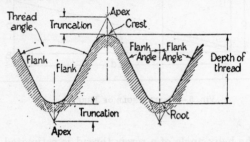

FIG. 3.—TRUNCATION OF THREAD.

Truncation.—The truncation at the crest of a thread is the radial distance between the crest and the adjacent apex. The truncation at the root of a thread is the radial distance between the root and the adjacent apex (Fig. 3).

Angle of Thread.—The angle of thread (thread angle) is the angle between the flanks measured in an axial plane section (Fig. 1).

Flank Angles.—The flank angles are the two angles between the

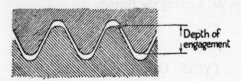

FIG. 4.—DEPTH OF ENGAGEMENT.

individual flanks and the perpendicular to the axis of the thread measured in an axial section (Fig. 3).

Depth of Engagement.—The depth of engagement between two mating screw threads is the radial distance by which their thread forms overlap each other (Fig. 4).

Mean Helix Angle.—The mean helix angle of a screw thread is the angle made by the thread helix at the pitch line with a diametrical plane of the thread. The helix angle of a thread increases continuously from the crest to the root of a thread.

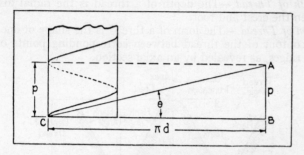

FIG. 5.—HELIX ANGLE OF THREAD.

Note.—The helix angle of a screw thread is estimated as follows (Fig. 5) :

In triangle ABC. θ = helix angle.

$$\tan \theta = \frac{AB}{BC} = \frac{p}{\pi d}$$

where p = pitch of thread and d = external diameter.

The thread on cylinder on left (Fig. 5) may be regarded as being formed by wrapping the triangular lamina ABC around the cylinder, the upper edge AC forming the thread.

TYPES OF VEE THREADS

The more widely used vee-type screw thread forms in the past and present include the following : (1) Whitworth ; (2) British Association (B.A.) ; (3) American National Standard (Sellers) ; (4) International Metric (Système Internationale) ; (5) British Standard Cycle (C.E.I.) ; (6) Löwenherz (German).

Of these the Whitworth thread angle is 55° ; the B.A., 47½° ; Sellers, 60° ; Metric, 60° ; C.E.I., 60° ; and Löwenherz. 53° 8 min.

(1) British Standard Whitworth (Fig. 6)

This thread form has been standardised by the British Standards Institution (B.S. No. 84—1940), and it is used for B.S. Whitworth, B.S. Fine and B.S. Pipe (parallel threads).

It is of symmetrical vee-form with angle between the flanks, measured in the axial plane, of 55°. One-sixth of the sharp vee is

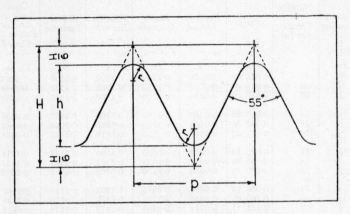

FIG. 6.—BRITISH STANDARD WHITWORTH THREAD.

truncated at the top and bottom, the thread being rounded equally at crests and roots by circular arcs blending tangentially with the flanks. The following are the thread proportions where p = pitch in inches.

$$\text{Height } H = 0 \cdot 960491p.$$
$$\text{Depth of thread } h = 0 \cdot 640327p.$$
$$\text{Radius of crest and root } r = 0 \cdot 137329p.$$

The nominal diameters, threads per inch, pitch and other essential data regarding the British Standard Whitworth, British Standard Fine and British Standard Pipe Screw Threads * are given in the following tables :

* Abstract from B.S. No. 84—1940.

BRITISH STANDARD WHITWORTH SCREW THREADS

1	2	3	4	5	6	7	8
Nominal Diameter	Number of Threads per In.	Pitch	Depth of Thread	Major Diameter	Effective Diameter	Minor Diameter	Cross Sectional Area at Bottom of Thread
In.		In.	In.	In.	In.	In.	Sq. in.
1/8	40	0·025 00	0·0160	0·1250	0·1090	0·0930	0·0068
3/16	24	0·041 67	0·0267	0·1875	0·1608	0·1341	0·0141
1/4	20	0·050 00	0·0320	0·2500	0·2180	0·1860	0·0272
5/16	18	0·055 56	0·0356	0·3125	0·2769	0·2413	0·0457
3/8	16	0·062 50	0·0400	0·3750	0·3350	0·2950	0·0683
7/16	14	0·071 43	0·0457	0·4375	0·3918	0·3461	0·0941
1/2	12	0·083 33	0·0534	0·5000	0·4466	0·3932	0·1214
9/16	12	0·083 33	0·0534	0·5625	0·5091	0·4557	0·1631
5/8	11	0·090 91	0·0582	0·6250	0·5668	0·5086	0·2032
11/16	11	0·090 91	0·0582	0·6875	0·6293	0·5711	0·2562
3/4	10	0·100 00	0·0640	0·7500	0·6860	0·6220	0·3039
7/8	9	0·111 11	0·0711	0·8750	0·8039	0·7328	0·4218
1	8	0·125 00	0·0800	1·0000	0·9200	0·8400	0·5542
1 1/8	7	0·142 86	0·0915	1·1250	1·0335	0·9420	0·6969
1 1/4	7	0·142 86	0·0915	1·2500	1·1585	1·0670	0·8942
1 1/2	6	0·166 67	0·1067	1·5000	1·3933	1·2866	1·300
1 3/4	5	0·200 00	0·1281	1·7500	1·6219	1·4938	1·753
2	4·5	0·222 22	0·1423	2·0000	1·8577	1·7154	2·311
2 1/4	4	0·250 00	0·1601	2·2500	2·0899	1·9298	2·925
2 1/2	4	0·250 00	0·1601	2·5000	2·3399	2·1798	3·732
2 3/4	3·5	0·285 71	0·1830	2·7500	2·5670	2·3840	4·464
3	3·5	0·285 71	0·1830	3·0000	2·8170	2·6340	5·449
3 1/4	3·25	0·307 69	0·1970	3·2500	3·0530	2·8560	6·406
3 1/2	3·25	0·307 69	0·1970	3·5000	3·3030	3·1060	7·577
3 3/4	3	0·333 33	0·2134	3·7500	3·5366	3·3232	8·674
4	3	0·333 33	0·2134	4·0000	3·7866	3·5732	10·03
4 1/2	2·875	0·347 83	0·2227	4·5000	4·2773	4·0546	12·91
5	2·75	0·363 64	0·2328	5·0000	4·7672	4·5344	16·15
5 1/2	2·625	0·380 95	0·2439	5·5000	5·2561	5·0122	19·73
6	2·5	0·400 00	0·2561	6·0000	5·7439	5·4878	23·65

B.S. WHITWORTH BOLTS

LIMITS AND TOLERANCES

CLOSE FIT

1	2	3	4	5	6	7	8	9	10	11
Nominal Diameter	Number of Threads per In.	Major Diameter			Effective Diameter			Minor Diameter		
		Max.	Tol.	Min.	Max.	Tol.	Min.	Max.	Tol.	Min.
In.		In.	In.	In.	In.	In.	In.	In.	In.	In.
⅛	40	0·1250	0·0035	0·1215	0·1090	0·0019	0·1071	0·0930	0·0040	0·0890
3/16	24	0·1875	0·0043	0·1832	0·1608	0·0023	0·1585	0·1341	0·0050	0·1291
¼	20	0·2500	0·0048	0·2452	0·2180	0·0026	0·2154	0·1860	0·0055	0·1805
5/16	18	0·3125	0·0052	0·3073	0·2769	0·0028	0·2741	0·2413	0·0059	0·2354
⅜	16	0·3750	0·0055	0·3695	0·3350	0·0030	0·3320	0·2950	0·0062	0·2888
7/16	14	0·4375	0·0059	0·4316	0·3918	0·0032	0·3886	0·3461	0·0067	0·3394
½	12	0·5000	0·0063	0·4937	0·4466	0·0034	0·4432	0·3932	0·0072	0·3860
9/16	12	0·5625	0·0065	0·5560	0·5091	0·0036	0·5055	0·4557	0·0074	0·4483
⅝	11	0·6250	0·0067	0·6183	0·5668	0·0037	0·5631	0·5086	0·0076	0·5010
11/16	11	0·6875	0·0068	0·6807	0·6293	0·0038	0·6255	0·5711	0·0077	0·5634
¾	10	0·7500	0·0072	0·7428	0·6860	0·0040	0·6820	0·6220	0·0081	0·6139
⅞	9	0·8750	0·0076	0·8674	0·8039	0·0043	0·7996	0·7328	0·0086	0·7242
1	8	1·0000	0·0080	0·9920	0·9200	0·0045	0·9155	0·8400	0·0091	0·8309
1⅛	7	1·1250	0·0086	1·1164	1·0335	0·0048	1·0287	0·9420	0·0097	0·9323
1¼	7	1·2500	0·0087	1·2413	1·1585	0·0049	1·1536	1·0670	0·0098	1·0572
1½	6	1·5000	0·0094	1·4906	1·3933	0·0053	1·3880	1·2866	0·0106	1·2760
1¾	5	1·7500	0·0102	1·7398	1·6219	0·0057	1·6162	1·4938	0·0115	1·4823
2	4·5	2·0000	0·0108	1·9892	1·8577	0·0061	1·8516	1·7154	0·0122	1·7032
2¼	4	2·2500	0·0114	2·2386	2·0899	0·0064	2·0835	1·9298	0·0129	1·9169
2½	4	2·5000	0·0116	2·4884	2·3399	0·0066	2·3333	2·1798	0·0131	2·1667
2¾	3·5	2·7500	0·0123	2·7377	2·5670	0·0070	2·5600	2·3840	0·0139	2·3701
3	3·5	3·0000	0·0125	2·9875	2·8170	0·0072	2·8098	2·6340	0·0141	2·6199

B.S. Whitworth Nuts

LIMITS AND TOLERANCES

CLOSE FIT

1	2	3	4	5	6	7	8	9
Nominal Diameter	Number of Threads per In.	Major Diameter	Effective Diameter			Minor Diameter		
		Min.	Max.	Tol.	Min.	Max.	Tol.	Min.
In.		In.	In.	In.	In.	In.	In.	In.
⅛	40	0·1250	0·1109	0·0019	0·1090	0·1020	0·0090	0·0930
3/16	24	0·1875	0·1631	0·0023	0·1608	0·1474	0·0133	0·1341
¼	20	0·2500	0·2206	0·0026	0·2180	0·2030	0·0170	0·1860
5/16	18	0·3125	0·2797	0·0028	0·2769	0·2594	0·0181	0·2413
⅜	16	0·3750	0·3380	0·0030	0·3350	0·3145	0·0195	0·2950
7/16	14	0·4375	0·3950	0·0032	0·3918	0·3674	0·0213	0·3461
½	12	0·5000	0·4500	0·0034	0·4466	0·4169	0·0237	0·3932
9/16	12	0·5625	0·5127	0·0036	0·5091	0·4794	0·0237	0·4557
⅝	11	0·6250	0·5705	0·0037	0·5668	0·5338	0·0252	0·5086
11/16	11	0·6875	0·6331	0·0038	0·6293	0·5963	0·0252	0·5711
¾	10	0·7500	0·6900	0·0040	0·6860	0·6490	0·0270	0·6220
⅞	9	0·8750	0·8082	0·0043	0·8039	0·7620	0·0292	0·7328
1	8	1·0000	0·9245	0·0045	0·9200	0·8720	0·0320	0·8400
1⅛	7	1·1250	1·0383	0·0048	1·0335	0·9776	0·0356	0·9420
1¼	7	1·2500	1·1634	0·0049	1·1585	1·1026	0·0356	1·0670
1½	6	1·5000	1·3986	0·0053	1·3933	1·3269	0·0403	1·2866
1¾	5	1·7500	1·6276	0·0057	1·6219	1·5408	0·0470	1·4938
2	4·5	2·0000	1·8638	0·0061	1·8577	1·7668	0·0514	1·7154
2¼	4	2·2500	2·0963	0·0064	2·0899	1·9863	0·0570	1·9298
2½	4	2·5000	2·3465	0·0066	2·3399	2·2368	0·0570	2·1798
2¾	3·5	2·7500	2·5740	0·0070	2·5670	2·4481	0·0641	2·3840
3	3·5	3·0000	2·8242	0·0072	2·8170	2·6981	0·0641	2·6340

B.S. Whitworth Bolts (contd.)
LIMITS AMD TOLERANCES
MEDIUM FIT

1	2	3	4	5	6	7	8	9	10	11
Nominal Diameter	Number of Threads per In.	Major Diameter			Effective Diameter			Minor Diameter		
		Max.	Tol.	Min.	Max.	Tol.	Min.	Max.	Tol.	Min.
In.		In.	In.	In.	In.	In.	In.	In.	In.	In.
⅛	40	0·1250	0·0045	0·1205	0·1090	0·0029	0·1061	0·0930	0·0061	0·0869
³⁄₁₆	24	0·1875	0·0055	0·1820	0·1608	0·0035	0·1573	0·1341	0·0076	0·1265
¼	20	0·2500	0·0061	0·2439	0·2180	0·0039	0·2141	0·1860	0·0084	0·1776
⁵⁄₁₆	18	0·3125	0·0066	0·3059	0·2769	0·0042	0·2727	0·2413	0·0089	0·2324
⅜	16	0·3750	0·0070	0·3680	0·3350	0·0045	0·3305	0·2950	0·0095	0·2855
⁷⁄₁₆	14	0·4375	0·0075	0·4300	0·3918	0·0048	0·3870	0·3461	0·0101	0·3360
½	12	0·5000	0·0081	0·4919	0·4466	0·0052	0·4414	0·3932	0·0110	0·3822
⁹⁄₁₆	12	0·5625	0·0082	0·5543	0·5091	0·0053	0·5038	0·4557	0·0111	0·4446
⅝	11	0·6250	0·0086	0·6164	0·5668	0·0056	0·5612	0·5086	0·0116	0·4970
¹¹⁄₁₆ *	11	0·6875	0·0088	0·6787	0·6293	0·0058	0·6235	0·5711	0·0118	0·5593
¾	10	0·7500	0·0092	0·7408	0·6860	0·0060	0·6800	0·6220	0·0123	0·6097
⅞	9	0·8750	0·0097	0·8653	0·8039	0·0064	0·7975	0·7328	0·0131	0·7197
1	8	1·0000	0·0103	0·9897	0·9200	0·0068	0·9132	0·8400	0·0139	0·8261
1⅛	7	1·1250	0·0110	1·1140	1·0335	0·0072	1·0263	0·9420	0·0148	0·9272
1¼	7	1·2500	0·0112	1·2388	1·1585	0·0074	1·1511	1·0670	0·0150	1·0520
1½	6	1·5000	0·0121	1·4879	1·3933	0·0080	1·3853	1·2866	0·0162	1.2704
1¾	5	1·7500	0·0131	1·7369	1·6219	0·0086	1·6133	1·4938	0·0175	1·4763
2	4·5	2·0000	0·0138	1·9862	1·8577	0·0091	1·8486	1·7154	0·0185	1·6969
2¼	4	2·2500	0·0146	2·2354	2·0899	0·0096	2·0803	1·9298	0·0196	1·9102
2½	4	2·5000	0·0150	2·4850	2·3399	0·0100	2·3299	2·1798	0·0200	2·1598
2¾	3·5	2·7500	0·0157	2·7343	2·5670	0·0104	2·5566	2·3840	0·0211	2·3629
3	3·5	3·0000	0·0161	2·9839	2·8170	0·0108	2·8062	2·6340	0·0215	2·6125

* To be dispensed with wherever possible.

E.W.D.—4*

B.S. Whitworth Nuts

LIMITS AND TOLERANCES

MEDIUM FIT

1	2	3	4	5	6	7	8	9
Nominal Diameter	Number of Threads per In.	Major Diameter	Effective Diameter			Minor Diameter		
		Min.	Max.	Tol.	Min.	Max.	Tol.	Min.
In.		In.	In.	In.	In.	In.	In.	In.
⅛	40	0·1250	0·1119	0·0029	0·1090	0·1020	0·0090	0·0930
3/16	24	0·1875	0·1643	0·0035	0·1608	0·1474	0·0133	0·1341
¼	20	0·2500	0·2219	0·0039	0·2180	0·2030	0·0170	0·1860
5/16	18	0·3125	0·2811	0·0042	0·2769	0·2594	0·0181	0·2413
⅜	16	0·3750	0·3395	0·0045	0·3350	0·3145	0·0195	0·2950
7/16	14	0·4375	0·3966	0·0048	0·3918	0·3674	0·0213	0·3461
½	12	0·5000	0·4518	0·0052	0·4466	0·4169	0·0237	0·3932
9/16	12	0·5625	0·5144	0·0053	0·5091	0·4794	0·0237	0·4557
⅝	11	0·6250	0·5724	0·0056	0·5668	0·5338	0·0252	0·5086
11/16	11	0·6875	0·6351	0·0058	0·6293	0·5963	0·0252	0·5711
¾	10	0·7500	0·6920	0·0060	0·6860	0·6490	0·0270	0·6220
⅞	9	0·8750	0·8103	0·0064	0·8039	0·7620	0·0292	0·7328
1	8	1·0000	0·9268	0·0068	0·9200	0·8720	0·0320	0·8400
1⅛	7	1·1250	1·0407	0·0072	1·0335	0·9776	0·0356	0·9420
1¼	7	1·2500	1·1659	0·0074	1·1585	1·1026	0·0356	1·0670
1½	6	1·5000	1·4013	0·0080	1·3933	1·3269	0·0403	1·2866
1¾	5	1·7500	1·6305	0·0086	1·6219	1·5408	0·0470	1·4938
2	4·5	2·0000	1·8668	0·0091	1·8577	1·7668	0·0514	1·7154
2¼	4	2·2500	2·0995	0·0096	2·0899	1·9868	0·0570	1·9298
2½	4	2·5000	2·3499	0·0100	2·3399	2·2368	0·0570	2·1798
2¾	3·5	2·7500	2·5774	0·0104	2·5670	2·4481	0·0641	2·3840
3	3·5	3·0000	2·8278	0·0108	2·8170	2·6981	0·0641	2·6340

B.S. Whitworth Bolts (*contd.*)
LIMITS AND TOLERANCES
FREE FIT

1	2	3	4	5	6	7	8	9	10	11
Nominal Diameter	Number of Threads per In.	Major Diameter			Effective Diameter			Minor Diameter		
		Max.	Tol.	Min.	Max.	Tol.	Min.	Max.	Tol.	Min.
In.		In.	In.	In.	In.	In.	In.	In.	In.	In.
⅛	40	0·1250	0·0059	0·1191	0·1090	0·0043	0·1047	0·0930	0·0075	0·0855
3⁄16	24	0·1875	0·0072	0·1803	0·1608	0·0052	0·1556	0·1341	0·0093	0·1248
¼	20	0·2500	0·0080	0·2420	0·2180	0·0058	0·2122	0·1860	0·0103	0·1757
5⁄16	18	0·3125	0·0087	0·3038	0·2769	0·0063	0·2706	0·2413	0·0110	0·2303
⅜	16	0·3750	0·0093	0·3657	0·3350	0·0068	0·3282	0·2950	0·0118	0·2832
7⁄16	14	0·4375	0·0100	0·4275	0·3918	0·0073	0·3845	0·3461	0·0126	0·3335
½	12	0·5000	0·0106	0·4894	0·4466	0·0077	0·4389	0·3932	0·0135	0·3797
9⁄16	12	0·5625	0·0109	0·5516	0·5091	0·0080	0·5011	0·4557	0·0138	0·4419
⅝	11	0·6250	0·0114	0·6136	0·5668	0·0084	0·5584	0·5086	0·0144	0·4942
11⁄16 *	11	0·6875	0·0116	0·6759	0·6293	0·0086	0·6207	0·5711	0·0146	0·5565
¾	10	0·7500	0·0122	0·7378	0·6860	0·0090	0·6770	0·6220	0·0153	0·6067
⅞	9	0·8750	0·0129	0·8621	0·8039	0·0096	0·7943	0·7328	0·0163	0·7165
1	8	1·0000	0·0137	0·9863	0·9200	0·0102	0·9098	0·8400	0·0173	0·8227
1⅛	7	1·1250	0·0145	1·1105	1·0335	0·0107	1·0228	0·9420	0·0183	0·9237
1¼	7	1·2500	0·0149	1·2351	1·1585	0·0111	1·1474	1·0670	0·0187	1·0483
1½	6	1·5000	0·0161	1·4839	1·3933	0·0120	1·3813	1·2866	0·0202	1·2664
1¾	5	1·7500	0·0174	1·7326	1·6219	0·0129	1·6090	1·4938	0·0218	1·4720
2	4·5	2·0000	0·0184	1·9816	1·8577	0·0137	1·8440	1·7154	0·0231	1·6923
2¼	4	2·2500	0·0194	2·2306	2·0899	0·0144	2·0755	1·9298	0·0244	1·9054
2½	4	2·5000	0·0199	2·4801	2·3399	0·0149	2·3250	2·1798	0·0249	2·1549
2¾	3·5	2·7500	0·0210	2·7290	2·5670	0·0157	2·5513	2·3840	0·0264	2·3576
3	3·5	3·0000	0·0214	2·9786	2·8170	0·0161	2·8009	2·6340	0·0268	2·6072

* To be dispensed with wherever possible.

B.S. Whitworth Nuts

LIMITS AND TOLERANCES

FREE FIT

1	2	3	4	5	6	7	8	9
Nom-inal Dia-meter	Number of Threads per In.	Major Diameter	Effective Diameter			Minor Diameter		
		Min.	Max.	Tol.	Min.	Max.	Tol.	Min.
In.		In.	In.	In.	In.	In.	In.	In.
⅛	40	0·1250	0·1133	0·0043	0·1090	0·1020	0·0090	0·0930
3/16	24	0·1875	0·1660	0·0052	0·1608	0·1474	0·0133	0·1341
¼	20	0·2500	0·2238	0·0058	0·2180	0·2030	0·0170	0·1860
5/16	18	0·3125	0·2832	0·0063	0·2769	0·2594	0·0181	0·2413
⅜	16	0·3750	0·3418	0·0068	0·3350	0·3145	0·0195	0·2950
7/16	14	0·4375	0·3991	0·0073	0·3918	0·3674	0·0213	0·3461
½	12	0·5000	0·4543	0·0077	0·4466	0·4169	0·0237	0·3932
9/16	12	0·5625	0·5171	0·0080	0·5091	0·4794	0·0237	0·4557
⅝	11	0·6250	0·5752	0·0084	0·5668	0·5338	0·0252	0·5086
11/16	11	0·6875	0·6379	0·0086	0·6293	0·5963	0·0252	0·5711
¾	10	0·7500	0·6950	0·0090	0·6860	0·6490	0·0270	0·6220
⅞	9	0·8750	0·8135	0·0096	0·8039	0·7620	0 0292	0 7328
1	8	1·0000	0·9302	0·0102	0·9200	0·8720	0·0320	0·8400
1⅛	7	1·1250	1·0442	0·0107	1·0335	0·9776	0·0356	0·9420
1¼	7	1·2500	1·1696	0·0111	1·1585	1·1025	0·0356	1·0670
1½	6	1·5000	1·4053	0·0120	1·3933	1·3269	0·0403	1·2866
1¾	5	1·7500	1·6348	0·0129	1·6219	1·5408	0·0470	1·4938
2	4·5	2·0000	1·8714	0·0137	1·8577	1·7668	0·0514	1·7154
2¼	4	2·2500	2·1043	0·0144	2·0899	1·9668	0·0570	1·9298
2½	4	2·5000	2·3548	0·0149	2·3399	2·2368	0·0570	2·1798
2¾	3·5	2·7500	2·5827	0·0157	2·5670	2·4481	0·0641	2·3840
3	3·5	3·0000	2·8331	0·0161	2·8170	2·6981	0·0641	2·6340

BRITISH STANDARD FINE SCREW THREADS

1	2	3	4	5	6	7	8
Nominal Diameter	Number of Threads per In.	Pitch	Depth of Thread	Major Diameter	Effective Diameter	Minor Diameter	Cross Sectional Area at Bottom of Thread
In.		In.	In.	In.	In.	In.	Sq. In.
3/16	32	0·031 25	0·0200	0·1875	0·1675	0·1475	0·0171
7/32	28	0·035 71	0·0229	0·2188	0·1959	0·1730	0·0235
1/4	26	0·038 46	0·0246	0·2500	0·2254	0·2008	0·0317
9/32	26	0·038 46	0·0246	0·2812	0·2566	0·2320	0·0423
5/16	22	0·045 45	0·0291	0·3125	0·2834	0·2543	0·0508
3/8	20	0·050 00	0·0320	0·3750	0·3430	0·3110	0·0760
7/16	18	0·055 56	0·0356	0·4375	0·4019	0·3663	0·1054
1/2	16	0·062 50	0·0400	0·5000	0·4600	0·4200	0·1385
9/16	16	0·062 50	0·0400	0·5625	0·5225	0·4825	0·1828
5/8	14	0·071 43	0·0457	0·6250	0·5793	0·5336	0·2236
11/16	14	0·071 43	0·0457	0·6875	0·6418	0·5961	0·2791
3/4	12	0·083 33	0·0534	0·7500	0·6966	0·6432	0·3249
13/16	12	0·083 33	0·0534	0·8125	0·7591	0·7057	0·3911
7/8	11	0·090 91	0·0582	0·8750	0·8168	0·7586	0·4520
1	10	0·100 00	0·0640	1·0000	0·9360	0·8720	0·5972
1 1/8	9	0·111 11	0·0711	1·1250	1·0539	0·9828	0·7586
1 1/4	9	0·111 11	0·0711	1·2500	1·1789	1·1078	0·9639
1 3/8	8	0·125 00	0·0800	1·3750	1·2950	1·2150	1·159
1 1/2	8	0·125 00	0·0800	0·5000	1·4200	1·3400	1·410
1 5/8	8	0·125 00	0·0800	1·6250	1·5450	1·4650	1·686
1 3/4	7	0·142 86	0·0915	1·7500	1·6585	1·5670	1·928
2	7	0·142 86	0·0915	2·0000	1·9085	1·8170	2·593
2 1/4	6	0·166 67	0·1067	2·2500	2·1433	2·0366	3·258
2 1/2	6	0·166 67	0·1067	2·5000	2·3933	2·2866	4·106
2 3/4	6	0·166 67	0·1067	2·7500	2·6433	2·5366	5·054
3	5	0·200 00	0·1281	3·0000	2·8719	2·7438	5·913
3 1/4	5	0·200 00	0·1281	3·2500	3·1219	2·9938	7·039
3 1/2	4·5	0·222 22	0·1423	3·5000	3·3577	3·2154	8·120
3 3/4	4·5	0·222 22	0·1423	3·7500	3·6077	3·4654	9·432
4	4·5	0·222 22	0·1423	4·0000	3·8577	3·7154	10·84
4 1/4	4	0·250 00	0·1601	4·2500	4·0899	3·9298	12·13

Note.—It is recommended that for larger diameters in this series four threads per in. be used.

B.S. FINE BOLTS

LIMITS AND TOLERANCES

CLOSE FIT

1	2	3	4	5	6	7	8	9	10	11
Nominal Diameter	Number of Threads per In.	Major Diameter			Effective Diameter			Minor Diameter		
		Max.	Tol.	Min.	Max.	Tol.	Min.	Max.	Tol.	Min.
In.		In.	In.	In.	In.	In.	In.	In.	In.	In.
$\frac{3}{16}$	32	0·1875	0·0040	0·1835	0·1675	0·0022	0·1653	0·1475	0·0045	0·1430
$\frac{7}{32}$	28	0·2188	0·0043	0·2145	0·1959	0·0024	0·1935	0·1730	0·0049	0·1681
$\frac{1}{4}$	26	0·2500	0·0045	0·2455	0·2254	0·0025	0·2229	0·2008	0·0050	0·1958
$\frac{9}{32}$	26	0·2812	0·0046	0·2766	0·2566	0·0026	0·2540	0·2320	0·0051	0·2269
$\frac{5}{16}$	22	0·3125	0·0048	0·3077	0·2834	0·0027	0·2807	0·2543	0·0055	0·2488
$\frac{3}{8}$	20	0·3750	0·0051	0·3699	0·3430	0·0029	0·3401	0·3110	0·0058	0·3052
$\frac{7}{16}$	18	0·4375	0·0055	0·4320	0·4019	0·0031	0·3988	0·3663	0·0062	0·3601
$\frac{1}{2}$	16	0·5000	0·0058	0·4942	0·4600	0·0033	0·4567	0·4200	0·0065	0·4135
$\frac{9}{16}$	16	0·5625	0·0059	0·5566	0·5225	0·0034	0·5191	0·4825	0·0066	0·4759
$\frac{5}{8}$	14	0·6250	0·0063	0·6187	0·5793	0·0036	0·5757	0·5336	0·0071	0·5265
$\frac{11}{16}$	14	0·6875	0·0064	0·6811	0·6418	0·0037	0·6381	0·5961	0·0072	0·5889
$\frac{3}{4}$	12	0·7500	0·0068	0·7432	0·6966	0·0039	0·6927	0·6432	0·0077	0·6355
$\frac{13}{16}$	12	0·8125	0·0069	0·8056	0·7591	0·0040	0·7551	0·7057	0·0078	0·6979
$\frac{7}{8}$	11	0·8750	0·0072	0·8678	0·8168	0·0042	0·8126	0·7586	0·0081	0·7505
1	10	1·0000	0·0076	0·9924	0·9360	0·0044	0·9316	0·8720	0·0085	0·8635
$1\frac{1}{8}$	9	1·1250	0·0079	1·1171	1·0539	0·0046	1·0493	0·9828	0·0089	0·9739
$1\frac{1}{4}$	9	1·2500	0·0081	1·2419	1·1789	0·0048	1·1741	1·1078	0·0091	1·0987
$1\frac{3}{8}$	8	1·3750	0·0085	1·3665	1·2950	0·0050	1·2900	1·2150	0·0096	1·2054
$1\frac{1}{2}$	8	1·5000	0·0087	1·4913	1·4200	0·0052	1·4148	1·3400	0·0098	1·3302

B.S. Fine Nuts

LIMITS AND TOLERANCES

CLOSE FIT

1	2	3	4	5	6	7	8	9
Nominal Diameter	Number of Threads per In.	Major Diameter	Effective Diameter			Minor Diameter		
		Min.	Max.	Tol.	Min.	Max.	Tol.	Min.
In.		In.	In.	In.	In.	In.	In.	In.
$\frac{3}{16}$	32	0·1875	0·1697	0·0022	0·1675	0·1577	0·0102	0·1475
$\frac{7}{32}$	28	0·2188	0·1983	0·0024	0·1959	0·1841	0·0111	0·1730
$\frac{1}{4}$	26	0·2500	0·2279	0·0025	0·2254	0·2125	0·0117	0·2008
$\frac{9}{32}$	26	0·2812	0·2592	0·0026	0·2566	0·2437	0·0117	0·2320
$\frac{5}{16}$	22	0·3125	0·2861	0·0027	0·2834	0·2684	0·0141	0·2543
$\frac{3}{8}$	20	0·3750	0·3459	0·0029	0·3430	0·3280	0·0170	0·3110
$\frac{7}{16}$	18	0·4375	0·4050	0·0031	0·4019	0·3844	0·0181	0·3663
$\frac{1}{2}$	16	0·5000	0·4633	0·0033	0·4600	0·4395	0·0195	0·4200
$\frac{9}{16}$	16	0·5625	0·5259	0·0034	0·5225	0·5020	0·0195	0·4825
$\frac{5}{8}$	14	0·6250	0·5829	0·0036	0·5793	0·5549	0·0213	0·5336
$\frac{11}{16}$	14	0·6875	0·6455	0·0037	0·6418	0·6174	0 0213	0·5961
$\frac{3}{4}$	12	0·7500	0·7005	0·0039	0·6966	0·6669	0·0237	0·6432
$\frac{13}{16}$	12	0·8125	0·7631	0·0040	0·7591	0·7294	0·0237	0·7057
$\frac{7}{8}$	11	0·8750	0·8210	0·0042	0·8168	0·7838	0·0252	0·7586
1	10	1·0000	0·9404	0·0044	0·9360	0·8990	0·0270	0·8720
$1\frac{1}{8}$	9	1·1250	1·0585	0·0046	1·0539	1·0120	0·0292	0·9828
$1\frac{1}{4}$	9	1·2500	1·1837	0·0048	1·1789	1·1370	0·0292	1·1078
$1\frac{3}{8}$	8	1·3750	1·3000	0·0050	1·2950	1·2470	0·0320	1·2150
$1\frac{1}{2}$	8	1·5000	1·4252	0·0052	1·4200	1·3720	0·0320	1·3400

B.S. Fine Bolts (*contd.*)

LIMITS AND TOLERANCES

MEDIUM FIT

1	2	3	4	5	6	7	8	9	10	11
Nominal Diameter	Number of Threads per In.	Major Diameter			Effective Diameter			Minor Diameter		
		Max.	Tol.	Min.	Max.	Tol.	Min.	Max.	Tol.	Min.
In.		In.	In.	In.	In.	In.	In.	In.	In.	In.
3/16	32	0·1875	0·0051	0·1824	0·1675	0·0033	0·1642	0·1475	0·0068	0·1407
7/32	28	0·2188	0·0055	0·2133	0·1959	0·0036	0·1923	0·1730	0·0074	0·1656
1/4	26	0·2500	0·0057	0·2443	0·2254	0·0037	0·2217	0·2008	0·0076	0·1932
9/32	26	0·2812	0·0059	0·2753	0·2566	0·0039	0·2527	0·2320	0·0078	0·2242
5/16	22	0·3125	0·0062	0·3063	0·2834	0·0041	0·2793	0·2543	0·0084	0·2459
3/8	20	0·3750	0·0066	0·3684	0·3430	0·0044	0·3386	0·3110	0·0089	0·3021
7/16	18	0·4375	0·0071	0·4304	0·4019	0·0047	0·3972	0·3663	0·0094	0·3569
1/2	16	0·5000	0·0075	0·4925	0·4600	0·0050	0·4550	0·4200	0·0100	0·4100
9/16	16	0·5625	0·0077	0·5548	0·5225	0·0052	0·5173	0·4825	0·0102	0·4723
5/8	14	0·6250	0·0081	0·6169	0·5793	0·0054	0·5739	0·5336	0·0107	0·5229
11/16	14	0·6875	0·0083	0·6792	0·6418	0·0056	0·6362	0·5961	0·0109	0·5852
3/4	12	0·7500	0·0088	0·7412	0·6966	0·0059	0·6907	0·6432	0·0117	0·6315
13/16	12	0·8125	0·0089	0·8036	0·7591	0·0060	0·7531	0·7057	0·0118	0·6939
7/8	11	0·8750	0·0092	0·8658	0·8168	0·0062	0·8106	0·7586	0·0122	0·7464
1	10	1·0000	0·0098	0·9902	0·9360	0·0066	0·9294	0·8720	0·0129	0·8591
1⅛	9	1·1250	0·0102	1·1148	1·0539	0·0069	1·0470	0·9828	0·0136	0·9692
1¼	9	1·2500	0·0105	1·2395	1·1789	0·0072	1·1717	1·1078	0·0139	1·0939
1⅜	8	1·3750	0·0110	1·3640	1·2950	0·0075	1·2885	1·2150	0·0146	1·2004
1½	8	1·5000	0·0112	1·4888	1·4200	0·0077	1·4123	1·3400	0·0148	1·3252

B.S. Fine Nuts

LIMITS AND TOLERANCES

MEDIUM FIT

1	2	3	4	5	6	7	8	9
Nominal Diameter	Number of Threads per In.	Major Diameter	Effective Diameter			Minor Diameter		
		Min.	Max.	Tol.	Min.	Max.	Tol.	Min.
In.		In.	In.	In.	In.	In.	In.	In.
$\frac{3}{16}$	32	0·1875	0·1708	0·0033	0·1675	0·1577	0·0102	0·1475
$\frac{7}{32}$	28	0·2188	0·1995	0·0036	0·1959	0·1841	0·0111	0·1730
$\frac{1}{4}$	26	0·2500	0·2291	0·0037	0·2254	0·2125	0·0117	0·2008
$\frac{9}{32}$	26	0·2812	0·2605	0·0039	0·2566	0·2437	0·0117	0·2320
$\frac{5}{16}$	22	0·3125	0·2875	0·0041	0·2834	0·2684	0·0141	0·2543
$\frac{3}{8}$	20	0·3750	0·3474	0·0044	0·3430	0·3280	0·0170	0·3110
$\frac{7}{16}$	18	0·4375	0·4066	0·0047	0·4019	0·3844	0·0181	0·3663
$\frac{1}{2}$	16	0·5000	0·4650	0·0050	0·4600	0·4395	0·0195	0·4200
$\frac{9}{16}$	16	0·5625	0·5277	0·0052	0·5225	0·5020	0·0195	0·4825
$\frac{5}{8}$	14	0·6250	0·5847	0·0054	0·5793	0·5549	0·0213	0·5336
$\frac{11}{16}$	14	0·6875	0·6474	0·0056	0·6418	0·6174	0·0213	0·5961
$\frac{3}{4}$	12	0·7500	0·7025	0·0059	0·6966	0·6669	0·0237	0·6432
$\frac{13}{16}$	12	0·8125	0·7651	0·0060	0·7591	0·7294	0·0237	0·7057
$\frac{7}{8}$	11	0·8750	0·8230	0·0062	0·8168	0·7838	0·0252	0·7586
1	10	1·0000	0·9426	0·0066	0·9360	0·8990	0·0270	0·8720
$1\frac{1}{8}$	9	1·1250	1·0608	0·0069	1·0539	1·0120	0·0292	0·9828
$1\frac{1}{4}$	9	1·2500	1·1861	0·0072	1·1789	1·1370	0·0292	1·1078
$1\frac{3}{8}$	8	1·3750	1·3025	0·0075	1·2950	1·2470	0·0320	1·2150
$1\frac{1}{2}$	8	1·5000	1·4277	0·0077	1·4200	1·3720	0·0320	1·3400

B.S. Fine Bolts (*contd.*)

LIMITS AND TOLERANCES

FREE FIT

1	2	3	4	5	6	7	8	9	10	11
Nominal Diameter	Number of Threads per In.	Major Diameter			Effective Diameter			Minor Diameter		
		Max.	Tol.	Min.	Max.	Tol.	Min.	Max.	Tol.	Min.
In.		In.	In.	In.	In.	In.	In.	In.	In.	In.
3/16	32	0·1875	0·0068	0·1807	0·1675	0·0050	0·1625	0·1475	0·0085	0·1390
7/32	28	0·2188	0·0072	0·2116	0·1959	0·0053	0·1906	0·1730	0·0091	0·1639
1/4	26	0·2500	0·0076	0·2424	0·2254	0·0056	0·2198	0·2008	0·0095	0·1913
9/32	26	0·2812	0·0078	0·2734	0·2566	0·0058	0·2508	0·2320	0·0097	0·2223
5/16	22	0·3125	0·0083	0·3042	0·2834	0·0062	0·2772	0·2543	0·0105	0·2438
3/8	20	0·3750	0·0088	0·3662	0·3430	0·0066	0·3364	0·3110	0·0111	0·2999
7/16	18	0·4375	0·0094	0·4281	0·4019	0·0070	0·3949	0·3663	0·0117	0·3546
1/2	16	0·5000	0·0099	0·4901	0·4600	0·0074	0·4526	0·4200	0·0124	0·4076
9/16	16	0·5625	0·0102	0·5523	0·5225	0·0077	0·5148	0·4825	0·0127	0·4698
5/8	14	0·6250	0·0108	0·6142	0·5793	0·0081	0·5712	0·5336	0·0134	0·5202
11/16	14	0·6875	0·0111	0·6764	0·6418	0·0084	0·6334	0·5961	0·0137	0·5824
3/4	12	0·7500	0·0117	0·7383	0·6966	0·0088	0·6878	0·6432	0·0146	0·6286
13/16	12	0·8125	0·0119	0·8006	0·7591	0·0090	0·7501	0·7057	0·0148	0·6909
7/8	11	0·8750	0·0123	0·8627	0·8168	0·0093	0·8075	0·7586	0·0153	0·7433
1	10	1·0000	0·0131	0·9869	0·9360	0·0099	0·9261	0·8720	0·0162	0·8558
1⅛	9	1·1250	0·0137	1·1113	1·0539	0·0104	1·0435	0·9828	0·0171	0·9657
1¼	9	1·2500	0·0141	1·2359	1·1789	0·0108	1·1681	1·1078	0·0175	1·0903
1⅜	8	1·3750	0·0148	1·3602	1·2950	0·0113	1·2837	1·2150	0·0184	1·1966
1½	8	1·5000	0·0151	1·4849	1·4200	0·0116	1·4084	1·3400	0·0187	1·3213

B.S. Fine Nuts

LIMITS AND TOLERANCES

FREE FIT

1	2	3	4	5	6	7	8	9
Nominal Diameter	Number of Threads per In.	Major Diameter	Effective Diameter			Minor Diameter		
		Min.	Max.	Tol.	Min.	Max.	Tol.	Min.
In.		In.	In.	In.	In.	In.	In.	In.
$\frac{3}{16}$	32	0·1875	0·1725	0·0050	0·1675	0·1577	0·0102	0·1475
$\frac{7}{32}$	28	0·2188	0·2012	0·0053	0·1959	0·1841	0·0111	0·1730
$\frac{1}{4}$	26	0·2500	0·2310	0·0056	0·2254	0·2125	0·0117	0·2008
$\frac{9}{32}$	26	0·2812	0·2624	0·0058	0·2566	0·2437	0·0117	0·2320
$\frac{5}{16}$	22	0·3125	0·2896	0·0062	0·2834	0·2684	0·0141	0·2543
$\frac{3}{8}$	20	0·3750	0·3496	0·0066	0·3430	0·3280	0·0170	0·3110
$\frac{7}{16}$	18	0·4375	0·4089	0·0070	0·4019	0·3844	0·0181	0·3663
$\frac{1}{2}$	16	0·5000	0·4674	0·4674	0·4600	0·4395	0·0195	0·4200
$\frac{9}{16}$	16	0·5625	0·5302	0·0077	0·5225	0·5020	0·0195	0·4825
$\frac{5}{8}$	14	0·6250	0·5874	0·0081	0·5793	0·5549	0·0213	0·5336
$\frac{11}{16}$	14	0·6875	0·6502	0·0084	0·6418	0·6174	0·0213	0·5961
$\frac{3}{4}$	12	0·7500	0·7054	0·0088	0·6966	0·6669	0·0237	0·6432
$\frac{13}{16}$	12	0·8125	0·7681	0·0090	0·7591	0·7294	0·0237	0·7057
$\frac{7}{8}$	11	0·8750	0·8261	0·0093	0·8168	0·7838	0·0252	0·7586
1	10	1·0000	0·9459	0·0099	0·9360	0·8990	0·0270	0·8720
$1\frac{1}{8}$	9	1·1250	1·0643	0·0104	1·0539	1·0120	0·0292	0·9828
$1\frac{1}{4}$	9	1·2500	1·1897	0·0108	1·1789	1·1370	0·0292	1·1078
$1\frac{3}{8}$	8	1·3750	1·3063	0·0113	1·2950	1·2470	0·0320	1·2150
$1\frac{1}{2}$	8	1·5000	1·4316	0·0116	1·4200	1·3720	0·0320	1·3400

BRITISH STANDARD PIPE THREADS (PARALLEL)

(FOR GENERAL ENGINEERING PURPOSES)

1	2	3	4	5	6	7	8
B.S.P. Size	Number of Threads per In.	Pitch	Depth of Thread	Major Diameter	Effective Diameter	Minor Diameter	Cross Sectional Area at Bottom of Thread
In.		In.	In.	In.	In.	In.	Sq. In.
⅛	28	0·035 71	0·0229	0·3830	0·3601	0·3372	0·0893
¼	19	0·052 63	0·0337	0·5180	0·4843	0·4506	0·1595
⅜	19	0·052 63	0·0337	0·6560	0·6223	0·5886	0·2721
½	14	0·071 43	0·0457	0·8250	0·7793	0·7336	0·4227
⅝	14	0·071 43	0·0457	0·9020	0·8563	0·8106	0·5161
¾	14	0·071 43	0·0457	1·0410	0·9953	0·9496	0·7082
⅞	14	0·071 43	0·0457	1·1890	1·1433	1·0976	0·9462
1	11	0·090 91	0·0582	1·3090	1·2508	1·1926	1·117
1¼	11	0·090 91	0·0582	1·6500	1·5918	1·5336	1·847
1½	11	0·090 91	0·0582	1·8820	1·8238	1·7656	2·448
1¾	11	0·090 91	0·0582	2·1160	2·0578	1·9996	3·140
2	11	0·090 91	0·0582	2·3470	2·2888	2·2306	3·908
2¼	11	0·090 91	0·0582	2·5870	2·5288	2·4706	4·794
2½	11	0·090 91	0·0582	2·9600	2·9018	2·8436	6·351
2¾	11	0·090 91	0·0582	3·2100	3·1518	3·0936	7·517
3	11	0·090 91	0·0582	3·4600	3·4018	3·3436	8·780

B.S. PIPE THREADS. BOLTS

LIMITS AND TOLERANCES

CLOSE FIT

1	2	3	4	5	6	7	8	9	10	11	12
	Number of Threads per In.	Length of Engagement	Major Diameter			Effective Diameter			Minor Diameter		
B.S.P. Size			Max.	Tol.	Min.	Max.	Tol.	Min.	Max.	Tol.	Min.
In.		In.	In.	In.	In.	In.	In.	In.	In.	In.	In.
1/8	28	3/8	0·3830	0·0047	0·3783	0·3601	0·0028	0·3573	0·3372	0·0053	0·3319
1/4	19	1/2	0·5180	0·0055	0·5125	0·4843	0·0032	0·4811	0·4506	0·0062	0·4444
3/8	19	1/2	0·6560	0·0056	0·6504	0·6223	0·0033	0·6190	0·5886	0·0063	0·5823
1/2	14	5/8	0·8250	0·0064	0·8186	0·7793	0·0037	0·7756	0·7336	0·0072	0·7264
5/8	14	5/8	0·9020	0·0065	0·8955	0·8563	0·0038	0·8525	0·8106	0·0073	0·8033
3/4	14	3/4	1·0410	0·0067	1·0343	0·9953	0·0040	0·9913	0·9496	0·0075	0·9421
7/8	14	3/4	1·1890	0·0067	1·1823	1·1433	0·0040	1·1393	1·0976	0·0075	1·0901
1	11	1/2	1·3090	0·0073	1·3017	1·2508	0·0043	1·2465	1·1926	0·0082	1·1844
1 1/4	11	1	1·6500	0·0076	1·6424	1·5918	0·0046	1·5872	1·5336	0·0085	1·5251
1 3/8	11	1 1/8	1·8820	0·0078	1·8742	1·8238	0·0048	1·8190	1·7656	0·0087	1·7569

B.S. PIPE THREADS. NUTS

LIMITS AND TOLERANCES
CLOSE FIT

1	2	3	4	5	6	7	8	9	10
B.S.P. Size	*Number of Threads per In.*	*Length of Engagement*	*Major Diameter*	*Effective Diameter*			*Minor Diameter*		
			Min.	*Max.*	*Tol.*	*Min.*	*Max.*	*Tol.*	*Min.*
In.		*In.*	*In.*	*In.*	*In.*	*In.*	*In.*	*In.*	*In.*
1/8	28	3/8	0·3830	0·3629	0·0028	0·3601	0·3483	0·0111	0·3372
1/4	19	1/2	0·5180	0·4875	0·0032	0·4843	0·4681	0·0175	0·4506
3/8	19	1/2	0·6560	0·6256	0·0033	0·6223	0·6061	0·0175	0·5886
1/2	14	5/8	0·8250	0·7830	0·0037	0·7793	0·7549	0·0213	0·7336
5/8	14	5/8	0·9020	0·8601	0·0038	0·8563	0·8319	0·0213	0·8106
3/4	14	3/4	1·0410	0·9993	0·0040	0·9953	0·9709	0·0213	0·9496
7/8	14	3/4	1·1890	1·1473	0·0040	1·1433	1·1189	0·0213	1·0976
1	11	7/8	1·3090	1·2551	0·0043	1·2508	1·2178	0·0252	1·1926
1 1/4	11	1	1·6500	1·5964	0·0046	1·5918	1·5588	0·0252	1·5336
1 1/2	11	1 1/8	1·8820	1·8286	0·0048	1·8238	1·7908	0·0252	1·7656

B.S. PIPE THREADS. BOLTS

LIMITS AND TOLERANCES

MEDIUM FIT

1	2	3	4	5	6	7	8	9	10	11	12
B.S.P. Size	Number of Threads per In.	Length of Engagement	Major Diameter			Effective Diameter			Minor Diameter		
			Max.	Tol.	Min.	Max.	Tol.	Min.	Max.	Tol.	Min.
In.		In.	In.	In.	In.	In.	In.	In.	In.	In.	In.
⅛	28	⅜	0·3830	0·0061	0·3769	0·3601	0·0042	0·3559	0·3372	0·0080	0·3292
¼	19	½	0·5180	0·0072	0·5108	0·4843	0·0049	0·4794	0·4506	0·0095	0·4411
⅜	19	½	0·6560	0·0073	0·6487	0·6223	0·0050	0·6173	0·5886	0·0096	0·5790
½	14	⅝	0·8250	0·0083	0·8167	0·7793	0·0056	0·7737	0·7336	0·0109	0·7227
⅝	14	⅝	0·9020	0·0083	0·8937	0·8563	0·0056	0·8507	0·8106	0·0109	0·7997
¾	14	¾	1·0410	0·0087	1·0323	0·9953	0·0060	0·9893	0·9496	0·0113	0·9383
⅞	14	¾	1·1890	0·0088	1·1802	1·1433	0·0061	1·1372	1·0976	0·0114	1·0862
1	11	⅞	1·3090	0·0095	1·2995	1·2508	0·0065	1·2443	1·1926	0·0125	1·1801
1¼	11	1	1·6500	0·0099	1·6401	1·5918	0·0069	1·5849	1·5336	0·0129	1·5207
1½	11	1⅛	1·8820	0·0102	1·8718	1·8238	0·0072	1·8166	1·7656	0·0132	1·7524

B.S. PIPE THREADS. NUTS

LIMITS AND TOLERANCES
MEDIUM FIT

1	2	3	4	5	6	7	8	9	10
			Major Diameter	Effective Diameter			Minor Diameter		
B.S.P. Size	Number of Threads per In.	Length of Engagement	Min.	Max.	Tol.	Min.	Max.	Tol.	Min.
In.		In.	In.	In.	In.	In.	In.	In.	In.
1/8	28	3/8	0·3830	0·3643	0·0042	0·3601	0·3483	0·0111	0·3372
1/4	19	1/2	0·5180	0·4892	0·0049	0·4843	0·4681	0·0175	0·4506
3/8	19	1/2	0·6560	0·6273	0·0050	0·6223	0·6061	0·0175	0·5886
1/2	14	5/8	0·8250	0·7849	0·0056	0·7793	0·7549	0·0213	0·7336
5/8	14	5/8	0·9020	0·8619	0·0056	0·8563	0·8319	0·0213	0·8106
3/4	14	3/4	1·0410	1·0013	0·0060	0·9953	0·9709	0·0213	0·9496
7/8	14	3/4	1·1890	1·1494	0·0061	1·1433	1·1189	0·0213	1·0976
1	11	7/8	1·3090	1·2573	0·0065	1·2508	1·2178	0·0252	1·1926
1¼	11	1	1·6500	1·5987	0·0069	1·5918	1·5588	0·0252	1·5336
1½	11	1⅛	1·8820	1·8310	0·0072	1·8238	1·7908	0·0252	1·7656

B.S. PIPE THREADS. BOLTS

LIMITS AND TOLERANCES

FREE FIT

1	2	3	4	5	6	7	8	9	10	11	12
	Number of Threads per In.	Length of Engagement	Major Diameter			Effective Diameter			Minor Diameter		
B.S.P. Size			Max.	Tol.	Min.	Max.	Tol.	Min.	Max.	Tol.	Min.
In.		In.	In.	In.	In.	In.	In.	In.	In.	In.	In.
⅛	28	⅜	0·3830	0·0083	0·3747	0·3601	0·0064	0·3537	0·3372	0·0102	0·3270
¼	19	½	0·5180	0·0096	0·5084	0·4843	0·0073	0·4770	0·4506	0·0119	0·4387
⅜	19	½	0·6560	0·0098	0·6462	0·6223	0·0075	0·6148	0·5886	0·0121	0·5765
½	14	⅝	0·8250	0·0111	0·8139	0·7793	0·0084	0·7709	0·7336	0·0137	0·7199
⅝	14	⅝	0·9020	0·0112	0·8908	0·8563	0·0085	0·8478	0·8106	0·0138	0·7968
¾	14	¾	1·0410	0·0116	1·0294	0·9953	0·0089	0·9864	0·9496	0·0142	0·9354
⅞	14	¾	1·1890	0·0118	1·1772	1·1433	0·0091	1·1342	1·0976	0·0144	1·0832
1	11	⅞	1·3090	0·0128	1·2962	1·2508	0·0098	1·2410	1·1926	0·0158	1·1768
1¼	11	1	1·6500	0·0133	1·6367	1·5918	0·0103	1·5815	1·5336	0·0163	1·5173
1½	11	1⅛	1·8820	0·0137	1·8683	1·8238	0·0107	1·8131	1·7656	0·0167	1·7489

B.S. PIPE THREADS. NUTS

Limits and Tolerances
FREE FIT

1	2	3	4	5	6	7	8	9	10
			Major Diameter	Effective Diameter			Minor Diameter		
B.S.P. Size	Number of Threads per In.	Length of Engagement	Min.	Max.	Tol.	Min.	Max.	Tol.	Min.
In.		In.	In.	In.	In.	In.	In.	In.	In.
1/8	28	3/8	0·3830	0·3665	0·0064	0·3601	0·3483	0·0111	0·3372
1/4	19	1/2	0·5180	0·4916	0·0073	0·4843	0·4681	0·0175	0·4506
3/8	19	1/2	0·6560	0·6298	0·0075	0·6223	0·6061	0·0175	0·5886
1/2	14	5/8	0·8250	0·7877	0·0084	0·7793	0·7549	0·0213	0·7336
5/8	14	5/8	0·9020	0·8648	0·0085	0·8563	0·8319	0·0213	0·8106
3/4	14	3/4	1·0410	1·0042	0·0089	0·9953	0·9709	0·0213	0·9496
7/8	14	3/4	1·1890	1·1524	0·0091	1·1433	1·1189	0·0213	1·0976
1	11	7/8	1·3090	1·2606	0·0098	1·2508	1·2178	0·0252	1·1926
1¼	11	1	1·6500	1·6021	0·0103	1·5918	1·5588	0·0252	1·5336
1½	11	1⅛	1·8820	1·8345	0·0107	1·8238	1·7908	0·0252	1·7656

WHITWORTH SCREW THREADS OF SPECIAL DIAMETERS, PITCHES, AND LENGTHS OF ENGAGEMENT

SERIES OF PITCHES

1	2	3	4
Number of Threads per In.	Pitch	Standard Depth of Thread	Double Standard Depth of Thread
	In.	In.	In.
40	0·025 00	0·0160	0·0320
36	0·027 78	0·0178	0·0356
32	0·031 25	0·0200	0·0400
28	0·035 71	0·0229	0·0458
26	0·038 46	0·0246	0·0492
24	0·041 67	0·0267	0·0534
20	0·050 00	0·0320	0·0640
18	0·055 56	0·0356	0·0712
16	0·062 50	0·0400	0·0800
14	0·071 43	0·0457	0·0914
12	0·083 33	0·0534	0·1068
10	0·100 00	0·0640	0·1280
8	0·125 00	0·0800	0·1600
6	0·166 67	0·1067	0·2134
4	0·250 00	0·1601	0·3202

Note.—Basic Effective Diameter = Basic Major Diameter — Standard Depth of Thread (Col. 3).

Basic Minor Diameter = Basic Major Diameter — Twice Standard Depth of Thread (Col. 4).

British Standard Truncated Whitworth Thread *

In the truncated Whitworth form of thread the basic rounded crests at the major diameter of the bolt and the minor diameter of the nut are removed at their junctions with the straight flanks of the basic thread (Fig. 7). The resulting flat crests of threads are given suitable manufacturing tolerances which are negative on the bolt and positive on the nut. The effective diameters of the bolt and nut and the major and minor diameters of the nut are the same as

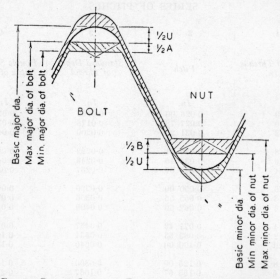

FIG. 7.—British Standard Truncated Whitworth Thread.

for B.S. Whitworth bolts and nuts. Truncated bolt threads are not used with "free fits."

Fig. 7 shows the upper and lower limiting outlines of a bolt and nut with truncated threads. For the bolt the major basic diameter is reduced by an amount equal to twice the normal rounded crest, denoted by U where

$$U = 0 \cdot 147835p \text{ where } p = \text{pitch.}$$

In the case of the nut, the basic minor diameter is increased by the same amount.

* B.S. 84—1940 (Amendment No. 3, August 1945).

TRUNCATED WHITWORTH THREADS WITH FLAT CRESTS

Unit = 0·001 in.

1	2	3	4	5
	BOLT.—Major Diameter		NUT.—Minor Diameter	
Threads per Inch	Nominal Truncation	Tolerance on Truncated Major Diameter	Nominal Truncation	Tolerance on Truncated Minor Diameter
	U	A	U	B
40	3·7	4·3	3·7	5·3
36	4·1	4·5	4·1	5·5
32	4·6	4·6	4·6	5·6
28	5·3	4·8	5·3	5·8
26	5·7	5·0	5·7	6·0
24	6·2	5·1	6·2	7·1
22	6·7	5·4	6·7	7·4
20	7·4	5·6	7·4	9·6
19	7·8	5·7	7·8	9·7
18	8·2	5·9	8·2	9·9
16	9·2	6·3	9·2	10·3
14	10·6	6·7	10·6	10·7
12	12·3	7·4	12·3	11·4
11	13·4	7·8	13·4	11·8
10	14·8	8·2	14·8	12·2
9	16·4	8·8	16·4	12·8
8	18·5	9·5	18·5	13·5
7	21·1	10·5	21·1	14·5
6	24·6	11·7	24·6	15·7
5	29·6	13·4	29·6	17·4
4½	32·9	14·5	32·9	18·5
4	37·0	16·0	37·0	20·0
3½	42·2	17·9	42·2	21·9

Notes.—1. To obtain the upper limit for the major diameter of the truncated thread of a bolt, subtract the value in col. 2 from its basic major diameter. To obtain the lower limit for the minor diameter of the truncated thread of a nut, add the value in col. 4 to its basic minor diameter.

2. The tolerances on bolts are negative and those on nuts positive.

3. The tolerances are the same for close, medium and free fits.

The tolerances on the flat crests at the major diameter of the bolt and on the flat crests at the minor diameter of the nut are denoted by A and B respectively. These tolerances are the same for close, medium and free classes of fits.

The following formulæ are used for determining A :

$$U + A = 0.2p + 0.003 \text{ in.}$$
$$A = \text{Difference between the rounded-off values of } (U + A) \text{ and } U.$$

In the case of the nut, the upper limit of tolerance for the flat crests at the minor diameter is :

$$U + B = 0.2p + 0.004 \text{ in. for 26 t.p.i. and finer.}$$
$$0.2p + 0.005 \text{ in. for 24 and 22 t.p.i.}$$
$$0.2p + 0.007 \text{ in. for 20 t.p.i. and coarser.}$$
$$B = \text{Difference between the rounded-off values of } (U + B) \text{ and } U.$$

The values of U, A and B are given in the table.

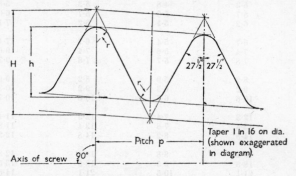

FIG. 8.—BRITISH STANDARD TAPER PIPE THREAD.

BRITISH STANDARD TAPER PIPE THREADS

The British Standard Whitworth form of thread with 55° thread angle is used. One-sixth of the sharp vee is truncated at the top and bottom, the threads being rounded equally at the crests and roots to a radius equal to 0·137329 times the pitch.

The standard taper of the B.S. Taper Pipe Thread * (Fig. 8) is 1 in 16. The flanks of the B.S. Whitworth thread make equal angles with the axis of the pipe, or screw.

* B.S. No. 21—1938.

The following are the proportions of the B.S. Taper Pipe Thread :
H = height of basic triangle, h = working height, r = root and crest radius, p = pitch.

$$H = 0.960237p.$$
$$h = 0.640327p.$$
$$r = 0.137278p.$$

It will be observed that these values are slightly different from those of the B.S. Whitworth parallel thread, on account of the taper of the thread.

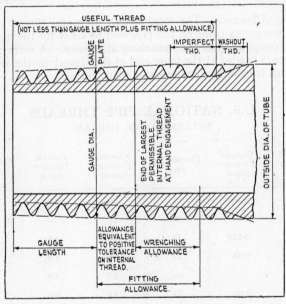

Fig. 9.—British Standard Taper Pipe Thread.

Nomenclature

The following definitions are used in the B.S. Taper Pipe Thread Specification (Fig. 9).

Gauge Diameter.—The basic major diameter of the thread, whether internal, external, parallel or taper.

Gauge Plane.—The plane in which the gauge diameter is located.

Gauge Length.—Distance of the gauge plane on an external taper screw from the small end of screw.

Complete Thread.—That part of the thread which is fully formed at both the crest and root.

Imperfect Thread.—That part of the thread fully formed at root, but truncated at the crest by its intersection with the cylindrical surface of the work.

Wash-out Thread.—That part of the thread not fully formed at the root. It is produced by the bevel at the start of the screwing tool.

Wrenching Allowance.—The additional length of useful thread to allow for the relative movement between the pipe end and coupling, beyond the position of hand engagement, due to the force applied by wrench.

Fitting Allowance.—The total length of useful thread required beyond the gauge plane on the pipe end to allow for the maximum oversize coupling, plus the wrenching allowance. A corresponding allowance is needed at the inner end of the thread in the coupling, unless this is chamfered or screwed right through.

U.S. NATIONAL PIPE THREADS
(SELLERS OR 60° THREAD)

Nominal Diameter (inch)	Outside Diameter (inch)	Threads per Inch	Nominal Diameter (inch)	Outside Diameter (inch)	Threads per Inch
$\frac{1}{8}$	0·405	27	$2\frac{1}{2}$	2·875	8
$\frac{1}{4}$	0·54	18	$2\frac{3}{4}$	—	—
$\frac{3}{8}$	0·675	18	3	3·5	8
$\frac{1}{2}$	0·84	14	$3\frac{1}{2}$	4·0	8
$\frac{5}{8}$	—	—	4	4·5	8
$\frac{3}{4}$	1·05	14	$4\frac{1}{2}$	5·0	8
$\frac{7}{8}$	—	—	5	5·563	8
1	1·315	$11\frac{1}{2}$	6	6·625	8
$1\frac{1}{4}$	1·66	$11\frac{1}{2}$	7	7·625	8
$1\frac{1}{2}$	1·90	$11\frac{1}{2}$	8	8·625	8
$1\frac{3}{4}$	—	—	9	9·688	8
2	2·375	$11\frac{1}{2}$	10	10·75	8
$2\frac{1}{4}$	—	—	12	12·75	8

BASIC SIZES FOR B.S. PIPE THREADS *

1	2	3	4	5	6	7	8	9	10	11	12
B.S.P. Size (Nominal Bore of Tube)	Outside Diameter of Black Tube				No. of Threads per Inch	Pitch	Depth of Thread	Diameters at Gauge Plane (Basic)			Gauge Length
	Maximum	Minimum	Mean	Tolerance				Major (Gauge Diameter)	Effective	Minor	
In.	*In.*	*In.*	*In.*	*In.*		*In.*	*In.*	*In.*	*In.*	*In.*	*In.*
1/8	0·412	0·387	0·400	0·025	28	0·03571	0·0229	0·383	0·3601	0·3372	0·1563
1/4	0·550	0·525	0·538	0·025	19	0·05263	0·0337	0·518	0·4843	0·4506	0·2367
3/8	0·688	0·663	0·676	0·025	19	0·05263	0·0337	0·656	0·6223	0·5886	0·2500
1/2	0·859	0·834	0·847	0·025	14	0·07143	0·0457	0·825	0·7793	0·7336	0·3214
3/4	1·075	1·050	1·063	0·025	14	0·07143	0·0457	1·041	0·9953	0·9496	0·3750
1	1·351	1·320	1·336	0·031	11	0·09091	0·0582	1·309	1·2508	1·1926	0·4091
1 1/4	1·692	1·661	1·677	0·031	11	0·09091	0·0582	1·650	1·5918	1·5336	0·5000
1 1/2	1·924	1·893	1·909	0·031	11	0·09091	0·0582	1·882	1·8238	1·7656	0·5000
2	2·403	2·358	2·381	0·045	11	0·09091	0·0582	2·347	2·2888	2·2306	0·6250
2 1/2	3·021	2·971	2·996	0·050	11	0·09091	0·0582	2·960	2·9018	2·8436	0·6875
3	3·526	3·471	3·499	0·055	11	0·09091	0·0582	3·460	3·4018	3·3436	0·8125
3 1/2	4·021	3·961	3·991	0·060	11	0·09091	0·0582	3·950	3·8918	3·8336	0·8750
4	4·526	4·461	4·494	0·065	11	0·09091	0·0582	4·450	4·3918	4·3336	1·0000
5	5·536	5·461	5·498	0·075	11	0·09091	0·0582	5·450	5·3918	5·3336	1·1250
6	6·541	6·461	6·501	0·080	11	0·09091	0·0582	6·450	6·3918	6·3336	1·1250
7	7·575	7·463	7·519	0·112	10	0·10000	0·0640	7·450	7·3860	7·3220	1·3750
8	8·585	8·463	8·524	0·122	10	0·10000	0·0640	8·450	8·3860	8·3220	1·5000
9	9·595	9·463	9·529	0·132	10	0·10000	0·0640	9·450	9·3860	9·3220	1·5000
10	10·605	10·463	10·534	0·142	10	0·10000	0·0640	10·450	10·3860	10·3220	1·5000
11	11·615	11·465	11·540	0·150	8	0·12500	0·0800	11·450	11·3700	11·2900	1·6250
12	12·625	12·465	12·545	0·160	8	0·12500	0·0800	12·450	12·3700	12·2900	1·6250

Note.—Tubes 7 in. and upwards : The ends shall be specially sized prior to screwing, in order to ensure ample thickness below the root of the thread. This condition shall be complied with for the screwing of cut tube at site.

* British Standard Specification B.S. 21—1938.

LIMITS OF SIZE FOR B.S. PIPE THREADS *

(TURNS OF THREAD)

1	2	3	4	5	6	7	8	9	10
B.S.P. Size (Nominal Bore of Tube)	*Gauge Length. (Distance of Gauge Plane from Pipe End)*				*Position of Gauge Plane on Internal Screws*	*Length of Useful Thread on Pipe End † not less than :*			*Fitting Allowance*
	Basic	*Tol. Plus and Minus*	*Max.*	*Min.*	*Tol. Plus and Minus*	*For Basic Gauge Length*	*For Max. Gauge Length*	*For Min. Gauge Length*	
In.									
$\frac{1}{8}$	$4\frac{3}{8}$	1	$5\frac{3}{8}$	$3\frac{3}{8}$	$1\frac{1}{4}$	$7\frac{1}{8}$	$8\frac{1}{8}$	$6\frac{1}{8}$	$2\frac{3}{4}$
$\frac{1}{4}$	$4\frac{1}{2}$	1	$5\frac{1}{2}$	$3\frac{1}{2}$	$1\frac{1}{4}$	$7\frac{1}{4}$	$8\frac{1}{4}$	$6\frac{1}{4}$	$2\frac{3}{4}$
$\frac{3}{8}$	$4\frac{3}{4}$	1	$5\frac{3}{4}$	$3\frac{3}{4}$	$1\frac{1}{4}$	$7\frac{1}{2}$	$8\frac{1}{2}$	$6\frac{1}{2}$	$2\frac{3}{4}$
$\frac{1}{2}$	$4\frac{1}{2}$	1	$5\frac{1}{2}$	$3\frac{1}{2}$	$1\frac{1}{4}$	$7\frac{1}{4}$	$8\frac{1}{4}$	$6\frac{1}{4}$	$2\frac{3}{4}$
$\frac{3}{4}$	$5\frac{1}{4}$	1	$6\frac{1}{4}$	$4\frac{1}{4}$	$1\frac{1}{4}$	8	9	7	$2\frac{3}{4}$
1	$4\frac{1}{2}$	1	$5\frac{1}{2}$	$3\frac{1}{2}$	$1\frac{1}{4}$	$7\frac{1}{4}$	$8\frac{1}{4}$	$6\frac{1}{4}$	$2\frac{3}{4}$
$1\frac{1}{4}$	$5\frac{1}{2}$	1	$6\frac{1}{2}$	$4\frac{1}{2}$	$1\frac{1}{4}$	$8\frac{1}{4}$	$9\frac{1}{4}$	$7\frac{1}{4}$	$2\frac{3}{4}$
$1\frac{1}{2}$	$5\frac{1}{2}$	1	$6\frac{1}{2}$	$4\frac{1}{2}$	$1\frac{1}{4}$	$8\frac{1}{4}$	$9\frac{1}{4}$	$7\frac{1}{4}$	$2\frac{3}{4}$
2	$6\frac{7}{8}$	1	$7\frac{7}{8}$	$5\frac{7}{8}$	$1\frac{1}{4}$	$10\frac{1}{8}$	$11\frac{1}{8}$	$9\frac{1}{8}$	$3\frac{1}{4}$
$2\frac{1}{2}$	$7\frac{9}{16}$	$1\frac{1}{2}$	$9\frac{1}{16}$	$6\frac{1}{16}$	$1\frac{1}{2}$	$11\frac{9}{16}$	$13\frac{1}{16}$	$10\frac{1}{16}$	4
3	$8\frac{15}{16}$	$1\frac{1}{2}$	$10\frac{7}{16}$	$7\frac{7}{16}$	$1\frac{1}{2}$	$12\frac{15}{16}$	$14\frac{7}{16}$	$11\frac{7}{16}$	4
$3\frac{1}{2}$	$9\frac{5}{8}$	$1\frac{1}{2}$	$11\frac{1}{8}$	$8\frac{1}{8}$	$1\frac{1}{2}$	$13\frac{5}{8}$	$15\frac{1}{8}$	$12\frac{1}{8}$	4
4	11	$1\frac{1}{2}$	$12\frac{1}{2}$	$9\frac{1}{2}$	$1\frac{1}{2}$	$15\frac{1}{2}$	17	14	$4\frac{1}{2}$
5	$12\frac{3}{8}$	$1\frac{1}{2}$	$13\frac{7}{8}$	$10\frac{7}{8}$	$1\frac{1}{2}$	$17\frac{3}{8}$	$18\frac{7}{8}$	$15\frac{7}{8}$	5
6	$12\frac{3}{8}$	$1\frac{1}{2}$	$13\frac{7}{8}$	$10\frac{7}{8}$	$1\frac{1}{2}$	$17\frac{3}{8}$	$18\frac{7}{8}$	$15\frac{7}{8}$	5
7	$13\frac{3}{4}$	2	$15\frac{3}{4}$	$11\frac{3}{4}$	2	$19\frac{1}{4}$	$21\frac{1}{4}$	$17\frac{1}{4}$	$5\frac{1}{2}$
8	15	2	17	13	2	$20\frac{1}{2}$	$22\frac{1}{2}$	$18\frac{1}{2}$	$5\frac{1}{2}$
9	15	2	17	13	2	$20\frac{1}{2}$	$22\frac{1}{2}$	$18\frac{1}{2}$	$5\frac{1}{2}$
10	$16\frac{1}{4}$	2	$18\frac{1}{4}$	$14\frac{1}{4}$	2	$21\frac{3}{4}$	$23\frac{3}{4}$	$19\frac{3}{4}$	$5\frac{1}{2}$
11	13	2	15	11	2	$18\frac{1}{2}$	$20\frac{1}{2}$	$16\frac{1}{2}$	$5\frac{1}{2}$
12	13	2	15	11	2	$18\frac{1}{2}$	$20\frac{1}{2}$	$16\frac{1}{2}$	$5\frac{1}{2}$

* *Note.*—This table applies to taper threads on pipe ends and taper threaded couplings. For parallel threaded couplings diametral tolerances equivalent to the length tolerances in col. 6 will apply.

† The design of internally-screwed parts must make allowance for receiving pipe ends up to the lengths given in col. 8. The lengths of useful thread shall in no case be less than those given in col. 9.

LIMITS OF SIZE FOR B.S. PIPE THREADS *

(LINEAR MEASURE)

1	2	3	4	5	6	7	8	9	10
B.S.P. Size (Nominal Bore of Tube)	Gauge Length. (Distance of Gauge Plane from Pipe End)				Position of Gauge Plane on Internal Screws	Length of Useful Thread on Pipe End † not less than :			Fitting Allowance
	Basic	Tol. Plus and Minus	Max.	Min.	Tol. Plus and Minus	For Basic Gauge Length	For Max. Gauge Length	For Min. Gauge Length	
In.	In.	In.	In.	In.	In.	In.	In.	In.	In.
⅛	0·1563	0·0357	0·1920	0·1206	0·0446	0·2545	0·2902	0·2188	0·0982
¼	0·2367	0·0526	0·2893	0·1841	0·0658	0·3814	0·4340	0·3288	0·1447
⅜	0·2500	0·0526	0·3026	0·1974	0·0658	0·3947	0·4473	0·3421	0·1447
½	0·3214	0·0714	0·3928	0·2500	0·0893	0·5178	0·5892	0·4464	0·1964
¾	0·3750	0·0714	0·4464	0·3036	0·0893	0·5714	0·6428	0·5000	0·1964
1	0·4091	0·0909	0·5000	0·3182	0·1136	0·6591	0·7500	0·5682	0·2500
1¼	0·5000	0·0909	0·5909	0·4091	0·1136	0·7500	0·8409	0·6591	0·2500
1½	0·5000	0·0909	0·5909	0·4091	0·1136	0·7500	0·8409	0·6591	0·2500
2	0·6250	0·0909	0·7159	0·5341	0·1136	0·9204	1·0113	0·8295	0·2954
2½	0·6875	0·1364	0·8239	0·5511	0·1364	1·0511	1·1875	0·9147	0·3636
3	0·8125	0·1364	0·9489	0·6761	0·1364	1·1761	1·3125	1·0397	0·3636
3½	0·8750	0·1364	1·0114	0·7386	0·1364	1·2386	1·3750	1·1022	0·3636
4	1·0000	0·1364	1·1364	0·8636	0·1364	1·4091	1·5455	1·2727	0·4091
5	1·1250	0·1364	1·2614	0·9886	0·1364	1·5795	1·7159	1·4431	0·4545
6	1·1250	0·1364	1·2614	0·9886	0·1364	1·5795	1·7159	1·4431	0·4545
7	1·3750	0·2000	1·5750	1·1750	0·2000	1·9250	2·1250	1·7250	0·5500
8	1·5000	0·2000	1·7000	1·3000	0·2000	2·0500	2·2500	1·8500	0·5500
9	1·5000	0·2000	1·7000	1·3000	0·2000	2·0500	2·2500	1·8500	0·5500
10	1·6250	0·2000	1·8250	1·4250	0·2000	2·1750	2·3750	1·9750	0·5500
11	1·6250	0·2500	1·8750	1·3750	0·2500	2·3125	2·5625	2·0625	0·6875
12	1·6250	0·2500	1·8750	1·3750	0·2500	2·3125	2·5625	2·0625	0·6875

* *Note.*—This table applies to taper threads on pipe ends and taper threaded couplings. For parallel threaded couplings diametral tolerances equivalent to the length tolerances in col. 6 will apply.

† The design of internally-screwed parts must make allowance for receiving pipe ends up to the lengths given in col. 8. The lengths of useful thread shall in no case be less than those given in col. 9.

(2) British Association Thread (B.A.)

This screw thread has a thread angle of $47\frac{1}{2}°$, and it is used for small diameters of bolts and nuts, the maximum outside diameter, viz. for No. 0, being 0·236 in. (6·0 mm.). The following are the thread proportions (Fig. 10) :

Depth of thread $h = 0·6p$.
Height of thread $H = 1·136p$.

Radius at top and bottom of thread $= \frac{2}{11}p = 0·18p$.

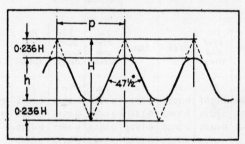

FIG. 10.—BRITISH ASSOCIATION THREAD.

The dimensions of B.A. threads are given in the table on page 128, but for full particulars, B.S. No. 93—1919 should be consulted.

BRITISH STANDARD SCREW THREAD SPECIFICATIONS*

The following British Standards Specifications relate to screw threads :

B.S. 84—1940.   Screw Threads of Whitworth Form.   (Add. June 1942 and April 1943.)

B.S. 93—1919.   Screw Threads, British Association, with Tolerances for Sizes Nos. 0 to 15 B.A.   (Add. August 1940.)

B.S. 95—1919.   Corrections to Effective Diameter required to compensate Pitch and Angle Errors in Screw Threads of Whitworth Form, Tables of.   (Under revision 1943.)

B.S. 1095—1943.   Metric Screw Threads, Système Internationale.

B.S. 1104—1943.   General-purpose Acme Screw Threads.

B.S. 811—1950.   Cycle Threads (formerly C.E.I. Threads).

B.S. 21—1938.   Pipe Threads, Part I.   Basic Sizes and Tolerances.

B.S. 1657—1950.   Buttress Threads.

B.S. 1580—1949.   Unified Screw Threads.

* British Standards Institution, 28 Victoria St., London, S.W.1.

B.S. 61—1946. Screw Threads for Copper Tubes.

B.S. 919—1952. Screw Thread Gauge Tolerances.

B.S. 84—1940 (Amendment No. 3, August 1945). Truncated Whitworth Form Screw Threads.

B.S. 949—1941. Screwing Taps, Dimensions, Limits and Tolerances for. (Add. May 1942.)

B.S. 57—1944. B.A. Bolts, Screws, Nuts and Washers.

B.S. 450—1932. Bright Countersunk, Round and Cheese Head Screws (British Standard Whitworth (B.S.W.) and British Standard Fine (B.S.F.)).

B.S. 451—1932. Bright Square Head Set-screws with Flat Chamfered Ends (British Standard Whitworth (B.S.W.) and British Standard Fine (B.S.F.)).

B.S. 768—1938. Grub Screws (B.S.W., B.S.F., B.A. and B.S.P.).

BRITISH ASSOCIATION (B.A.) THREADS

No.	Diameter		Pitch		Depth of Thread	Core Diameter	Cross Sectional Area at Bottom of Thread
	Mm.	In.	Mm.	In.	Mm.	Mm.	Sq. mm.
0	6·0	0·236	1·0	0·0394	0·6	4·8	18·10
1	5·3	0·209	0·90	0·0354	0·54	4·22	13·99
2	4·7	0·185	0·81	0·0319	0·485	3·73	10·93
3	4·1	0·161	0·73	0·0287	0·44	3·22	8·14
4	3·6	0·142	0·66	0·0260	0·395	2·81	6·20
5	3·2	0·126	0·59	0·0232	0·355	2·49	4·87
6	2·8	0·110	0·53	0·0209	0·32	2·16	3·66
7	2·5	0·098	0·48	0·0189	0·29	1·92	2·89
8	2·2	0·087	0·43	0·0169	0·26	1·68	2·22
9	1·9	0·075	0·39	0·0154	0·235	1·43	1·61
10	1·7	0·067	0·35	0·0138	0·21	1·28	1·29
11	1 5	0·059	0·31	0·0122	0·185	1·13	1·00
12	1·3	0·051	0·28	0·0110	0·17	0·96	0·72
13	1·2	0·047	0·25	0·0098	0·15	0·90	0·64
14	1·0	0·039	0·23	0·0091	0·14	0·72	0·41
15	0·90	0·035	0·21	0·0083	0·125	0·65	0·33
16	0·79	0·031	0·19	0·0075	0·115	0·56	0·25
17	0·70	0·028	0·17	0·0067	0·10	0·50	0·20
18	0·62	0·024	0·15	0·0059	0·09	0·44	0·15
19	0·54	0·021	0·14	0·0055	0·085	0·37	0·11
20	0·48	0·019	0·12	0·0047	0·07	0·34	0·091
21	0·42	0·017	0·11	0·0043	0·065	0·29	0·066
22	0·37	0·015	0·10	0·0039	0·06	0·25	0·049
23	0·33	0·013	0·09	0·0035	0·055	0·22	0·038
24	0 29	0·011	0·08	0·0031	0·05	0·19	0·028
25	0·25	0·010	0 07	0·0028	0·04	0·17	0·023

(3) American National Standard (Sellers) Thread

The thread angle is 60° and one-eighth of the theoretical depth of the crests and roots are truncated (Fig. 11). The following are the thread proportions:

$$\text{Depth of thread } h = 0.75H = 0.649519p.$$
$$\text{Theoretical depth } H = 0.866p.$$
$$\text{Width of flat } f = 0.125p.$$
$$\text{Depth of truncation} = 0.125p.$$

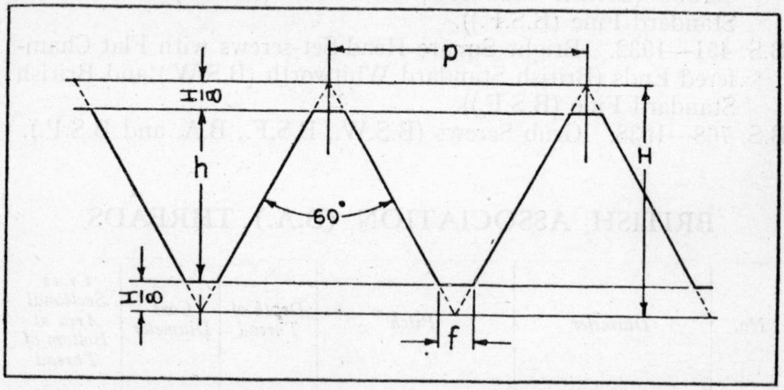

FIG. 11.—AMERICAN NATIONAL STANDARD (SELLERS) THREAD.

There are five series of American National Standard thread, viz. *Coarse Thread* (N.C.), *Fine Thread* (N.F.), 8-*Pitch* (N.), 12-*Pitch* (N.) and 16-*Pitch* (N.).

Usually the coarse-pitch series is employed for general engineering purposes.

The Society of Automotive Engineers' Standard Threads

These screw threads are identical in thread form to the American National Standard Thread. They have been developed in a wide range of sizes and fits from the original Association of Licenced Automobile Manufacturers (A.L.A.M.), recommended standards of 1906. These standards covered threads of $\frac{1}{4}$- to $\frac{3}{4}$-in. diameter, with 28 to 16 threads per inch.

The A.L.A.M. standard was adopted and extended to $1\frac{1}{2}$ in. diameter in 1911, by the S.A.E., as the *S.A.E. Screw Standard*. In 1915 this series was again extended and referred to as the *S.A.E. Coarse Series*, and an *S.A.E. Fine Series* for $1\frac{5}{8}$-in. diameter and larger sizes adopted with 16 threads per inch. In 1918, the S.A.E.

Fine Series was extended downward from $1\frac{1}{2}$ in. to $\frac{1}{4}$ in., chiefly for aeronautical use.

The present *Coarse (N.C.) Series* was the former American National Standard ; the *S.A.E. Fine (N.F.) Series* was the previous S.A.E. Coarse Series extended to include the numbered sizes ; and the present *S.A.E. Extra Fine (E.F.)* was the former S.A.E. Fine Series.

The 8-, 12-, and 16-threads per Inch Series were adopted by the S.A.E. in 1935. The *16-thread Series*, Class 2, for screws and nuts, and sizes $4\frac{1}{4}$ in. to 6 in. inclusive in the Class 3 table series for screws and nuts, were added to the S.A.E. standard in 1942.

In the *Extra Fine Series* the pitch for the $1\frac{5}{8}$-in. diameter and larger sizes is 16 threads per inch.

For standard pitches finer than the *Standard Fine (N.F.) Series*, the *S.A.E. Standard Extra Fine Series* from $\frac{1}{4}$ to $1\frac{1}{2}$ in. in diameter in both Class 2 and Class 3 fits are issued in tabular form.

Full particulars of the S.A.E. are given in the S.A.E. Handbook, issued yearly by the Society of Automotive Engineers, 29 West 39 Street, New York City, U.S.A.

Clearance in the Nut.—A clearance shall be provided at the minor diameter of the thread in the nut by truncation such that the basic depth of thread shall be reduced by $\frac{1}{8}$ or more, depending upon the size and pitch.

A clearance at the major diameter of the thread in the nut shall be provided by decreasing the depth of the truncation triangle any desired amount down to $\frac{1}{3}$ of its theoretical value.

Length of Engagement.—The tolerances are given in the original tables, except for the 8-, 12- and 16-pitch threads, are based on a length of engagement which does not exceed the nominal or major diameter of the screw. Where greater lengths of engagement are required, a corresponding increase in the accuracy of lead and thread form is necessary. The length of engagement for the 8-, 12- and 16-pitch threads is noted in each case under the tables.*

Tolerance and Allowance.—In the Class 2 and Class 3 fits the following characteristics hold : the minimum nut and the maximum screw are basic ; the tolerance is plus on the nut and minus on the screw ; the allowance between pitch diameters of the maximum screw and minimum nut is zero for all pitches and diameters.

Uniform Tap Drill Sizes.—The maximum and minimum minor diameters and the consequent minor-diameter tolerances are the same for all nuts of a given size and pitch for all classes of fit. This permits uniform tap drill sizes for all classes of fit.

* Not reproduced.

SOCIETY OF AUTOMOTIVE ENGINEERS (S.A.E.) THREADS

Size	Basic Major Diam.	Threads per Inch						Size
		Coarse (N.C.)	Fine (N.F.)	Extra Fine (N.E.F.)	8-Thread Series (8N)	12-Thread Series (12N)	16-Thread Series (16N)	
	In.							
0	0·0600	—	80*	—	—	—	—	0
1	0·0730	64*	72*	—	—	—	—	1
2	0·0860	56*	64*	—	—	—	—	2
3	0·0990	48*	56*	—	—	—	—	3
4	0·1120	40*	48*	—	—	—	—	4
5	0·1250	40*	44*	—	—	—	—	5
6	0·1380	32*	40*	—	—	—	—	6
8	0·1640	32*	36*	—	—	—	—	8
10	0·1900	24*	32*	—	—	—	—	10
12	0·2160	24	28	32	—	—	—	12
1/4	0·2500	20*	28*	32*	—	—	—	1/4
5/16	0·3125	18*	24*	32*	—	—	—	5/16
3/8	0·3750	16*	24*	32*	—	—	—	3/8
7/16	0·4375	14*	20*	28*	—	—	—	7/16
1/2	0·5000	13*	20*	28*	—	12	—	1/2
9/16	0·5625	12*	18*	24*	—	12	—	9/16
5/8	0·6250	11*	18*	24*	—	12	—	5/8
11/16	0·6875	*11**	*16**	*24**	—	12	—	11/16
3/4	0·7500	10*	16*	20*	—	12	16	3/4
13/16	0·8125	*10**	*16**	*20**	—	12	16	13/16
7/8	0·8750	9*	14*	20*	—	12	16	7/8
15/16	0·9375	*9**	*14**	*20**	—	12	16	15/16
1	1·0000	8*	14*	20*	8	12	16	1
1 1/16	1·0625	—	—	*18**	*8**	12*	16	1 1/16
1 1/8	1·1250	7	12	18*	8*	12*	16	1 1/8
1 3/16	1·1875	—	—	*18**	—	12*	16	1 3/16
1 1/4	1·2500	7	12	18*	8*	12*	16	1 1/4
1 5/16	1·3125	—	—	*18**	—	12*	16	1 5/16
1 3/8	1·3750	6	12	18*	8*	12*	16	1 3/8
1 7/16	1·4375	—	—	*18**	—	12*	16	1 7/16
1 1/2	1·5000	6	12	18*	8*	12*	16	1 1/2
1 9/16	1·5625	—	—	*18**	—	—	16	1 9/16
1 5/8	1·6250	—	—	*18**	8*	12*	16	1 5/8
1 11/16	1·6875	—	—	*18**	—	—	16	1 11/16
1 3/4	1·7500	5	—	16	8*	12*	16*	1 3/4
1 13/16	1·8125	—	—	—	—	—	16*	1 13/16
1 7/8	1·8750	—	—	—	8*	12*	16*	1 7/8
1 15/16	1·9375	—	—	—	—	—	16*	1 15/16
2	2·0000	4 1/2	—	16	8*	12*	16*	2
2 1/16	2·0625	—	—	—	—	—	16*	2 1/16

Note.—Threads per inch marked with one asterisk (*) are *also* S.A.E. Aeronautical Standard. Those in italics with two asterisks (**) are S.A.E. Aeronautical Standard *only*.

For the modified thread form (rounded root) in the external threads of the standard aeronautical series, applying to 28 pitch and larger, see S.A.E. Aeronautical Standard AS83.

Society of Automotive Engineers (S.A.E.) Threads (contd.)

Size	Basic Major Diam.	Threads per Inch						Size
		Coarse (N.C.)	Fine (N.F.)	Extra Fine (N.E.F.)	8-Thread Series (8N)	12-Thread Series (12N)	16-Thread Series (16N)	
	In.							
2⅛	2·1250	—	—	—	8*	12*	16*	2⅛
2 3/16	2·1875	—	—	—	—	—	16*	2 3/16
2¼	2·2500	4½	—	16	8*	12*	16*	2¼
2 5/16	2·3125	—	—	—	—	—	16*	2 5/16
2⅜	2·3750	—	—	—	—	12*	16*	2⅜
2 7/16	2·4375	—	—	—	—	—	16*	2 7/16
2½	2·5000	4	—	16	8*	12*	16*	2½
2⅝	2·6250	—	—	—	—	12*	16*	2⅝
2¾	2·7500	4	—	16	8*	12*	16*	2¾
2⅞	2·8750	—	—	—	—	12*	16*	2⅞
3	3·0000	4	—	16	8*	12*	16*	3
3⅛	3·1250	—	—	—	—	12*	16*	3⅛
3¼	3·2500	4	—	16	8*	12*	16*	3¼
3⅜	3·3750	—	—	—	—	12*	16*	3⅜
3½	3·5000	4	—	16	8*	12*	16*	3½
3⅝	3·6250	—	—	—	—	12*	16*	3⅝
3¾	3·7500	4	—	16	8*	12*	16*	3¾
3⅞	3·8750	—	—	—	—	12*	16*	3⅞
4	4·0000	4	—	16	8*	12*	16*	4
4¼	4·2500	—	—	16	8	12	—	4¼
4½	4·5000	—	—	16	8	12	—	4½
4¾	4·7500	—	—	16	8	12	—	4¾
5	5·0000	—	—	16	8	12	—	5
5¼	5·2500	—	—	16	8	12	—	5¼
5½	5·5000	—	—	16	8	12	—	5½
5¾	5·7500	—	—	16	8	12	—	5¾
6	6·0000	—	—	16	8	12	—	6

S.A.E. STANDARD PIPE THREADS

The S.A.E. Standard Pipe Threads are based on the American (National) Standard Taper Pipe Thread and for full thread length conform in all respects to the Dryseal American (National) Standard Taper Pipe Thread published in the tentative revision of American Standard B2.1. The Short Dryseal Taper Pipe Thread is an S.A.E. design exclusively which conforms in all respects to the Dryseal American (National) Standard Taper Pipe Thread, except in length of full thread which is reduced for economy of material, clearances, etc.

Taper and Form of Thread.—The angle between the sides of the thread is 60° when measured in an axial plane, and the line bisecting this angle is perpendicular to the axis for either taper or straight pipe threads.

The modification of thread form wherein the Dryseal American (National) Standard Taper Pipe Thread (N.P.T.F.) differs from the American (National) Standard (N.P.T.) consists of a change in

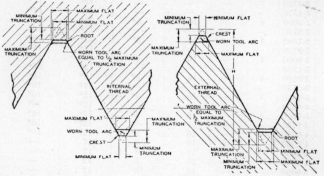

Fig. 12.—Dryseal American (National) Standard External and Internal Pipe Threads.
(Pressure tight Joints without Lubricant or Sealer)

truncation of root and crest to insure their contact before flanks engage. The elimination of clearance at crest and root prevents spiral leakage and renders joints pressure-tight without lubricant or sealer.

The root and crest of threads as specified are flat, although commercially manufactured threads appear rounded.

The taper of taper pipe thread shall be 1 in 16, or 0·75 in. per ft., measured on the diameter and along the axis with a tolerance of plus or minus five per cent.

Diameter and Length of Thread.—Diameter and length of thread for different pipe sizes are based on the following formulæ :

Pitch diameter of thread at end of pipe (N.P.T.F.) :

$$E_0 = D - (0.05d \text{ plus } 1.1)p.$$

Pitch diameter of thread at end of pipe (N.P.T.F.—S.A.E. Short) :

$$E_0 \text{ Short} = D - (0.05D \text{ plus } 1.037)p.$$

Pitch diameter of thread at large end of internal thread (N.P.T.F.) :

$E_1 = E_0 + (0.0625 \times \text{Basic } L_1)$ for all sizes except $\frac{1}{8}$ and $\frac{1}{4}$.

For $\frac{1}{8}$ and $\frac{1}{4}$ sizes $E_1 = E_0 + (0.0625 \times \text{corrected } L_1)$:

Pitch diameter of thread at large end of internal thread (N.P.T F. —S.A.E. Short) :

$$E_1 \text{ Short} = E_0 + (0.0625 \times L_1 \text{ Short}).$$

Length of effective thread (N.P.T.F.) :

$$L_2 = (0.8D + 6.8)p.$$

Length of effective thread (N.P.T.F.—S.A.E. Short) :

$$L_2 \text{ Short} = (0.8D + 5.8)p.$$

When :

D = Outside diameter of pipe.

p = Pitch of thread.   (All dimensions are in inches.)

The length of effective thread includes approximately two usable threads slightly imperfect at the crest, on pipe.

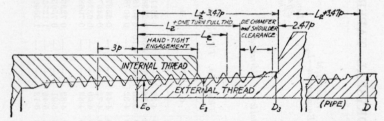

Fig. 13.—Dryseal American (National) Standard Taper Pipe Thread (N.P.T.F. (Pressure-tight Joints without Lubricant or Sealer)

Standard Length of Engagement (*N.P.T.F.*).—As the number of threads engaged by hand and the number of threads remaining for wrench take-up are disproportionate in the American (National) Standard Taper Pipe Thread (N.P.T.) for the $\frac{1}{8}$- and $\frac{1}{4}$-in. sizes as compared to all other sizes, tapped hole dimensions controlling amount of hand and wrench engagement have been adjusted on those sizes in the Dryseal American (National) Standard Taper Pipe Thread (N.P.T.F.) to make the relation of hand and wrench engagement proportionate to that of all other sizes.

S.A.E. DRYSEAL TAPER PIPE THREAD (N.P.T.F.)

N.P.T.F. Size and T.P.I.	Pitch p	P.D. at End of External Thread E_0	P.D. at End of Internal Thread E_1	Hand-tight Engagement—L_1 Basic		Corrected		Length of Effective Thread L_2		Vanish Threads "V" Plus Effective Thread Tolerance Plus Shoulder Clear. $V + 1p + .47p$		Fitting L'gth $L_2 + 3.47p$	External Thread for Draw L_2—Hand Engagement		Length of Internal Thread (Min.) Hand Engagement $+ 3p$		Outside Dia. of Fitting D_3	Outside Dia. of Pipe D
	In.	In.	In.	In.	Th'ds	In.	Th'ds	In.	Th'ds	In.	Th'ds	In.	In.	Th'ds	In.	Th'ds	In.	In.
1	2	3	4	5	6	7	8	9	10	11	12	13	14	15	16	17	18	19
$\frac{1}{16}$–27	·03704	0·27118	0·28118	·160	4·32	·1615	4·36	0·2611	7·05	·1285	3·47	0·3896	·1011	2·73	0·2711	7·32	0·315	0·3125
$\frac{1}{8}$–27	·03704	0·36351	0·37360	·180	4·86	·2278	4·10	0·2638	7·12	·1285	3·47	0·3923	·1023	2·76	0·2726	7·36	0·407	0·405
$\frac{1}{4}$–18	·05556	0·47739	0·49163	·200	3·60	—	—	0·4018	7·23	·1928	3·47	0·5946	·1740	3·13	0·3945	7·10	0·546	0·540
$\frac{3}{8}$–18	·55556	0·61201	0·62701	·240	4·32	—	—	0·4078	7·34	·1928	3·47	0·6006	·1678	3·02	0·4067	7·32	0·681	0·675
$\frac{1}{2}$–14	·07143	0·75843	0·77843	·320	4·48	—	—	0·5337	7·47	·2478	3·47	0·7815	·2137	2·99	0·5343	7·48	0·850	0·840
$\frac{3}{4}$–14	·07143	0·96768	0·98887	·339	4·75	—	—	0·5457	7·64	·2478	3·47	0·7935	·2067	2·89	0·5533	7·75	1·060	1·050
1–11½	·08696	1·21363	1·23363	·400	4·60	—	—	0·6828	7·85	·3017	3·47	0·9845	·2828	3·25	0·6609	7·60	1·327	1·315
1¼–11½	·08696	1·55713	1·58338	·420	4·83	—	—	0·7068	8·13	·3017	3·47	1·0085	·2868	3·30	0·6809	7·83	1·672	1·660
1½–11½	·08696	1·79609	1·82234	·420	4·83	—	—	0·7235	8·32	·3017	3·47	1·0252	·3035	3·49	0·6809	7·83	1·912	1·900
2–11½	·08696	2·26902	2·29627	·436	5·01	—	—	0·7565	8·70	·3017	3·47	1·0582	·3205	3·69	0·6969	8·01	2·387	2·375
2½–8	·12500	2·71953	2·76216	·682	5·46	—	—	1·1375	9·10	·4337	3·47	1·5712	·4555	3·64	1·0570	8·46	2·920	2·875
3–8	·12500	3·34063	3·38850	·766	6·13	—	—	1·2000	9·60	·4337	3·47	1·6337	·4340	3·47	1·1410	9·13	3·545	3·500

(4) International Metric Threads

This form of screw thread was adopted in 1898 by the International Congress. It has a thread angle of 60° and the diameters of screws specified range from 6 mm. (1-mm. pitch) to 80 mm. (6-mm. pitch) (Fig. 14).

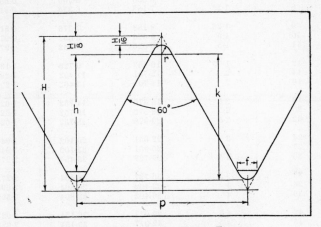

FIG. 14.—INTERNATIONAL METRIC THREAD.

The depth H $= 0·866p$.
Depth of engagement of mating
    threads, h $= 0·6495p$.
Depth of screw k $= 0·7035p$.
Radius of crest or root r $= 0·0633p$ (max.) ; $0·054p$ (min.)
Width of flat f $= 0·125p$.
Tap drill size $=$ major diameter $-$ pitch p.

BRITISH STANDARD METRIC THREAD DIMENSIONS*

Major Diameter (Nominal and Basic)	Pitch p	Effective Diameter (Basic)	Minor Diameter (Basic)	Depth of Thread (Basic) h
mm.	mm.	mm.	mm.	mm.
6	1	5·350	4·700	0·650
7	1	6·350	5·700	0·650
8	1·25	7·188	6·376	0·812
9	1·25	8·188	7·376	0·812
10	1·5	9·026	8·052	0·974
11	1·5	10·026	9·052	0·974
12	1·75	10·863	9·726	1·137
14	2	12·701	11·402	1·299
16	2	14·701	13·402	1·299
18	2·5	16·376	14·752	1·624
20	2·5	18·376	16·752	1·624
22	2·5	20·376	18·752	1·624
24	3	22·051	20·102	1·949
27	3	25·051	23·102	1·949
30	3·5	27·727	25·454	2·273
33	3·5	30·727	28·454	2·273
36	4	33·402	30·804	2·598
39	4	36·402	33·804	2·598
42	4·5	39·077	36·154	2·923
45	4·5	42·077	39·154	2·923
48	5	44·752	41·504	3·248
52	5	48·752	45·504	3·248
56	5·5	52·428	48·856	3·572
60	5·5	56·428	52·856	3·572
64	6	60·103	56·206	3·897
68	6	64·103	60·206	3·897
72	6	68·103	64·206	3·897
76	6	72·103	68·206	3·897
80	6	76·103	72·206	3·897
85	6	81·103	77·206	3·897
90	6	86·103	82·206	3·897
95	6	91·103	87·206	3·897
100	6	96·103	92·206	3·897
105	6	101·103	97·206	3·897
110	6	106·103	102·206	3·897
115	6	111·103	107·206	3·897
120	6	116·103	112·206	3·897
125	6	121·103	117·206	3·897
etc., in steps of 5 mm.				

* Abstract from B.S. 1093—1943.

BRITISH STANDARD METRIC THREAD TOLERANCES
Metric Bolts.   Limits and Tolerances
(CLOSE FIT)

1	2	3	4	5	6	7	8	9
Nominal Diameter	Pitch	Major Diameter			Effective Diameter			Minor Diameter
		Max.	Tol.	Min.	Max.	Tol.	Min.	Max.
mm.	mm.	mm.	mm.	mm.	mm.	mm.	mm.	mm.
6	1	6·000	0·158	5·842	5·350	0·064	5·286	4·700
7	1	7·000	0·158	6·842	6·350	0·067	6·283	5·700
8	1·25	8·000	0·185	7·815	7·188	0·072	7·116	6·376
9	1·25	9·000	0·185	8·815	8·188	0·075	8·113	7·376
10	1·5	10·000	0·212	9·788	9·026	0·079	8·947	8·052
11	1·5	11·000	0·212	10·788	10·026	0·081	9·945	9·052
12	1·75	12·000	0·239	11·761	10·863	0·086	10·777	9·726
14	2	14·000	0·266	13·734	12·701	0·091	12·610	11·402
16	2	16·000	0·266	15·734	14·701	0·094	14·607	13·402
18	2·5	18·000	0·320	17·680	16·376	0·102	16·274	14·752
20	2·5	20·000	0·320	19·680	18·376	0·105	18·271	16·752
22	2·5	22·000	0·320	21·680	20·376	0·108	20·268	18·752
24	3	24·000	0·374	23·626	22·051	0·114	21·937	20·102
27	3	27·000	0·374	26·626	25·051	0·118	24·933	23·102
30	3·5	30·000	0·428	29·572	27·727	0·125	27·602	25·454
33	3·5	33·000	0·428	32·572	30·727	0·128	30·599	28·454
36	4	36·000	0·482	35·518	33·402	0·134	33·268	30·804
39	4	39·000	0·482	38·518	36·402	0·138	36·264	33·804
42	4·5	42·000	0·536	41·464	39·077	0·143	38·934	36·154
45	4·5	45·000	0·536	44·464	42·077	0·146	41·931	39·154
48	5	48·000	0·590	47·410	44·752	0·152	44·600	41·504
52	5	52·000	0·590	51·410	48·752	0·155	48·597	45·504
56	5·5	56·000	0·644	55·356	52·428	0·161	52·267	48·856
60	5·5	60·000	0·644	59·356	56·428	0·164	56·264	52·856

Metric Nuts. Tolerances

(CLOSE FIT)

1	2	3	4	5	6	7	8	9
Nominal Diameter	Pitch	Major Diameter	Effective Diameter			Minor Diameter		
		Min.	Max.	Tol.	Min.	Max.	Tol.	Min.
mm.	mm.	mm.	mm.	mm.	mm.	mm.	mm.	mm.
6	1	6·000	5·414	0·064	5·350	5·026	0·163	4·863
7	1	7·000	6·417	0·067	6·350	6·026	0·163	5·863
8	1·25	8·000	7·260	0·072	7·188	6·782	0·203	6·579
9	1·25	9·000	8·263	0·075	8·188	7·892	0·203	7·579
10	1·5	10·000	9·105	0·079	9·026	8·539	0·244	8·295
11	1·5	11·000	10·107	0·081	10·026	9·539	0·244	9·295
12	1·75	12·000	10·949	0·086	10·863	10·295	0·284	10·011
14	2	14·000	12·792	0·091	12·701	12·051	0·324	11·727
16	2	16·000	14·795	0·094	14·701	14·051	0·324	13·727
18	2·5	18·000	16·478	0·102	16·376	15·564	0·406	15·158
20	2·5	20·000	18·481	0·105	18·376	17·564	0·406	17·158
22	2·5	22·000	20·484	0·108	20·376	19·564	0·406	19·158
24	3	24·000	22·165	0·114	22·051	21·077	0·487	20·590
27	3	27·000	25·169	0·118	25·051	24·077	0·487	23·590
30	3·5	30·000	27·852	0·125	27·727	26·590	0·568	26·022
33	3·5	33·000	30·855	0·128	30·727	29·590	0·568	29·022
36	4	36·000	33·536	0·134	33·402	32·103	0·650	31·453
39	4	39·000	36·540	0·138	36·402	35·103	0·650	34·453
42	4·5	42·000	39·220	0·143	39·077	37·616	0·731	36·885
45	4·5	45·000	42·223	0·146	42·077	40·616	0·731	39·885
48	5	48·000	44·904	0·152	44·752	43·128	0·812	42·316
52	5	52·000	48·907	0·155	48·752	47·128	0·812	46·316
56	5·5	56·000	52·589	0·161	52·428	50·641	0·893	49·748
60	5·5	60·000	56·592	0·164	56·428	54·641	0·893	53·748

Metric Bolts. Tolerances

(MEDIUM FIT)

1	2	3	4	5	6	7	8	9
Nominal Diameter	Pitch	Major Diameter			Effective Diameter			Minor Diameter
		Max.	Tol.	Min.	Max.	Tol.	Min.	Max.
mm.	mm.	mm.	mm.	mm.	mm.	mm.	mm.	mm.
6	1	6·000	0·158	5·842	5·350	0·096	5·254	4·700
7	1	7·000	0·158	6·842	6·350	0·100	6·250	5·700
8	1·25	8·000	0·185	7·815	7·188	0·108	7·080	6·376
9	1·25	9·000	0·185	8·815	8·188	0·112	8·076	7·376
10	1·5	10·000	0·212	9·788	9·026	0·119	8·907	8·052
11	1·5	11·000	0·212	10·788	10·026	0·122	9·904	9·052
12	1·75	12·000	0·239	11·761	10·863	0·128	10·735	9·726
14	2	14·000	0·266	13·734	12·701	0·137	12·564	11·402
16	2	16·000	0·266	15·734	14·701	0·142	14·559	13·402
18	2·5	18·000	0·320	17·680	16·376	0·153	16·223	14·752
20	2·5	20·000	0·320	19·680	18·376	0·157	18·219	16·752
22	2·5	22·000	0·320	21·680	20·376	0·162	20·214	18·752
24	3	24·000	0·374	23·626	22·051	0·171	21·880	20·102
27	3	27·000	0·374	26·626	25·051	0·177	24·874	23·102
30	3·5	30·000	0·428	29·572	27·727	0·187	27·540	25·454
33	3·5	33·000	0·428	32·572	30·727	0·192	30·535	28·454
36	4	36·000	0·482	35·518	33·402	0·202	33·200	30·804
39	4	39·000	0·482	38·518	36·402	0·206	36·196	33·804
42	4·5	42·000	0·536	41·464	39·077	0·215	38·862	36·154
45	4·5	45·000	0·536	44·464	42·077	0·219	41·858	39·154
48	5	48·000	0·590	47·410	44·752	0·227	44·525	41·504
52	5	52·000	0·590	51·410	48·752	0·233	48·519	45·504
56	5·5	56·000	0·644	55·356	52·428	0·242	52·186	48·856
60	5·5	60·000	0·644	59·356	56·428	0·247	56·181	52·856

Metric Nuts. Tolerances
(MEDIUM FIT)

1	2	3	4	5	6	7	8	9
Nominal Diameter	Pitch	Major Diameter	Effective Diameter			Minor Diameter		
		Min.	Max.	Tol.	Min.	Max.	Tol.	Min.
mm.	mm.	mm.	mm.	mm.	mm.	mm.	mm.	mm.
6	1	6·000	5·446	0·096	5·350	5·026	0·163	4·863
7	1	7·000	6·450	0·100	6·350	6·026	0·163	5·863
8	1·25	8·000	7·296	0·108	7·188	6·782	0·203	6·579
9	1·25	9·000	8·300	0·112	8·188	7·782	0·203	7·579
10	1·5	10·000	9·145	0·119	9·026	8·539	0·244	8·295
11	1·5	11·000	10·148	0·122	10·026	9·539	0·244	9·295
12	1·75	12·000	10·991	0·128	10·863	10·295	0·284	10·011
14	2	14·000	12·838	0·137	12·701	12·051	0·324	11·727
16	2	16·000	14·843	0·142	14·701	14·051	0·324	13·727
18	2·5	18·000	16·529	0·153	16·376	15·564	0·406	15·158
20	2·5	20·000	18·533	0·157	18·376	17·564	0·406	17·158
22	2·5	22·000	20·538	0·162	20·376	19·564	0·406	19·158
24	3	24·000	22·222	0·171	22·051	21·077	0·487	20·590
27	3	27·000	25·228	0·177	25·051	24·077	0·487	23·590
30	3·5	30·000	27·914	0·187	27·727	26·590	0·568	26·022
33	3·5	33·000	30·919	0·192	30·727	29·590	0·568	29·022
36	4	36·000	33·604	0·202	33·402	32·103	0·650	31·453
39	4	39·000	36·608	0·206	36·420	35·103	0·650	34·453
42	4·5	42·000	39·292	0·215	39·077	37·616	0·731	36·885
45	4·5	45·000	42·296	0·219	42·077	40·616	0·731	39·885
48	5	48·000	44·979	0·227	44·752	43·128	0·812	42·316
52	5	52·000	48·985	0·233	48·752	47·128	0·812	46·316
56	5·5	56·000	52·670	0·242	52·428	50·641	0·893	49·748
60	5·5	60·000	56·675	0·247	56·428	54·641	0·893	53·748

Metric Bolts. Tolerances
(FREE FIT)

1	2	3	4	5	6	7	8	9
Nominal Diameter	Pitch	Major Diameter			Effective Diameter			Minor Diameter
		Max.	Tol.	Min.	Max.	Tol.	Min.	Max.
mm.	mm.	mm.	mm.	mm.	mm.	mm.	mm.	mm.
6	1	6·000	0·158	5·842	5·350	0·144	5·206	4·700
7	1	7·000	0·158	6·842	6·350	0·151	6·199	5·700
8	1·25	8·000	0·185	7·815	7·188	0·162	7·026	6·376
9	1·25	9·000	0·185	8·815	8·188	0·168	8·020	7·376
10	1·5	10·000	0·212	9·788	9·026	0·178	8·848	8·052
11	1·5	11·000	0·212	10·788	10·026	0·183	9·843	9·052
12	1·75	12·000	0·239	11·761	10·863	0·192	10·671	9·726
14	2	14·000	0·266	13·734	12·701	0·206	12·495	11·402
16	2	16·000	0·266	15·734	14·701	0·213	14·488	13·402
18	2·5	18·000	0·320	17·680	16·376	0·229	16·147	14·752
20	2·5	20·000	0·320	19·680	18·376	0·236	18·140	16·752
22	2·5	22·000	0·320	21·680	20·376	0·243	20·133	18·752
24	3	24·000	0·374	23·626	22·051	0·256	21·795	20·102
27	3	27·000	0·374	26·626	25·051	0·266	24·785	23·102
30	3·5	30·000	0·428	29·572	27·727	0·280	27·447	25·454
33	3·5	33·000	0·428	32·572	30·727	0·288	30·439	28·454
36	4	36·000	0·482	35·518	33·402	0·302	33·100	30·804
39	4	39·000	0·482	38·518	36·402	0·310	36·092	33·804
42	4·5	42·000	0·536	41·464	39·077	0·322	38·755	36·154
45	4·5	45·000	0·536	44·464	42·077	0·329	41·748	39·154
48	5	48·000	0·590	47·410	44·752	0·341	44·411	41·504
52	5	52·000	0·590	51·410	48·752	0·349	48·403	45·504
56	5·5	56·000	0·644	55·356	52·428	0·362	52·066	48·856
60	5·5	60·000	0·644	59·356	56·428	0·370	56·958	52·856

Metric Nuts. Tolerances
(FREE FIT)

1	2	3	4	5	6	7	8	9
Nominal Diameter	Pitch	Major Diameter	Effective Diameter			Minor Diameter		
		Min.	Max.	Tol.	Min.	Max.	Tol.	Min.
mm.	mm.	mm.	mm.	mm.	mm.	mm.	mm.	mm.
6	1	6·000	5·494	0·144	5·350	5·026	0·163	4·863
7	1	7·000	6·501	0·151	6·350	6·026	0·163	5·863
8	1·25	8·000	7·350	0·162	7·188	6·782	0·203	6·579
9	1·25	9·000	8·356	0·168	8·188	7·782	0·203	7·579
10	1·5	10·000	9·204	0·178	9·026	8·539	0·244	8·295
11	1·5	11·000	10·209	0·183	10·026	9·539	0·244	9·295
12	1·75	12·000	11·055	0·192	10·863	10·295	0·284	10·011
14	2	14·000	12·907	0·206	12·701	12·051	0·324	11·727
16	2	16·000	14·914	0·213	14·701	14·051	0·324	13·727
18	2·5	18·000	16·605	0·229	16·376	15·564	0·406	15·158
20	2·5	20·000	18·612	0·236	18·376	17·564	0·406	17·158
22	2·5	22·000	20·619	0·243	20·376	19·564	0·406	19·158
24	3	24·000	22·307	0·256	22·051	21·077	0·487	20·590
27	3	27·000	25·317	0·266	25·051	24·077	0·487	23·590
30	3·5	30·000	28·007	0·280	27·727	26·590	0·568	26·022
33	3·5	33·000	31·015	0·288	30·727	29·590	0·568	29·022
36	4	36·000	33·704	0·302	33·402	32·103	0·650	31·453
39	4	39·000	36·712	0·310	36·402	35·103	0·650	34·453
42	4·5	42·000	39·399	0·322	39·077	37·616	0·731	36·885
45	4·5	45·000	42·406	0·329	42·077	40·616	0·731	39·885
48	5	48·000	45·093	0·341	44·752	43·128	0·812	42·316
52	5	52·000	49·101	0·349	48·752	47·128	0·812	46·316
56	5·5	56·000	52·790	0·362	52·428	50·641	0·893	49·748
60	5·5	60·000	56·798	0·370	56·428	54·641	0·893	53·748

(5) Cycle Engineers' Institute (C.E.I.) Threads

This form of thread was recommended in the C.E.I. *Proceedings* (1902) to give a thread of suitable design and strength for the bolts, nuts, nipples, spokes and other threaded parts of cycles and motor cycles.

In 1938 the British Standards Institution issued a specification, known as the B.S. 811—1938. This was revised and the present specification, namely, B.S. 811—1950 published for Cycle (B.S.C.) Threads. Particulars of these later standards are given, following Table III, on page 151. The original C.E.I. thread system included a series of threads applicable to any size of stock, rather than to progressive sizes, so that the B.S. system standardized only a selection of the more commonly used sizes.

The form of thread is 60° triangular, with the crest and root rounded off to a distance of one-sixth of the pitch, the radius of the curve being one-sixth of the pitch.

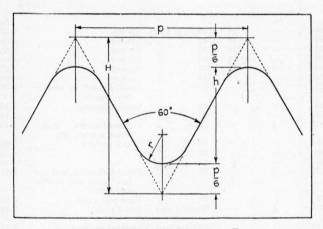

FIG. 15.—CYCLE ENGINEERS' INSTITUTE THREAD.

The following are the thread proportions (Fig. 15) :

$$H = 0\cdot866p$$
$$h = 0\cdot5327p$$
$$r = \frac{p}{6} = 0\cdot166p.$$

CYCLE ENGINEERS' INSTITUTE (C.E.I.) THREADS

TABLE I

Diameters in Inches	Threads per Inch
0·050 to 0·084	62
0·085 to 0·099	56
0·100 to 0·124	44
0·125 to 0·154	40
0·155 to 0·199	32
0·200 to 1·000	26
Above 1·000	24

TABLE II

Diameters in Decimals	Diameters in Fractions	Nos. on I.W.G.	Threads per Inch	Suitable for such Parts as	Theoretical Diameter Bottom of Thread
In.	In.				In.
0·056	—	17	62 right hand	Spokes	0·0388
0·064	—	16	62 ,, ,,	Spokes	0 0468
0·072	—	15	62 ,, ,,	Spokes	0·0598
0·080	—	14	62 ,, ,,	Spokes	0·0628
0·092	—	13	56 ,, ,,	Spokes	0·0729
0·104	—	12	44 ,, ,,	Spokes	0·0798
0·125	$\frac{1}{8}$	—	40 ,, ,,	Small screws, as used in free-wheels	0·0984
0·154	—	—	40 ,, ,,	Chain coupling	0·1274
0·175	—	—	32 ,, ,,		0·1417
0·1875	$\frac{3}{16}$	—	32 ,, ,,	Chain-adjusters, brake-screw screws, etc.	0·1542
0·250	$\frac{1}{4}$	—	26 ,, ,,	Crank cotters	0·2091
0·266	—	—	26 ,, ,,		—
0·281	—	—	26 ,, ,,		—
0·3125	$\frac{5}{16}$	—	26 ,, ,,	Front-hub axles, seat and head pins and saddle-clip bolts	0·2715
0·375	$\frac{3}{8}$	—	26 ,, ,,	Rear-hub axles	0·3341
0·5625 *	$\frac{9}{16}$	—	20 right and left	Pedal pins	0·498
0·9675 *	—	—	30 right hand	Steering column	0·932
1·000	1	—	26 ,, ,,	Steering column	0·959
1·290	—	—	24 left hand	Hub lock-ring	1·2456
1·370	—	—	24 right hand	Hub chain-wheel	1·3256
1·4375	$1\frac{7}{16}$	—	24 left hand	Multiple motor, or hubs with $\frac{5}{16}$-in. balls for lock-ring	1·393
1·500	$1\frac{1}{2}$	—	24 right hand	Multiple motor, or hubs with $\frac{5}{16}$-in. balls for chain-wheel	1·4556

* Exceptional thread.

Table III

Diameter of Screw	Threads per Inch	Theoretical Diameter Bottom of Thread	Diameter of Screw	Threads per Inch	Theoretical Diameter Bottom of Thread
In.		*In.*	*In.*		*In.*
$\frac{1}{8}$	40	0·0984	$\frac{5}{16}$	26	0·2715
$\frac{5}{32}$	32	0·1229	$\frac{3}{8}$	26	0·3341
$\frac{3}{16}$	32	0·1542	$\frac{7}{16}$	26	0·3966
$\frac{7}{32}$	26	0·1778	$\frac{1}{2}$	26	0·4591
$\frac{1}{4}$	26	0·2091	$\frac{9}{16}$	26	0·5216
$\frac{9}{32}$	26	0·2403			

(5a) British Standard Cycle (B.S.C.) Threads

Formerly known as the C.E.I. Threads, this system is described in B.S. 811—1950. In view of the close resemblance between the B.S.C. and the Whitworth and B.A. threads it is strongly recommended that the use of the B.S.C. thread is restricted to bolts, nuts and screwed parts to be used in cycle and motor cycle manufacture.

The B.S.C. basic thread is identical in form to that shown in Fig. 15 and the same thread proportion formulæ also apply.

The Specification includes B.S.C. bolts and nuts in Close, Medium and Free fit Classes ; B.S.C. spokes and nipples in the Medium Class ; B.S.C. threads in the Medium Class, for special application, and B.S.W. bolts and nuts (20 T.P.I.) in the Medium Class.

When *stainless steel* is used for screws and nuts, there is a tendency for closely fitting threaded parts to seize when tightened together, so that it is recommended that the maximum permissible size for all stainless steel bolts and externally-threaded parts should be 0·001 in. below their basic size.

The Specification includes tables of basic dimensions, limits and tolerances, the tables of basic dimensions being here reproduced :

BRITISH STANDARD CYCLE THREADS FOR BOLTS AND NUTS AND SIMILAR APPLICATIONS*

Basic Dimensions

1	2	3	4	5	6	7
Nominal Diameter of Screw	No. of Threads per Inch	Pitch	Depth of Thread	Basic Diameters		
				Major	Effective	Minor
In.		In.	In.	In.	In.	In.
$\frac{1}{8}$	40	0·02500	0·0133	0·1250	0·1117	0·0984
$\frac{5}{32}$	32	0·03125	0·0166	0·1563	0·1397	0·1231
$\frac{3}{16}$	32	0·03125	0·0166	0·1875	0·1709	0·1543
$\frac{7}{32}$	26	0·03846	0·0205	0·2188	0·1983	0·1778
$\frac{1}{4}$	26	0·03846	0·0205	0·2500	0·2295	0·2090
$\frac{9}{32}$	26	0·03846	0·0205	0·2813	0·2608	0·2403
$\frac{5}{16}$	26	0·03846	0·0205	0·3125	0·2920	0·2715
$\frac{3}{8}$	26	0·03846	0·0205	0·3750	0·3545	0·3340
$\frac{7}{16}$	26	0·03846	0·0205	0·4375	0·4170	0·3965
$\frac{1}{2}$	26	0·03846	0·0205	0·5000	0·4795	0·4590
$\frac{9}{16}$	26	0·03846	0·0205	0·5625	0·5420	0·5215
$\frac{5}{8}$	26	0·03846	0·0205	0·6250	0·6045	0·5840
$\frac{11}{16}$	26	0·03846	0·0205	0·6875	0·6670	0·6465
$\frac{3}{4}$	26	0·03846	0·0205	0·7500	0·7295	0·7090

* B.S. 811—1950.

BRITISH STANDARD CYCLE THREADS FOR SPOKES AND NIPPLES *

Basic Dimensions

1	2	3	4	5	6	7	8
Nominal Diameter of Wire†		Number of Threads per In. (R.H.)	Pitch	Depth of Thread	Basic Diameters		
					Major	Effective	Minor
S.W.G.	In.		In.	In.	In.	In.	In.
16	0·064	56	0·01786	0·0095	0·0735	0·0640	0·0545
15	0·072	56	0·01786	0·0095	0·0815	0·0720	0·0625
14	0·080	56	0·01786	0·0095	0·0895	0·0800	0·0705
13	0·092	56	0·01786	0·0095	0·1015	0·0920	0·0825
12	0·104	56	0·01786	0·0095	0·1135	0·1040	0·0945
11	0·116	44	0·02273	0·0121	0·1281	0·1160	0·1039
10	0·128	40	0·02500	0·0133	0·1413	0·1280	0·1147
9	0·144	40	0·02500	0·0133	0·1573	0·1440	0·1307
8	0·160	32	0·03125	0·0166	0·1766	0·1600	0·1434

* B.S. 811—1950.
† The diameter is that of the end portion of the spoke on which the thread is rolled, and is not necessarily the same as that of the body of the spoke : it is equal to the basic (maximum) effective diameter of the spoke thread (col. 7).

BRITISH STANDARD CYCLE THREADS FOR SPECIAL APPLICATIONS*

Basic Dimensions

Nominal Diameter of Screw	t.p.i.	Pitch	Depth of Thread	Basic Diameters			Application
				Major	Effective	Minor	
In.		In.	In.	In.	In.	In.	
$\frac{17}{64}$	26 R.H.	0·03846	0·0205	0·2656	0·2451	0·2246	Cycle and motor cycle crank cotters.
$\frac{7}{8}$	24 R.H.	0·04167	0·0222	0·8750	0·8528	0·8306	Steering columns of juvenile cycles.
$\frac{31}{32}$ 1	30 R.H. 24 R.H.	0·03333 0·04167	0·0178 0·0222	0·9688 1·0000	0·9510 0·9778	0·9332 0·9556	Steering columns.
$1\frac{1}{8}$	26 R.H.	0·03846	0·0205	1·1250	1·1045	1·0840	Motor cycle and tandem steering columns.
1·290	24 L.H.	0·04167	0·0222	1·2900	1·2678	1·2456	Lock rings for sprockets on rear hubs.
1·370 1·370	24 R.H.⎫ 24 L.H.⎭	0·04167	0·0222	1·3700	1·3478	1·3256	Hub sprockets and bottom bracket cups.
1·450 1·450	26 R.H.⎫ 26 L.H.⎭	0·03846	0·0205	1·4500	1·4295	1·4090	Tandem bottom bracket cups.
$1\frac{9}{16}$ $1\frac{5}{8}$	24 L.H. 24 R.H.	0·04167 0·04167	0·0222 0·0222	1·5625 1·6250	1·5403 1·6028	1·5181 1·5806	Carrier cycle sprockets and lock rings.

* B.S. 811—1950.

(6) Löwenherz Thread

This screw thread, which is used on German precision instruments and apparatus, has a thread angle of 53° 8 min.   The crests and roots of the threads are flat, as in the Sellers thread form.   The following are the general thread proportions :
Total depth of thread, between apices H = p, where p = pitch.
Distance from apex to flat on crest or

$$\text{root} = \frac{H}{8}.$$

Effective depth of thread, between flats

$$\text{on crest and root} = \frac{3H}{4}.$$

Steinlen Thread

This thread form is used in Switzerland for screws machined on the lathe.   The thread angle is 53° 8 min.   The crests and roots of the thread are rounded off.   The following are the general thread proportions :
Total depth of thread between apices H = p, where p = pitch.

$$\text{Distance from apex to crest or root} = \frac{H}{8}.$$

$$\text{Radius of curve of crest and apex} = 0.1011p.$$

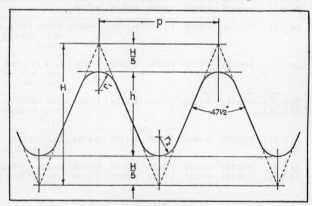

Fig. 16.—Swiss or Thury Thread.

Swiss or Thury Thread

This thread is similar to and forms the basis of the British Association thread.   It has the same thread angle, viz. $47\frac{1}{2}°$, but differs in regard to the radius of the crest and root.

SWISS OR THURY SCREW THREADS

No.	Inches (approximately)		Threads per Inch	Millimetres (exact)	
	Diameter	Pitch		Diameter	Pitch
25	·010	·0028	353	·25	·072
24	·011	·0031	317	·29	·080
23	·013	·0035	285	·33	·089
22	·015	·0039	259	·37	·098
21	·017	·0043	231	·42	·11
20	·019	·0047	212	·48	·12
19	·021	·0055	181	·54	·14
18	·024	·0059	169	·62	·15
17	·027	·0067	149	·70	·17
16	·031	·0075	134	·79	·19
15	·035	·0083	121	·90	·21
14	·039	·0091	110	1·0	·23
13	·044	·0098	101	1·2	·25
12	·051	·0110	90·7	1·3	·28
11	·059	·0122	81·9	1·5	·31
10	·067	·0138	72·6	1·7	·35
9	·075	·0154	65·1	1·9	·39
8	·086	·0169	59·1	2·2	·43
7	·098	·0189	52·9	2·5	·48
6	·110	·0209	47·9	2·8	·53
5	·126	·0232	43·0	3·2	·59
4	·142	·0260	38·5	3·6	·66
3	·161	·0287	34·8	4·1	·73
2	·185	·0319	31·4	4·7	·81
1	·209	·0354	28·2	5·3	·90
0	·236	·0394	25·4	6·0	1·00
− 1	·268	—	22·85	6·81	1·11
− 2	·304	—	20·65	7·73	1·23
− 3	·345	—	18·54	8·77	1·37
− 4	·392	—	16·73	9·95	1·52
− 5	·445	—	15·02	11·3	1·69
− 6	·504	—	13·48	12·8	1·88
− 7	·571	—	12·15	14·5	2·09
− 8	·650	—	10·94	16·5	2·32
− 9	·736	—	9·84	18·7	2·58
− 10	·835	—	8·85	21·2	2·87
− 11	·949	—	7·97	24·1	3·19
− 12	1·079	—	7·17	27·4	3·54
− 13	1·205	—	6·46	31·0	3·93
− 14	1·386	—	5·81	35·2	4·37
− 15	1·575	—	5·22	40·0	4·86
− 16	1·787	—	4·84	45·4	5·40
− 17	2·028	—	4·23	51·5	6·00
− 18	2·299	—	3·82	58·4	6·66
− 19	2·610	—	3·43	66·3	7·40
− 20	2·961	—	3·08	75·2	8·23

In the Thury thread one-fifth of the depth, between the apices of the thread triangle, is rounded off at the top and bottom of the triangle.

The following are the thread proportions :

$$\text{Height of thread H} = 0{\cdot}6p.$$
$$\text{Radius of crest of thread} = 0{\cdot}1666p.$$
$$\text{Radius of root of thread} = 0{\cdot}2000p.$$

The largest screw (No. 0) in the positive series has a diameter of 6 mm. and pitch of 1 mm. Each size-smaller screw in the series is approximately $\frac{9}{10}$ of the preceding diameter. The negative screws have increasing diameters in similar proportions or ratios.

WHITWORTH SCREW THREADS FOR WATCHES AND INSTRUMENTS

Diameter in Thousandths of an Inch	No. of Threads per Inch	Diameter in Thousandths of an Inch	No. of Threads per Inch
10	400	34	150
11	400	36	150
12	350	38	120
13	350	40	120
14	300	45	120
15	300	50	100
16	300	55	100
17	250	60	100
18	250	65	80
19	250	70	80
20	210	75	80
22	210	80	60
24	210	85	60
26	180	90	60
28	180	95	50
30	180	100	50
32	150		

SQUARE THREADS

The square thread is used chiefly for power-transmission purposes where relatively high end-thrust loads have to be withstood. The " flanks " of the square thread are approximately parallel to the diametral plane, i.e. at right angles to the axis, and take the end thrusts in either direction. Square thread screws are employed for screw presses, machine-tool feeds and similar purposes. There is no bursting stress on the nuts, as in the vee-thread type.

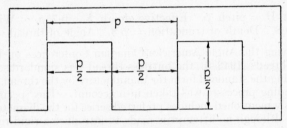

FIG. 17.—SQUARE THREAD.

The following are the proportions of square threads (Fig. 17) :

Width of tooth $= 0.5p$.

Width of tooth space $= 0.5p$.

Depth of thread $= 0.5p$.

BUTTRESS THREADS

This type of screw thread may be regarded as a modification of the square thread in that the screw has to withstand its maximum

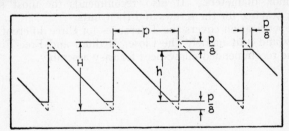

FIG. 18.—THE ORDINARY BUTTRESS THREAD.

end thrust in one direction only, viz. on the face normal to the axis of the screw. It combines the advantages of the square thread with the strength of the vee-form thread. The thrust side is usually made perpendicular to the thread axis, so that there is little radial pressure. On these accounts the buttress thread is particularly suitable when tubular members are screwed together. It is used for quick-action vices, breech mechanisms of large guns, aeroplane hubs and columns of hydraulic presses.

Before the standardisation of the Buttress Thread (B.S. 1657—1950) the form used was that shown in Fig. 18, and the proportions were as follows :

Depth H = pitch p. Effective depth $h = 0.75p$. Width of flat $= p/8$. Depth of truncation $= p/8$. Angle of thread $= 45°$.

Following the Anglo-American-Canadian Conferences on Unified Screw Threads (1943–5), the buttress thread was standardised, and in selecting the standard form the manufacture by the thread milling and grinding processes was taken into account. The Specification previously mentioned includes preferred series for the diameters and pitches, although no attempt is made to introduce a rigid relationship.

Fig. 19 shows the British Standard form of buttress thread. The following are proportions of this thread :

Depth H $= 0.89064p$.   Effective depth A $= 0.50586p$.
Width of flat F $= 0.27544p$.   Depth of truncation $f = 0.24532p$.
$h = 0.61172p$. $r = 0.12055p$.   B $= 0.4p$. $s = 0.13946p$.

The numerical data for this thread is given in the table on page 160.

The British Standard also includes a formula for calculating effective diameter tolerances and gives the tolerances for the major and minor diameters. It also recommends the most suitable gauging practice for the screws and their nuts.

The Specification covers the Tolerances for three different classes of screw and nut, namely the Close, Medium and Free Fits, and gives the recommended allowances for easy assembly.

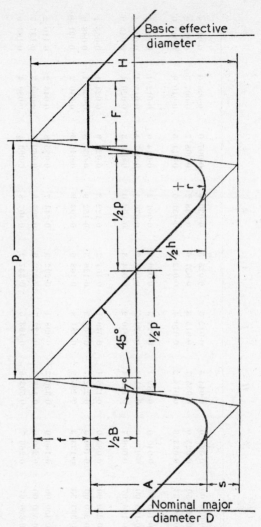

Fig. 19.—British Standard form of Buttress Thread.

NUMERICAL DATA FOR B.S. FORM BUTTRESS SCREW THREADS
(see Fig. 19 on page 159)

t.p.i.	Pitch (p)	B	H	f	A	h	s	r	F
20	0·050 00	0·020 0	0·044 5	0·012 3	0·025 3	0·030 6	0·007 0	0·006 0	0·013 8
16	0·062 50	0·025 0	0·055 7	0·015 3	0·031 6	0·038 2	0·008 7	0·007 5D	0·017 2
12	0·083 33	0·033 3	0·074 2	0·020 4	0·042 1	0·051 0	0·011 6	0·010 0	0·023 0
10	0·100 00	0·040 0	0·089 1	0·024 5	0·050 6	0·061 2	0·014 0	0·012 1	0·027 5
8	0·125 00	0·050 0	0·111 3	0·030 7	0·063 2	0·076 5	0·017 4	0·015 1	0·034 4
6	0·166 67	0·066 7	0·148 4	0·040 9	0·084 3	0·102 0	0·023 3	0·020 1	0·045 9
5	0·200 00	0·080 0	0·178 1	0·049 1	0·101 2	0·122 3	0·027 9	0·024 1	0·055 1
4	0·250 00	0·100 0	0·222 7	0·061 3	0·126 5	0·152 9	0·034 9	0·030 1	0·068 9
3	0·333 33	0·133 3	0·296 9	0·081 8	0·168 6	0·203 9	0·046 5	0·040 2	0·091 8
2·5	0·400 00	0·160 0	0·356 3	0·098 1	0·202 3	0·244 7	0·055 8	0·048 2	0·110 2
2	0·500 00	0·200 0	0·445 3	0·122 7	0·252 9	0·305 9	0·069 7	0·060 3	0·137 7
1·5	0·666 67	0·266 7	0·593 8	0·163 5	0·337 2	0·407 8	0·093 ½	0·080 4	0·183 6
1·25	0·800 00	0·320 0	0·712 5	0·196 3	0·404 7	0·489 4	0·111 6	0·096 4	0·220 4
1	1·000000	0·400 0	0·890 6	0·245 3	0·505 9	0·611 7	0·139 5	0·120 6	0·275 4

KNUCKLE THREAD

This is a modification of the square thread and is used in instances where the corners of the latter would be liable to damage, as in heavy outdoor applications such as for railway-carriage coupling screws. There is an increased amount of screw friction with this pattern of thread, so that rather more clearance between the screw and nut is necessary.

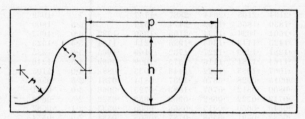

FIG. 19.—KNUCKLE THREAD.

The following are the proportions of the knuckle thread (Fig. 19) :

$$\text{Depth of thread } h = \frac{p}{2}.$$

$$\text{Radius of crest and root} = \frac{p}{4}.$$

Note.—Circular arcs of radii $\frac{p}{4}$ are used to form the thread.

THE ACME THREAD

This type may be regarded as a modification of the square thread in the direction of the flat-topped or truncated vee-type thread. It is stronger than the square thread and easier to machine. It is much used for strong power-transmission screws where half-nuts are engaged, as in lathe lead screws, since it gives an easier engagement than the square thread.

E.W.D.—6

STANDARD SCREW THREAD DEPTHS IN INCHES

Formula for Depth	Pitch × ·64033	Pitch × ·6495	Pitch × ·61343	Pitch × ·8660	(Pitch ÷ 2) + ·010″	Pitch × ·5327	Pitch × ·7036 S.I.		Pitch × ·600 B.A.	
No. of Threads per In.	Whit. *	U.S.S.	Unified Thread	Sharp Vee	Acme	B.S.Cy.	Pitch mm.	Depth Inches	No.	Depth Inches
3	·2134	·2165	·2044	·2887	·1767		7	·1939		
3½	·1830	·1856	·1752	·2474	·1529		6·5	·1800		
4	·1601	·1624	·1534	·2165	·1350	·1332	6·0	·1662		
4½	·1423	·1443	·1363	·1925	·1211	·1184	5·5	·1523		
5	·1281	·1299	·1227	·1732	·1100	·1065	5·0	·1385		
5½	·1164	·1181	·1115	·1575	·1009	·0969	4·5	·1246		
6	·1067	·1083	·1022	·1443	·0933	·0888	4·0	·1108		
7	·0915	·0928	·0876	·1237	·0814	·0761	3·5	·0969		
8	·0800	·0812	·0767	·1083	·0725	·0666	3·0	·0831		
9	·0712	·0722	·0682	·0962	·0655	·0592	2·5	·0692		
10	·0640	·0650	·0613	·0866	·0600	·0533	2·1	·0582		
11	·0582	·0591	·0558	·0787	·0505	·0484	2·0	·0554		
12	·0534	·0541	·0511	·0722	·0467	·0444	1·8	·0499		
13	·0493	·0500	·0472	·0666		·0410	1·75	·0484		
14	·0457	·0464	·0438	·0619	·0407	·0381	1·7	·0471		
15	·0427	·0433	·0409	·0577		·0355	1·66	·0460		
16	·0400	·0406	·0383	·0541	·0362	·0333	1·5	·0415		
17	·0377	·0382	·0355	·0509		·0313	1·25	·0346		
18	·0356	·0361	·0341	·0481		·0296	1·0	·0277	0	·0236
19	·0338	·0343	·0323	·0457		·0280	·90	·0249	1	·0212
20	·0320	·0325	·0307	·0433		·0266	·85	·0235		
21	·0305	·0309	·0292	·0412		·0254	·81	·0224	2	·0191
22	·0291	·0295	·0276	·0394		·0242	·80	·0222		
24	·0267	·0271	·0256	·0361		·0222	·75	·0208		
25	·0256	·0260	·0245	·0346		·0213	·73	·0202	3	·0172
26	·0246	·0250	·0236	·0333		·0205	·70	·0194		
27	·0237	·0241	·0227	·0321		·0197	·66	·0183	4	·0156
28	·0229	·0232	·0219	·0309		·0190	·60	·0166		
30	·0213	·0217	·0204	·0289		·0178	·59	·0163	5	·0139
32	·0200	·0203	·0192	·0271		·0166	·55	·0152		
34	·0188	·0191	·0180	·0255		·0157	·53	·0146	6	·0125
35	·0183	·0186	·0175	·0247		·0152	·50	·0139		
36	·0178	·0180	·0170	·0241		·0148	·48	·0133	7	·0113
37	·0173	·0176	·0166	·0234		·0144	·45	·0125		
38	·0169	·0171	·0161	·0228		·0140	·43	·0119	8	·0101
40	·0160	·0162	·0153	·0216		·0133	·39	·0108	9	·0092
42	·0152	·0155	·0146	·0206		·0127	·35	·0096	10	·0083
48	·0133	·0135	·0128	·0180		·0111	·25	·0069	11	·0073
50	·0128	·0130	·0123	·0173		·0107			12	·0066
56	·0114	·0116	·0109	·0155		·0095			13	·0059
60	·0107	·0108	·0102	·0144		·0089			14	·005

[*Alfred Herbert Ltd., Coventry.*]

* Also B.S.F., B.S.P., Std. Brass, Adm. Fine, Conduit and Copper Tube.

The thread angle is 29°. The clearance is obtained by making the Acme nut oversize by 0·020 in.

The proportions of the thread (Fig. 20) are as follows :

Depth of thread h $\qquad = \dfrac{p}{2} + 0·010$ in.

Diameter of nut at root = Overall diameter of screw + 0·010 in.
Diameter of nut at crest = Root diameter of screw + 0·010 in.
Width of crest d $\qquad = 0·3707p$ (for screws)
Width of root d $\qquad = 0·3707p - 0·0052$ in. (for screws)

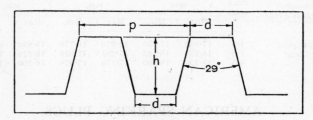

FIG. 20.—ACME THREAD.

General Purpose Acme Thread*

This thread has the 29° angle and a basic depth $h = 0·5p$.
The basic width of flat $d = 0·37069p$.
The basic thickness of thread at a distance of $p/4$ from the top of thread (corresponding to a diameter smaller than the outside diameter by $p/2$) is equal to $p/2$.
Width of root $d = 0·3706p - (0·52 \times$ clearance).
A clearance of 0·010 in. is added to the basic thread depth for threads of 10-pitch and coarser pitches, and 0·005 in. on finer pitches.

BRITISH MOTOR TYRE VALVE THREAD (S.M.M.T.)

The screwed ends of inner tube valves have the 60° system International thread of 0·302 in. diameter and 32 threads per inch.

* B.S. 1104 —1943 and U.S.A. Standards Handbook H/28.

Sparking Plug Screw Threads

Two main sizes of thread are used for aircraft and automobile engines, namely, the 14 mm. and 18 mm.

The 60° thread, Metric or Systéme Internationale Standard, is used for automobile engines.

The 14-mm. thread has a pitch of 1·25 mm.

The 18-mm. thread has a pitch of 1·5 mm.

The standard sparking plug dimensions recommended by the British Standards Institution (Report No. 45—1928 and 2E9)* are shown in the table, all sizes being in millimetres.

Automobile Sparking Plugs	Pitch mm.	Full Diameter mm.		Effective Diameter mm.		Core Diameter mm.	
		Max.	Min.	Max.	Min.	Max.	Min.
Sparking plug .	1·5	17·950	17·750	16·976	16·776	15·839	15·639
Tapped hole .	1·5	18·337	18·162	17·201	17·026	16·226	16·051
Taps . .	1·5	18·330	18·200	17·170	17·070	16·200	16·070

AMERICAN SPARKING PLUGS
(S.A.E. Standard)

(1) Sparking Plug Threads

Sparking Plug	Major Diameter		Pitch Diameter		Minor Diameter
	Max.	Min.	Max.	Min.	Max.
⅞ in.–18	0·8750	0·8668	0·8384	0·8343	0·8068
18–1·5 mm.	0·7077	0·7028	0·6693	0·6644	0·6246

(2) Tapped Hole Threads

Sparking Plug	Major Diameter	Pitch Diameter		Minor Diameter	
	Min.	Max.	Min.	Max.	Min.
⅞ in.–18	0·8750	0·8430	0·8389	0·8209	0·8149
18–1·5 mm.	0·7160	0·6762	0·6713	0·6378	0·6329

* Also see B.S. 45—1938 for Dimensions of Sparking Plugs, Plug Holes, Taps for Plug Holes and Copper Asbestos Washers (for Automobile Engines).

UNIFIED SCREW THREADS

The principal screw-thread systems that have been in use in Great Britain are the Whitworth (55°) and the B.A. (47½°), whilst in the United States and Canada the American National Thread System (60°) developed from the Sellers was used.

From the 1914–18 war onwards it became apparent that a common standard for screw threads in the three countries was desirable. In 1926, 1943, 1945 and 1948 meetings were held between technical representatives of the three countries, and as a result a compromise between the differing views was reached. The British Standard* proposed, subsequently, is believed to represent the best technical compromise found possible by the Screw Thread Committees in all three countries.

The dimensions and tolerances for both the Unified Coarse and Unified Fine Thread Series in this standard agree with the corresponding values in the American Standard (A.S.A.B1.1—1949). Some of the tolerances in the tables of Special Threads differ in the last place of decimals from the American ones, but these differences are considered to be insignificant.

The three countries have agreed upon the following designations for Unified Screw Threads : (A) Unified Coarse Thread, *UNC*. (B) Unified Fine Thread, *UNF*. (C) Unified Special Thread, *UNS*.

These designations are to be preceded by the nominal diameter and the number of threads per inch.

The Specification given in the footnote was issued as a provisional British Standard, to be reviewed at the end of six months, to confirm it as one of the series of British Standards for screw threads.

The preparation of a British Standard for the general dimensions of bolts, nuts and screws with Unified Screw Threads is in hand.

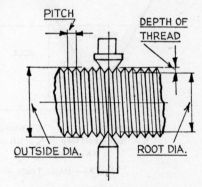

Fig. 21.—Thread Micrometer
(*see page* 167).

Early in 1948 the British Governmental Inter-Services Engineering Standards Co-ordinating Committee indicated its intention of

* B.S. 1580—1949.

adopting the Unified Screw Thread System in new designs of certain Service products.

The British Standard relates to parallel screw threads and includes :

(1) A Coarse Thread Series from $\frac{1}{4}$ in. to 4 in. diameter.

(2) A Fine Thread Series from $\frac{1}{4}$ in. to $1\frac{1}{2}$ in. diameter.

The full Specification, which should be consulted for detailed information in regard to bases of tolerances, gauges, tolerances on pitch and angle in relation to tolerance on effective diameter, tables of sizes, pitches, tolerances, etc., is B.S. 1580—1949.

FORM OF UNIFIED SCREW THREAD

The basic form of the Unified Screw Thread is shown in heavy line in Fig. 22. The outline, defined by the lower cross-hatching, is

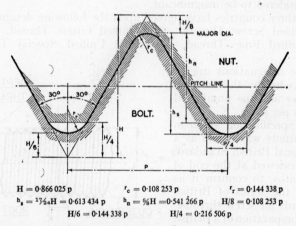

$H = 0.866\,025\,p$	$r_c = 0.108\,253\,p$	$r_r = 0.144\,338\,p$
$h_s = {}^{17}\!/_{24}H = 0.613\,434\,p$	$h_n = \tfrac{5}{8}H = 0.541\,266\,p$	$H/8 = 0.108\,253\,p$
$H/6 = 0.144\,338\,p$	$H/4 = 0.216\,506\,p$	

Fig. 22.—Basic Form of Unified Thread.

also that of a bolt in its maximum metal condition ; *both the crest and root are rounded.* The thread angle is 60°. The outline shown by the upper cross hatching is the design form of a nut in its maximum metal condition ; *the root is rounded* but *the crest is flat.*

CLASSES OF BOLTS AND NUTS

Three classes of bolts and nuts are specified :

Class 1A bolt. Class 1B nut.—These are for screw threads of ordinary commercial quality.

Class 2A bolt. Class 2B nut.—These are for the better grade of ordinary interchangeable screw threads.

Class 3A bolt. Class 3B nut.—For screw threads requiring a snug fit as in highest quality production, with very efficient system of gauging and inspection.

The Specification includes tables for sizes and tolerances of these classes in the coarse and fine threads.

DESIGNATION OF UNIFIED SCREW THREADS

It is recommended that these threads should be referred to on drawings, etc., by their basic major diameter and number of threads per inch, followed by the appropriate abbreviations of the diameter-pitch series to which they belong and also the class.

The following are typical examples :

	Designation	*Example*
Unified Coarse Thread Series .	UNC	$\frac{1}{4}$—20. UNC—3A.
Unified Fine Thread Series .	UNF	$\frac{3}{8}$—24. UNF—2B.
Unified Special Series . .	UNS	5·75—8. UNS—1A.
Unified thread form (untabulated diameters and pitches) . .	UN	3·83—16. UN—1A.
Left-handed threads. (Symbol LH to follow recognised abbreviation.)	—	$\frac{1}{2}$—12. UNC—3A.LH.

GAUGING SCREW THREADS

(1) Micrometer Method (Fig. 21)

The thread micrometer is provided with special anvil and point to suit the screw thread form to be gauged. When gauging screw threads the angle of the point and the sides of the vee-anvil, i.e. the

BRITISH STANDARD UNIFIED SCREW THREADS
NUMERICAL DATA FOR STANDARD PITCHES*

For key to designated letters see Fig. 22.

Number of Threads per Inch	Pitch p	$p/4$ $= 0.250\,000p$	H $= 0.866\,025p$	$\dfrac{H}{8} = r_c$ $= 0.108\,253p$	$\dfrac{H}{6} = r_r$ $= 0.144\,338p$	$\dfrac{H}{4}$ $= 0.216\,506p$	h_s $= \dfrac{17}{24}H$ $= 0.613\,434p$	h_n $= 5/8\,H$ $= 0.541\,266p$
	In.	*In.*	*In.*	*In.*	*In.*	*In.*	*In.*	*In.*
36	0·027 778	0·006 94	0·024 06	0·003 01	0·004 01	0·006 01	0·017 04	0·015 04
28	0·035 714	0·008 93	0·030 93	0·003 87	0·005 16	0·007 74	0·021 91	0·019 33
24	0·041 667	0·010 42	0·036 08	0·004 51	0·006 01	0·009 02	0·025 56	0·022 55
20	0·050 000	0·012 50	0·043 30	0·005 41	0·007 22	0·010 83	0·030 67	0·027 06
18	0·055 556	0·013 89	0·048 11	0·006 01	0·008 02	0·012 03	0·034 08	0·030 07
16	0·062 500	0·015 62	0·054 13	0·006 77	0·009 02	0·013 53	0·038 34	0·033 83
14	0·071 429	0·017 86	0·061 86	0·007 73	0·010 31	0·015 46	0·043 82	0·038 66
12	0·083 333	0·020 83	0·072 17	0·009 02	0·012 03	0·018 04	0·051 12	0·045 11
11	0·090 909	0·022 73	0·078 73	0·009 84	0·013 12	0·019 68	0·055 77	0·049 21
10	0·100 000	0·025 00	0·086 60	0·010 83	0·014 43	0·021 65	0·061 34	0·054 13
9	0·111 111	0·027 78	0·096 22	0·012 03	0·016 04	0·024 06	0·068 16	0·060 14
8	0·125 000	0·031 25	0·108 25	0·013 53	0·018 04	0·027 06	0·076 68	0·067 66
7	0·142 857	0·035 71	0·123 72	0·015 46	0·020 62	0·030 93	0·087 63	0·077 32
6	0·166 667	0·041 67	0·144 34	0·018 04	0·024 06	0·036 08	0·102 24	0·090 21
5	0·200 000	0·050 00	0·173 21	0·021 65	0·028 87	0·043 30	0·122 69	0·108 25
4½	0·222 222	0·055 56	0·192 45	0·024 06	0·032 08	0·048 11	0·136 32	0·120 28
4	0·250 000	0·062 50	0·216 51	0·027 06	0·036 08	0·054 13	0·153 36	0·135 23

* Table 1. B.S. 1580—1949.

flanks of the thread, should contact the thread. The zero position of the contacts (Fig. 23) should be such that the micrometer scale reads zero.

If correctly adjusted and used, the micrometer reading gives the *pitch diameter*, which is intermediate between the crest and root of the thread. The value should correspond with that obtained by measurement of the outside diameter and the pitch, as follows :

$$PD = OD - d,$$

where PD = pitch diameter, OD = outside diameter and d = depth of thread.

For Whitworth screw threads :

$$PD = OD - 0{\cdot}6403p$$

where p = pitch in inches,

$$\text{or } PD = OD - \frac{0{\cdot}6403}{n}$$

where n = number of threads per inch.

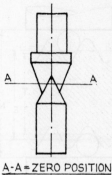

A-A = ZERO POSITION

Fig. 23.

SCREW MICROMETER READINGS FOR WHITWORTH THREADS

Diameter O.D. (inch)	Threads per Inch (n)	Screw Micrometer Reading P.D. (inch)	$\dfrac{0 \cdot 6403}{n}$
$\frac{1}{4}$	20	0·2180	0·0320
$\frac{5}{16}$	18	0·2769	0·0355
$\frac{3}{8}$	16	0·3350	0·0400
$\frac{7}{16}$	14	0·3918	0·0457
$\frac{1}{2}$	12	0·4467	0·0533
$\frac{9}{16}$	12	0·5092	0·0533
$\frac{5}{8}$	11	0·5668	0·0582
$\frac{11}{16}$	11	0·6293	0·0582
$\frac{3}{4}$	10	0·6860	0·0640
$\frac{13}{16}$	10	0·7485	0·0640
$\frac{7}{8}$	9	0·8039	0·0711
$\frac{15}{16}$	9	0·8664	0·0711
1	8	0·9200	0·0800
$1\frac{1}{8}$	7	1·0336	0·0914
$1\frac{1}{4}$	7	1·1586	0·0914
$1\frac{3}{8}$	6	1·2684	0·1066
$1\frac{1}{2}$	6	1·3934	0·1066
$1\frac{5}{8}$	5	1·4970	0·1280
$1\frac{3}{4}$	5	1·6220	0·1280
$1\frac{7}{8}$	$4\frac{1}{2}$	1·7328	0·1422
2	$4\frac{1}{2}$	1·8578	0·1422
$2\frac{1}{8}$	$4\frac{1}{2}$	1·9828	0·1422

(2) The Two-wire Method (Fig. 24)

This method is employed for ascertaining the effective diameter, rom measurements over a pair of wires or rods of equal diameter, placed in the thread grooves on opposite sides of the axis of the screw (Fig. 24).

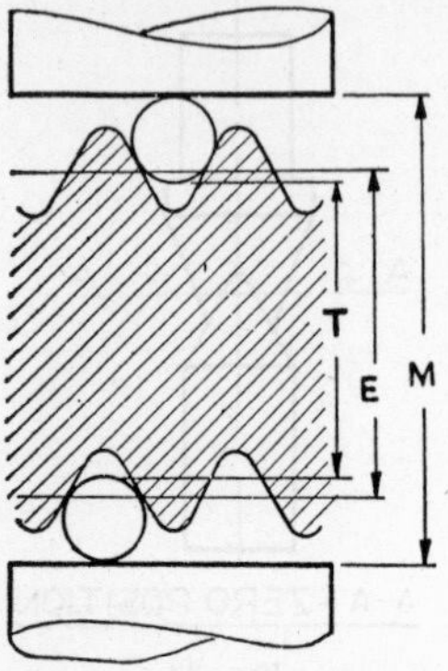

The effective diameter of the thread
E = T + P
where T = dimension between the wires
= M − 2d.

d = diameter of the wires.

P = a constant, the value of which depends upon the diameter of the wire and pitch of thread.

If p = pitch of thread, then,

For Whitworth threads P = 0·9605p − 1·1657d.

For British Association threads P = 1·136p − 1·483d.

For Sellers (American National) and Metric threads P = 0·866p − d.

FIG. 24.—TWO-WIRE METHOD.

(3) Three-wire Method (Fig. 25)

It is generally more convenient to employ one wire on one side and two wires on the opposite side of the thread (Fig. 25). This avoids micrometer tilting errors.

The same formulæ can be used as in the two-wire method, but the following is an alternative method, based upon the micrometer reading M.

For Whitworth threads M = D − 1·6008p + 3·1657d, where D = outside diameter of thread.

Thus D = M + 1·6008p − 3·1657d.

For British Association threads D = M + 1·7363p − 3·4829d.

For Sellers (American National) and Metric threads D = M + 1·5155p − 3d.

The basis of these formulæ, which can be worked out from first principles, is as follows :

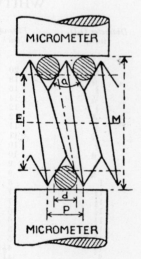

FIG. 25.—THREE WIRE METHOD.

$$D = M + \frac{p}{2 \tan \dfrac{a}{2}} - d - \frac{d}{\sin \dfrac{a}{2}} - c,$$

where a = angle of thread and c is a constant to compensate for the obliquity of the wires in the thread. It is usually of a very small order and, except for quick-pitch threads of appreciable obliquity, can be neglected.

Diameter of Rod or Wire

The diameter of the rod selected for use in the three-wire method must be such that it contacts the straight flanks of the vee-threads, i.e. does not touch the crest or root curves.

For each size of thread there is a definite maximum and minimum diameter of rod, and one " best " diameter, i.e. one that contacts the threads on the pitch line.

For Whitworth threads maximum diameter of rod $d = 0 \cdot 853 p$.

            minimum   ,,   ,, $= 0 \cdot 506 p$.

            best diameter $d_1 = 0 \cdot 56368 p$.

For British Association threads maximum diameter $d = 0 \cdot 730 p$.

            minimum   ,, $= 0 \cdot 498 p$.

For International Metric threads maximum diameter $d = 1 \cdot 010 p$.

            minimum   ,, $= 0 \cdot 505 p$.

For American National (Sellers) maximum diameter $d = 0 \cdot 90 p$.

            minimum   ,, $= 0 \cdot 56 p$.

            best diameter $d_1 = 0 \cdot 57735 p$.

Formula for Best Diameter

If a = one-half thread angle, p = pitch, d_1 = best diameter,

$$d_1 = \frac{p}{2 \cos a} = \frac{p \sec a}{2}.$$

The rods or wires used for the three-wire method should be ground truly cylindrical, with hardened working surfaces, and of working surface length 1 in. The wires must be straight to within $0 \cdot 00002$ in. per $0 \cdot 25$ in. length and cylindrical to within $0 \cdot 00002$ in. All three rods should have the same basic diameter within $0 \cdot 00003$ in.

Acme Thread Checking

Diameter of rod such that top of rod is flush with flat crests of thread is given by

$$d = 0.48725p.$$

For fuller data on checking screw threads the reader should consult *Notes on Screw Gauges*, issued by the National Physical

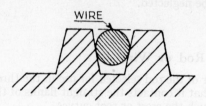

FIG. 26.—ACME THREAD CHECKING.

Laboratory (H.M. Stationery Office, Kingsway, London, W.C.2), and *Engineering Precision Measurements*, A. W. Judge (Chapman & Hall, Ltd.).

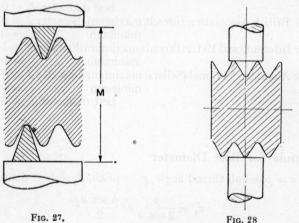

FIG. 27.   FIG. 28

Measurement of Core and Outside Diameter

Small hardened prisms are used on the micrometer contacts, such that the prism angle is less than the thread angle and the radius at the end of the prism is smaller than the root radius of the thread.

For Whitworth threads the prism angle is 45°; for 60° thread angles the prism angle is 45° to 50°.

The Matrix prism measuring system is shown in Fig. 26.

If M = micrometer reading, h = height of prism, then core diameter = M − 2h.

The *outside diameter* is measured with a micrometer having contacts of diameter somewhat greater than the pitch of the thread to be measured (Fig. 28).

Instead of prisms, contacts with spherical ball-ends of smaller radius than the root radius of the thread to be measured are used in thread-measuring comparators, e.g. the Cooke horizontal comparator.

FIG. 29.—THREAD PROFILE CHECKING

Thread Form Checking

The optical projector method, whereby an enlarged image of the screw thread is shown on a ground-glass screen, enables the thread form to be compared with an accurate comparison thread outline form or template on the screen (Fig. 29). Any inaccuracies of thread form are clearly shown. The usual magnifications of engineering optical projectors are 10, 25, 50 and 100.

Lathe Screw-cutting Gear Trains

The pitch of a thread cut in the centre lathe is determined by the ratio of the gears between the spindle and lead screw and the pitch of the lead screw. The general formula for screw-cutting gears on the lathe is as follows :

If p = pitch of screw to be cut, and p_1 = pitch of lead screw,

$$\frac{p}{p_1} = \frac{\text{T.P.I. on lead screw}}{\text{T.P.I. to be cut}} = \frac{\text{No. teeth on driving-wheel}}{\text{No. teeth on lead-screw wheel}}$$

Simple Gear Train (Fig. 30)

If a, b and c denote numbers of teeth on lathe spindle gear, intermediate gear and lead-screw gear, respectively, then :

$$\frac{p}{p_1} = \frac{\text{teeth on driving-wheel}}{\text{teeth on lead screw}} = \frac{a}{c}.$$

Note.—The number of teeth on gear wheel b has no effect on this ratio.

Example 1.—Given lead screw = $\frac{1}{2}$-in. pitch. Screw to be cut = $\frac{1}{8}$-in. pitch.

$$\frac{p}{p_1} = \frac{\frac{1}{8}}{\frac{1}{2}} = \frac{2}{8} = \frac{1}{4} = \frac{20}{80} = \frac{\text{spindle gear}}{\text{lead-screw gear}}.$$

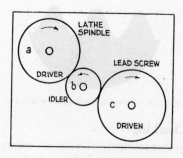

FIG. 30.—SIMPLE LATHE GEAR TRAIN.

Thus the ratio of spindle to lead-screw gear is 1 : 4, and any pairs of wheels, e.g. 20 and 80 or 30 and 120, having this ratio can be used.

Example 2.—Lead screw = 4 T.P.I. Screw to be cut = 24 T.P.I.

Here $p_1 = \frac{1}{4}$ and $p = \frac{1}{24}$,

$$\frac{p}{p_1} = \frac{4}{24} = \frac{1}{6} = \frac{10}{60} = \frac{20}{120}.$$

Thus there can be a 20 gear on spindle and 120 gear on lead screw.

Compound Gear Trains (Fig. 31)

If a, b, c and d denote the numbers of teeth on the gearwheels and p_1 and p the pitches of the lead screw and thread to be cut, respectively,

Then

$$\frac{p}{p_1} = \frac{a}{b} \times \frac{c}{d}$$

Example 3.—Lead screw = $\frac{1}{6}$-in. pitch. Screw to be cut = 40 T.P.I. or $p = \frac{1}{40}$.

Then

$$\frac{p}{p_1} = \frac{6}{40} = \frac{3 \times 2}{5 \times 8} = \frac{30 \times 20}{50 \times 80}$$

Thus there will be a 30 gear on spindle driving a 50 gear on intermediate stud, to which is keyed a 20 gear gearing with an 80 gear on lead screw.

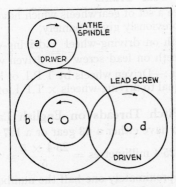

FIG. 31.—COMPOUND GEAR TRAIN.

Cutting Fractional Pitches

Fractional threads can only be screw-cut if the ratio of the gears can be expressed as a fraction.

Example 1.—Lead screw = $\frac{1}{2}$-in. pitch. Screw to be cut = $\frac{3}{16}$-in. pitch.

Here

$$\frac{p}{p_1} = \frac{3 \times 2}{16 \times 1} = \frac{30 \times 20}{80 \times 20}.$$

Thus there will be a 30 on spindle gearing into an 80 on intermediate stud to which is keyed a 20, which meshes with another 20 on lead screw.

If the ratio cannot be factorised, the thread can only be cut approximately.

Example 2.—Lead screw = $\frac{1}{4}$-in. pitch. Screw to be cut = 41·9 threads in 8 in.

Here

$$p = \frac{8}{41 \cdot 9} \text{ in.}$$

and

$$\frac{p}{p_1} = \frac{8 \times 4}{41 \cdot 9} = \frac{320}{419}.$$

As 419 cannot be factorised, the nearest whole number that can be factorised must be taken, namely, $419 + 1 = 420$.

$$\frac{320}{420} \text{ can be written as } \frac{16}{21} = \frac{4 \times 4}{3 \times 7} = \frac{40 \times 40}{30 \times 70}.$$

This compound train of gears will cut the thread accurately for most practical purposes.

To Prove Lathe Gear Trains

To check or prove a set of gearwheels which have been estimated from the formula previously given, namely,

$$\frac{p}{p_1} = \frac{\text{teeth on driving-wheel}}{\text{teeth on lead screw}} = \frac{\text{driving-wheels}}{\text{driven wheels}}.$$

Multiply together:—Driven wheels by T.P.I. of lead screw. The product must be equal to driving-wheels × T.P.I. of screw to be cut.

Cutting Metric Pitch Threads on English Lathes

It is necessary to have either a 63 gear or a 127 gear, the reason being that 1 in. = 25·4 millimetres = $\frac{25 \cdot 4 \times 5}{5} = \frac{127}{5}$.

The 63 gear is approximately one-half the number of teeth of the 127, but it does not give such accurate results.

The formula for metric pitches is :

$$\frac{\text{teeth on drivers}}{\text{teeth on driven}} = \text{T.P.I. of lead screw} \times \frac{5p}{127},$$

where p = pitch of thread to be cut, in millimetres.

Example 1.—Pitch of lead screw = $\frac{1}{2}$ in. Screw to be cut = 7-mm. pitch.

T.P.I. of lead screw = 2.

From formula :

$$\frac{\text{drivers}}{\text{driven}} = \frac{2 \times 5 \times 7}{127} = \frac{70}{127} = \frac{35 \times 40}{127 \times 20}.$$

Thus a 35 on spindle gears with a 20, to which is keyed a 40, which gears with a 127 on lead screw.

Note.—When cutting metric threads on English lathes the 127 (or 63) gear is arranged on the lead screw.

Example 2.—Pitch of lead screw = $\frac{1}{4}$. Screw to be cut = 3-mm. pitch. Gearwheel with 63 teeth to be used.

In this case the formula becomes :

$$\frac{\text{drivers}}{\text{driven}} = \text{T.P.I. of lead screw} \times \frac{2 \cdot 5 p}{63}.$$

In the example T.P.I. of lead screw = 4 :

$$\frac{\text{drivers}}{\text{driven}} = \frac{4 \times 2 \cdot 5 \times 3}{63} = \frac{10 \times 3}{63} = \frac{20 \times 30}{20 \times 63}.$$

Thus there will be a 20 on spindle driving a 20, to which is keyed a 30 meshing with a 63 on lead screw.

Cutting English Threads on Metric Lathe

The formula in this application is as follows :

$$\frac{\text{drivers}}{\text{driven}} = \frac{127}{5p} \times \frac{1}{\text{T.P.I. to be cut.}}, \quad p = \text{metric lead-screw pitch.}$$

Example 3.—Pitch of lead screw = 3 mm. Screw to be cut = 24 T.P.I.

$$\frac{\text{drivers}}{\text{driven}} = \frac{127}{5 \times 3 \times 24} = \frac{127 \times 20}{90 \times 80}.$$

There will be a 127 on spindle geared to a 90 on intermediate stud, to which is keyed a 20 driving an 80 on lead screw.

Note.—In this case the 127 gear is mounted on the lathe spindle.

Prime Numbers

In English lathes, when the T.P.I. of the work to be cut and the lead screw are even numbers, the selection of the most suitable gears is straightforward.

When either of these T.P.I.s is an odd number, it is sometimes impossible to arrange suitable gears.

The following are prime numbers of threads per inch which are impossible to screw-cut accurately, since these numbers cannot be factorised : 23, 29, 31, 37, 41, 43, 47, 53, 59, 61, 67, 71, 73, 79, 83.

It is sometimes sufficiently accurate when cutting short lengths of screw thread to use the nearest whole number that can be factorised;

this can generally be effected by adding or subtracting 1 from the prime number.

For special purposes where accuracy is essential it is necessary to have special gearwheels with odd numbers of teeth, or multiples of unfactorisable odd numbers, e.g. 46, 58, 62, 74, etc.

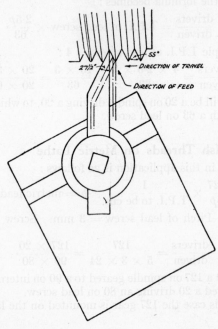

FIG. 32.—METHOD OF SETTING SLIDE REST AT ANGLE FOR SCREW-CUTTING.

Screw-cutting Whitworth Thread

A useful method is to set the top slide rest over to one-half the thread angle, namely, $\frac{1}{2}$ of $55° = 27\frac{1}{2}°$. (For U.S. and Metric threads this angle will be 30°.)

The screw-cutting tool (Fig. 32) cuts only on the left-hand side, and with this arrangement the cut is increased by moving the top slide feed screw, when the cutting edge always remains parallel with the left-hand flank of the thread being cut.

HELIX ANGLES OF SCREW THREADS

Dia.	B.S.W. T.P.I.	B.S.W. Helix Angle	B.S.F. T.P.I.	B.S.F. Helix Angle	Std. Brass T.P.I.	Std. Brass Helix Angle	Adm. Fine T.P.I.	Adm. Fine Helix Angle	Am. N. Coarse T.P.I.	Am. N. Coarse Helix Angle	Am. N. Fine T.P.I.	Am. N. Fine Helix Angle
3/16″	24	4° 44′										
No. 10	24	3° 57′	28	3° 18′					24	4° 44′	32	3° 24′
No. 12	20	4° 11′	26	3° 7′					24	4° 9′	28	3° 24′
1/4″	18	3° 40′	26	2° 44′	26	3° 7′	24	3° 24′	20	4° 11′	28	2° 52′
5/16″	16	3° 24′	22	2° 56′	26	2° 0′	24	2° 11′	18	3° 40′	24	2° 40′
3/8″	14	3° 20′	20	2° 40′	26	1° 29′	20	1° 57′	16	3° 24′	24	2° 11′
7/16″	12	3° 24′	18	2° 31′	26	1° 10′	20	1° 32′	14	3° 20′	20	2° 15′
1/2″	12	2° 59′	16	2° 29′	26	0° 58′	14	1° 51′	13	3° 7′	20	1° 57′
9/16″	11	2° 56′	16	2° 11′	26	0° 50′	14	1° 34′	12	2° 59′	18	1° 55′
5/8″	11	2° 38′	14	2° 15′	26	0° 43′	12	1° 36′	11	2° 56′	18	1° 43′
11/16″	10	2° 40′	14	2° 2′	26	0° 38′						
3/4″	10	2° 26′	12	2° 11′	26	0° 34′	12	1° 25′	10	2° 40′	16	1° 36′
13/16″	9	2° 31′	12	2° 0′	26	0° 29′						
7/8″	9	2° 20′	11	2° 2′			12	1° 16′	9	2° 31′	14	1° 34′
15/16″	8	2° 29′										
1″	8	2° 31′	10	1° 57′			12	1° 3′	8	2° 29′	14	1° 22′
1 1/8″	7	2° 15′	9	1° 55′			12	0° 54′	7	2° 31′	12	1° 25′
1 1/4″	7	2° 24′	9	1° 43′					7	2° 15′	12	1° 16′
1 3/8″	6	2° 11′	8	1° 46′					6	2° 11′	12	1° 3′
1 1/2″	6	2° 26′	8	1° 36′								
1 5/8″	5	2° 15′	8	1° 29′					5	2° 15′		
1 3/4″	5	2° 20′	7	1° 34′								
1 7/8″	4½	2° 11′										
2″	4½	2° 11′	7	1° 22′	26	0° 29′	8	1° 11′	4½	2° 11′	12	1° 3′

Nom. Dia.	B.S.P. T.P.I.	B.S.P. Helix Angle	Briggs T.P.I.	Briggs Helix Angle	Copper Tube T.P.I.	Copper Tube Helix Angle	Conduit T.P.I.	Conduit Helix Angle	Copper Stay T.P.I.	Copper Stay Helix Angle	Copper Stay T.P.I.	Copper Stay Helix Angle
1/8″	28	1° 48′	27	1° 52′	28	2° 53′	18	2° 11′				
1/4″	19	1° 59′	18	2° 2′	20	2° 34′	18	1° 43′				
3/8″	19	1° 32′	18	1° 36′	20	1° 54′	16	1° 36′				
1/2″	14	1° 40′	14	1° 40′	20	1° 30′						
5/8″	14	1° 31′			20	1° 15′						
3/4″	14	1° 19′	14	1° 19′	20	1° 4′						

Size	t.p.i.	Helix Angle	t.p.i.	Helix Angle	t.p.i.	Helix Angle	t.p.i.	Helix Angle	t.p.i.	Helix Angle	t.p.i.	Helix Angle
7/8"	14	1° 8'	11½	1° 41'	20	0° 56'	16	1° 11'				
15/16"	11	1° 46'			20	0° 49'						
1 1/16"			11½	1° 20'	20	0° 45'	16	0° 57'	12	1° 51'	11	2° 2'
1 1/8"	11	1° 23'					14	0° 54'	12	1° 43'	11	1° 53'
1 3/16"	11	1° 9'	11½	1° 6'	16	0° 37'	14	0° 40'	12	1° 36'	11	1° 46'
1 1/4"	11	0° 59'			16	0° 40'			12	1° 30'	11	1° 39'
1 3/8"	11	0° 51'	11½	0° 49'	16	0° 35'			12	1° 25'	11	1° 33'
2"									12	1° 20'	11	1° 28'
									12	1° 16'	11	1° 23'

	S.I. & Swiss Std.		Swiss Fine		Lowenherz		B.A.			
Dia. mm.	Pitch mm.	Helix Angle	Pitch mm.	Helix Angle	Pitch mm.	Helix Angle	No.	Dia. mm.	Pitch mm.	Helix Angle
4	0·70	3° 36'	0·35	1° 44'	0·80	3° 19'	4	3·60	0·66	3° 45'
5	0·70	3° 43'	0·50	1° 57'	1·00	3° 28'	3	4·10	0·73	3° 37'
6	1·00	3° 24'	0·75	2° 29'	1·00	3° 15'	2	4·70	0·81	3° 31'
7	1·00	2° 52'	0·75	2° 6'	1·20	3° 5'	1	5·30	0·90	3° 26'
8	1·25	3° 10'	1·00	2° 29'	1·30	2° 57'	0	6·00	1·00	3° 24'
9	1·25	2° 47'	1·00	2° 11'	1·40	2° 51'				
10	1·50	3° 2'	1·00	1° 57'						
11	1·50	2° 44'	1·00	1° 46'	1·60	2° 42'				
12	1·75	2° 56'	1·25	2° 2'	1·80	2° 36'				
14	2·00	2° 52'	1·25	1° 44'	2·00	2° 31'				
16	2·00	2° 29'	1·25	1° 30'	2·20	2° 27'				
18	2·50	2° 47'	1·50	1° 36'	2·40	2° 24'				
20	2·50	2° 29'	1·50	1° 26'	2·80	2° 33'				
22	2·50	2° 14'	1·50	1° 18'	2·80	2° 20'				
24	3·00	2° 29'	1·50	1° 11'	3·20	2° 28'				
26										
27	3·00	2° 11'	2·00	1° 25'	3·20	2° 17'				
28	3·50	2° 18'			3·60	2° 14'				
30			2·00	1° 16'	3·60	2° 14'				
32										
33	3·50	2° 5'	2·00	1° 9'						
36	4·00	2° 11'	2·00	1° 3'	4·00	2° 11'				
39	4·00	2° 0'	2·00	0° 58'						
40					4·00	1° 57'				

These Tables are useful in selecting chaser holders for Alfred Herbert Tangic, Landmatic, Tangar, Tangel and Landex Dieheads.

[Alfred Herbert Ltd., Coventry.]

HELIX ANGLES FOR SCREW THREADS

English Diameters and Pitches

Diameter

Threads per Inch	3/16″	1/4″	5/16″	3/8″	7/16″	1/2″	9/16″	5/8″	3/4″	7/8″	1″	1 1/8″	1 1/4″
36	2° 59′	2° 11′	1° 43′	1° 25′	1° 12′	1° 3′	56′	50′	42′	35′	31′	27′	25′
32	3° 24′	2° 29′	1° 57′	1° 36′	1° 22′	1° 11′	1° 3′	57′	47′	40′	35′	31′	28′
28	3° 57′	2° 52′	2° 15′	1° 51′	1° 34′	1° 22′	1° 12′	1° 5′	54′	46′	40′	35′	32′
26	4° 19′	3° 7′	2° 26′	2° 0′	1° 42′	1° 29′	1° 18′	1° 10′	58′	50′	43′	38′	34′
24	4° 44′	3° 24′	2° 40′	2° 11′	1° 51′	1° 36′	1° 25′	1° 16′	1° 3′	54′	47′	42′	37′
22	5° 14′	3° 45′	2° 56′	2° 24′	2° 2′	1° 46′	1° 33′	1° 23′	1° 9′	59′	51′	45′	41′
20	5° 52′	4° 11′	3° 15′	2° 40′	2° 15′	1° 57′	1° 43′	1° 32′	1° 16′	1° 5′	57′	50′	45′
18	6° 40′	4° 44′	3° 40′	2° 59′	2° 31′	2° 15′	1° 55′	1° 43′	1° 25′	1° 12′	1° 3′	56′	50′
16	7° 43′	5° 26′	4° 11′	3° 24′	2° 52′	2° 29′	2° 11′	1° 57′	1° 36′	1° 22′	1° 11′	1° 3′	57′
14		6° 22′	4° 53′	3° 57′	3° 20′	2° 52′	2° 31′	2° 15′	1° 51′	1° 34′	1° 22′	1° 12′	1° 5′
13		6° 59′	5° 20′	4° 19′	3° 37′	3° 7′	2° 44′	2° 26′	2° 0′	1° 42′	1° 29′	1° 18′	1° 10′
12			5° 52′	4° 44′	3° 57′	3° 45′	2° 59′	2° 40′	2° 11′	1° 51′	1° 36′	1° 25′	1° 16′
11½					4° 22′	4° 44′	3° 17′	2° 56′	2° 17′	1° 56′	1° 41′	1° 29′	1° 20′
11					4° 53′	5° 26′	3° 40′	3° 15′	2° 24′	2° 2′	1° 46′	1° 33′	1° 23′
10							4° 8′	3° 40′	2° 40′	2° 15′	1° 57′	1° 43′	1° 32′
9							4° 44′	4° 11′	2° 59′	2° 31′	2° 11′	1° 55′	1° 43′
8								4° 53′	3° 24′	2° 52′	2° 29′	2° 11′	1° 57′
7									3° 58′	3° 20′	2° 52′	2° 31′	2° 15′
6									4° 44′	3° 58′	3° 24′	2° 59′	2° 40′
5½										4° 22′	3° 45′	3° 17′	2° 56′
5										4° 53′	4° 11′	3° 40′	3° 15′
4½											4° 44′	4° 7′	3° 40′
4											5° 26′	4° 44′	4° 11′
3½												5° 32′	4° 53′
3¼													5° 20′
3													5° 52′
2													

HELIX ANGLES FOR SCREW THREADS

English Diameters and Pitches (continued)

Threads per Inch	Diameter													
	1⅜″	1½″	1⅝″	1¾″	1⅞″	2″	2¼″	2½″	2¾″	3″	3¼″	3½″	3¾″	4″
36	22′	21′	19′	18′	16′	15′	—	—	—	—	—	—	—	—
32	25′	23′	21′	20′	18′	17′	15′	—	—	—	—	—	—	—
28	29′	26′	24′	23′	21′	20′	18′	16′	—	—	—	—	—	—
26	31′	29′	26′	24′	23′	21′	19′	17′	15′	—	—	—	—	11′
24	34′	31′	28′	26′	25′	23′	21′	18′	17′	15′	14′	13′	12′	11′
22	37′	34′	31′	29′	27′	25′	22′	20′	18′	17′	15′	14′	13′	13′
20	41′	37′	33′	32′	30′	28′	25′	22′	20′	18′	17′	16′	15′	14′
18	45′	42′	38′	35′	33′	31′	27′	25′	22′	21′	19′	18′	16′	15′
16	51′	47′	43′	40′	37′	35′	31′	28′	25′	23′	21′	20′	18′	17′
14	59′	54′	49′	46′	43′	40′	35′	32′	29′	26′	24′	23′	21′	20′
13	1°3′	58′	53′	49′	46′	43′	38′	34′	31′	29′	26′	24′	23′	21′
12	1°9′	1°3′	58′	54′	50′	47′	42′	37′	34′	31′	29′	26′	25′	23′
11½	1°12′	1°6′	1°1′	56′	52′	49′	43′	39′	35′	32′	30′	28′	26′	24′
11	1°16′	1°9′	1°3′	59′	55′	51′	45′	41′	37′	34′	31′	29′	27′	25′
10	1°23′	1°16′	1°10′	1°5′	1°0′	57′	50′	45′	41′	37′	34′	32′	29′	28′
9	1°33′	1°25′	1°18′	1°12′	1°7′	1°3′	56′	50′	45′	42′	38′	35′	33′	31′
8	1°46′	1°36′	1°29′	1°22′	1°16′	1°11′	1°3′	57′	51′	47′	43′	40′	37′	35′
7	2°2′	1°51′	1°42′	1°34′	1°28′	1°22′	1°12′	1°5′	59′	54′	49′	46′	43′	40′
6	2°24′	2°11′	2°0′	1°51′	1°43′	1°36′	1°25′	1°16′	1°9′	1°3′	58′	54′	50′	47′
5½	2°38′	2°24′	2°12′	2°2′	1°53′	1°46′	1°33′	1°23′	1°16′	1°9′	1°3′	59′	55′	51′
5	2°56′	2°40′	2°26′	2°15′	2°5′	1°57′	1°43′	1°32′	1°23′	1°16′	1°10′	1°5′	1°0′	57′
4½	3°17′	2°59′	2°44′	2°31′	2°20′	2°11′	1°55′	1°43′	1°33′	1°25′	1°18′	1°12′	1°7′	1°3′
4	3°45′	3°24′	3°7′	2°52′	2°40′	2°29′	2°11′	1°57′	1°46′	1°36′	1°29′	1°22′	1°16′	1°11′
3½	4°22′	3°57′	3°37′	3°20′	3°5′	2°52′	2°31′	2°15′	2°2′	1°51′	1°42′	1°34′	1°28′	1°22′
3¼	4°46′	4°18′	3°56′	3°37′	3°21′	3°7′	2°44′	2°26′	2°12′	2°0′	1°50′	1°42′	1°35′	1°29′
3	5°14′	4°44′	4°18′	3°57′	3°40′	3°24′	2°59′	2°40′	2°24′	2°11′	2°0′	1°51′	1°43′	1°36′
2	—	—	6°59′	6°23′	5°52′	5°26′	4°44′	4°11′	3°45′	3°24′	3°7′	2°52′	2°40′	2°29′

[Alfred Herbert Ltd.]

HELIX ANGLES FOR SCREW THREADS
Metric Diameters and Pitches

Diameter Mm.

Pitch Mm.	4	4·5	5	5·5	6	7	8	9	10	11	12	14	16	18	20	22	24	27	30
0·6	3° 2'	2° 40'	2° 22'	2° 8'	1° 57'	1° 39'	1° 26'	1° 16'	1° 8'	1° 2'	57'	48'	42'	37'	33'	30'	28'	25'	22'
0·75	3° 53'	3° 24'	3° 2'	2° 44'	2° 29'	2° 6'	1° 49'	1° 36'	1° 26'	1° 18'	1° 11'	1° 1'	53'	47'	42'	38'	35'	31'	28'
0·9	4° 48'	4° 11'	3° 43'	3° 20'	3° 2'	2° 33'	2° 13'	1° 57'	1° 45'	1° 35'	1° 26'	1° 13'	1° 4'	57'	51'	46'	42'	37'	34'
1	5° 26'	4° 44'	4° 11'	3° 45'	3° 24'	2° 52'	2° 29'	2° 11'	1° 57'	1° 46'	1° 36'	1° 22'	1° 11'	1° 3'	57'	51'	47'	42'	37'
1·25	7° 6'	6° 9'	5° 25'	4° 51'	4° 23'	3° 41'	3° 10'	2° 47'	2° 29'	2° 14'	2° 2'	1° 44'	1° 30'	1° 20'	1° 11'	1° 5'	59'	52'	47'
1·5	8° 58'	7° 43'	6° 46'	6° 1'	5° 25'	4° 32'	3° 53'	3° 24'	3° 2'	2° 44'	2° 29'	2° 6'	1° 49'	1° 36'	1° 26'	1° 18'	1° 11'	1° 3'	57'
1·75	11° 1'	9° 24'	8° 12'	7° 17'	6° 32'	5° 26'	4° 38'	4° 3'	3° 36'	3° 14'	2° 56'	2° 29'	2° 9'	1° 54'	1° 42'	1° 32'	1° 24'	1° 14'	1° 6'
2	—	11° 15'	9° 46'	8° 37'	7° 43'	6° 22'	5° 26'	4° 44'	4° 11'	3° 45'	3° 24'	2° 52'	2° 29'	2° 11'	1° 57'	1° 46'	1° 36'	1° 25'	1° 16'
2·5	—	—	—	11° 36'	10° 18'	8° 25'	7° 7'	6° 9'	5° 26'	4° 51'	4° 23'	3° 41'	3° 10'	2° 47'	2° 29'	2° 14'	2° 2'	1° 48'	1° 36'
3	—	—	—	—	—	10° 42'	8° 58'	7° 43'	6° 46'	6° 1'	5° 25'	4° 32'	3° 53'	3° 24'	3° 2'	2° 44'	2° 29'	2° 11'	1° 57'
3·5	—	—	—	—	—	—	11° 0'	9° 24'	8° 13'	7° 17'	6° 32'	5° 26'	4° 38'	4° 3'	3° 36'	3° 14'	2° 56'	2° 35'	2° 18'
4	—	—	—	—	—	—	—	11° 15'	9° 46'	8° 37'	7° 43'	6° 22'	5° 26'	4° 44'	4° 11'	3° 45'	3° 24'	2° 59'	2° 40'
4·5	—	—	—	—	—	—	—	—	11° 26'	10° 4'	8° 57'	7° 22'	6° 15'	5° 25'	4° 48'	4° 18'	3° 53'	3° 24'	3° 2'
5	—	—	—	—	—	—	—	—	—	11° 36'	10° 18'	8° 25'	7° 7'	6° 9'	5° 26'	4° 51'	4° 23'	3° 50'	3° 24'
5·5	—	—	—	—	—	—	—	—	—	—	11° 44'	9° 32'	8° 1'	6° 55'	6° 5'	5° 26'	4° 54'	4° 16'	3° 47'
6	—	—	—	—	—	—	—	—	—	—	—	10° 42'	8° 58'	7° 43'	6° 46'	6° 1'	5° 26'	4° 43'	4° 11'
6·5	—	—	—	—	—	—	—	—	—	—	—	—	9° 58'	8° 32'	7° 28'	6° 38'	5° 58'	5° 11'	4° 35'
7	—	—	—	—	—	—	—	—	—	—	—	—	11° 0'	9° 24'	8° 12'	7° 17'	6° 34'	5° 40'	5° 0'
7·5	—	—	—	—	—	—	—	—	—	—	—	—	—	10° 18'	8° 58'	7° 56'	7° 7'	6° 9'	5° 26'
8	—	—	—	—	—	—	—	—	—	—	—	—	—	11° 15'	9° 46'	8° 37'	7° 43'	6° 40'	5° 52'
10	—	—	—	—	—	—	—	—	—	—	—	—	—	—	—	—	—	—	—
12	—	—	—	—	—	—	—	—	—	—	—	—	—	—	—	—	—	—	—

[Alfred Herbert Ltd.]

HELIX ANGLES FOR SCREW THREADS
Metric Diameters and Pitches (continued)

Diameter Mm.

Pitch Mm.	33	36	39	42	45	48	52	56	60	64	68	72	76	80	84	88	92	96	100
0·6	20'	18'	17'	16'	15'	14'	13'	—	—	—	—	—	—	—	—	—	—	—	—
0·75	25'	23'	21'	20'	18'	17'	16'	15'	—	—	—	—	—	—	—	—	—	—	—
0·9	30'	28'	26'	24'	22'	21'	19'	18'	17'	16'	—	—	—	—	—	—	—	—	—
1	34'	31'	29'	26'	25'	23'	21'	20'	18'	17'	16'	—	—	—	—	—	—	—	—
1·25	42'	39'	36'	33'	31'	29'	27'	25'	23'	22'	20'	19'	—	—	—	—	—	—	—
1·5	51'	47'	43'	40'	37'	35'	32'	30'	28'	26'	24'	23'	22'	—	—	—	—	—	—
1·75	1° 0'	55'	51'	47'	44'	41'	38'	35'	33'	30'	29'	27'	26'	24'	—	—	—	—	—
2	1° 9'	1° 3'	58'	54'	50'	47'	43'	40'	37'	35'	33'	31'	29'	28'	26'	—	—	—	—
2·5	1° 27'	1° 20'	1° 13'	1° 8'	1° 3'	59'	54'	50'	47'	44'	41'	39'	37'	35'	33'	32'	—	—	—
3	1° 46'	1° 36'	1° 29'	1° 22'	1° 16'	1° 11'	1° 6'	1° 1'	57'	53'	50'	47'	44'	42'	40'	38'	36'	—	—
3·5	2° 5'	1° 54'	1° 44'	1° 36'	1° 30'	1° 24'	1° 17'	1° 11'	1° 6'	1° 2'	58'	55'	52'	49'	47'	45'	43'	41'	—
4	2° 24'	2° 11'	2° 0'	1° 51'	1° 43'	1° 36'	1° 29'	1° 22'	1° 16'	1° 11'	1° 7'	1° 3'	1° 0'	57'	54'	51'	49'	47'	45'
4·5	2° 44'	2° 29'	2° 16'	2° 6'	1° 57'	1° 49'	1° 40'	1° 33'	1° 26'	1° 21'	1° 16'	1° 11'	1° 7'	1° 4'	1° 1'	58'	55'	53'	51'
5	3° 4'	2° 47'	2° 33'	2° 21'	2° 11'	2° 2'	1° 52'	1° 44'	1° 36'	1° 30'	1° 24'	1° 20'	1° 15'	1° 11'	1° 8'	1° 5'	1° 2'	59'	57'
5·5	3° 24'	3° 5'	2° 50'	2° 37'	2° 25'	2° 15'	2° 4'	1° 55'	1° 47'	1° 40'	1° 33'	1° 28'	1° 23'	1° 19'	1° 15'	1° 11'	1° 8'	1° 5'	1° 2'
6	3° 45'	3° 24'	3° 7'	2° 52'	2° 40'	2° 29'	2° 16'	2° 6'	1° 57'	1° 49'	1° 42'	1° 36'	1° 31'	1° 26'	1° 22'	1° 18'	1° 15'	1° 11'	1° 8'
6·5	4° 7'	3° 43'	3° 24'	3° 8'	2° 54'	2° 42'	2° 29'	2° 17'	2° 8'	1° 59'	1° 52'	1° 45'	1° 39'	1° 34'	1° 29'	1° 25'	1° 21'	1° 17'	1° 14'
7	4° 29'	4° 3'	3° 42'	3° 24'	3° 9'	2° 56'	2° 41'	2° 29'	2° 18'	2° 9'	2° 1'	1° 54'	1° 47'	1° 42'	1° 36'	1° 32'	1° 28'	1° 24'	1° 20'
7·5	4° 51'	4° 23'	4° 0'	3° 41'	3° 24'	3° 10'	2° 54'	2° 40'	2° 29'	2° 19'	2° 10'	2° 2'	1° 55'	1° 49'	1° 44'	1° 39'	1° 34'	1° 30'	1° 26'
8	5° 14'	4° 43'	4° 18'	3° 57'	3° 40'	3° 24'	3° 7'	2° 52'	2° 40'	2° 29'	2° 19'	2° 11'	2° 4'	1° 57'	1° 51'	1° 46'	1° 41'	1° 36'	1° 32'
10	6° 51'	6° 9'	5° 36'	5° 7'	4° 43'	4° 23'	4° 0'	3° 41'	3° 24'	3° 10'	2° 58'	2° 47'	2° 37'	2° 29'	2° 21'	2° 14'	2° 8'	2° 2'	1° 57'
12	—	7° 43'	6° 59'	6° 22'	5° 52'	5° 26'	4° 56'	4° 32'	4° 11'	3° 53'	3° 38'	3° 24'	3° 12'	3° 2'	2° 52'	2° 44'	2° 36'	2° 29'	2° 22'

[Alfred Herbert Ltd.]

*BRITISH STANDARD PRECISION HEXAGON BOLTS, SCREWS, NUTS AND PLAIN WASHERS**

In 1951 the British Standards Institution issued a new Specification, superseding the earlier one of 1944, given in the last edition of this volume.   It refers to bolts, nuts and screws made to given mechanical properties and tolerances.   Further, in place of the $\frac{3}{16}$ in. B.S.W. and B.S.F. threads, the Institution recommends the No. 2 B.A. thread.

The Specification gives details of the materials, finish, length of bolts and screws, particulars of the screw threads and the threaded and unthreaded portion lengths, squareness of nut face to thread, chamfering, washer-facing, split-pin holes and slots, method of marking and fitting bolts.   It contains also a section giving the dimensions of split cotter pins and plain washers.   The last section deals with methods of inspection and testing.

Length of Bolts and Screws.—The nominal length is the distance from the underside of the head to the extreme end of the shank, including any chamfering or radius.   Various tolerances are tabulated in regard to these lengths.

Screw Threads.—For bolts and screws the threads may be either cut or rolled but must conform to the limits and tolerances for " medium fit," specified in B.S. 84, Screw threads of Whitworth form or B.S. 93, British Association, with tolerances for sizes Nos. 0 to 15 B.A.   In regard to nuts, the screw threads must conform to the limits and tolerances for " free fit " specified in B.S. 84, and in the case of 2 B.A. in B.S. 93.

Length of Screwed Thread.—In the case of long bolts, the length of thread is the distance from the end of the bolt to the leading face of the nut which has been screwed on as far as possible by hand.

For short bolts the length is unspecified but they should be threaded to leave a limited length of unthreaded shank under the head.

Screws should be threaded to allow a nut being screwed by hand to within a distance from the underside of the head of twice the pitch for B.S.F. and B.S.W. threads and from $1\frac{1}{2}$ to $2\frac{1}{2}$ times the pitch for B.A. threads.

* Abstract from B.S. 1083—1951.

B.S. HEXAGON HEAD BOLTS AND SCREWS *

Nominal Size D	Number of Threads per Inch		Diameter of Unthreaded Portion of Shank B		Width Across Flats A		Width Across Corners C	Diameter of Washer Face E		Thickness of Head F		Radius Under Head R	Split Cotter Pin Holes — Diameter of Hole		Drill No. or Letter‡	Max. Off-centre Distance between Centre Line of Hole and Thread
	B.S.W.	B.S.F.	Max.	Min.	Max.	Min.	Max.	Max.	Min.	Max.	Min.	Max.	Max.	Min.		Max.
			In.	In.	In.	In.	In.	In.	In.	In.	In.	In.	In.	In.		In.
2 B.A.	—	—	0·185 0	0·182 0	0·324	0·319	0·37	0·319	0·309	0·139	0·132	0·015			—	—
1/4	20	26	0·250 0	0·246 5	0·445	0·438	0·51	0·428	0·418	0·19	0·18	1/32	0·075	0·070	50	0·006
5/16	18	22	0·312 5	0·309 0	0·525	0·518	0·61	0·508	0·498	0·22	0·21	1/32	0·075	0·070	50	0·006
3/8	16	20	0·375 0	0·371 5	0·600	0·592	0·69	0·582	0·572	0·27	0·26	1/32	0·075	0·070	50	0·006
7/16	14	18	0·437 5	0·433 5	0·710	0·702	0·82	0·690	0·680	0·33	0·32	1/32	0·110	0·104	37	0·007
1/2	12	16	0·500 0	0·496 0	0·820	0·812	0·95	0·800	0·790	0·38	0·37	1/32	0·110	0·104	37	0·007
9/16	12	16	0·562 5	0·558 5	0·920	0·912	1·06	0·900	0·890	0·44	0·43	1/32	0·143	0·136	29	0·008
5/8	11	14	0·625 0	0·619 0	1·010	1·000	1·17	0·985	0·975	0·49	0·48	1/32	0·143	0·136	29	0·008
3/4	10	12	0·750 0	0·744 0	1·200	1·190	1·39	1·175	1·165	0·60	0·59	1/32	0·174	0·166	19	0·009
7/8	9	11	0·875 0	0·867 0	1·300	1·288	1·50	1·273	1·263	0·66	0·65	1/32	0·174	0·166	19	0·009
1	8	10	1·000 0	0·992 0	1·480	1·468	1·71	1·453	1·443	0·77	0·76	3/64	0·208	0·199	8	0·010
1 1/8	7	9	1·125 0	1·117 0	1·670	1·658	1·93	1·638	1·628	0·88	0·87	3/64	0·208	0·199	8	0·010
1 1/4	7	9	1·250 0	1·242 0	1·860	1·845	2·15	1·825	1·815	0·98	0·96	3/64	0·238	0·228	1	0·011
1 3/8†	—	8	1·375 0	1·365 0	2·050	2·035	2·37	2·015	2·005	1·09	1·07	3/64	0·238	0·228	1	0·011
1 1/2	6	8	1·500 0	1·490 0	2·220	2·200	2·56	2·180	2·170	1·20	1·18	3/64	0·238	0·228	G	0·011
1 3/4	5	7	1·750 0	1·740 0	2·580	2·555	2·98	2·530	2·520	1·42	1·40	3/64	0·271	0·261	G	0·012
2	4·5	7	2·000 0	1·990 0	2·760	2·735	3·19	2·710	2·700	1·53	1·51	3/64	0·333	0·323	P	0·015

* B.S. 1083—1951.

† Not standard with B.S.W. thread.

‡ In deference to past general usage drill number and letter sizes are included in this table, but B.S. 328—1950 recommends that these drills be regarded as non-preferred and advises the use of alternative metric sizes.

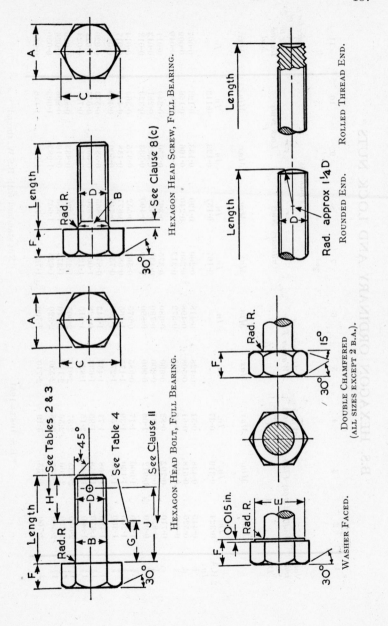

Hexagon Head Screw, Full Bearing.

Rolled Thread End.

Rounded End.

Rad. approx 1¼D

Hexagon Head Bolt, Full Bearing.

See Tables 2 & 3

See Table 4

See Clause 11

Double Chamfered
(all sizes except 2 b.a.).

Washer Faced.

0·015 in.

B.S. HEXAGON ORDINARY AND LOCK NUTS *

1	2	3	4	5	6	7	8	9	10	11
	Width Across Flats A		Width Across Corners C	Diameter of Washer Face B		Thickness				Tolerance for Squareness of Face to Thread Nut
						Ordinary Nuts E		Lock Nuts F		
Nominal Size D	Max.	Min.	Max.	Max.	Min.	Max.	Min.	Max.	Min.	Max.
	In.	In.	In.	In.	In.	In.	In.	In.	In.	In.
2 B.A. In.	0·324	0·319	0·37	—	—	0·167	0·157	0·123	0·113	—
1/4	0·445	0·438	0·51	0·428	0·418	0·200	0·190	0·133	0·123	0·007
5/16	0·525	0·518	0·61	0·508	0·498	0·250	0·240	0·166	0·156	0·009
3/8	0·600	0·592	0·69	0·582	0·572	0·312	0·302	0·208	0·198	0·010
7/16	0·710	0·702	0·82	0·690	0·680	0·375	0·365	0·250	0·240	0·011
1/2	0·820	0·812	0·95	0·800	0·790	0·437	0·427	0·291	0·281	0·013
9/16	0·920	0·912	1·06	0·900	0·890	0·500	0·490	0·333	0·323	0·013
5/8	1·010	1·000	1·17	0·985	0·975	0·562	0·552	0·375	0·365	0·014
3/4	1·200	1·190	1·39	1·175	1·165	0·687	0·677	0·458	0·448	0·017
7/8	1·300	1·288	1·50	1·273	1·263	0·750	0·740	0·500	0·490	0·020
1	1·480	1·468	1·71	1·453	1·443	0·875	0·865	0·583	0·573	0·020
1 1/8	1·670	1·658	1·93	1·638	1·628	1·000	0·990	0·666	0·656	0·024
1 1/4	1·860	1·845	2·15	1·825	1·815	1·125	1·105	0·750	0·730	0·024
1 3/8†	2·050	2·035	2·37	2·015	2·005	1·250	1·230	0·833	0·813	0·026
1 1/2	2·220	2·200	2·56	2·180	2·170	1·375	1·355	0·916	0·896	0·026
1 3/4†	2·580	2·555	2·98	2·530	2·520	1·625	1·605	1·083	1·063	0·030
2	2·760	2·735	3·19	2·710	2·700	1·750	1·730	1·166	1·146	0·030

* B.S. 1083—1951. † Not standard with B.S.W. thread.

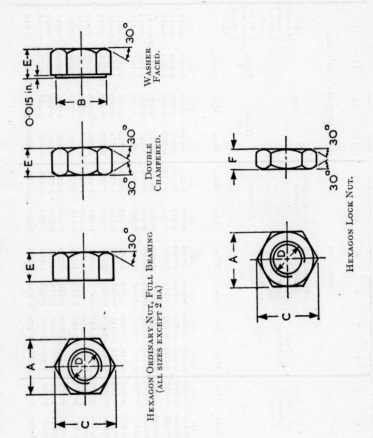

HEXAGON ORDINARY NUT, FULL BEARING
(ALL SIZES EXCEPT 2 BA)

DOUBLE CHAMFERED.

WASHER FACED.

HEXAGON LOCK NUT.

B.S. HEXAGON SLOTTED NUTS AND CASTLE NUTS *

1	2	3	4	5	6	7	8	9	10	11	12	13	14	15	16
	Slotted Nuts				Castle Nuts						Slotted and Castle Nuts				
Nominal Size D	Thickness G		Lower Face of Nut to Bottom of Slots H		Total Thickness J		Thickness of Hexagon Portion and from Lower Face of Nut to Bottom of Slots K		Castellated Portion Diameter L		Slots Width M		Slots Depth N	Max. Off-centre Distance Between Centre Line of Slots and Tapped Hole	Tolerance for Squareness of Face to Thread of Nut
	Max.	Min.	Max.	Min.	Max.	Min.	Max.	Min.	Max.	Min.	Max.	Min.	Approx.		Max.
In.	*In.*	*In.*	*In.*	*In.*	*In.*	*In.*	*In.*	*In.*	*In.*	*In.*	*In.*	*In.*	*In.*	*In.*	*In.*
¼	0·260	0·250	0·170	0·160	0·290	0·280	0·200	0·190	0·430	0·425	0·100	0·090	0·090	0·012	0·007
⁵⁄₁₆	0·280	0·270	0·190	0·180	0·340	0·330	0·250	0·240	0·510	0·500	0·100	0·090	0·090	0·012	0·009
⅜	0·312	0·302	0·222	0·212	0·402	0·392	0·312	0·302	0·585	0·575	0·100	0·090	0·090	0·012	0·010
⁷⁄₁₆	0·375	0·365	0·235	0·225	0·515	0·505	0·375	0·365	0·695	0·685	0·135	0·125	0·140	0·014	0·011
½	0·437	0·427	0·297	0·287	0·577	0·567	0·437	0·427	0·805	0·795	0·135	0·125	0·140	0·014	0·013
⁹⁄₁₆	0·500	0·490	0·313	0·303	0·687	0·677	0·500	0·490	0·905	0·895	0·175	0·165	0·187	0·017	0·013
⅝	0·562	0·552	0·375	0·365	0·749	0·739	0·562	0·562	0·995	0·985	0·175	0·165	0·187	0·017	0·014
¾	0·687	0·677	0·453	0·443	0·921	0·911	0·687	0·677	1·185	1·165	0·218	0·208	0·234	0·022	0·017
⅞	0·750	0·740	0·516	0·506	0·984	0·974	0·750	0·740	1·285	1·265	0·218	0·208	0·234	0·022	0·020
1	0·875	0·865	0·595	0·585	1·155	1·145	0·875	0·865	1·465	1·445	0·260	0·250	0·280	0·027	0·020
1⅛	1·000	0·990	0·720	0·710	1·280	1·270	1·000	0·990	1·655	1·635	0·260	0·250	0·280	0·027	0·024
1¼	1·125	1·105	0·797	0·777	1·453	1·433	1·125	1·105	1·845	1·825	0·300	0·290	0·328	0·030	0·024
1⅜†	1·250	1·230	0·922	0·902	1·578	1·558	1·250	1·230	2·035	2·015	0·300	0·290	0·328	0·030	0·026
1½	1·375	1·355	1·047	1·027	1·703	1·683	1·375	1·355	2·200	2·180	0·300	0·290	0·328	0·030	0·026
1¾	1·625	1·605	1·250	1·230	2·000	1·980	1·625	1·605	2·555	2·535	0·343	0·333	0·375	0·034	0·030
2	1·750	1·730	1·282	1·262	2·218	2·198	1·750	1·730	2·735	2·715	0·426	0·416	0·468	0·042	0·030

* B.S. 1083—1195.
† Not standard with B.S.W. thread.   For widths across flats, width across corners, and diameter of washer face see table on page 186.

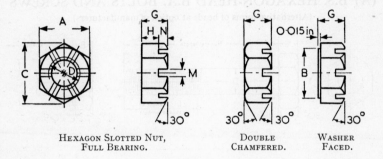

HEXAGON SLOTTED NUT, FULL BEARING.   DOUBLE CHAMFERED.   WASHER FACED.

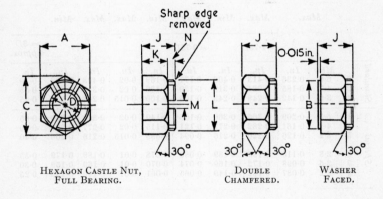

Sharp edge removed

HEXAGON CASTLE NUT, FULL BEARING.   DOUBLE CHAMFERED.   WASHER FACED.

(A) B.S. HEXAGON-HEAD B.A. BOLTS AND SCREWS

(Alternative forms of heads at option of manufacturers)

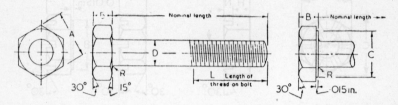

1	2	3	4	5	6	7	8	9	10	11	12
B.A. No.		Diameter of Shank and Major Diameter of Thread D		Width across Flats A		Thickness of Head B		Radius under Head R	Diameter of Washer Face C		Length of Thread on Bolts L
		Max.		Max.	Min.	Max.	Min.	Max.	Max.	Min.	
				= 1·75D		= 0·75D					= 3D approx.
Standard	0	Mm. 6·0	In. 0·236	In. 0·413	In. 0·408	In. 0·177	In. 0·169	In. 0·02	In. 0·408	In. 0·398	In. 0·70
	2	4·7	0·185	0·324	0·319	0·139	0·132	0·02	0·319	0·309	0·55
	4	3·6	0·142	0·248	0·243	0·106	0·100	0·015	0·243	0·233	0·45
Special	1	5·3	0·209	0·365	0·360	0·156	0·149	0·02	0·360	0·350	0·65
	3	4·1	0·161	0·282	0·277	0·121	0·115	0·02	0·277	0·267	0·50
	5	3·2	0·126	0·220	0·216	0·094	0·089	0·015	0·216	0·206	0·40
	6	2·8	0·110	0·193	0·189	0·083	0·078	0·01	0·189	0·179	0·35
	7	2·5	0·098	0·172	0·169	0·074	0·070	0·01	0·169	0·159	0·30
	8	2·2	0·087	0·152	0·149	0·065	0·061	0·01	0·149	0·139	0·25

(B) BRITISH STANDARD B.A. ORDINARY AND THIN NUTS

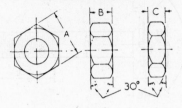

1	2	3	4	5	6	7	8	9	10
		Nominal Diameter of Thread *D*		Width across Flats *A*		Thickness			
						Ordinary Nuts *B*		Thin (or Lock) Nuts *C*	
B.A. No.		Nominal		Max.	Min.	Max.	Min.	Max.	Min.
				= 1·75D		See Note.		= ⅔D	
		Mm.	In.	In.	In.	In.	In.	In.	In.
Standard	0	6·0	0·236	0·413	0·408	0·213	0·203	0·157	0·147
	2	4·7	0·185	0·324	0·319	0·167	0·157	0·123	0·113
	4	3·6	0·142	0·248	0·243	0·135	0·125	0·094	0·084
	6	2·8	0·110	0·193	0·189	0·105	0·095	0·073	0·063
	8	2·2	0·087	0·152	0·149	0·082	0·075	—	—
	10	1·7	0·067	0·117	0·114	0·064	0·057	—	—
	12	1·3	0·051	0·090	0·088	0·049	0·044	—	—
Special	1	5·3	0·209	0·365	0·360	0·188	0·178	0·139	0·129
	3	4·1	0·161	0·282	0·277	0·153	0·143	0·108	0·098
	5	3·2	0·126	0·220	0·216	0·120	0·110	0·084	0·074
	7	2·5	0·098	0·172	0·169	0·094	0·087	—	—
	9	1·9	0·075	0·131	0·128	0·071	0·064	—	—
	11	1·5	0·059	0·103	0·101	0·056	0·051	—	—
	13	1·2	0·047	0 083	0·081	0·045	0·040	—	—
	14	1 0	0·039	0 069	0·067	0·037	0·032	—	—
	15	0 9	0·035	0·062	0 060	0 034	0·029	—	—
	16	0·79	0·031	0·056	0 054	0·029	0 024	—	—

Note.—The maximum thicknesses for ordinary nuts, sizes **0, 1** and **2** B.A., are derived from the formula $B = 0.9D$; for smaller sizes the formula $B = 0.95D$ has been used.

E.W.D.—7

(C) BRITISH STANDARD B.A. COUNTERSUNK-HEAD BOLTS AND SCREWS

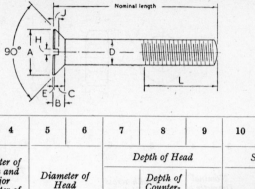

1	2	3	4	5	6	7	8	9	10	11
		Diameter of Shank and Major Diameter of Thread D		Diameter of Head A		Depth of Head			Slot	
	B.A. No.					Total B	Depth of Countersunk Portion C	E	Width H	Depth J
		Max.		Max.	Min.	Nom.	Nom.	Max.	Nom.	Nom.
				See Note			$= \frac{3}{4}D$ approx.			
		Mm.	In.	In.	In.	In.	In.	In.	In.	In.
Standard	0	6·0	0·236	0·413	0·403	0·099	0·089	0·010	0·048	0·052
	2	4·7	0·185	0·319	0·309	0·077	0·067	0·010	0·040	0·043
	4	3·6	0·142	0·252	0·242	0·065	0·055	0·010	0·032	0·032
	6	2·8	0·110	0·194	0·184	0·051	0·042	0·009	0·024	0·025
	8	2·2	0·087	0·158	0·148	0·044	0·036	0·008	0·024	0·020
	10	1·7	0·067	0·111	0·106	0·029	0·022	0·007	0·018	0·016
	12	1·3	0·051	0·096	0·091	0·029	0·023	0·006	0·0124	0·014
Special	1	5·3	0·209	0·365	0·355	0·088	0·078	0·010	0·048	0·047
	3	4·1	0·161	0·285	0·275	0·072	0·062	0·010	0·040	0·036
	5	3·2	0·126	0·221	0·211	0·058	0 048	0·010	0·032	0·030
	7	2·5	0·098	0·175	0·165	0·048	0·039	0·009	0·024	0·022
	9	1·9	0·075	0·127	0·122	0·034	0·026	0·008	0·018	0·018
	11	1·5	0·059	0·111	0·106	0·033	0·026	0·007	0·018	0·015
	13	1·2	0·047	0·080	0·075	0·023	0·017	0·006	0·0124	0·013
	14	1·0	0·039	0·064	0·059	0·019	0·013	0·006	0·0124	0·011
	15	0·9	0·035	0·064	0·059	0·021	0·015	0·006	0·0116	0·007
	16	0·79	0·031	0·058	0·054	0·019	0·014	0·005	0·010	0·007

Note.—The diameters in Col. 5 are based on the relationship $A = 1·75D$, but the limits have been so selected as to permit of the use of readily available commercial diameters of round bars.

(D) BRITISH STANDARD B.A. ROUND-HEAD BOLTS AND SCREWS

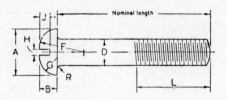

1	2	3	4	5	6	7	8	9	10	11
B.A. No.		Diameter of Shank and Major Diameter of Thread D		Diameter of Head A		Depth of Head B		Radius under Head R	Slot	
									Width H	Depth J
		Max.		Max.	Min.	Max.	Min.	Max.	Nom.	Nom.
				See Note		= 0·7D				= 0·42D
		Mm.	In.	In.	In.	In.	In.	In.	In.	In.
Standard	0	6·0	0·236	0·413	0·403	0·165	0·157	0·02	0·048	0·099
	2	4·7	0·185	0·319	0·309	0·130	0·123	0·02	0·040	0·078
	4	3·6	0·142	0·252	0·242	0·099	0·093	0·015	0·032	0·060
	6	2·8	0·110	0·194	0·184	0·077	0·072	0·01	0·024	0·046
	8	2·2	0·087	0·158	0·148	0·061	0·057	0·01	0·024	0·037
	10	1·7	0·067	0·111	0·106	0·047	0·043	0·01	0·018	0·028
	12	1·3	0·051	0·096	0·091	0·036	0·033	0·005	0·0124	0·021
Special	1	5·3	0·209	0·365	0·355	0·146	0·139	0·02	0·048	0·088
	3	4·1	0·161	0·285	0·275	0·113	0·107	0·02	0·040	0·068
	5	3·2	0·126	0·221	0·211	0·088	0·083	0·015	0·032	0·053
	7	2·5	0·098	0·175	0·165	0·069	0·065	0·01	0·024	0·041
	9	1·9	0·075	0·127	0·122	0·052	0·048	0·01	0·018	0·032
	11	1·5	0·059	0·111	0·106	0·041	0·038	0·005	0·018	0·025
	13	1·2	0·047	0·080	0·075	0·033	0·030	0·005	0·0124	0·020
	14	1·0	0·039	0·064	0·059	0·028	0·025	0·005	0·0124	0·016
	15	0·9	0·035	0·064	0·059	0·025	0·022	0·005	0·0116	0·015
	16	0·79	0·031	0·058	0·054	0·022	0·019	0·005	0·010	0·013

Notes.—Shape of Head. The shape of the head shall closely approximate to a half ellipse. This shape is given to a very close approximation by radii *F* and *G* equal to dimensions *A* and *B* respectively.

(E) BRITISH STANDARD B.A. CHEESE-HEAD BOLTS AND SCREWS

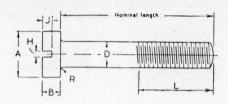

1	2	3	4	5	6	7	8	9	10	11
	B.A. No.	Diameter of Shank and Major Diameter of Thread D		Diameter of Head A		Depth of Head B		Radius under Head R	Slot	
									Width H	Depth J
		Max.		Max.	Min.	Max.	Min.	Max.	Nom.	Nom.
						= 0·7D				= $\frac{3}{8}D$
		Mm.	In.	In.	In.	In.	In.	In.	In.	In.
Standard	0	6·0	0·236	0·413	0·403	0·165	0·157	0·02	0·048	0·089
	2	4·7	0·185	0·319	0·309	0·130	0·123	0·02	0·040	0·069
	4	3·6	0·142	0·252	0·242	0·099	0·093	0·015	0·032	0·053
	6	2·8	0·110	0·194	0·184	0·077	0·072	0·01	0·024	0·041
	8	2·2	0·087	0·158	0·148	0·061	0·057	0·01	0·024	0·032
	10	1·7	0·067	0·111	0·106	0·047	0·043	0·01	0·018	0·025
	12	1·3	0·051	0·096	0·091	0·036	0·033	0·005	0·0124	0·019
Special	1	5·3	0·209	0·365	0·355	0·146	0·139	0·02	0·048	0·078
	3	4·1	0·161	0·285	0·275	0·113	0·107	0·02	0·040	0·061
	5	3·2	0·126	0·221	0·211	0·088	0·083	0·015	0·032	0·047
	7	2·5	0·098	0·175	0·165	0·069	0·065	0·01	0·024	0·037
	9	1·9	0·075	0·127	0·122	0·052	0·048	0·01	0·018	0·028
	11	1·5	0·059	0·111	0·106	0·041	0·038	0·005	0·018	0·022
	13	1·2	0·047	0·080	0·075	0·033	0·030	0·005	0·0124	0·018
	14	1·0	0·039	0·064	0·059	0·028	0·025	0·005	0·0124	0·015
	15	0·9	0·035	0·064	0·059	0·025	0·022	0·005	0·0116	0·013
	16	0·79	0·031	0·058	0·054	0·022	0·019	0·005	0·010	0·012

BRITISH STANDARD WING NUTS *

British Standard wing nuts in cold-forged mild steel or brass, hot brass or other non-ferrous stampings, malleable-iron castings and hot-steel stampings are specified by the nominal size of screw thread, e.g. " British Standard 2 B.A. Wing Nut." Their dimensions are given in the following Tables (A) and (B). The wing nuts must be supplied smooth and free from fins and sharp edges. The bases of the nuts must be flat and square with the axis of the screw thread.

(A) Dimensions of Wing Nuts

(Hot-brass or non-ferrous stampings. Malleable-iron castings. Hot-steel stampings.)

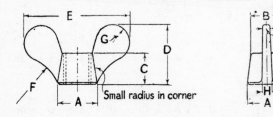

Small radius in corner

1	2	3	4	5	6	7	8	9	10	11	12
	Nominal Size of Screw Thread										
No.†	*B.S.W. and B.S.F.*	*B.A.*	A	B	C	D	E	F	G	H	J
	In.		*In.*	*In.*	*In.*	*In.*	*In.*	*In.*	*In.*	*In.*	*In.*
1	$\frac{1}{8}$	4 and 5	$\frac{11}{32}$	$\frac{1}{4}$	$\frac{9}{32}$	$\frac{17}{32}$	$\frac{7}{8}$	$\frac{3}{4}$	$\frac{3}{64}$	$\frac{3}{32}$	$\frac{1}{16}$
2	$\frac{3}{16}$	2 and 3	$\frac{13}{32}$	$\frac{5}{16}$	$\frac{11}{32}$	$\frac{19}{32}$	1	$\frac{3}{4}$	$\frac{5}{32}$	$\frac{3}{32}$	$\frac{1}{16}$
3	$\frac{1}{4}$	0 and 1	$\frac{1}{2}$	$\frac{3}{8}$	$\frac{7}{16}$	$\frac{23}{32}$	$1\frac{3}{16}$	$\frac{3}{4}$	$\frac{3}{16}$	$\frac{3}{32}$	$\frac{1}{16}$
4	$\frac{5}{16}$	—	$\frac{5}{8}$	$\frac{15}{32}$	$\frac{1}{2}$	$\frac{22}{32}$	$1\frac{1}{2}$	$\frac{3}{4}$	$\frac{1}{4}$	$\frac{1}{8}$	$\frac{3}{32}$
5	$\frac{3}{8}$	—	$\frac{11}{16}$	$\frac{9}{16}$	$\frac{9}{16}$	1	$1\frac{3}{4}$	$\frac{3}{4}$	$\frac{9}{32}$	$\frac{3}{16}$	$\frac{1}{8}$
6	$\frac{7}{16}$	—	$\frac{3}{4}$	$\frac{5}{8}$	$\frac{19}{32}$	$1\frac{1}{4}$	2	1	$\frac{5}{16}$	$\frac{3}{16}$	$\frac{1}{8}$
7	$\frac{1}{2}$	—	$\frac{7}{8}$	$\frac{11}{16}$	$\frac{21}{32}$	$1\frac{1}{4}$	$2\frac{5}{16}$	1	$\frac{3}{8}$	$\frac{7}{32}$	$\frac{5}{32}$
8	$\frac{5}{8}$	—	1	$\frac{13}{16}$	$\frac{3}{4}$	$1\frac{7}{16}$	$2\frac{1}{2}$	$1\frac{1}{4}$	$\frac{13}{32}$	$\frac{1}{4}$	$\frac{5}{16}$
9	$\frac{3}{4}$	—	$1\frac{1}{4}$	$1\frac{1}{16}$	$\frac{7}{8}$	$1\frac{5}{8}$	$3\frac{1}{16}$	$1\frac{1}{4}$	$\frac{15}{32}$	$\frac{9}{32}$	$\frac{7}{32}$

* Abstract from B.S. No. 856—1939.

† The numbers given in this column are the customary trade designations for the sizes of the nut blanks.

(B) Dimensions of Wing Nuts

(Mild steel, cold forged.   Brass, cold forged)

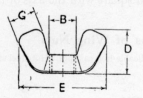
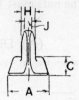

1	2	3	4	5	6	7	8	9	10	11
No.*	Nominal Size of Screw Thread		A	B	C	D	E	G	H	J
	B.S.W. and B.S.F.	B.A.								
	In.		In.	In.	In.	In.	In.	In.	In.	In.
1	$\frac{1}{8}$	4 and 5	$\frac{5}{16}$	$\frac{13}{64}$	$\frac{1}{8}$	$\frac{11}{32}$	$\frac{21}{32}$	$\frac{13}{64}$	$\frac{3}{32}$	$\frac{3}{64}$
2	$\frac{3}{16}$	2 and 3	$\frac{27}{64}$	$\frac{15}{64}$	$\frac{11}{64}$	$\frac{7}{16}$	$\frac{27}{32}$	$\frac{17}{64}$	$\frac{1}{8}$	$\frac{5}{64}$
3	$\frac{1}{4}$	0 and 1	$\frac{31}{64}$	$\frac{9}{16}$	$\frac{13}{64}$	$\frac{1}{2}$	$1\frac{1}{16}$	$\frac{5}{16}$	$\frac{5}{32}$	$\frac{3}{32}$
4	$\frac{5}{16}$	—	$\frac{9}{16}$	$\frac{3}{8}$	$\frac{15}{64}$	$\frac{5}{8}$	$1\frac{7}{32}$	$\frac{3}{8}$	$\frac{3}{16}$	$\frac{7}{64}$
5	$\frac{3}{8}$	—	$\frac{43}{64}$	$\frac{15}{32}$	$\frac{17}{64}$	$\frac{23}{32}$	$1\frac{13}{32}$	$\frac{7}{16}$	$\frac{7}{32}$	$\frac{1}{8}$
6	$\frac{7}{16}$	—	$\frac{7}{8}$	$\frac{5}{8}$	$\frac{29}{64}$	$\frac{29}{32}$	$1\frac{7}{8}$	$\frac{19}{32}$	$\frac{19}{64}$	$\frac{11}{64}$
7	$\frac{1}{2}$	—	$\frac{7}{8}$	$\frac{5}{8}$	$\frac{3}{8}$	$\frac{29}{32}$	$1\frac{7}{8}$	$\frac{19}{32}$	$\frac{19}{64}$	$\frac{11}{64}$
8	$\frac{5}{8}$	—	$1\frac{3}{32}$	$\frac{7}{8}$	$\frac{17}{32}$	$1\frac{1}{8}$	$2\frac{1}{16}$	$\frac{11}{16}$	$\frac{3}{8}$	$\frac{1}{4}$
9	$\frac{3}{4}$	—	$1\frac{5}{32}$	$\frac{7}{8}$	$\frac{17}{32}$	$1\frac{3}{8}$	$2\frac{11}{16}$	$\frac{11}{16}$	$\frac{3}{8}$	$\frac{7}{16}$

* The numbers given in this column are the customary trade designations for the sizes of the nut blanks.

BRITISH STANDARD BRIGHT SCREWS *

The British Standards Institution has standardised the dimensions and other requirements of bright countersunk-, round-and cheese-head screws with British Standard Whitworth and British Standard Fine Threads.

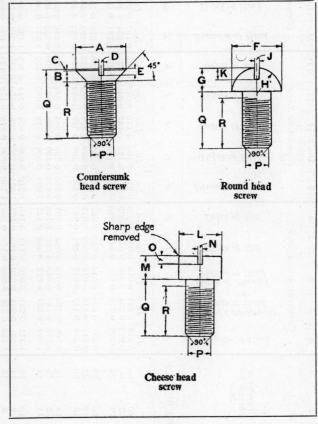

Countersunk head screw

Round head screw

Cheese head screw

Fig. 1.

* Abstract, B.S. 450—1932.

DIMENSIONS OF BRIGHT COUNTERSUNK, ROUND, AND CHEESE-HEAD SCREWS

1	2	3	Countersunk-head Screw					Round-head Screw					Cheese-head Screw				18
	4	5	6	7	8	9	10	11	12	13	14	15	16	17	
Nominal Size and Maximum Diameter of Screw	Number of Threads per Inch		Diameter of Head	Depth of Countersunk Portion of Head	Depth of Parallel Portion of Head	Width of Slot	Depth of Slot	Diameter of Head	Depth of Head	Radius of Head	Width of Slot	Depth of Slot	Diameter of Head	Depth of Head	Width of Slot	Depth of Slot	Nominal Size and Maximum Diameter of Screw
	B.S.W.	B.S.F.	A	B	C	D	E	F	G	H	J	K	L	M	N	O	
_In._			_In._	_In._	_In._	_In._	_In._	_In._	_In._	_In._	_In._	_In._	_In._	_In._	_In._	_In._	_In._
1/8	40	—	0.219	0.047	0.010	0.032	0.033	0.219	0.100	0.110	0.032	0.050	0.187	0.100	0.032	0.040	1/8
5/32	32	—	0.273	0.058	0.010	0.040	0.039	0.273	0.125	0.137	0.040	0.062	0.234	0.125	0.040	0.050	5/32
3/16	24	32	0.328	0.070	0.010	0.040	0.045	0.328	0.150	0.165	0.040	0.075	0.281	0.150	0.040	0.060	3/16
1/4	20	26	0.437	0.094	0.010	0.062	0.057	0.437	0.200	0.220	0.062	0.100	0.375	0.200	0.062	0.080	1/4
5/16	18	22	0.547	0.117	0.015	0.062	0.073	0.547	0.250	0.274	0.062	0.125	0.469	0.250	0.062	0.100	5/16
3/8	16	20	0.656	0.141	0.015	0.084	0.085	0.656	0.300	0.329	0.084	0.150	0.562	0.300	0.084	0.120	3/8
7/16	14	18	0.766	0.164	0.015	0.084	0.097	0.766	0.350	0.384	0.084	0.175	0.656	0.350	0.084	0.123	7/16
1/2	12	16	0.875	0.187	0.015	0.093	0.108	0.875	0.400	0.439	0.093	0.200	0.750	0.400	0.093	0.140	1/2
9/16	11	14	1.094	0.234	0.020	0.093	0.137	1.094	0.500	0.549	0.093	0.250	0.937	0.500	0.093	0.175	9/16
5/8	10	12	1.312	0.281	0.020	0.144	0.160	1.312	0.600	0.659	0.144	0.300	1.125	0.600	0.144	0.210	5/8
3/4	9	11	1.531	0.328	0.020	0.160	0.184	1.531	0.700	0.769	0.160	0.350	1.312	0.700	0.160	0.245	3/4
1	8	10	1.750	0.375	0.020	0.176	0.207	1.750	0.800	0.878	0.176	0.400	1.500	0.800	0.176	0.280	1

BRITISH STANDARD SET (OPEN-ENDED)
SPANNERS *

The British Standard B.S.W. and B.S.F. open-ended carbon-steel spanners are specified for dimensions, proof test and the angle between the head and shank, namely 15°.

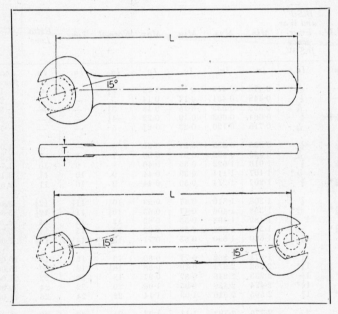

FIGS. 2 and 3.—BRITISH STANDARD SET (OPEN-ENDED) SPANNERS.

* B.S. 192—1924. Dimensions of Spanners.

DIMENSIONS AND PROOF TEST MOMENTS

1	2	3	4	5	6	7	8	9	10
Nominal Size of Spanner (Diameter of Corresponding Bolt)		Width between Jaws		Thickness of Spanner Head (T. Figs. 3 and 4)		Length of Spanner (L. Figs. 3 and 4)			Turning Moment for Proof Test
B.S.W.	B.S.F. and War Emergency B.S.W.	Min.	Max.	Min.	Max.	Normal	Long	Extra Long	
In.	In.	In.	In.	In.	In.	In.	In.	In.	Inch-pounds
—	7/32	0·416	0·419	0·10	0·12	2¼	—	—	110
—	¼	0·448	0·451	0·12	0·14	3	—	—	230
¼	5/16	0·529	0·533	0·15	0·18	3¾	—	—	380
5/16	⅜	0·604	0·608	0·19	0·22	4½	—	—	560
⅜	7/16	0·715	0·720	0·23	0·27	5	—	—	780
7/16	½	0·825	0·830	0·27	0·31	6	—	—	1,000
½	9/16	0·926	0 932	0·31	0·36	7	8	9	1,300
9/16	⅝	1·016	1·022	0·35	0·40	8	9	10	1,700
⅝	11/16 *	1·107	1·114	0·39	0·44	9	10	11	2,100
11/16 *	¾	1·207	1·214	0·39	0·44	9	10	11	2,500
¾	⅞	1·308	1·316	0·47	0·53	10½	11½	12½	3,100
13/16 *	15/16 *	1·398	1·406	0·47	0·53	10½	11½	12½	3,800
⅞	1	1·489	1·498	0·55	0·62	12	13	14	4,700
15/16 *	—	1·589	1·598	0·55	0·62	12	13	14	5,700
1	1⅛	1·680	1·690	0·63	0·71	13½	14½	16½	7,000
1⅛	1¼	1·871	1 882	0·71	0·80	15	16½	18	10,000
1¼	1⅜ *	2·062	2 074	0·79	0·88	16½	18	20	15,000
1⅜ *	1½	2·233	2·246	0·87	0·97	18	20	22	21,000
1½ *	1⅝ *	2·424	2·438	0·95	1·06	20	22	24	30,000
1⅝ *	1¾	2·595	2·610	1·03	1·14	22	24	26	41,000
1¾ *	2	2·776	2·792	1·11	1·23	24	26	28	55,000
1⅞ *	—	3·037	3·054	1·22	1·35	26	28	31	75,000
2	2¼	3·168	3·186	1·27	1·40	28	31	34	96,000

* In the relevant specifications for bolts and nuts, it is recommended that, for general use, these sizes be dispensed with.

CLEARANCE DIAGRAM FOR BOLTS AND NUTS

The diagram (Fig. 4) shows the recommendations of the British Standards Institution for the guidance of designers. It indicates how near together nuts or bolt heads on a straight line may be put to permit a spanner to operate through 70° between them.

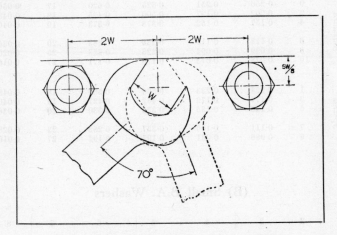

FIG. 4.—CLEARANCE DIAGRAM FOR BOLTS AND NUTS.

BRITISH STANDARD B.A. WASHERS *

British Standard B.A. Washers are designated by the number of the B.A. screw which they fit and are supplied in "large" and "small" sizes.

* Abstract, B.S. 57—1944.

(A) Large B.A. Washers

1	2	3	4	5	6	7	8
	B.A. No.	Diameter of Hole		Outside Diameter		Thickness	
		Max.	Min.	Max.	Min.		
		In.	In.	In.	In.	S.W.G.	In.
Standard	0	0·256	0·251	0·625	0·620	17	0·056
	2	0·202	0·197	0·500	0·495	18	0·048
	4	0·157	0·152	0·378	0·373	19	0·040
	6	0·123	0·118	0·288	0·283	20	0·036
	8	0·099	0·094	0·228	0·223	25	0·020
	10	0·078	0·073	0·176	0·171	27	0·0164
Special	1	0·228	0·223	0·565	0·560	18	0·048
	3	0·177	0·172	0·432	0·427	19	0·040
	5	0·140	0·135	0·335	0·330	20	0·036
	7	0·111	0·106	0·257	0·252	22	0·028
	9	0·086	0·081	0·197	0·192	27	0·0164

(B) Small B.A. Washers

1	2	3	4	5	6	7	8
	B.A. No.	Diameter of Hole		Outside Diameter		Thickness	
		Max.	Min.	Max.	Min.		
		In.	In.	In.	In.	S.W.G.	In.
Standard	0	0·256	0·251	0·500	0·495	19	0·040
	2	0·202	0·197	0·391	0·386	21	0·032
	4	0·157	0·152	0·301	0·296	22	0·028
	6	0·123	0·118	0·233	0·228	23	0·024
	8	0·099	0·094	0·185	0·180	25	0·020
Special	1	0·228	0·223	0·443	0·438	20	0·036
	3	0·177	0·172	0·341	0·336	22	0·028
	5	0·140	0·135	0·268	0·263	23	0·024
	7	0·111	0·106	0·208	0·203	24	0·022

B.S. PLAIN WASHERS*

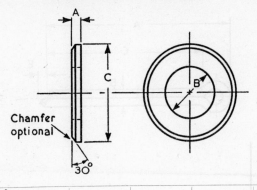

1	2	3	4	5	6
Nominal Size of Bolt or Screw D	Diameter of Hole B		Outside Diameter C	Thickness (approx.) A	
	Max.	Min.			
In.	In.	In.	In.	S.W.G.	In.
2 B.A.	0·202	0·197	½ (large)	18	0·048
2 B.A.	0·202	0·197	$\frac{25}{64}$ (small)	21	0·032
¼	0·270	0·265	$\frac{9}{16}$	17	0·056
$\frac{5}{16}$	0·333	0·328	⅝	15	0·072
⅜	0·395	0·390	¾	15	0·072
$\frac{7}{16}$	0·458	0·453	⅞	13	0·092
½	0·520	0·515	1	13	0·092
$\frac{9}{16}$	0·593	0·588	1⅛	12	0·104
⅝	0·656	0·651	1¼	11	0·116
¾	0·781	0·776	1½	9	0·144
⅞	0·906	0·901	1⅝	9	0·144
1	1·031	1·026	1⅞	8	0·160
1⅛	1·156	1·151	2⅛	7	0·176
1¼	1·281	1·276	2⅜	7	0·176
1⅜	1·406	1·401	2⅝	6	0·192
1½	1·531	1·526	2⅞	6	0·192
1¾	1·781	1·776	3⅜	5	0·212
2	2·031	2·026	3⅝	5	0·212

Note.—The dimensions given in col. 6 for the thickness of the washers shall be subject to the normal manufacturing tolerances on the sheet or strip.

* B.S. 1083—1951.

B.S. SPLIT COTTER–PINS*

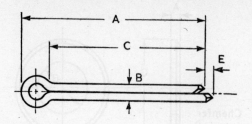

1	2	3	4	5	6
Nominal Size of Bolt or Screw D	Diameter B		Nominal Length A	Effective Length C	Additional Length of Long Leg E
	Nominal	Max.	Nominal	Approx.	Approx.
In.	In.	In.	In.	In.	In.
$\frac{1}{4}$	$\frac{1}{16}$	0·062	1	$\frac{7}{8}$	$\frac{3}{32}$
$\frac{5}{16}$	$\frac{1}{16}$	0·062	1	$\frac{7}{8}$	$\frac{3}{32}$
$\frac{3}{8}$	$\frac{1}{16}$	0·062	1	$\frac{7}{8}$	$\frac{3}{32}$
$\frac{7}{16}$	$\frac{3}{32}$	0·093	$1\frac{1}{4}$	$1\frac{1}{16}$	$\frac{3}{32}$
$\frac{1}{2}$	$\frac{3}{32}$	0·093	$1\frac{1}{4}$	$1\frac{1}{16}$	$\frac{3}{32}$
$\frac{9}{16}$	$\frac{1}{8}$	0·124	$1\frac{1}{2}$	$1\frac{1}{4}$	$\frac{1}{8}$
$\frac{5}{8}$	$\frac{1}{8}$	0·124	$1\frac{1}{2}$	$1\frac{1}{4}$	$\frac{1}{8}$
$\frac{3}{4}$	$\frac{5}{32}$	0·155	2	$1\frac{11}{16}$	$\frac{1}{8}$
$\frac{7}{8}$	$\frac{5}{32}$	0·155	2	$1\frac{11}{16}$	$\frac{1}{8}$
1	$\frac{3}{16}$	0·186	$2\frac{1}{4}$	$1\frac{7}{8}$	$\frac{1}{8}$
$1\frac{1}{8}$	$\frac{3}{16}$	0·186	$2\frac{1}{2}$	$2\frac{1}{8}$	$\frac{1}{8}$
$1\frac{1}{4}$	$\frac{7}{32}$	0·217	$2\frac{3}{4}$	$2\frac{5}{16}$	$\frac{1}{8}$
$1\frac{3}{8}$	$\frac{7}{32}$	0·217	3	$2\frac{9}{16}$	$\frac{1}{8}$
$1\frac{1}{2}$	$\frac{7}{32}$	0·217	$3\frac{1}{4}$	$2\frac{13}{16}$	$\frac{1}{8}$
$1\frac{3}{4}$	$\frac{1}{4}$	0·249	$3\frac{3}{4}$	$3\frac{1}{4}$	$\frac{1}{8}$
2	$\frac{5}{16}$	0·311	4	$3\frac{3}{8}$	$\frac{1}{8}$

Note.—When ordering split cotter-pins the nominal length (col. 4) and nominal diameter (col. 2) should be quoted.

* B.S. 1083—1951.

AMERICAN S.A.E. SPLIT-PINS (COTTER-PINS)

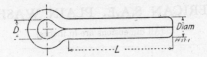

(All dimensions are in inches)

Length (L)	\(\frac{1}{16}\)	\(\frac{3}{32}\)	\(\frac{1}{8}\)	\(\frac{5}{32}\)	\(\frac{3}{16}\)	\(\frac{7}{32}\)	\(\frac{1}{4}\)	\(\frac{5}{16}\)
			Nominal Trade Diameter (D)					
\(\frac{5}{16}\)	*							
\(\frac{7}{16}\)	*							
\(\frac{1}{2}\)	*	*						
\(\frac{5}{8}\)	*	*						
\(\frac{3}{4}\)	*	*						
\(\frac{7}{8}\)	*	*	*					
1		*	*					
\(1\frac{1}{8}\)		*	*					
\(1\frac{1}{4}\)			*	*				
\(1\frac{3}{8}\)			*	*				
\(1\frac{1}{2}\)			*	*				
\(1\frac{5}{8}\)			*	*	*			
\(1\frac{3}{4}\)			*	*	*			
2				*	*	*		
\(2\frac{1}{4}\)				*	*	*	*	*
\(2\frac{1}{2}\)				*	*	*	*	*
\(2\frac{3}{4}\)					*	*	*	*
3						*	*	*
Diameter Limits †	0·061 0·058	0·090 0·086	0·122 0·118	0·150 0·146	0·176 0·172	0·207 0·202	0·225 0·220	0·280 0·275

† Actual cotter-pin or wire diameter limits.

AMERICAN S.A.E. PLAIN WASHERS

(All dimensions are in inches)

Nominal Sizes	Inside Diameter	Outside Diameter	Thickness ± 0·010 in.
2 (0·086)	$\frac{3}{32}$	$\frac{1}{4}$	$\frac{1}{32}$
4 (0·112)	$\frac{1}{8}$	$\frac{5}{16}$	$\frac{1}{32}$
6 (0·138)	$\frac{5}{32}$	$\frac{3}{8}$	$\frac{3}{64}$
8 (0·164)	$\frac{3}{16}$	$\frac{7}{16}$	$\frac{3}{64}$
10 (0·190)	$\frac{7}{32}$	$\frac{1}{2}$	$\frac{1}{16}$
12 (0·216)	$\frac{1}{4}$	$\frac{9}{16}$	$\frac{1}{16}$
$\frac{1}{4}$	$\frac{9}{32}$	$\frac{5}{8}$	$\frac{1}{16}$
$\frac{5}{16}$	$\frac{11}{32}$	$\frac{11}{16}$	$\frac{1}{16}$
$\frac{3}{8}$	$\frac{13}{32}$	$\frac{13}{16}$	$\frac{1}{16}$
$\frac{7}{16}$	$\frac{15}{32}$	$\frac{15}{16}$	$\frac{1}{16}$
$\frac{1}{2}$	$\frac{17}{32}$	$1\frac{1}{16}$	$\frac{3}{32}$
$\frac{9}{16}$	$\frac{19}{32}$	$1\frac{3}{16}$	$\frac{3}{32}$
$\frac{5}{8}$	$\frac{21}{32}$	$1\frac{5}{16}$	$\frac{3}{32}$
$\frac{11}{16}$	$\frac{23}{32}$	$1\frac{3}{8}$	$\frac{3}{32}$
$\frac{3}{4}$	$\frac{13}{16}$	$1\frac{1}{2}$	$\frac{1}{8}$
$\frac{7}{8}$	$\frac{15}{16}$	$1\frac{3}{4}$	$\frac{1}{8}$
1	$1\frac{1}{16}$	2	$\frac{1}{8}$
$1\frac{1}{8}$	$1\frac{3}{16}$	$2\frac{1}{4}$	$\frac{1}{8}$
$1\frac{1}{4}$	$1\frac{5}{16}$	$2\frac{1}{2}$	$\frac{5}{32}$
$1\frac{3}{8}$	$1\frac{7}{16}$	$2\frac{3}{4}$	$\frac{5}{32}$
$1\frac{1}{2}$	$1\frac{9}{16}$	3	$\frac{5}{32}$

Note.—All washers must be flat and free from burrs.

SPRING LOCK WASHERS. S.A.E. STANDARD

These spring lock washers are standardised for automobile and general engineering use for: (1) spring take-up devices to compensate for developed looseness and the loss of tension between component parts of an assembly; (2) hardened thrust bearings to facilitate assembly and dismantling of bolted fastenings by decreasing frictional resistance between the bolted surface and bearing face of bolt head or nut. The following are the standard requirements:

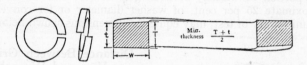

Washer Section.—The section of finished washers shall be slightly trapezoidal in shape with thickness at the inner periphery greater than thickness at the outer periphery by an amount varying from a minimum of 0·0005 in. to a maximum of 0·001 in. per $\frac{1}{64}$ in. of section width. The minimum thickness specified in the table of dimensions represents the nominal mean thickness of the trapezoid. Reduced to formulæ, the increase in thickness from the outer periphery to inner periphery shall be 0·032 W (min.) and 0·064 W (max.)

Finish.—Plated washers shall be baked to relieve hydrogen or acid embrittlement.

Coiling.—Washers shall be coiled so that free height is approximately twice the thickness of washer section. Gap and relationship of severed ends shall be such as to prevent washers tangling.

Quality of Finish.—The flat faces of washers and the inner and outer peripheries shall be smooth and free from knurling, serrations, die marks, deep scratches, etc., although slight feed roll marks are permissible. Washers shall also be free of burrs, rust, pit marks and loose scale, with internal and external circumferential edges rounded sufficiently to avoid heat checks.

Material and Hardness.—Washers shall be made from carbon steel fabricated and heat treated to a Rockwell hardness of 47–53 C scale. They shall be ground down to remove decarburisation before testing hardness. They shall also meet the test requirements of this specification.

210

Temper Test.—After a first compression to flat, the free height of a washer shall be at least $\frac{5}{8}$ of the original free height. Subsequent compression under the same load shall not further reduce this free height.

Toughness Test.—A portion of washer shall be firmly gripped in vice jaws having sharp edges. Ends of washer shall be free and an axis passing through slot shall be parallel to top of vice. An equal portion of washer shall be gripped in wrench jaws. Edges of wrench jaws shall be sharp and in a plane parallel to top of vice. Free portion of washer, between grip of vice and wrench, shall approximate 25 per cent. of washer diameter or for convenience and uniformity of test, may equal the dimensions shown below.

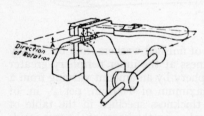

Direction of Rotation

Distance Between Grip of Vice and Wrench

Nominal Size	A	Nominal Size	A	Nom. Size	A
2 to 8 incl.	$\frac{1}{16}$	$\frac{11}{16}, \frac{3}{4}, \frac{13}{16}$	$\frac{5}{16}$	$1\frac{5}{16}$	$\frac{17}{32}$
10, 12	$\frac{3}{32}$	$\frac{7}{8}, \frac{15}{16}$	$\frac{3}{8}$	$1\frac{3}{8}$	$\frac{9}{16}$
$\frac{1}{4}, \frac{5}{16}$	$\frac{1}{8}$	$1, 1\frac{1}{16}$	$\frac{7}{16}$	$1\frac{7}{16}$	$1\frac{9}{32}$
$\frac{3}{8}, \frac{7}{16}$	$\frac{3}{16}$	$1\frac{1}{8}, 1\frac{3}{16}$	$\frac{15}{32}$	$1\frac{1}{2}$	$\frac{5}{8}$
$\frac{1}{2}, \frac{9}{16}, \frac{5}{8}$	$\frac{1}{4}$	$1\frac{1}{4}$	$\frac{1}{2}$	—	—

Movement of wrench in a direction that increases the free height of the washer shall twist the lock washer through 90 degrees without sign of fracture. When a washer fractures, the structure at the point of fracture shall show a fine grain, and shall deliver, at the instant of fracture, a tough, springy, reactive shear.

Lock washers shall be specified or designated by the Nominal Size and the Series, e.g. $\frac{1}{4}$-in. Light, $\frac{1}{4}$-in. Medium, $\frac{1}{4}$-in. Heavy or $\frac{1}{4}$-in. Extra Heavy.

Spring Lock Washers. S.A.E. Standard (Sizes in Inches)

Nominal Size	Clearance Nominal Bolt Size Min.	Max.	Washer Section, Min. Medium Width	Medium Thick	Light Width	Light Thick	Heavy Width	Heavy Thick	Extra Heavy Width	Extra Heavy Thick	Inside Diameter Min.	Outside Diameter Max. Medium	Light	Heavy	Extra Heavy
No. 2 (·086)	·002	·011	·035	·020	·030	·015	·040	·025	·053	·027	·088	0·175	0·165	0·185	0·211
No. 3 (·099)	·002	·011	·040	·025	·035	·020	·047	·031	·062	·034	·102	0·198	0·188	0·212	0·242
No. 4 (·112)	·003	·012	·040	·025	·035	·020	·047	·031	·062	·034	·115	0·212	0·202	0·226	0·256
No. 5 (·125)	·003	·012	·047	·031	·040	·025	·055	·040	·079	·045	·128	0·239	0·225	0·255	0·303
No. 6 (·138)	·003	·013	·047	·031	·040	·025	·055	·040	·079	·045	·141	0·251	0·237	0·267	0·315
No. 8 (·164)	·004	·014	·055	·040	·047	·031	·062	·047	·096	·057	·168	0·296	0·280	0·310	0·378
No. 10 (·190)	·004	·015	·062	·047	·055	·040	·070	·056	·112	·068	·194	0·337	0·323	0·353	0·437
No. 12 (·216)	·005	·016	·070	·056	·062	·047	·077	·063	·130	·080	·221	0·380	0·364	0·394	0·500
¼	·005	·017	·109	·062	·107	·047	·110	·077	·132	·084	·255	0·493	0·489	0·495	0·539
⁵⁄₁₆	·006	·020	·125	·078	·117	·056	·130	·097	·143	·108	·319	0·591	0·575	0·601	0·627
⅜	·007	·023	·141	·094	·136	·070	·145	·115	·170	·123	·382	0·688	0·678	0·696	0·746
⁷⁄₁₆	·008	·026	·156	·109	·154	·085	·160	·133	·186	·143	·446	0·784	0·780	0·792	0·844
½	·009	·029	·171	·125	·170	·099	·176	·151	·204	·162	·509	0·879	0·877	0·889	0·945
⁹⁄₁₆	·010	·032	·188	·141	·186	·113	·193	·170	·223	·182	·573	0·979	0·975	0·989	1·049
⅝	·011	·035	·203	·156	·201	·126	·210	·189	·242	·202	·636	1·086	1·082	1·100	1·164
¹¹⁄₁₆	·012	·038	·219	·172	·216	·138	·227	·207	·260	·221	·700	1·184	1·178	1·200	1·266
¾	·013	·041	·234	·188	·233	·153	·244	·226	·279	·241	·763	1·279	1·277	1·299	1·369
¹³⁄₁₆	·014	·044	·250	·203	·249	·168	·262	·246	·298	·261	·827	1·377	1·375	1·401	1·473
⅞	·015	·047	·266	·219	·264	·179	·281	·266	·322	·285	·890	1·474	1·470	1·504	1·586
¹⁵⁄₁₆	·016	·050	·281	·234	·277	·191	·298	·284	·345	·308	·954	1·570	1·562	1·604	1·698
1	·017	·053	·297	·250	·289	·202	·319	·306	·366	·330	1·017	1·672	1·656	1·716	1·810
1 ¹⁄₁₆	·018	·056	·312	·266	·301	·213	·338	·326	·389	·352	1·081	1·768	1·746	1·820	1·922
1 ⅛	·019	·059	·328	·281	·314	·224	·356	·345	·411	·375	1·144	1·865	1·837	1·921	2·031
1 ³⁄₁₆	·020	·062	·344	·297	·324	·234	·373	·364	·431	·396	1·208	1·963	1·923	2·021	2·137
1 ¼	·021	·065	·359	·312	·336	·244	·393	·384	·452	·417	1·271	2·058	2·012	2·126	2·244
1 ⁵⁄₁₆	·022	·068	·375	·328	·346	·254	·410	·403	·472	·438	1·335	2·156	2·098	2·226	2·350
1 ⅜	·023	·071	·391	·344	·356	·264	·427	·422	·491	·458	1·398	2·253	2·183	2·325	2·453
1 ⁷⁄₁₆	·024	·074	·406	·359	·366	·273	·442	·440	·509	·478	1·462	2·349	2·269	2·421	2·555
1 ½	·025	·077	·422	·375	·375	·282	·458	·458	·526	·496	1·525	2·446	2·352	2·518	2·654

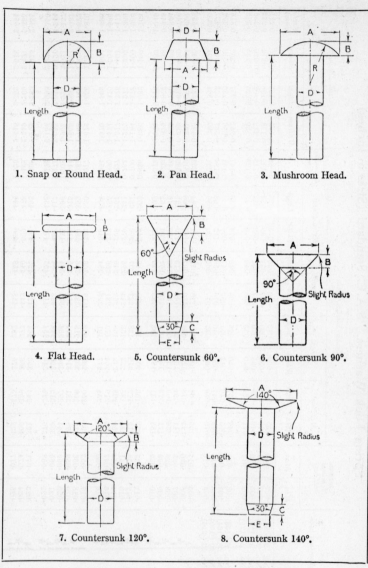

1. Snap or Round Head.   2. Pan Head.   3. Mushroom Head.

4. Flat Head.   5. Countersunk 60°.   6. Countersunk 90°.

7. Countersunk 120°.   8. Countersunk 140°.

FIG. 5.—BRITISH STANDARD RIVET PROPORTIONS.

RIVET PROPORTIONS (FERROUS AND NON-FERROUS)

The proportions of rivets in diameters up to $\frac{1}{2}$ in. have been standardised by the British Standards Institution (B.S. No. 641—1935), and the various types are illustrated ; formulæ for their proportions and tabular values are given.

Eight types of rivets are specified, viz. : (1) Snap or Round Head (Ferrous and Non-ferrous). (2) Pan Head (Ferrous and Non-ferrous). (3) Mushroom Head (Ferrous and Non-ferrous). (4) Flat Head (Ferrous and Non-ferrous). (5) Countersunk Head, 60° (non-ferrous). (6) Countersunk Head, 90° (Ferrous and Non-ferrous). (7) Countersunk Head, 120° (Ferrous) ; and (8) Countersunk Head 140° (Non-ferrous). These rivets are illustrated on page 212.

FORMULÆ FOR RIVET PROPORTIONS

Reference should be made to the lettered dimensions given on page 186.

(1) *Snap- or Round-head Rivets (Ferrous and Non-ferrous)*
$$A = 1 \cdot 75D \qquad B = 0 \cdot 75D \qquad R = 0 \cdot 885D$$

(2) *Pan-head Rivets (Ferrous and Non-ferrous)*
$$A = 1 \cdot 6D \qquad B = 0 \cdot 7D$$

(3) *Mushroom-head Rivets (Ferrous and Non-ferrous)*
$$A = 2 \cdot 25D \qquad B = 0 \cdot 5D \qquad R = 1 \cdot 516D$$

(4) *Flat-head Rivets (Ferrous and Non-ferrous)*
$$A = 2 \cdot 0D \qquad B = 0 \cdot 25D$$

(5) *Countersunk-head Rivets 60° (Non-ferrous)*
$$A = 1 \cdot 75D \qquad B = 0 \cdot 65D \qquad C = 0 \cdot 4D \qquad E = 0 \cdot 79D$$

(6) *Countersunk-head Rivets 90° (Ferrous and Non-ferrous)*
$$A = 2D \qquad B = 0 \cdot 5D$$

(7) *Countersunk-head Rivets 120° (Ferrous)*
$$A = 2D \qquad B = 0 \cdot 29D$$

(8) *Countersunk-head Rivets 140° (Non-ferrous)*
$$A = 2 \cdot 75D \qquad C = 0 \cdot 4D \qquad E = 0 \cdot 79D$$

where D = shank diameter.

B.S. TABULAR PROPORTIONS OF RIVETS

(1) Snap- or Round-head Rivets (Ferrous and Non-ferrous)

Nominal Diameter	Diameter of Head	Depth of Head	Radius of Head
D	A	B	R
In.	In.	In.	In.
$\frac{1}{16}$	0·109	0·047	0·055
$\frac{3}{32}$	0·164	0·070	0·083
$\frac{1}{8}$	0·219	0·094	0·111
$\frac{5}{32}$	0·273	0·117	0·138
$\frac{3}{16}$	0·322	0·141	0·166
$\frac{1}{4}$	0·438	0·188	0·221
$\frac{5}{16}$	0·547	0·234	0·277
$\frac{3}{8}$	0·656	0·281	0·332
$\frac{7}{16}$	0·766	0·328	0·387

(2) B.S. Pan-head Rivets (Ferrous and Non-ferrous)

Nominal Diameter	Diameter of Head	Depth of Head
D	A	B
In.	In.	In.
$\frac{3}{16}$	0·300	0·131
$\frac{1}{4}$	0·400	0·175
$\frac{5}{16}$	0·500	0·219
$\frac{3}{8}$	0·600	0·263
$\frac{7}{16}$	0·700	0·306

(3) B.S. Mushroom-head Rivets (Ferrous and Non-ferrous)

Nominal Diameter		Diameter of Head	Depth of Head	Radius of Head
D		A	B	R
In.		In.	In.	In.
$\frac{1}{16}$		0·141	0·031	0·095
	$\frac{3}{32}$	0·211	0·047	0·142
$\frac{1}{8}$		0·281	0·063	0·189
	$\frac{5}{32}$	0·352	0·078	0·237
$\frac{3}{16}$		0·422	0·094	0·284
	$\frac{1}{4}$	0·563	0·125	0·379
$\frac{5}{16}$		0·703	0·156	0·474
	$\frac{3}{8}$	0·844	0·188	0·568
$\frac{7}{16}$		0·984	0·219	0·663

(4) B.S. Flat-head Rivets (Ferrous and Non-ferrous)

Nominal Diameter		Diameter of Head	Depth of Head
D		A	B
In.		In.	In.
$\frac{1}{16}$		0·125	0·016
	$\frac{1}{32}$	0·188	0·023
$\frac{1}{8}$		0·250	0·031
	$\frac{5}{32}$	0·313	0·039
$\frac{3}{16}$		0·375	0·047
	$\frac{1}{4}$	0·500	0·063
$\frac{5}{16}$		0·625	0·078
	$\frac{3}{8}$	0·750	0·094
$\frac{7}{16}$		0·875	0·109

(5) B.S. Countersunk-head Rivets. 60° (Non-ferrous)

Nominal Diameter	Diameter of Head	Depth of Head	Depth of Point	Diameter of Point
D	A	B	C	E
In.	In.	In.	In.	In.
$\frac{3}{32}$	0·164	0·061	0·038	0·074
$\frac{1}{8}$	0·219	0·081	0·050	0·099
$\frac{5}{32}$	0·273	0·101	0·063	0·123
$\frac{3}{16}$	0·322	0·122	0·075	0·148
$\frac{1}{4}$	0·438	0·162	0·100	0·198
$\frac{5}{16}$	0·547	0·203	0·125	0·247
$\frac{3}{8}$	0·656	0·244	0·150	0·296

(6) B.S. Countersunk-head Rivets. 90° (Ferrous and Non-ferrous)

Nominal Diameter	Diameter of Head	Depth of Head
D	A	B
In.	In.	In.
$\frac{1}{16}$	0·125	0·031
$\frac{3}{32}$	0·188	0·047
$\frac{1}{8}$	0·250	0·063
$\frac{5}{32}$	0·313	0·078
$\frac{3}{16}$	0·375	0·094
$\frac{1}{4}$	0·500	0·125
$\frac{5}{16}$	0·625	0·156
$\frac{3}{8}$	0·750	0·188
$\frac{7}{16}$	0·875	0·219

(7) B.S. Countersunk-head Rivets. 120° (Ferrous)

Nominal Diameter	Diameter of Head	Depth of Head
D	A	B
In.	In.	In.
$\frac{1}{8}$	0·250	0·037
$\frac{3}{16}$	0·375	0·054
$\frac{1}{4}$	0·500	0·072
$\frac{5}{16}$	0·625	0·090
$\frac{3}{8}$	0·750	0·109

(8) B.S. Countersunk-head Rivets. 140° Non ferrous)

Nominal Diameter		Dimensions of Rivets			Dimensions of Washers		
		Diameter of Head	Depth of Point	Diameter of Point	Diameter	Thickness	Diameter of Hole
D		A	C	E	A		
S.W.G.	In.	In.	In.	In.	In.	S.W.G.	In.
12	0·104	0·286	0·042	0·082	0·286	20	0·036
11	0·116	0·319	0·046	0·092	0·319	19	0·040
10	0·128	0·352	0·051	0·101	0·352	19	0·040
							The diameter
9	0·144	0·396	0·058	0·114	0·396	18	0·048	of the hole
8	0·160	0·440	0·064	0·126	0·440	18	0·048	shall be such
7	0·176	0·484	0·070	0·139	0·484	18	0·048	that the
							washer is a
6	0·192	0·528	0·077	0·152	0·528	18	0·048	driving fit on
5	0·212	0·583	0·085	0·167	0·583	16	0·064	the shank of
4	0·232	0·638	0·093	0·183	0·638	16	0·064	the rivet.
—	¼*	0·688	0·100	0·198	0·688	16	0·064
—	5⁄16	0·859	0·125	0·247	0·859	14	0·080
—	⅜	1·031	0·150	0·296	1·031	14	0·080

* Approximately equals 3 S.W.G.

KEYS AND KEYWAYS

The British Standard Specification for Keys and Keyways and Coned Shaft Ends (B.S. No. 46, Part I—1929) gives the nomenclature for various types of keys and keyways and illustrates each of the various types used in engineering work. It specifies the material for steel keys and its mechanical strength properties. Four grades of steel, designated No. 46/1 (Black-rolled—35 tons min.), No. 46/2 (Black-rolled—52 tons min.), 46/3 (Bright drawn—35 tons min.), and 46/4 (Bright drawn—50 tons min.), are specified.

The standard taper for *coned* and *keyed shaft ends* is 1 in 10 on the diameter.

The sizes and lengths of keys are given in tables included in the Specifications.

The sizes of rectangular parallel keys, keyways and keybars, square parallel keys, plain rectangular taper keys, plain square taper keys, gib-head rectangular taper keys, gib-head square taper keys, peg feather keys, Woodruff keys and tangential keys are tabulated. The following tables are abstracted from B.S. No. 46, Part I—1929.

B.S. PLAIN RECTANGULAR TAPER

Taper 1 in 100

(All Dimensions

1	2	3	4	5	6	7	8	9	10
	Shaft Diameters		Key					Keyway	
Designation	Over	Up to and including	Nominal Size		Min. Width W	Min. Thickness at Large End	Max. Width in Shaft and Hub	Minimum Depth on Centre Line	
			Width	Thickness				In Shaft	In Hub at Deep End
B.S.K. 1/16 P.R.T.†	3/32	1/8	3/32 (0·09375)	3/32 (0·09375)	0·0938	0·097	0·0938	0·0584	0·0354
B.S.K. 1/8 P.R.T.†	1/4	3/8	1/8 (0·125)	1/8 (0·125)	0·1250	0·129	0·1250	0·0766	0·0474
B.S.K. 5/32 P.R.T.†	3/8	1/2	5/32 (0·15625)	5/32 (0·15625)	0·1563	0·160	0·1563	0·0935	0·0618
B.S.K. 3/16 P.R.T.	1/2	3/4	3/16 (0·1875)	5/32 (0·15625)	0·1875	0·160	0·1875	0·0935	0·0618
B.S.K. 1/4 P.R.T.	3/4	1	1/4 (0·25)	3/16 (0·1875)	0·2500	0·191	0·2500	0·1130	0·0725
B.S.K. 5/16 P.R.T.	1	1 1/4	5/16 (0·3125)	7/32 (0·21875)	0·3125	0·222	0·3125	0·1325	0·0843
B.S.K. 3/8 P.R.T.	1 1/4	1 1/2	3/8 (0·375)	1/4 (0·25)	0·3750	0·254	0·3750	0·1521	0·0959
B.S.K. 7/16 P.R.T.	1 1/2	1 3/4	7/16 (0·4375)	9/32 (0·28125)	0·4375	0·286	0·4375	0·1721	0·1082
B.S.K. 1/2 P.R.T.	1 3/4	2	1/2 (0·5)	11/32 (0·34375)	0·5000	0·348	0·5000	0·2073	0·1355
B.S.K. 9/16 P.R.T.	2	2 1/4	9/16 (0·5625)	3/8 (0·375)	0·5625	0·380	0·5625	0·2269	0·1471
B.S.K. 5/8 P.R.T.	2 1/4	2 1/2	5/8 (0·625)	13/32 (0·40625)	0·6250	0·411	0·6250	0·2465	0·1588
B.S.K. 11/16 P.R.T.	2 1/2	2 3/4	11/16 (0·6875)	15/32 (0·46875)	0·6875	0·475	0·6875	0·2822	0·1866
B.S.K. 3/4 P.R.T.	2 3/4	3	3/4 (0·75)	1/2 (0·5)	0·7500	0·507	0·7500	0·3018	0·1982
B.S.K. 7/8 P.R.T.	3	3 1/2	7/8 (0·875)	5/8 (0·625)	0·8750	0·632	0·8750	0·3746	0·2504
B.S.K. 1 P.R.T.	3 1/2	4	1	11/16 (0·6875)	1·0000	0·694	1·0000	0·4137	0·2738
B.S.K. 1 1/8 P.R.T.	4	4 1/2	1 1/8 (1·125)	3/4 (0·75)	1·1250	0·757	1·1250	0·4528	0·2962
B.S.K. 1 1/4 P.R.T.	4 1/2	5	1 1/4 (1·25)	13/16 (0·8125)	1·2500	0·819	1·2500	0·4920	0·3195
B.S.K. 1 3/8 P.R.T.	5	5 1/2	1 3/8 (1·375)	15/16 (0·9375)	1·3750	0·945	1·3750	0·5629	0·3746
B.S.K. 1 1/2 P.R.T.	5 1/2	6	1 1/2 (1·5)	1	1·5000	1·008	1·5000	0·6021	0·3979
B.S.K. 1 5/8 P.R.T.	6	6 1/2	1 5/8 (1·625)	1 1/16 (1·0625)	1·6250	1·070	1·6250	0·6413	0·4212
B.S.K. 1 3/4 P.R.T.	6 1/2	7	1 3/4 (1·75)	1 3/16 (1·1875)	1·7500	1·195	1·7500	0·7117	0·4758
B.S.K. 1 7/8 P.R.T.	7	7 1/2	1 7/8 (1·875)	1 1/4 (1·25)	1·8750	1·260	1·8750	0·7513	0·4997
B.S.K. 2 P.R.T.	7 1/2	8	2	1 3/8 (1·375)	2·0000	1·385	2·0000	0·8217	0·5543
B.S.K. 2 1/4 P.R.T.	8	9	2 1/4 (2·25)	1 1/2 (1·5)	2·2500	1·510	2·2500	0·9046	0·5964
B.S.K. 2 1/2 P.R.T.	9	10	2 1/2 (2·5)	1 5/8 (1·625)	2·5000	1·635	2·5000	0·9829	0·6431
B.S.K. 2 3/4 P.R.T.	10	11	2 3/4 (2·75)	1 7/8 (1·875)	2·7500	1·887	2·7500	1·1248	0·7532
B.S.K. 3 P.R.T.	11	12	3	2	3·0000	2·012	3·0000	1·2031	0·7999

* Where Key Bars are required to produce keys for which a fitting allowance is not desired, they can be col. 17.

† These keys are identical with the B.S. Plain Square Taper Keys of the corresponding sizes.

KEYS, KEYWAYS AND KEY BARS

are in inches)

11	12	13	14	15	16	17	18	19	20
Finished Key Bar *		Tolerances					Standard Lengths L		
		On Key		On Keyway		On Key Bar			
Min. Width	Min. Thickness	Width −·0000	Thickness −·0000	Width +·0000	Depth −·0000	Width and Thickness −·0000	Min.	In-creasing by	Max.
0·0978	0·0978	+·0010	+·0020	−·0010	+·0010	+·0020	3/8	1/8	3/4
0·1290	0·1290	+·0010	+·0020	−·0010	+·0010	+·0020	1/2	1/8	1
0·1603	0·1603	+·0010	+·0020	−·0010	+·0010	+·0020	5/8	1/8	1 1/4
0·1915	0·1603	+·0010	+·0020	−·0010	+·0010	+·0020	3/4	1/4	1 1/2
0·2540	0·1915	+·0010	+·0020	−·0010	+·0010	+·0020	1	1/4	2
0·3165	0·2228	+·0010	+·0020	−·0010	+·0010	+·0020	1 1/2	1/4	2 1/2
0·3790	0·2540	+·0010	+·0020	−·0010	+·0010	+·0020	1 1/2	1/4	3
0·4425	0·2863	+·0015	+·0020	−·0015	+·0010	+·0020	1 3/4	1/4	3 1/2
0·5050	0·3488	+·0015	+·0040	−·0015	+·0010	+·0020	2	1/2	4
0·5675	0·3800	+·0015	+·0040	−·0015	+·0010	+·0020	2 1/2	1/2	4 1/2
0·6300	0·4113	+·0015	+·0040	−·0015	+·0010	+·0020	2 1/2	1/2	5
0·6945	0·4758	+·0020	+·0040	−·0020	+·0015	+·0030	3	1/2	5 1/2
0·7570	0·5070	+·0020	+·0040	−·0020	+·0015	+·0030	3	1/2	6
0·8820	0·6320	+·0020	+·0040	−·0020	+·0015	+·0030	3 1/2	1/2	7
1·0070	0·6945	+·0020	+·0040	−·0020	+·0015	+·0030	4	1	8
1·1320	0·7570	+·0020	+·0040	−·0020	+·0015	+·0030	5	1	9
1·2570	0·8195	+·0020	+·0040	−·0020	+·0015	+·0030	5	1	10
1·3830	0·9455	+·0025	+·0050	−·0025	+·0015	+·0040	6	1	11
1·5080	1·0080	+·0025	+·0050	−·0025	+·0015	+·0040	6	1	12
1·6330	1·0705	+·0025	+·0050	−·0025	+·0015	+·0040	7	1	13
1·7580	1·1955	+·0025	+·0050	−·0025	+·0015	+·0040	7	1	14
1·8850	1·2600	+·0030	+·0050	−·0030	+·0020	+·0040	8	1	15
2·0100	1·3850	+·0030	+·0050	−·0030	+·0020	+·0040	8	2	16
2·2600	1·5100	+·0030	+·0050	−·0030	+·0020	+·0040	10	2	18
2·5100	1·6350	+·0030	+·0050	−·0030	+·0020	+·0040	10	2	20
2·7620	1·8870	+·0040	+·0050	−·0040	+·0020	+·0050	12	2	22
3·0120	2·0120	+·0040	+·0050	−·0040	+·0020	+·0050	12	2	24

obtained to the nominal width and thickness of the keys (cols. 4 and 5) with the plus tolerances specified in

B.S. RECTANGULAR PARALLEL

T | L

(All Dimensions

1	2	3	4	5	6	7	8	9	10
	Shaft Diameters		Key		Depth of Immersion of Key on Centre Line (Nominal)		Keyway		
Designation	Over	Up to and including	Nominal and Min. Width W	Nominal and Min. Thickness T	In Shaft	In Hub	Max. Width in Shaft and Hub	Min. Depth on Centre Line In Shaft	In Hub
B.S.K. 3/32 R.†	3/16	1/4	3/32 (0·09375)	3/32 (0·09375)	0·0574	0·0364	0·0938	0·0584	0·0374
B.S.K. 1/8 R.†	1/4	3/8	1/8 (0·125)	1/8 (0·125)	0·0756	0·0494	0·1250	0·0766	0·0504
B.S.K. 5/32 R.†	3/8	1/2	5/32 (0·15625)	5/32 (0·15625)	0·0925	0·0638	0·1563	0·0935	0·0648
B.S.K. 3/16 R.	1/2	3/4	3/16 (0·1875)	5/32 (0·15625)	0·0925	0·0638	0·1875	0·0935	0·0648
B.S.K. 1/4 R.	3/4	1	1/4 (0·25)	3/16 (0·1875)	0·1120	0·0755	0·2500	0·1130	0·0765
B.S.K. 5/16 R.	1	1 1/4	5/16 (0·3125)	7/32 (0·21875)	0·1315	0·0873	0·3125	0·1325	0·0883
B.S.K. 3/8 R.	1 1/4	1 1/2	3/8 (0·375)	1/4 (0·25)	0·1511	0·0989	0·3750	0·1521	0·0999
B.S.K. 7/16 R.	1 1/2	1 3/4	7/16 (0·4375)	9/32 (0·28125)	0·1706	0·1107	0·4375	0·1721	0·1122
B.S.K. 1/2 R.	1 3/4	2	1/2 (0·5)	11/32 (0·34375)	0·2058	0·1380	0·5000	0·2073	0·1395
B.S.K. 9/16 R.	2	2 1/4	9/16 (0·5625)	3/8 (0·375)	0·2254	0·1496	0·5625	0·2269	0·1511
B.S.K. 5/8 R.	2 1/4	2 1/2	5/8 (0·625)	13/32 (0·40625)	0·2450	0·1613	0·6250	0·2465	0·1628
B.S.K. 11/16 R.	2 1/2	2 3/4	11/16 (0·6875)	15/32 (0·46875)	0·2802	0·1886	0·6875	0·2822	0·1906
B.S.K. 3/4 R.	2 3/4	3	3/4	1/2 (0·5)	0·2998	0·2002	0·7500	0·3018	0·2022
B.S.K. 7/8 R.	3	3 1/2	7/8 (0·875)	5/8 (0·625)	0·3726	0·2524	0·8750	0·3746	0·2544
B.S.K. 1 R.	3 1/2	4	1	11/16 (0·6875)	0·4117	0·2758	1·0000	0·4137	0·2778
B.S.K. 1 1/8 R.	4	4 1/2	1 1/8 (1·125)	3/4 (0·75)	0·4508	0·2992	1·1250	0·4528	0·3012
B.S.K. 1 1/4 R.	4 1/2	5	1 1/4 (1·25)	13/16 (0·8125)	0·4900	0·3225	1·2500	0·4920	0·3245
B.S.K. 1 3/8 R.	5	5 1/2	1 3/8 (1·375)	15/16 (0·9375)	0·5604	0·3771	1·3750	0·5629	0·3796
B.S.K. 1 1/2 R.	5 1/2	6	1 1/2 (1·5)	1	0·5996	0·4004	1·5000	0·6021	0·4029
B.S.K. 1 5/8 R.	6	6 1/2	1 5/8 (1·625)	1 1/16 (1·0625)	0·6388	0·4237	1·6250	0·6413	0·4262
B.S.K. 1 3/4 R.	6 1/2	7	1 3/4 (1·75)	1 3/16 (1·1875)	0·7092	0·4783	1·7500	0·7117	0·4808
B.S.K. 1 7/8 R.	7	7 1/2	1 7/8 (1·875)	1 1/4 (1·25)	0·7483	0·5017	1·8750	0·7513	0·5047
B.S.K. 2 R.	7 1/2	8	2	1 3/8 (1·375)	0·8187	0·5563	2·0000	0·8217	0·5593
B.S.K. 2 1/4 R.	8	9	2 1/4 (2·25)	1 1/2 (1·5)	0·9016	0·5984	2·2500	0·9046	0·6014
B.S.K. 2 1/2 R.	9	10	2 1/2 (2·5)	1 5/8 (1·625)	0·9799	0·6451	2·5000	0·9829	0·6481
B.S.K. 2 3/4 R.	10	11	2 3/4 (2·75)	1 7/8 (1·875)	1·1208	0·7542	2·7500	1·1248	0·7582
B.S.K. 3 R.	11	12	3	2	1·1991	0·8009	3·0000	1·2031	0·8049

* Where Key Bars are required to produce keys for which a fitting allowance is not desired, they can be col. 16.

† These keys are identical with the B.S. Square Parallel Keys of the corresponding sizes.

KEYS, KEYWAYS AND KEY BARS

←—W—→

are in inches)

11	12	13	14	15	16	17	18	19
Finished Key Bar *		Tolerances				Standard Lengths L		
		On Key	On Keyway		On Key Bar			
Min. Width	Min. Thickness	Width and Thickness − ·0000	Width + ·0000	Depth − ·0000	Width and Thickness − ·0000	Min.	Increasing by	Max.
0·0978	0·0978	+ ·0010	− ·0010	+ ·0010	+ ·0020	⅜	⅛	¾
0·1290	0·1290	+ ·0010	− ·0010	+ ·0010	+ ·0020	½	⅛	1
0·1603	0·1603	+ ·0010	− ·0010	+ ·0010	+ ·0020	⅝	⅛	1¼
0·1915	0·1603	+ ·0010	− ·0010	+ ·0010	+ ·0020	¾	¼	1½
0·2540	0·1915	+ ·0010	− ·0010	+ ·0010	+ ·0020	1	¼	2
0·3165	0·2228	+ ·0010	− ·0010	+ ·0010	+ ·0020	1¼	¼	2½
0·3790	0·2540	+ ·0010	− ·0010	+ ·0010	+ ·0020	1½	¼	3
0·4425	0·2863	+ ·0015	− ·0015	+ ·0010	+ ·0020	1¾	¼	3½
0·5050	0·3488	+ ·0015	− ·0015	+ ·0010	+ ·0020	2	½	4
0·5675	0·3800	+ ·0015	− ·0015	+ ·0010	+ ·0020	2½	½	5
0·6300	0·4113	+ ·0015	− ·0015	+ ·0010	+ ·0020	2½	½	5
0·6945	0·4758	+ ·0020	− ·0020	+ ·0015	+ ·0030	3	½	6
0·7570	0·5070	+ ·0020	− ·0020	+ ·0015	+ ·0030	3	½	6
0·8820	0·6320	+ ·0020	− ·0020	+ ·0015	+ ·0030	3½	½	7
1·0070	0·6945	+ ·0020	− ·0020	+ ·0015	+ ·0030	4	1	8
1·1320	0·7570	+ ·0020	− ·0020	+ ·0015	+ ·0030	5	1	10
1·2570	0·8195	+ ·0020	− ·0020	+ ·0015	+ ·0030	5	1	10
1·3830	0·9455	+ ·0025	− ·0025	+ ·0015	+ ·0040	6	1	12
1·5080	1·0080	+ ·0025	− ·0025	+ ·0015	+ ·0040	6	1	12
1·6330	1·0705	+ ·0025	− ·0025	+ ·0015	+ ·0040	7	1	14
1·7580	1·1955	+ ·0025	− ·0025	+ ·0015	+ ·0040	7	1	14
1·8850	1·2600	+ ·0030	− ·0030	+ ·0020	+ ·0040	8	1	16
2·0100	1·3850	+ ·0030	− ·0030	+ ·0020	+ ·0040	8	2	16
2·2600	1·5100	+ ·0030	− ·0030	+ ·0020	+ ·0040	10	2	20
2·5100	1·6350	+ ·0030	− ·0030	+ ·0020	+ ·0040	10	2	20
2·7620	1·8870	+ ·0040	− ·0040	+ ·0020	+ ·0050	12	2	24
3·0120	2·0120	+ ·0040	− ·0040	+ ·0020	+ ·0050	12	2	24

obtained to the nominal width and thickness of the keys (cols. 4 and 5) with the plus tolerances specified in

BRITISH STANDARD WOODRUFF KEYS AND KEYWAYS

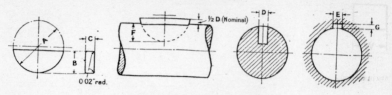

(All Dimensions are in inches)

1	2	3	4	5	6	7	8	9
B.S. Key No.	Diameter of Key A + 0 − 0·005	Depth of Key B + 0 − 0·005	Thickness of Key C + 0 − 0·001	Width of Keyway in Shaft D − 0 + 0·001	Width of Keyway in Hub or Boss E − 0 + 0·001	Depth of Keyway in Shaft F − 0 + 0·005	Depth of Keyway in Hub at Centre Line G − 0 + 0·005	Corresponding B.S. Woodruff Cutter Nos.
10	0·500	0·203	0·0635	0·0615	0·0635	0·1668	0·042	1
20	0·500	0·203	0·0948	0·0928	0·0948	0·1511	0·057	2
30	0·500	0·203	0·1260	0·1240	0·1260	0·1355	0·073	3
40	0·625	0·250	0·0948	0·0928	0·0948	0·1981	0·057	4
50	0·625	0·250	0·1260	0·1240	0·1260	0·1825	0·073	5
60	0·625	0·250	0·1573	0·1553	0·1573	0·1669	0·089	6
70	0·750	0·313	0·1260	0·1240	0·1260	0·2455	0·073	7
80	0·750	0·313	0·1573	0·1553	0·1573	0·2299	0·089	8
90	0·750	0·313	0·1885	0·1865	0·1885	0·2143	0·104	9
100	0·875	0·375	0·1573	0·1553	0·1573	0·2919	0·089	10
110	0·875	0·375	0·1885	0·1865	0·1885	0·2763	0·104	11
115	0·875	0·375	0·2510	0·2490	0·2510	0·2450	0·136	A
130	1·000	0·438	0·1885	0·1865	0·1885	0·3393	0·104	13
150	1·000	0·438	0·2510	0·2490	0·2510	0·3080	0·136	15
155	1·000	0·438	0·3135	0·3115	0·3135	0·2768	0·167	B
160	1·125	0·484	0·1885	0·1865	0·1885	0·3853	0·104	16
180	1·125	0·484	0·2510	0·2490	0·2510	0·3540	0·136	18
185	1·125	0·484	0·3135	0·3115	0·3135	0·3228	0·167	C
210	1·250	0·547	0·2510	0·2490	0·2510	0·4170	0·136	21
215	1·250	0·547	0·3135	0·3115	0·3135	0·3858	0·167	D
225	1·250	0·547	0·3760	0·3740	0·3760	0·3545	0·198	E
230	1·375	0·594	0·3135	0·3115	0·3135	0·4328	0·167	23
235	1·375	0·594	0·3760	0·3740	0·3760	0·4015	0·198	F
240	1·500	0·641	0·2510	0·2490	0·2510	0·5110	0·136	24
250	1·500	0·641	0·3135	0·3115	0·3135	0·4798	0·167	25
255	1·500	0·641	0·3760	0·3740	0·3760	0·4485	0·198	G

For particulars of the British Standard Cutters for producing the Woodruff Keyways see Table 31 I of B.S. Specification No. 122 for Milling Cutters and Reamers.

SPLINE SHAFTS FOR AIRCRAFT PURPOSES

The British Standards Institution has standardised the splined shafts and holes for aircraft purposes in their Specification A.20, April, 1942. It gives the nomenclature employed, fits and tolerances and includes comprehensive tables of Four Spline Shafts and Holes, Bottom Fitting, Deep for Splines of nominal sizes for holes of 0·3760 in. to 4·500 in. ; Four Spline Holes and Shafts, Bottom Fitting, Shallow (0·0426 in. to 5·100 in.) ; Six Spline Holes and Shafts, Bottom Fitting, Deep (0·0426 in. to 5·100 in.) and Six Spline Shafts and Holes, Bottom Fitting, Shallow (0·4510 in. to 5·400 in.). Diagrams are given in connection with these tables, in the specification.

SPLINED SHAFTS FOR AUTOMOBILE PURPOSES

The British Standard Specification No. 5015—1927 specifies Splines (Bottom Fitting) for Automobiles, Dimensions for. This Specification, at the time of compilation of this book was under revision.

BRITISH STANDARDS FOR AIRCRAFT MATERIALS AND COMPONENTS*

The various materials employed in aircraft construction and the components used in aircraft have been standardised in a large number of instances, and a series of Specifications is issued, at a cost of one shilling each, under the following headings :

A. *Bolts*, etc. These include Tensile Test Pieces, Magneto Couplings, Engine Mountings, Serrations and Gauges, Spline Shafts and Holes, etc.

B. *Brass, Copper*, etc. Castings, Bars, Whitemetal.

D. *Dope and Ingredients.*

E. *Electrical.* Sparking Plugs, Cords, Cables, Lamps, etc.

F. *Fabric.*

K. *Cast Iron.* Piston-ring Pots. Valve Guides, etc.

L. *Aluminium and Light Alloys.* Castings, Forgings, Bars, Sheets, etc.

S. *Steels.* Carbon and Alloy Steels, Bars, Forgings, etc.

S.P. *Standard Details.*

T. *Tubes.*

V. *Timber, Glues, Plywoods*, etc.

W. *Wire, Wire Ropes*, etc.

X. *Paints and Varnishes.*

* British Standards Institution, 2, Park Street, W.1.

SECTION 6

MACHINE-CUT GEARS

SPUR GEARS

Definitions

Pitch Circle.—This is the equivalent circle that would represent the diameter of friction disc which, in contact with a similar disc, would transmit the same relative motion as the pair of similar gears (Fig. 1).

In Fig. 1 A and B represent two meshing spur gears, the pitch circles of which are shown by the full circular lines.

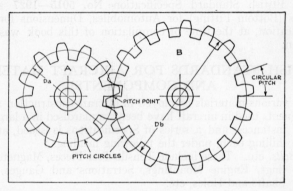

FIG. 1.

Pitch Diameter.—The diameter of the pitch circle. In Fig. 1 the pitch diameters are Da and Db.

Base Circle.—The generating circle from which an involute-gear tooth profile is generated.

Diametral Pitch (D.P.).—This is the number of teeth N of a gear divided by the pitch diameter.

Circular Pitch.—This is the circumference of the pitch circle divided by the number of teeth N.

Module (M).—The module of a gear is the reciprocal of the diametral pitch, i.e. the pitch diameter per tooth. The term *Module* is generally used on the Continent for metrical measurements of gear teeth.

Chordal Pitch.—The length of the chord of the pitch circle connecting two similarly located points on two contiguous teeth.

Chordal Thickness.*—The thickness or length of chord of a tooth at the pitch circle. Machined gears are often checked by measuring the chordal thickness with a gear-tooth caliper (Fig. 2).

Addendum.—The distance measured radially from the pitch circle to the crest of the gear tooth (Fig. 3).

Dedendum.—The distance measured radially from the pitch circle to the root of a gear tooth (or to the bottom of the space between two contiguous gear teeth)

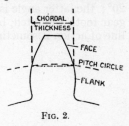

Fig. 2.

Clearance.—The width of the space between the crest of a tooth and the root of the two mating teeth, when in full mesh.

Whole Depth of Tooth.—The radial distance between circles containing the periphery of the teeth and the bottoms of the tooth spaces, i.e. the sum of the addendum and dedendum distances.

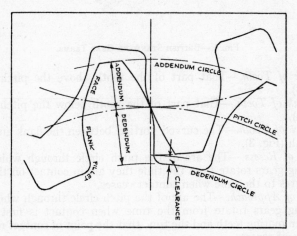

Fig. 3.

Working Depth of Tooth.—The depth in tooth space to which tooth of mating gear extends. Equal to sum of addenda of the two gears.

Line of Action.—In properly designed involute-gear teeth the line drawn at right angles to the meshing teeth at the pitch point

* See also Fig. 22.

226

(Fig. 4).* This line is also a common tangent to the two base circles.

It is also called the *Pressure Angle*. This angle is usually 14½° or 20°; the latter angle is shown in Fig. 4, which shows for an involute-gear tooth the pitch, base, addendum and dedendum circles. The line of action is sometimes termed the *Angle of Obliquity*.

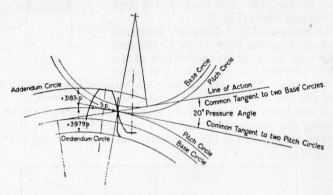

FIG. 4.—BRITISH STANDARD GEAR TERMS.

Face of Tooth.—That part of the tooth above the pitch circle (Fig. 3).

Flank of Tooth.—That part of the tooth below the pitch circle (Fig. 3).

Fillet of Tooth.—The curved portion between the flank and root of tooth (Fig. 3).

Arc of Recess.—The arc of the pitch circle through which the meshing gears rotate from the time they are in contact on the line of centres to the time when contact ceases.

Arc of Approach.—The arc of the pitch circle through which the meshing gears rotate from the time when contact is first made between mating teeth and the time that the point of contact reaches the line of centres.

Width of Tooth Face.—The length of the surface of contact of two mating gears ; this is generally equal to the full thickness of the gear wheel.

Thickness of Tooth.—The chordal thickness at the pitch circle of a tooth.

* British Standards Institution.

Interference.—When the points of contact of the mating teeth do not fall on the line of action interference is said to occur and the angular motions of the wheels are not uniform. Interference is more liable with a $14\frac{1}{2}°$ pressure angle; for this reason a 20° angle

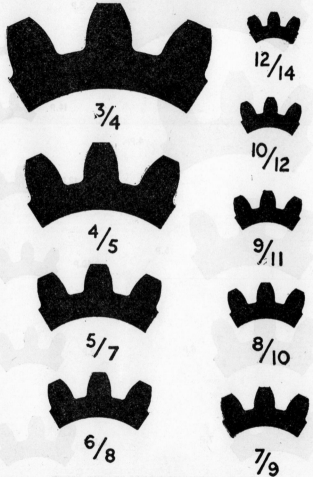

FIG. 5.—COMPARATIVE SIZES OF GEAR TEETH.

These sizes and shapes (slightly reduced) are based on a pinion having 15 teeth of Brown and Sharpe involute form, with 20° pressure angle.

[*Courtesy Inst. of Autom. Engrs.*]

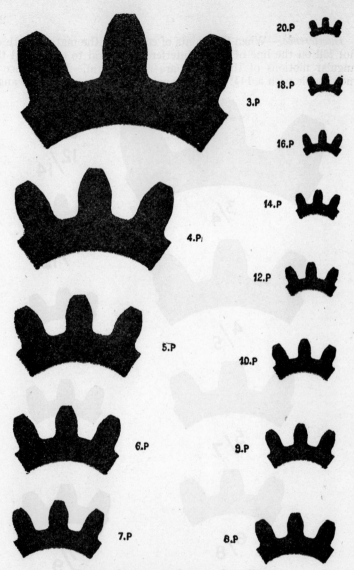

FIG. 6.—COMPARATIVE SIZES OF GEAR TEETH.
These outlines of gear teeth are based on an involute gear having 15 teeth of Brown and Sharpe form with $14\frac{1}{2}°$ pressure angle.   [*Courtesy Inst. of Autom. Engrs.*]

was recommended by the British Standards Institution (Fig. 4). It gives increased pressure on the bearings, however. In $14\frac{1}{2}°$ pressure angle gear-teeth interference occurs when the number of teeth is below 52 ; and for 20° teeth, below 17.   Interference may be reduced by increasing the pressure angle ; or reducing the addendum ; the latter method gives the well-known *stub teeth* ; a combination of both methods gives satisfactory results in practice.

Backlash.—The clearance between meshing gear teeth to allow for errors in tooth form and in the distance between the centres. In stub-teeth gears the backlash is usually about 0·03 to 0·05 inch for 1-inch diametral pitch teeth.

SPUR-GEAR TEETH FORMULÆ

CLASS A.—BRITISH STANDARD 20° PRESSURE ANGLE.   (PRECISION-MACHINED GEARS) *

Measurement	Expressed in Circular Pitch (C.P.)	Expressed in Diametral Pitch (D.P.)
Addendum . . .	0·3183 C.P.	$\dfrac{1}{\text{D.P.}}$
Dedendum . . .	0·4583 C.P.	$\dfrac{1·44}{\text{D.P.}}$
Total Depth . . .	0·7766 C.P.	$\dfrac{2·44}{\text{D.P.}}$
Working Depth . .	0·6366 C.P.	$\dfrac{2}{\text{D.P.}}$
Thickness at Pitch Line .	0·5000 C.P.	$\dfrac{1·5708}{\text{D.P.}}$

CLASS B.—BRITISH STANDARD 20° PRESSURE ANGLE.   (HIGH-CLASS OR COMMERCIAL CUT GEARS)

Measurement	Expressed in Circular Pitch (C.P.)	Expressed in Diametral Pitch (D.P.)
Addendum . . .	0·3183 C.P.	$\dfrac{1}{\text{D.P.}}$
Dedendum . . .	0·3979 C.P.	$\dfrac{1·25}{\text{D.P.}}$
Total Depth . . .	0·7162 C.P.	$\dfrac{2·25}{\text{D.P.}}$
Working Depth . .	0·6366 C.P.	$\dfrac{2}{\text{D.P.}}$
Thickness at Pitch Line .	0·5000 C.P.	$\dfrac{1·5708}{\text{D.P.}}$

* Abstract from B.S. 436—1940.

OTHER GENERAL FORMULÆ

Measurement	Expressed in Circular Pitch (C.P.)	Expressed in Diametral Pitch (D.P.)
Minimum Clearance . .	0·05 C.P.	$\dfrac{0\cdot157}{D.P.}$
Pitch Diameter . .	0·3183 × N * × C.P.	$\dfrac{N}{D.P.}$
Outside Diameter . .	0·3183 (N + 2) C.P.	$\dfrac{N + 2}{D.P.}$
Radius of Fillet . .	1·3 × clearance or 0·065 C.P.	$\dfrac{2\cdot20}{D.P.}$

* N = number of teeth.

Diametral Pitch	$\dfrac{25\cdot4}{Module}$
Diametral Pitch	$\dfrac{N}{pitch\ diameter}$
Circular Pitch	$\dfrac{\pi \times pitch\ diameter}{N}$
Circular Pitch	$\dfrac{\pi}{D.P.}$
Pitch Diameter	Module × N

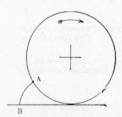

FIG. 7.—CYCLOID CURVE.

GEAR-TOOTH FORMS. CONSTRUCTION

1. Cycloidal Teeth

When a circular disc rolls on a flat plane any selected point A on the circumference describes a *cycloid curve* (Fig. 7).

When a circle rolls on the outside of another circle any point A on the circumference describes an *epicycloid* curve (Fig. 8).

When a circle rolls inside another circle any point on the circle describes a *hypocycloid* (Fig. 9).

In cycloidal-tooth gearing the face portion of the tooth is an epicycloid and the flank portion a hypocycloid.

The tooth proportions depend upon the relative diameters of the base (rolling) and pitch circles. When the diameter of the base circle is less than the radius of the pitch circle a weak-tooth form results ; when it is equal to the radius of pitch circle the

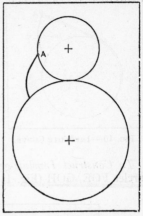

FIG. 8.—EPICYCLOID CURVE.

hypocycloid or flank portion becomes a radial line of the pitch circle.

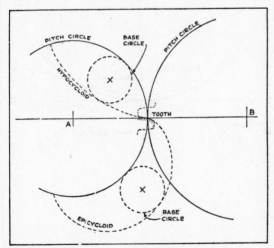

FIG. 9.—EPICYCLOID AND HYPOCYCLOID CURVES.

2. Involute Teeth

The involute is the curve traced out by a point A on the end of a fine cord or ribbon as it unwinds from a circle. The string always

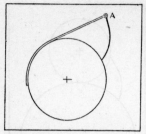

FIG. 10.—INVOLUTE CURVE.

remains tangential to this *base circle*; the latter is not to be confused with the pitch or dedendum circles (Fig. 10).

The involute form of tooth is stronger than the cycloidal one, and can more readily be machined. Moreover, if the gear-wheel centre distance is slightly different from the theoretically correct one, the involute gears will still mesh correctly and give the correct velocity ratio; this is not the case with cycloidal gears.

To Construct Involute-gear Teeth Shapes.—First draw the pitch circles FOE, GOH (Fig. 11), touching at the pitch point O. Join

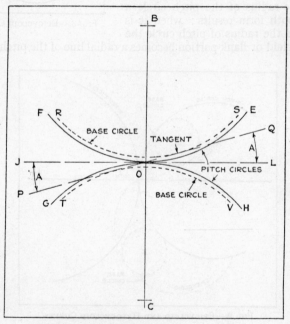

FIG. 11.—CONSTRUCTING INVOLUTE-GEAR TEETH.

centres BC. Draw the tangent JOL common to both pitch circles. Draw line POQ at the required pressure angle A to JOL.

Finally, draw the two circles RS and TV (dotted) to touch line POQ. The circles RS and TV are the required base circles of the two gears.

To draw the involute curve use a circular disc of any material MPN of diameter equal to that of base circle (Fig. 12). Take a straight-edge having a scribing pencil point P on its edge. Place the point P

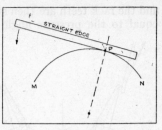

Fig. 12.

on base circle and roll the straight-edge around the circle, without slipping. P will trace out the involute curve. In Fig. 11 the points where POQ touch the base circles are the *interference points*, and represent the ends of the maximum path of contact of the gear teeth and the largest addendum circles that should be employed. If the base circle for the smaller gear comes between the pitch and root circles the involute curve cannot be extended down to the fillet ; the flank-extension line is then made a radial line, tangential to involute curve.

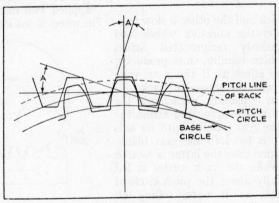

Fig. 13.—Involute Rack Gear.
A = pressure angle.

Rack and Pinion

When the diameter of one of a pair of involute gears is increased continuously the shape of its teeth becomes modified, progressively, until when the diameter is infinitely large the gear becomes a rack,

E.W.D.—8*

and the rack teeth are then straight-sided ones, of slope or obliquity equal to the pressure angle A (Fig. 13). The pitch circle of the larger gear, as the diameter is increased, gradually approaches a straight line and, for the infinitely great diameter is a straight line tangential to the pinion-pitch circle. The rack-and-pinion basic principle is employed in certain gear-generating machines, e.g. the Maag-Sulzer. This uses a pair of grinding wheels mounted at angles equivalent to the sides of the teeth of an involute rack (Fig. 14). The gear to be ground is mounted on a spindle to which are applied two movements,

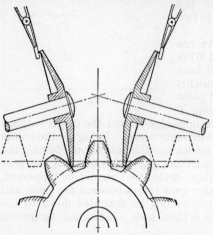

FIG. 14.—MAAG-SULZER GEAR-GENERATION PRINCIPLE.

one a quick and the other a slow one. The wheel is fed longitudinally under the abrasive wheels and simultaneously reciprocated across the machine rapidly, thus producing the same effect as if the gear were in mesh with the equivalent rack.

In gear "planing" machines the rack cutter is reciprocated across the face of the gear parallel with its axis whilst it is fed into the gear blank. At the same time the latter is rotated slowly while the rack cutter is fed tangentially along the pitch circle of the blank, as it were, rolling on the pitch line of the rack cutter (Fig. 15).

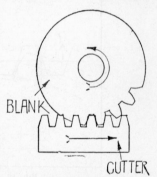

FIG. 15.—PLANING GEAR PRINCIPLE.

TABLE OF EQUIVALENT DIAMETRAL AND CIRCULAR PITCHES *

(Including Metric Pitches)

Standard Pitches in Bold Type, Equivalents in Small

Dia-metral	*Circular in In.*	*Module in Mm.*	*Dia-metral*	*Circular in In.*	*Module in Mm.*	*Dia-metral*	*Circular in In.*	*Module in Mm.*
$\frac{1}{2}$	6·2832	50·7991	**$1\frac{1}{4}$**	2·5133	20·3196	2·2848	**$1\frac{3}{8}$**	11·1168
·5080	6·1844	**50**	1·2566	**$2\frac{1}{2}$**	20·2123	2·3090	1·3606	**11**
·5236	**6**	48·5095	1·2700	2·4737	**20**	**$2\frac{1}{2}$**	1·2560	10·1598
·5644	5·5659	**45**	1·3963	**$2\frac{1}{4}$**	19·1911	2·5133	**$1\frac{1}{4}$**	10·1062
·5712	**$5\frac{1}{2}$**	44·4671	1·4111	2·2264	**18**	2·5400	1·2369	**10**
·6283	**5**	40·4246	**$1\frac{1}{2}$**	2·0944	16·9330	**$2\frac{3}{4}$**	1·1424	9·2362
·6350	4·9475	**40**	1·5708	**2**	16·1698	2·7925	**$1\frac{1}{8}$**	9·0955
·6981	**$4\frac{1}{2}$**	36·3822	1·5875	1·9790	**16**	2·8222	1·1132	**9**
·7257	4·3290	**35**	1·6755	**$1\frac{7}{8}$**	15·1592	**3**	1·0472	8·4665
$\frac{3}{4}$	4·1888	33·8661	1·6933	1·8553	**15**	3·1416	**1**	8·0849
·7854	**4**	32·3397	**$1\frac{3}{4}$**	1·7952	14·5140	3·1749	·9895	**8**
·8378	**$3\frac{3}{4}$**	30·3185	1·7952	**$1\frac{3}{4}$**	14·1486	3·3510	**$\frac{15}{16}$**	7·5796
·8467	3·7106	**30**	1·8143	1·7316	**14**	**$3\frac{1}{2}$**	·8976	7·2570
·8976	**$3\frac{1}{2}$**	28·2972	1·9333	**$1\frac{5}{8}$**	13·1380	3·5904	**$\frac{7}{8}$**	7·0743
·9666	**$3\frac{1}{4}$**	26·2760	1·9538	1·6079	**13**	3·6285	·8658	**7**
1	3·1416	25·3995	**2**	1·5708	12·6998	3·8666	**$\frac{13}{16}$**	6·5690
1·0160	3·0922	**25**	2·0944	**$1\frac{1}{2}$**	12·1274	3·9076	·8040	**$6\frac{1}{2}$**
1·0472	**3**	24·2548	2·1166	1·4842	**12**	**4**	·7854	6·3499
1·1424	**$2\frac{3}{4}$**	22·2335	**$2\frac{1}{4}$**	1·3963	11·2887	4·1888	**$\frac{3}{4}$**	6·0637

* B.S. No. 545—1934.

TABLE OF EQUIVALENT DIAMETRAL AND CIRCULAR PITCHES * (*contd.*)

(Including Metric Pitches)

Standard Pitches in Bold Type, Equivalents in Small

Dia-metral	Circular in In.	Module in Mm.	Dia-metral	Circular in In.	Module in Mm.	Dia-metral	Circular in In.	Module in Mm.
4·2333	·7421	**6**	10·0531	$\frac{5}{16}$	2·5265	25·1327	$\frac{1}{8}$	1·0106
4·5696	$\frac{11}{16}$	5·5584	10·1598	·3092	**2½**	25·3995	·1237	**1**
4·6181	·6803	**5½**	**11**	·2856	2·3090	**26**	·1208	·9769
5	·6283	5·0799	**12**	·2618	2·1166	**28**	·1122	·9071
5·0265	$\frac{5}{8}$	5·0531	12·5664	$\frac{1}{4}$	2·0212	**30**	·1047	·8467
5·0799	·6184	**5**	12·6998	·2474	**2**	**32**	·0932	·7847
5·5851	$\frac{9}{16}$	4·5478	**13**	·2417	1·9538	**34**	·0924	·7470
5·6443	·5566	**4½**	**14**	·2244	1·8143	**36**	·0873	·7055
6	·5236	4·2333	**15**	·2094	1·6933	**38**	·0827	·6684
6·2832	$\frac{1}{2}$	4·0425	**16**	·1963	1·5875	**40**	·0785	·6350
6·3499	·4947	**4**	16·7562	$\frac{3}{16}$	1·5159	**42**	·0748	·6048
7	·4488	3·6285	16·9330	·1855	**1½**	**44**	·0714	·5773
7·1808	$\frac{7}{16}$	3·5372	**17**	·1848	1·4941	**46**	·0683	·5522
7·2530	·4329	**3½**	**18**	·1745	1·4111	**48**	·0654	·5292
8	·3927	3·1749	**19**	·1653	1·3368	**50**	·0628	·5080
8·3776	$\frac{3}{8}$	3·0318	**20**	·1571	1·2700	50·2655	$\frac{1}{16}$	·5053
8·4665	·3711	**3**	**22**	·1428	1·1545	50·7991	·0618	$\frac{1}{2}$
9	·3491	2·8222	**24**	·1309	1·0583	**56**	·0561	·4536
10	·3142	2·5400	**25**	·1257	1·0160	**60**	·0524	·4233

* B.S. No. 545—1934.

BROWN AND SHARPE SPUR GEARS

Proportions of Standard Depth Teeth

NOTATION (Fig. 16)

P = diametral pitch. P′ = circular pitch. s = addendum.
$s + f$ = dedendum. t = thickness of tooth on pitch line.
f = clearance at bottom of teeth. D″ = working depth of tooth.
D″ + f = whole depth of tooth. D′ = pitch diameter. N = number of teeth.

D = outside diameter. $t″$ = chordal thickness of tooth. D‴ = bottom diameter.

$\theta = \frac{1}{4}$ of angle subtended by circular pitch. Module is in millimetres $= \dfrac{1}{P}$.

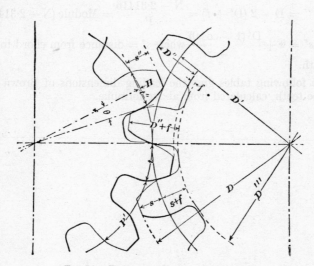

FIG. 16.—BROWN AND SHARPE SPUR GEARS.

FORMULÆ

$$s = \frac{1}{P} = \frac{P'}{\pi} = 0\cdot 3183\,P' = \frac{D'}{N}.$$

$$t = \frac{P'}{2} = \frac{\pi}{2P} = \frac{1\cdot 5708}{P} = 1\cdot 5708 \text{ module.}$$

$$f = \frac{t}{10} = 0 \cdot 1571 \text{ module.}$$

$$s + f = \frac{1 \cdot 157}{P} = 0 \cdot 3683 \text{ P}' = 1 \cdot 1571 \text{ module.}$$

$$D'' = 2s = \frac{2}{P} = 0 \cdot 6366 \text{ P}' = 2 \text{ module.}$$

$$D' = \frac{N}{P} = \frac{NP'}{\pi} = 0 \cdot 3183 \text{ P}'N.$$

$$D = D' + 2s = \frac{N + 2}{P}.$$

$$\theta = \frac{90°}{N}.$$

$$t'' = D' \sin \theta.$$

$$D''' = D - 2 \, (D'' + f) = \frac{N - 2 \cdot 31416}{P} = \text{Module (N} - 2 \cdot 31416.)$$

$$s'' = s + \frac{D' \, (1 - \cos \theta)}{2} \text{ where } s'' = \text{distance from chord to top}$$

of tooth.

The following tables give the leading dimensions of Brown and Sharpe teeth, calculated from above formulæ.

TABLE OF BROWN AND SHARPE GEAR TEETH
(Standard Depth)

Circular Pitch	Threads or Teeth per In. Linear	Diametral Pitch	Thickness of Tooth on Pitch Line	Addendum and Module	Working Depth of Tooth	Depth of Space below Pitch Line	Whole Depth of Tooth	Width of Thread-tool at End	Width of Thread at Top
P'	$\frac{1''}{P'}$	P	t	s	D''	s + f	D'' + f	P' × ·3095	P' × ·3354
2	½	1·5708	1·0000	·6366	1·2732	·7366	1·3732	·6190	·6707
1⅞	8/15	1·6755	·9375	·5968	1·1937	·6906	1·2874	·5803	·6288
1¾	4/7	1·7952	·8750	·5570	1·1141	·6445	1·2016	·5416	·5869
1⅝	8/13	1·9333	·8125	·5173	1·0345	·5985	1·1158	·5029	·5450
1½	⅔	2·0944	·7500	·4775	·9549	·5525	1·0299	·4642	·5030
1 7/16	16/23	2·1855	·7187	·4576	·9151	·5294	·9870	·4449	·4821
1⅜	8/11	2·2848	·6875	·4377	·8754	·5064	·9441	·4256	·4611
1⅓	¾	2·3562	·6666	·4244	·8488	·4910	·9154	·4127	·4471
1 5/16	16/21	2·3936	·6562	·4178	·8356	·4834	·9012	·4062	·4402
1¼	⅘	2·5133	·6250	·3979	·7958	·4604	·8583	·3869	·4192
1 3/16	16/19	2·6456	·5937	·3780	·7560	·4374	·8154	·3675	·3982
1⅛	8/9	2·7925	·5625	·3581	·7162	·4143	·7724	·3482	·3773
1 1/16	16/17	2·9568	·5312	·3382	·6764	·3913	·7295	·3288	·3563
1	1	3·1416	·5000	·3183	·6366	·3683	·6866	·3095	·3354
15/16	1 1/15	3·3510	·4687	·2984	·5968	·3453	·6437	·2902	·3141
⅞	1⅐	3·5904	·4375	·2785	·5570	·3223	·6007	·2708	·2934
13/16	1 3/13	3·8666	·4062	·2586	·5173	·2993	·5579	·2515	·2725
⅘	1¼	3·9270	·4000	·2546	·5092	·2946	·5492	·2476	·2686
¾	1⅓	4·1888	·3750	·2387	·4775	·2762	·5150	·2321	·2515
11/16	1 5/11	4·5696	·3437	·2189	·4377	·2532	·4720	·2128	·2306
⅔	1½	4·7124	·3333	·2122	·4244	·2455	·4577	·2063	·2236
⅝	1⅗	5·0265	·3125	·1889	·3979	·2301	·4291	·1934	·2096
⅗	1⅔	5·2360	·3000	·1910	·3820	·2210	·4120	·1857	·2012
4/7	1¾	5·4978	·2857	·1819	·3638	·2105	·3923	·1769	·1916
9/16	1 7/9	5·5851	·2812	·1790	·3581	·2071	·3862	·1741	·1886

TABLE OF BROWN AND SHARPE GEAR TEETH
(Standard Depth)

Circular Pitch	*Threads or Teeth per In. Linear*	*Diametral Pitch*	*Thickness of Tooth on Pitch Line*	*Addendum and Module*	*Working Depth of Tooth*	*Depth of Space below Pitch Line*	*Whole Depth of Tooth*	*Width of Thread-tool at End*	*Width of Thread at Top*
P′	$\frac{1''}{P'}$	P	*t*	*s*	D″	*s* + *f*	D″ + *f*	P′ × ·3095	P′ × ·3354
$\frac{1}{2}$	2	6·2832	·2500	·1592	·3183	·1842	·3433	·1547	·1677
$\frac{4}{9}$	$2\frac{1}{4}$	7·0685	·2222	·1415	·2830	·1637	·3052	·1376	·1490
$\frac{7}{16}$	$2\frac{2}{7}$	7·1808	·2187	·1393	·2785	·1611	·3003	·1354	·1467
$\frac{3}{7}$	$2\frac{1}{3}$	7·3304	·2143	·1364	·2728	·1578	·2942	·1326	·1437
$\frac{2}{5}$	$2\frac{1}{2}$	7·8540	·2000	·1273	·2546	·1473	·2746	·1238	·1341
$\frac{3}{8}$	$2\frac{2}{3}$	8·3776	·1875	·1194	·2387	·1381	·2575	·1161	·1258
$\frac{4}{11}$	$2\frac{3}{4}$	8·6394	·1818	·1158	·2316	·1340	·2498	·1125	·1219
$\frac{1}{3}$	3	9·4248	·1666	·1061	·2122	·1228	·2289	·1032	·1118
$\frac{5}{16}$	$3\frac{1}{5}$	10·0531	·1562	·0995	·1989	·1151	·2146	·0967	·1048
$\frac{3}{10}$	$3\frac{1}{3}$	10·4719	·1500	·0955	·1910	·1105	·2060	·0928	·1006
$\frac{2}{7}$	$3\frac{1}{2}$	10·9956	·1429	·0909	·1819	·1052	·1962	·0884	·0958
$\frac{1}{4}$	4	12·5664	·1250	·0796	·1591	·0921	·1716	·0774	·0838
$\frac{2}{9}$	$4\frac{1}{2}$	14·1372	·1111	·0707	·1415	·0818	·1526	·0688	·0745
$\frac{1}{5}$	5	15·7080	·1000	·0637	·1273	·0737	·1373	·0619	·0671
$\frac{3}{16}$	$5\frac{1}{3}$	16·7552	·0937	·0597	·1194	·0690	·1287	·0580	·0629
$\frac{2}{11}$	$5\frac{1}{2}$	17·2788	·0909	·0579	·1158	·0670	·1249	·0563	·0610
$\frac{1}{6}$	6	18·8496	·0833	·0531	·1061	·0614	·1144	·0516	·0559
$\frac{2}{13}$	$6\frac{1}{2}$	20·4203	·0769	·0489	·0978	·0566	·1055	·0476	·0516
$\frac{1}{7}$	7	21·9911	·0714	·0455	·0910	·0526	·0981	·0442	·0479
$\frac{2}{15}$	$7\frac{1}{2}$	23·5619	·0666	·0425	·0850	·0492	·0917	·0413	·0447
$\frac{1}{8}$	8	25·1327	·0625	·0398	·0796	·0460	·0858	·0387	·0419
$\frac{1}{9}$	9	28·2743	·0555	·0354	·0707	·0409	·0763	·0344	·0373
$\frac{1}{10}$	10	31·4159	·0500	·0318	·0637	·0368	·0687	·0309	·0335
$\frac{1}{16}$	16	50·2655	·0312	·0199	·0398	·0230	·0429	·0193	·0210
$\frac{1}{20}$	20	62·8318	·0250	·0159	·0318	·0184	·0343	·0155	·0168

TABLE OF BROWN AND SHARPE GEAR TEETH
(Standard Depth)

Diametral Pitch	Circular Pitch	Thickness of Tooth on Pitch Line	Addendum and Module	Working Depth of Tooth	Depth of Space below Pitch Line	Whole Depth of Tooth
P	P'	t	s	D″	s + f	D″ + f
½	6·2832	3·1416	2·0000	4·0000	2·3142	4·3142
¾	4·1888	2·0944	1·3333	2·6666	1·5428	2·8761
1	3·1416	1·5708	1·0000	2·0000	1·1571	2·1571
1¼	2·5133	1·2566	·8000	1·6000	·9257	1·7257
1½	2·0944	1·0472	·6666	1·3333	·7714	1·4381
1¾	1·7952	·8976	·5714	1·1429	·6612	1·2326
2	1·5708	·7854	·5000	1·0000	·5785	1·0785
2¼	1·3963	·6981	·4444	·8888	·5143	·9587
2½	1·2566	·6283	·4000	·8000	·4628	·8628
2¾	1·1424	·5712	·3636	·7273	·4208	·7844
3	1·0472	·5236	·3333	·6666	·3857	·7190
3½	·8976	·4488	·2857	·5714	·3306	·6163
4	·7854	·3927	·2500	·5000	·2893	·5393
5	·6283	·3142	·2000	·4000	·2314	·4314
6	·5236	·2618	·1666	·3333	·1928	·3595
7	·4488	·2244	·1429	·2857	·1653	·3081
8	·3927	·1963	·1250	·2500	·1446	·2696
9	·3491	·1745	·1111	·2222	·1286	·2397
10	·3142	·1571	·1000	·2000	·1157	·2157
11	·2856	·1428	·0909	·1818	·1052	·1961
12	·2618	·1309	·0833	·1666	·0964	·1798
13	·2417	·1208	·0769	·1538	·0890	·1659
14	·2244	·1122	·0714	·1429	·0826	·1541

TABLE OF BROWN AND SHARPE GEAR TEETH
(Standard Depth)

Diametral Pitch	Circular Pitch	Thickness of Tooth on Pitch Line	$\frac{1}{P}$ or the Addendum and Module	Working Depth of Tooth	Depth of Space below Pitch Line	Whole Depth of Tooth
P	P′	t	s	D″	s + f	D″ + f
15	·2094	·1047	·0666	·1333	·0771	·1438
16	·1963	·0982	·0625	·1250	·0723	·1348
17	·1848	·0924	·0588	·1176	·0681	·1269
18	·1745	·0873	·0555	·1111	·0643	·1198
19	·1653	·0827	·0526	·1053	·0609	·1135
20	·1571	·0785	·0500	·1000	·0579	·1079
22	·1428	·0714	·0455	·0909	·0526	·0980
24	·1309	·0654	·0417	·0833	·0482	·0898
26	·1208	·0604	·0385	·0769	·0445	·0829
28	·1122	·0561	·0357	·0714	·0413	·0770
30	·1047	·0524	·0333	·0666	·0386	·0719
32	·0982	·0491	·0312	·0625	·0362	·0674
34	·0924	·0462	·0294	·0588	·0340	·0634
36	·0873	·0436	·0278	·0555	·0321	·0599
38	·0827	·0413	·0263	·0526	·0304	·0568
40	·0785	·0393	·0250	·0500	·0289	·0539
42	·0748	·0374	·0238	·0476	·0275	·0514
44	·0714	·0357	·0227	·0455	·0263	·0490
46	·0683	·0341	·0217	·0435	·0252	·0469
48	·0654	·0327	·0208	·0417	·0241	·0449
50	·0628	·0314	·0200	·0400	·0231	·0431
56	·0561	·0280	·0178	·0357	·0207	·0385
60	·0524	·0262	·0166	·0333	·0193	·0360

TABLE OF BROWN AND SHARPE GEAR TEETH
(Stub-tooth Standard *)

Diametral Pitch	Circular Pitch	Thickness of Tooth on Pitch Line	$\frac{0.8}{P}$ or the Addendum	Working Depth of Tooth	$\frac{1}{P}$ or Depth of Space below Pitch Line	Whole Depth of Tooth
P	P′	t	s	D″	s + f	D″ + f
1	3·1416	1·5708	·8000	1·6000	1·0000	1·8000
1¼	2·5133	1·2566	·6400	1·2800	·8000	1·4400
1½	2·0944	1·0472	·5333	1·0666	·6666	1·2000
1¾	1·7952	·8926	·4571	·9142	·5714	1·0285
2	1·5708	·7854	·4000	·8000	·5000	·9000
2¼	1·3963	·6981	·3555	·7110	·4444	·8000
2½	1·2566	·6283	·3200	·6400	·4000	·7200
2¾	1·1424	·5712	·2909	·5818	·3636	·6545
3	1·0472	·5236	·2666	·5333	·3333	·6000
3½	·8976	·4488	·2286	·4571	·2857	·5143
4	·7854	·3927	·2000	·4000	·2500	·4500
5	·6283	·3142	·1600	·3200	·2000	·3600
6	·5236	·2618	·1333	·2667	·1666	·3000
7	·4488	·2244	·1143	·2286	·1429	·2572
8	·3927	·1963	·1000	·2000	·1250	·2250
9	·3491	·1745	·0889	·1778	·1111	·2000
10	·3142	·1571	·0800	·1600	·1000	·1800
12	·2618	·1309	·0667	·1333	·0833	·1500
14	·2244	·1122	·0572	·1144	·0714	·1286
16	·1963	·0982	·0500	·1000	·0625	·1125
18	·1745	·0873	·0444	·0888	·0555	·1000
20	·1571	·0785	·0400	·0800	·0500	·0900
22	·1428	·0714	·0364	·0728	·0455	·0819
24	·1309	·0654	·0333	·0667	·0417	·0750
28	·1122	·0561	·0286	·0572	·0357	·0643
30	·1047	·0524	·0266	·0533	·0333	·0600
32	·0982	·0491	·0250	·0500	·0312	·0562
36	·0873	·0436	·0222	·0444	·0278	·0500

* American Association Standards.

Stub-gear Tooth Proportions

The proportions of the stub tooth of the American Gear Manufacturers Association (A.G.N.A. Standard) are given in the table below, the following notation being employed:

s = addendum. f = clearance at bottom of teeth.
D'' = working depth of tooth. D' = pitch diameter.
D = outside diameter. A = pressure angle. N = number of teeth. $D.P.$ = diametral pitch. $C.P.$ = circular pitch.

Dimension	Diametral Pitch	Circular Pitch
Addendum s . . .	$\dfrac{0\cdot8}{\text{D.P.}}$	0·2546 C.P.
Dedendum $(s + f)$ . .	$\dfrac{1}{\text{D.P.}}$	0·3183 C.P.
Working Depth D'' .	$\dfrac{1\cdot6}{\text{D.P.}}$	0·5092 C.P.
Whole Depth $(D'' + f)$.	$\dfrac{1\cdot8}{\text{D.P.}}$	0·5729 C.P.
Pitch Diameter D' . .	$\dfrac{N}{\text{D.P.}}$	0·3183 C.P. × N
Outside Diameter D . .	$\dfrac{N + 1\cdot6}{\text{D.P.}}$	$D' + 2s$
Pressure Angle A . .	20°	20°

In the case of these teeth the chordal thickness and height of arc are the same as for standard teeth.

Involute-gear Cutters

Theoretically, since the dimensions of spur-gear teeth are proportional to the diametral (or circular) pitch, a different cutter is required for gears having different numbers of teeth. In practice, however, it is found satisfactory to use a set of eight cutters each, for the $14\frac{1}{2}°$ and 20° pressure-angle teeth, respectively. The following is a table of involute-gear tooth cutters, showing their designations and the range of gears (numbers of teeth) that they will machine.

Involute-gear Cutter No.	Range of Teeth that can be Cut
1	135 teeth to a rack
2	55 to 134 teeth
3	35 to 54 teeth
4	26 to 34 teeth
5	21 to 25 teeth
6	17 to 20 teeth
7	14 to 16 teeth
8	12 to 13 teeth

Involute-gear Cutters for More Accurate Teeth

Gear cutters are also made in half-numbers for more accurate or finer division of the number of teeth, as follows :

Involute-gear Cutter No.	Range of Teeth that can be Cut
$1\frac{1}{2}$	80 to 134 teeth
$2\frac{1}{2}$	42 to 54 teeth
$3\frac{1}{2}$	30 to 34 teeth
$4\frac{1}{2}$	23 to 25 teeth
$5\frac{1}{2}$	19 to 20 teeth
$6\frac{1}{2}$	15 to 16 teeth
$7\frac{1}{2}$	13 teeth

Epicycloidal or Double-curve Gear Cutters

Cutter Designation	Range of Teeth Cut	Cutter Designation	Range of Teeth Cut
A	12 teeth	M	27 to 29 teeth
B	13 teeth	N	30 to 33 teeth
C	14 teeth	O	34 to 37 teeth
D	15 teeth	P	38 to 42 teeth
E	16 teeth	Q	43 to 49 teeth
F	17 teeth	R	50 to 59 teeth
G	18 teeth	S	60 to 74 teeth
H	19 teeth	T	75 to 99 teeth
I	20 teeth	U	100 to 149 teeth
J	21 to 22 teeth	V	150 to 249 teeth
K	23 to 24 teeth	W	250 to a rack
L	25 to 26 teeth	X	Rack

[Brown and Sharpe]

Chordal Thickness and Height

For accurate checking of spur-gear teeth the chordal thickness AB (Fig. 17) and chordal height h are measured with vernier gear calipers (Fig. 18) or similar means. The following formulæ are used, where tables are unavailable:

$$s = h - x$$
$$x = R (1 - \cos \theta)$$
$$\text{Chord } AB = 2 R \sin \theta$$
$$\theta = \frac{90°}{N}$$

where s = distance from pitch circle to top of addendum.

R = radius of pitch circle.

N = number of teeth.

2θ = angle subtended by tooth at centre.

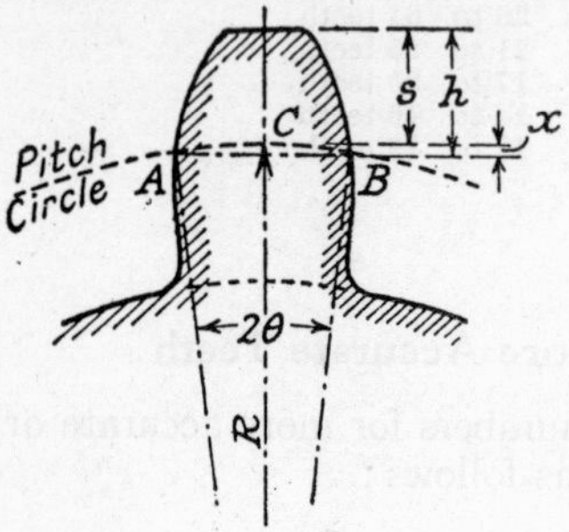

Fig. 17.—Chordal Thickness.

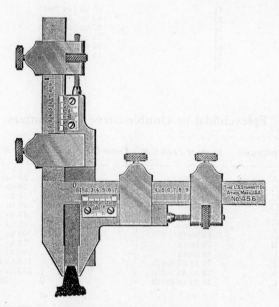

Fig. 18.—Vernier Gear Caliper.

CHORDAL THICKNESS OF GEAR TEETH

(1 Diametral Pitch)

No. of Teeth	Chordal AB	Distance x	No. of Teeth	Chordal AB	Distance x	No. of Teeth	Chordal AB	Distance x
						94	1·5707	·0066
6	1·5529	·1022	50	1·5705	·0123	95	1·5707	·0065
7	1·5568	·0873	51	1·5706	·0121	96	1·5707	·0064
8	1·5607	·0769	52	1·5706	·0119	97	1·5707	·0064
9	1·5628	·0684	53	1·5706	·0117	98	1·5707	·0063
10	1·5643	·0616	54	1·5706	·0114	99	1·5707	·0062
11	1·5654	·0559	55	1·5706	·0112	100	1·5707	·0061
12	1·5663	·0514	56	1·5706	·0110	101	1·5707	·0061
13	1·5670	·0474	57	1·5706	·0108	102	1·5707	·0060
14	1·5675	·0440	58	1·5706	·0106	103	1·5707	·0060
15	1·5679	·0411	59	1·5706	·0105	104	1·5707	·0059
16	1·5683	·0385	60	1·5706	·0102	105	1·5707	·0059
17	1·5686	·0362	61	1·5706	·0101	106	1·5707	·0058
18	1·5688	·0342	62	1·5706	·0100	107	1·5707	·0058
19	1·5690	·0324	63	1·5706	·0098	108	1·5707	·0057
20	1·5692	·0308	64	1·5706	·0097	109	1·5707	·0057
21	1·5694	·0294	65	1·5706	·0095	110	1·5707	·0056
22	1·5695	·0281	66	1·5706	·0094	111	1·5707	·0056
23	1·5696	·0268	67	1·5706	·0092	112	1·5707	·0055
24	1·5697	·0257	68	1·5706	·0091	113	1·5707	·0055
25	1·5698	·0247	69	1·5707	·0090	114	1·5707	·0054
26	1·5698	·0237	70	1·5707	·0088	115	1·5707	·0054
27	1·5699	·0228	71	1·5707	·0087	116	1·5707	·0053
28	1·5700	·0220	72	1·5707	·0086	117	1·5707	·0053
29	1·5700	·0213	73	1·5707	·0085	118	1·5707	·0053
30	1·5701	·0208	74	1·5707	·0084	119	1·5707	·0052
31	1·5701	·0199	75	1·5707	·0083	120	1·5707	·0052
32	1 5702	·0193	76	1·5707	·0081	121	1·5707	·0051
33	1·5702	·0187	77	1·5707	·0080	122	1·5707	·0051
34	1·5702	·0181	78	1·5707	·0079	123	1·5707	·0050
35	1·5702	·0176	79	1·5707	·0078	124	1·5707	·0050
36	1·5703	·0171	80	1·5707	·0077	125	1·5707	·0049
37	1·5703	·0167	81	1·5707	·0076	126	1·5707	·0049
38	1·5703	·0162	82	1·5707	·0075	127	1·5707	·0049
39	1·5704	·0158	83	1·5707	·0074	128	1·5707	·0048
40	1·5704	·0154	84	1·5707	·0074	129	1·5707	·0048
41	1·5704	·0150	85	1·5707	·0073	130	1·5707	·0047
42	1·5704	·0147	86	1·5707	·0072	131	1·5708	·0047
43	1·5705	·0143	87	1·5707	·0071	132	1·5708	·0047
44	1·5705	·0140	88	1·5707	·0070	133	1·5708	·0047
45	1·5705	·0137	89	1·5707	·0069	134	1·5708	·0046
46	1·5705	·0134	90	1·5707	·0068	135	1·5708	·0046
47	1·5705	·0131	91	1·5707	·0068	150	1·5708	·0045
48	1·5705	·0129	92	1·5707	·0067	250	1·5708	·0025
49	1·5705	·0126	93	1·5707	·0067	Rack	1·5708	·0000

[Brown and Sharpe]

BEVEL GEARS

Definitions

The motions obtained by means of bevel gearing may be regarded as the same as those obtained by a pair of cones rolling together in frictional contact (Fig. 19). Power may be transmitted from one shaft to another shaft whose axis makes any given *centre angle* with the axis of the first shaft by means of friction cones A and B, where the two axes intersect. As shown the axes are mutually at right

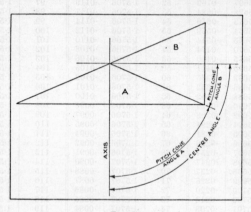

FIG. 19.

angles, but they may be inclined at angles greater or less than a right angle.

Ratio of Bevel Gears.—The ratio is that of the numbers of teeth of the two bevel gears.

Pitch Cones.—The pitch cones of a pair of bevel gears are the equivalent friction cones which will roll together without slip.

Pitch Circles.—The circles which form the bases of the two pitch cones.

Pitch Diameter.—The diameter of its pitch circle (D, Fig. 20).*

Cone Distance.—The length of the generating line of the two cones from the pitch circle to the apex (C, Fig. 20).

Pitch Point.—The point of tangency of the pitch circles.

Back Cones.—The complementary cones generated by lines at right angles to the pitch-cone generator at the pitch circles and intersecting the axes.

* B.S. No. 545—1934.

Pressure Angle.—The acute angle between the common normal to the tooth curves at the pitch point and the common tangent to the two pitch circles passing through the pitch point. (Fig. 21 * is

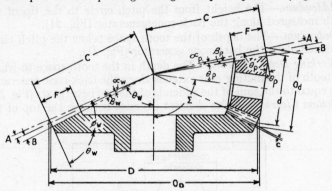

FIG. 20.—BRITISH STANDARD BEVEL GEARS.

a developed view on a plane tangential to the back cones at the pitch point.)

Circular Pitch.—The length of the arc of pitch circle between similar faces on consecutive teeth (Fig. 21).

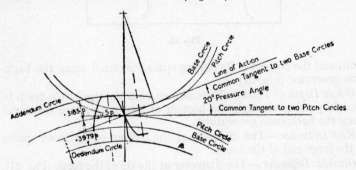

FIG. 21.—BRITISH STANDARD INVOLUTE TOOTH TERMS.

Normal Pitch of a helical bevel gear is the circular pitch multiplied by the cosine of the spiral angle at the pitch circle.

Diametral Pitch.—The number of teeth divided by the pitch diameter in inches.

* B.S. No. 545—1934.

Module.—The pitch diameter divided by the number of teeth. The reciprocal of the diametral pitch. Usually expressed in millimetres.

Addendum.—The height from pitch circle to the tip of the tooth measured along the back-cone generator (Fig. 21).

Dedendum.—The depth of the tooth space below the pitch circle measured along the back-cone generator (Fig. 21).

Working Depth of Tooth.—The depth in the tooth space to which the tooth of the mating gear extends along the back-cone generator. It is equal to the sum of the addenda of the two bevel gears (Fig. 21).

Bottom Clearance.—The shortest distance between the top of the

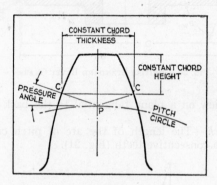

FIG. 22.

tooth and the bottom of its mating space measured along the back-cone generator (Fig. 21).

Whole Depth of Tooth.—The distance from the tips of the teeth to a circle passing through the bottom of the tooth space measured along the back-cone generator.

Root Diameter.—The diameter at the bottom of the tooth spaces at the large end of the tooth.

Outside Diameter.—The diameter at the tip of the teeth (Fig. 21).

Tooth Thickness.—The length of arc of the pitch circle between opposite faces of the same tooth (Fig. 21).

Face Width.—The width measured in the direction of the common generator of the two pitch cones.

Constant Chord.—The chord between two points on the gear-tooth profile which make contact with the basic rack (Fig. 22).

Fillet.—The rounded corner at the bottom of the tooth space.

Back Cone Angle.—The angle between the back-cone generating line and the axis of the gear, i.e. 90° minus the pitch angle.

Addendum Angle.—The angle between the pitch-cone surface and the base of the tooth.

Dedendum Angle.—The angle between the pitch-cone surface and the root of the tooth.

Face Angle.—The angle between the tip of the tooth and the axis of the gear, i.e. the pitch angle plus addendum angle (ϕ, Fig. 20).

Shaft Angle.—The angle between the intersecting axis within which the pitch point lies, i.e. the sum of the pitch angles of wheel and pinion.

British Standard Bevel Gears *

The British Standard form of tooth for straight bevel gears (Fig. 23) is generated from a straight-sided tool having an angle of 20° except that it has a slight easing of the tip of the tooth. The

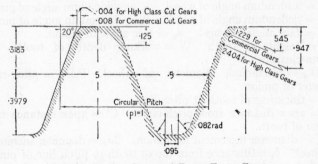

FIG. 23.—BRITISH STANDARD BEVEL TOOTH FORM.

amount of this easing must not exceed the following values measured on the basic rack :

Class B. High-class Cut Gears.—Easing Amount = 0·004 × circular pitch extending to 0·125 × circular pitch in depth.

Class C. Commercial Cut Gears.—Easing Amount = 0·008 × circular pitch extending to 0·125 × circular pitch in depth.

The bottom clearance space at the small end of the tooth is a smooth, continuous curve of approximately semicircular form.

The B.S. Specification (B.S. No. 545—1934) gives details of the

* B.S. No. 545—1934.

tooth correction, permissible pitch errors and tolerances, strength and horse-power rating, factor of safety, bending-stress factors, calculations and charts of zone factors, speed and pitch factors.

Bevel-gear Formulæ

NOTATION

D = diameter of wheel.   d = diameter of pinion.   C = cone distance.

A = addendum.   B = dedendum.   O = outside diameter.   F = face width.

θ = pitch angle.   α = addendum angle.   β = dedendum angle.   φ = face angle.

ε = shaft angle. N_w = Number of teeth of wheel. N_p ε = Number of teeth of pinion.

C.P. = circular pitch.   D.P. = diametral pitch.

$θ_w$ = pitch angle of wheel. $θ_p$ = pitch angle of pinion.

$α_w$ = addendum angle of wheel. $α_p$ = addendum angle of pinion.

$β_w$ = dedendum angle of wheel. $β_p$ = dedendum angle of pinion.

$φ_w$ = face angle of wheel. $φ_p$ = face angle of pinion.

H = height of tooth.   W = working depth of tooth.   c = bottom clearance.

P.D.$_w$ = pitch-circle diameter of wheel.   P.D.$_p$ = pitch-circle diameter of pinion.

T = thickness of tooth at pitch line.

C = apex distance from pitch circle.   C' = apex distance from bottom of tooth.

$2a_p$ = diameter increment for pinion. $2a_w$ = diameter increment for wheel. b_p = distance from top of tooth to pitch line of pinion. b_w = distance from top of tooth to pitch line of wheel. f_w = face distance for wheel. f_p = face distance for pinion.

FORMULÆ

$$C = \frac{\sqrt{N_w{}^2 + N_p{}^2}}{2 \text{ D.P.}} = \frac{\sqrt{N_w{}^2 + N_p{}^2} \times \text{C.P.}}{2\pi}$$

$$C' = \frac{X}{\cos \beta_p}$$

$$\tan \theta_w = \frac{N_w}{N_p}$$

$$\tan \theta_p = \frac{N_p}{N_w}$$

$$\tan \alpha = \frac{A}{C}$$

$$\tan \beta = \frac{A + c}{C}$$

$$\phi_w = \phi_p - \beta$$
$$\phi_p = \phi_w + \beta$$

Cutting angle of wheel $= \phi_w - \beta_w$
Cutting angle of pinion $= \phi_p - \beta_w$

$$P.D._w = \frac{N_w}{D.P.} = \frac{N_w \times C.P.}{\pi}$$

$$P.D._p = \frac{N_p}{D.P.} = \frac{N_p \times C.P.}{\pi}$$

Outside diameter of wheel $O_w = P.D._w + 2a_w$
Outside diameter of pinion $O_p = P.D._p + 2a_p$

$$2a_w = 2A \cos \theta_w$$
$$2a_p = 2A \cos \theta_p$$
$$b_w = a_p$$
$$b_p = a_w$$

$$F = \frac{C}{3} \text{ to } \frac{C}{4}$$

$$f_w = F \sin \phi_w$$
$$f_p = F \sin \phi_p$$

Note.—The involute-gear tooth proportions are the same as for spur gears.

$$\text{Diametral Pitch D.P.} = \frac{\pi}{C.P.} = \frac{3 \cdot 1416}{C.P.} = \frac{N}{D}$$

$$\text{Circular Pitch C.P.} = \frac{\pi}{D.P.} = \frac{3 \cdot 1416}{D.P.} = \frac{3 \cdot 1416 \, D}{N}$$

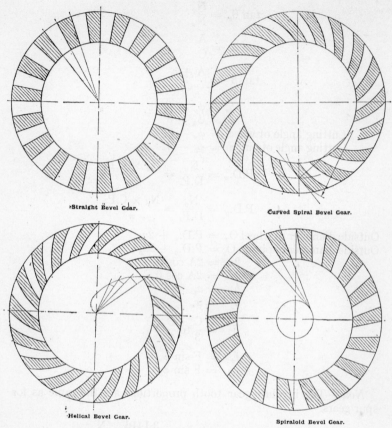

FIG. 24.—BRITISH STANDARD TYPES OF BEVEL GEARS.

TYPES OF BEVEL GEARS

The four types of straight and other bevel gears standardised by the British Standards Institution * are illustrated above, the nomenclature adopted being given below the diagrams. The methods of gear-tooth generation are also shown on the diagrams.

* B.S. No. 545—1934.

HELICAL GEARS

Definitions

The helix angle θ (Fig. 25) is the angle θ of a right-angled triangle of height C equal to the circumference of the upper cylinder and base equal to the lead of the spiral line *abcd*.

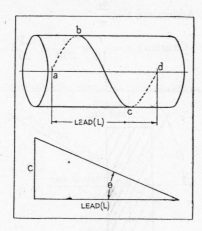

FIG. 25.

NOTATION

D = pitch-circle diameter.   P = normal diametral pitch.   L = lead of spiral.   *d* = outside diameter.

θ = helix angle.   N = number of teeth.   C.P. = circular pitch. M = module (mm.).   Addendum = *f*.   Clearance = *c*.

Helix angle. $\text{Tan } \theta = \dfrac{\pi D}{L}$

$$\cos \theta = \frac{N}{PD} = \frac{N \times \text{C.P.}}{\pi D} = \frac{MN}{D}$$

Number of teeth $N = PD \cos \theta = \dfrac{\pi D \cos \theta}{\text{C.P.}} = \dfrac{D \cos \theta}{M}$

Pitch-circle diameter $D = \dfrac{N}{P \cos \theta} = \dfrac{N \times \text{C.P.}}{\pi \cos \theta} = \dfrac{MN}{\cos \theta}$

$$\text{Outside diameter } d = D + \frac{2}{P} = D + \frac{2 \text{ C.P.}}{\pi} = D + 2\,M$$

$$\text{Addendum } f = \frac{1}{P} = \frac{\text{C.P.}}{\pi} = M$$

$$\left.\begin{array}{c}\text{Normal thickness of tooth}\\ \text{on pitch line}\end{array}\right\} t = \frac{\pi}{2P} = \frac{\text{C.P.}}{2} = \frac{\pi M}{2}$$

$$\text{Addendum } f = \frac{2t}{\pi}$$

$$\text{Clearance } c = \frac{t}{10} \text{ or } \frac{\pi}{20P} = \frac{\text{C.P.}}{20} = \frac{\pi M}{20}$$

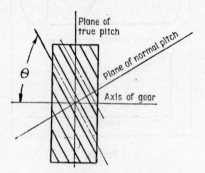

FIG. 26.—SPIRAL GEAR TERMS

$$\text{Whole depth of tooth} = 2f + c.$$

Diameter at bottom of tooth $= D - 2\,(f + c) = d - 2$ (depth of [tooth)

$$\left.\begin{array}{c}\text{Number of teeth for select-}\\ \text{ing cutter}\end{array}\right\} = \frac{N}{\cos^3 \theta}$$

$$\text{Diametral pitch } P = \frac{\pi}{\text{C.P.}} = \frac{25 \cdot 4}{M}$$

Note.—In the above formulæ all dimensions except M are in inches, M being in millimetres.

PROPORTIONS OF SPECIAL BEVEL AND SPIRAL-GEAR TEETH *

Module (Millimetres)	D.P.	Circular Pitch	Addendum · Standard Form 85 per cent. Stub (wheel and pinion)	Addendum · Wheel · Standard Gleason Correction	Addendum · Wheel · Gleason Correction 85 per cent. Stub	Addendum · Pinion · Standard Gleason Correction	Addendum · Pinion · Gleason Correction 85 per cent. Stub	Whole Depth Wheel and Pinion · Standard	Whole Depth Wheel and Pinion · 85 per cent. Stub	Depth below Pitch Line · Standard Form 85 per cent. Stub (wheel and pinion)	Depth below · Wheel · Standard Gleason Correction	Depth below · Wheel · Gleason Correction 85 per cent. Stub	Depth below · Pinion · Standard Gleason Correction	Depth below · Pinion · Gleason Correction 85 per cent. Stub
	20	0·1571	0·0425	0·0300	0·0255	0·0700	0·0595	0·1079	0·0917	0·0492	0·0779	0·0692	0·0379	0·0322
	19†	0·1653	0·0447	0·0316	0·0269	0·0736	0·0626	0·1135	0·0965	0·0518	0·0819	0·0696	0·0399	0·0339
	18	0·1745	0·0472	0·0333	0·0283	0·0777	0·0660	0·1198	0·1018	0·0546	0·0865	0·0735	0·0421	0·0358
	17†	0·1848	0·0500	0·0353	0·0300	0·0823	0·0700	0·1269	0·1079	0·0579	0·0916	0·0779	0·0446	0·0379
1½		0·1855	0·0502	0·0355	0·0302	0·0826	0·0702	0·1274	0·1083	0·0581	0·0919	0·0781	0·0448	0·0381
		3/16	0·0507	0·0358	0·0304	0·0836	0·0711	0·1287	0·1094	0·0587	0·0929	0·0790	0·0451	0·0383
	16	0·1963	0·0531	0·0375	0·0319	0·0875	0·0744	0·1348	0·1146	0·0615	0·0973	0·0827	0·0473	0·0402
	15†	0·2094	0·0566	0·0400	0·0340	0·0932	0·0792	0·1438	0·1222	0·0656	0·1038	0·0882	0·0506	0·0430
1¾		0·2164	0·0586	0·0413	0·0351	0·0965	0·0820	0·1486	0·1263	0·0677	0·1073	0·0912	0·0521	0·0443
	14	0·2244	0·0607	0·0428	0·0364	0·1000	0·0850	0·1541	0·1310	0·0703	0·1113	0·0946	0·0541	0·0460
	13†	0·2417	0·0654	0·0461	0·0392	0·1077	0·0915	0·1659	0·1410	0·0756	0·1198	0·1018	0·0582	0·0495
2		0·2474	0·0669	0·0472	0·0401	0·1102	0·0937	0·1698	0·1443	0·0774	0·1226	0·1042	0·0596	0·0506
		¼	0·0677	0·0478	0·0406	0·1114	0·0947	0·1716	0·1459	0·0784	0·1238	0·1053	0·0602	0·0512
	12	0·2618	0·0708	0·0500	0·0425	0·1166	0·0991	0·1798	0·1528	0·0820	0·1298	0·1103	0·0632	0·0537
2¼		0·2783	0·0753	0·0532	0·0452	0·1240	0·1054	0·1911	0·1624	0·0871	0·1379	0·1172	0·0671	0·0570
	11	0·2856	0·0773	0·0545	0·0463	0·1273	0·1082	0·1961	0·1667	0·0894	0·1416	0·1204	0·0688	0·0585
2½		0·3092	0·0836	0·0590	0·0501	0·1378	0·1171	0·2123	0·1805	0·0969	0·1533	0·1304	0·0745	0·0633
		5/16	0·0846	0·0597	0·0507	0·1393	0·1184	0·2146	0·1824	0·0978	0·1549	0·1317	0·0753	0·0640
	10	0·3142	0·0850	0·0600	0·0510	0·1400	0·1190	0·2157	0·1833	0·0983	0·1557	0·1323	0·0757	0·0643
2¾		0·3401	0·0921	0·0650	0·0552	0·1516	0·1289	0·2335	0·1985	0·1064	0·1685	0·1433	0·0819	0·0696
	9	0·3491	0·0944	0·0667	0·0567	0·1555	0·1322	0·2397	0·2037	0·1093	0·1730	0·1470	0·0842	0·0715
3		0·3710	0·1004	0·0709	0·0603	0·1653	0·1405	0·2548	0·2166	0·1162	0·1839	0·1563	0·0895	0·0761
		3/8	0·1015	0·0716	0·0609	0·1672	0·1421	0·2575	0·2189	0·1174	0·1859	0·1580	0·0903	0·0768
	8	0·3927	0·1062	0·0750	0·0638	0·1750	0·1487	0·2696	0·2294	0·1232	0·1946	0·1656	0·0946	0·0807

* Inst. of Autom. Engrs. † These sizes are now usually dispensed with.

Proportions of Special Bevel- and Spiral-gear Teeth (*contd.*)

D.P.	Module (Millimetres)	Circular Pitch	Addenda: Standard Form Stub 85 per cent. Stub (wheel and pinion)	Addenda Wheel: Standard Gleason Correction	Addenda Wheel: Gleason Correction 85 per cent. Stub	Addenda Pinion: Standard Gleason Correction	Addenda Pinion: Gleason Correction 85 per cent. Stub	Whole Depth Wheel and Pinion: Standard	Whole Depth Wheel and Pinion: 85 per cent. Stub	Depth below Pitch Line: Standard Form Stub 85 per cent. (wheel and pinion)	Depth below P.L. Wheel: Standard Gleason Correction	Depth below P.L. Wheel: Gleason Correction 85 per cent. Stub	Depth below P.L. Pinion: Standard Gleason Correction	Depth below P.L. Pinion: Gleason Correction 85 per cent. Stub
	3½	0·4329	0·1171	0·0827	0·0703	0·1929	0·1640	0·2972	0·2526	0·1355	0·2145	0·1823	0·1043	0·0886
		7/16	0·1184	0·0836	0·0711	0·1950	0·1657	0·3003	0·2553	0·1369	0·2167	0·1842	0·1053	0·0896
7		0·4488	0·1215	0·0857	0·0728	0·2000	0·1700	0·3081	0·2619	0·1404	0·2224	0·1891	0·1081	0·0919
	4	0·4947	0·1339	0·0945	0·0803	0·2205	0·1874	0·3391	0·2882	0·1543	0·2446	0·2079	0·1186	0·1008
		1/2	0·1352	0·0955	0·0812	0·2229	0·1895	0·3433	0·2918	0·1566	0·2478	0·2106	0·1204	0·1023
6		0·5236	0·1416	0·1000	0·0850	0·2333	0·1983	0·3595	0·3056	0·1640	0·2595	0·2206	0·1262	0·1073
	4½	0·5566	0·1506	0·1063	0·0904	0·2481	0·2109	0·3821	0·3248	0·1742	0·2758	0·2344	0·1340	0·1139
		9/16	0·1521	0·1074	0·0913	0·2506	0·2130	0·3862	0·3283	0·1762	0·2788	0·2370	0·1356	0·1153
	5	0·6184	0·1673	0·1181	0·1004	0·2755	0·2342	0·4246	0·3609	0·1936	0·3065	0·2605	0·1491	0·1267
		5/8	0·1691	0·1193	0·1014	0·2785	0·2367	0·4291	0·3647	0·1956	0·3098	0·2633	0·1506	0·1280
5		0·6283	0·1700	0·1200	0·1020	0·2800	0·2380	0·4314	0·3667	0·1967	0·3114	0·2647	0·1514	0·1287
	5½	0·6803	0·1840	0·1299	0·1104	0·3031	0·2576	0·4671	0·3970	0·2130	0·3372	0·2866	0·1640	0·1394
		11/16	0·1861	0·1313	0·1116	0·3065	0·2605	0·4720	0·4012	0·2151	0·3407	0·2896	0·1655	0·1407
	6	0·7421	0·2008	0·1417	0·1204	0·3307	0·2811	0·5095	0·4331	0·2323	0·3678	0·3127	0·1788	0·1520
		3/4	0·2029	0·1432	0·1217	0·3342	0·2841	0·5150	0·4377	0·2348	0·3718	0·3160	0·1808	0·1536
4		0·7854	0·2125	0·1500	0·1275	0·3500	0·2975	0·5393	0·4584	0·2459	0·3893	0·3309	0·1893	0·1609
		13/16	0·2198	0·1552	0·1319	0·3620	0·3077	0·5579	0·4742	0·2544	0·4027	0·3423	0·1959	0·1665
	7	0·8658	0·2343	0·1654	0·1406	0·3858	0·3279	0·5945	0·5053	0·2710	0·4291	0·3647	0·2087	0·1774
		7/8	0·2367	0·1671	0·1420	0·3899	0·3314	0·6007	0·5106	0·2739	0·4336	0·3686	0·2108	0·1792
3½		0·8976	0·2428	0·1714	0·1457	0·4000	0·3400	0·6163	0·5239	0·2811	0·4449	0·3782	0·2163	0·1839
		15/16	0·2536	0·1790	0·1521	0·4178	0·3551	0·6437	0·5471	0·2935	0·4647	0·3950	0·2259	0·1920
	8	0·9895	0·2677	0·1890	0·1606	0·4410	0·3748	0·6794	0·5775	0·3098	0·4904	0·4169	0·2384	0·2027
		1	0·2706	0·1910	0·1623	0·4456	0·3788	0·6866	0·5836	0·3130	0·4956	0·4213	0·2410	0·2048
3		1·0472	0·2833	0·2000	0·1700	0·4666	0·3966	0·7190	0·6111	0·3278	0·5190	0·4411	0·2524	0·2145

EPICYCLIC-GEAR TRAINS *

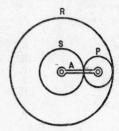

FIG. 27.

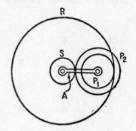

FIG. 28.

Letters denote diameters or numbers of teeth.

S = sun pinion.
P = planet pinion.
A = arm carrying P.
R = internally geared rack.

P_1 = planet wheel gearing with R.
P_2 = planet wheel gearing with S (P_1 coupled to P_2).

TABLE FOR FIG. 27

Case	Stationary Member	Driving Member	Driven Member	Revs. of Driven Member ÷ Revs. of Driving Member =	Revs.† of P on its Own Axis = Revs. of Driver × by
1	A	S	R	$\dfrac{S}{R}$	$\dfrac{S}{P}$
2	A	R	S	$\dfrac{R}{S}$	$\dfrac{R}{P}$
3	R	A	S	$\dfrac{R+S}{S}$	$\dfrac{R}{P}$
4	S	A	R	$\dfrac{R+S}{R}$	$\dfrac{S}{P}$
5	R	S	A	$\dfrac{S}{R+S}$	$\dfrac{S}{R+S} \times \dfrac{R}{P}$
6	S	R	A	$\dfrac{R}{R+S}$	$\dfrac{R}{R+S} \times \dfrac{S}{P}$

* Inst. of Autom. Engrs.
† This column gives the revs. of P relatively to the pin carrying it, which is fixed to the arm.

TABLE FOR FIG. 28

Case	Stationary Member	Driving Member	Driven Member	Revs. of Driven Member ÷ Revs. of Driving Member =	Revs.* of P_1 and P_2 = Revs. of Driver × by
1	A	S	R	$\dfrac{S}{P_2} \times \dfrac{P_1}{R}$	$\dfrac{S}{P_2}$
2	A	R	S	$\dfrac{R}{P_1} \times \dfrac{P_2}{S}$	$\dfrac{R}{P_1}$
3	R	A	S	$\dfrac{P_1 S + P_2 R}{P_1 S}$	$\dfrac{R}{P_1}$
4	S	A	R	$\dfrac{P_1 S + P_2 R}{P_2 R}$	$\dfrac{S}{P_2}$
5	R	S	A	$\dfrac{P_1 S}{P_1 S + P_2 R}$	$\dfrac{P_1 S}{P_1 S + P_2 R} \times \dfrac{R}{P_1}$
6	S	R	A	$\dfrac{P_2 R}{P_1 S + P_2 R}$	$\dfrac{P_2 R}{P_1 S + P_2 R} \times \dfrac{S}{P_2}$

* This column gives the revs. of P_2 and P_1 relatively to the pin carrying them, which is fixed to the arm.

[*Inst. of Autom. Engrs.*]

WORM GEARS

The chief types include (1) The Parallel or Straight Worm (A, Fig. 29). (2) Hindley or Hour Glass. (3) David Brown and Sharpe or D.B.S. Worm.

The Hindley Worm (B, Fig. 29) has a curved pitch line to correspond with that of the worm wheel. It has the big advantage over

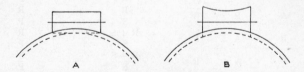

FIG. 29.—TYPES OF WORM GEAR.

the straight worm of giving a greater area of contact. The worm wheel can also be undercut so as to give a greater area of tooth contact.

The worm gear enables much greater reductions of speed to be made between two shafts with their axes at right angles, within a limited space, than other simple gears.

The efficiency of a well-designed and lubricated worm gear is very high ; for machine-cut gears of the usual ratios the efficiency is usually from 90 to 95 per cent. The Lanchester worm gear developed for rear-axle drive of automobiles had an efficiency of 96 to 98 per cent. ; ball or roller bearings were used throughout.

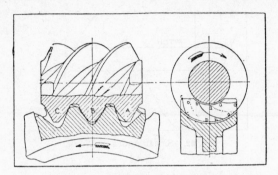

FIG. 30.—THE D.B.S. WORM GEAR.

The Hindley worm gear gives several teeth in contact with the worm at the same time.

The D.B.S. worm gear (Fig. 30), instead of using straight teeth on a section which contains the axis of the worm, are straight-sided on a section taken at a selected distance from the axis. Thus, the pitch line, instead of being half-way down the working depth, is at the bottom of the working depth or throat diameter of the worm wheel. This gives a high efficiency, namely, 96 to 97 per cent. for well-made gears running in an oil bath. In Fig. 30 the teeth A, B and C are in contact with the worm wheel. The Guest worm gear (Fig. 31) is another efficient type using tooth profiles generated on the hour-glass system. The tooth profiles are of such a shape as to give a large area of

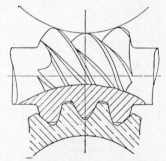

FIG. 31.—THE GUEST WORM GEAR.

contact between the worm and wheel. A special gear-generating machine is used to produce these large-contact-area worm gears.

The teeth of the worm may be either the involute or cycloidal form. For straight-sided teeth (on the axial section) the involute $14\frac{1}{2}°$ or one of $15°$ is usually employed, the cross-sectional dimensions being similar to those of the rack for a $14\frac{1}{2}°$ involute gear. The $30°$ tooth is often used for automobile worm gears. When the lead angle is more than $20°$ the tooth dimensions are based on the normal pitch.

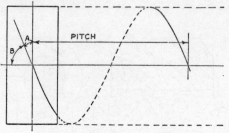

FIG. 32.—SPIRAL ANGLE OF WORM.

Nomenclature

Ratio of Gears.—The gear ratio is that of the number of teeth in the worm to the number of starts, e.g. for a single-start thread it is **1** ; for a three-start thread it is **3.**

Worm Spiral Angle.—This is the complement of the lead angle.

Worm Lead Angle.—The slope of the helix.

The spiral angle B (Fig. 32) is the complement of the helix angle A.

Worm Pitch Cylinder.—The worm pitch cylinder (Fig. 33) is the theoretical plain cylinder which, in rolling in frictional contact with the *Worm-wheel Pitch Circle*, gives the same motion as the actual worm and worm wheel.

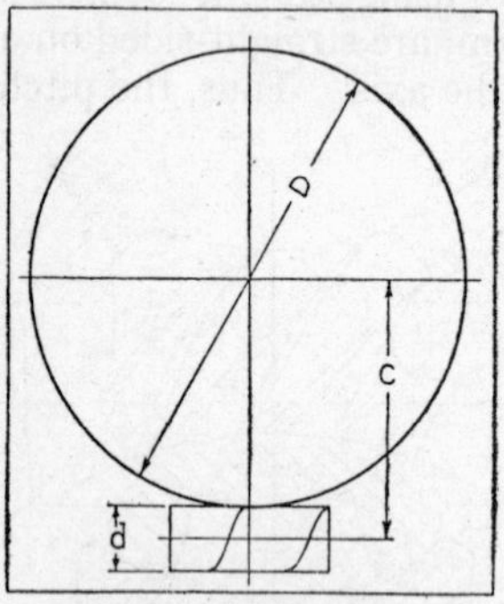

Centre Distance.—The distance between the axis of worm and centre of worm wheel (C, Fig. 33).

FIG. 33.—WORM PITCH CYLINDER.

Normal Circular Pitch.—The distance between the centres of adjacent threads measured round the pitch cylinder and the normal to helix.

Axial Pitch.—The axial pitch of the worm threads is the distance between the centre lines of two adjacent threads on the axial section.

Axial Pressure Angle.—The angle of inclination of worm profile at any point on an axial section to the perpendicular to the worm axis.

Normal Pressure Angle.—The angle between the tangent plane at any point on the tooth profile and a perpendicular to the axis at the same point.

Lead of Worm.—The axial advance per revolution of the worm.

Circular Pitch of Worm Wheel.—The circular arc distances between the centres of adjacent teeth as measured on the pitch circle.

The addendum, dedendum and clearance definitions are similar to those of spur gears.

Worm Crest Diameter.—The overall diameter of the worm threads or that of the enveloping cylinder.

Worm Root Diameter.—The diameter at the roots of the worm threads.

Worm-wheel Throat Diameter.—The diameter of the wheel at the bottom of the curved tooth face.

Overall Diameter of Worm Wheel.—The maximum diameter of the worm-wheel rim.

Worm-wheel Root Diameter.—The diameter at the base of the worm-wheel teeth.

Worm-gear Formulæ

NOTATION

L = lead. P = pitch of worm. C.P. = circular pitch of wheel. N.P. = normal pitch. N = R.P.M. of worm wheel. n = R.P.M. of worm.

G = gear ratio. Lead angle = A. Spiral angle = B (Fig. 32). Centre distance = C. Worm-wheel pitch diameter = D. Worm pitch-circle diameter = d.

T_w = number of teeth on worm wheel.

$$\text{Ratio of gearing } G = \frac{n}{N} = \frac{T_w}{\text{No. of starts on worm}}.$$

$$\text{Number of teeth on worm wheel } T_w \left\{ = \frac{n}{G}. \right.$$

$$\text{Linear pitch of worm } P = \frac{L}{\text{No. of starts}}.$$

$$\text{Circular pitch of wheel C.P.} = \frac{\pi D}{T_w}$$

$$= \frac{D \times 3 \cdot 1416}{T_w}.$$

$$\text{Normal pitch N.P.} = \text{C.P. cos A.}$$

$$\text{Lead L} = \text{pitch of worm} \times \text{number of starts}$$

$$= \frac{\pi D}{\cotan A}$$

$$= \frac{\pi D}{\tan B}$$

$$= \cotan B \times \pi D$$

$$= \tan A \times \pi D$$

$$= \frac{\pi D}{\text{gear ratio}} \text{ or } \frac{\pi D}{G}$$

$$= \frac{\pi D \times \text{number of starts}}{T_w}.$$

$$\text{Cotan lead angle.} \quad \text{Cotan A} = \frac{\pi D}{L}$$

$$= \cotan (90° - B).$$

$$\text{Tan spiral angle.} \quad \text{Tan B} = \frac{\pi D}{L}$$

$$= \text{Tan } (90° - A).$$

$$\text{Tan linear thread angle} = \frac{\tan \text{ normal thread angle}}{\cos \text{ lead angle A}}.$$

$$\text{Addendum} = \text{normal pitch of worm} \times 0 \cdot 3183.$$

$$\text{Dedendum} = \text{normal pitch of worm} \times 0 \cdot 3683.$$

$$\text{Worm pitch-circle diameter } d = \frac{2C}{1 + G \tan A} \text{ (approx.)}$$

$$= 2C - D.$$

$$\text{Centre distance C} = \frac{D + d}{2}.$$

When lead angle B exceeds 20° :

$$\text{Addendum} = 0 \cdot 3183 \text{ normal circular pitch.}$$

$$\text{Dedendum} = 0 \cdot 3683 \text{ normal circular pitch.}$$

$$\text{Worm-crest diameter} = d + 2 \times \text{addendum.}$$

$$\text{Worm-root diameter} = d - 2 \times \text{dedendum.}$$

$$\text{Wheel-throat diameter} = D + 2 \times \text{(wheel tooth-throat addendum).}$$

$$\text{Overall wheel diameter} = D + 3 \times \text{(wheel tooth-throat addendum).}$$

If N = R.P.M. of worm wheel; n = R.P.M. of worm; V = worm-wheel peripheral velocity; v = worm peripheral velocity:

$$V = 0.262 \text{ DN feet per minute.}$$
$$v = 0.262 \, dn \quad \text{feet per minute.}$$

Rubbing velocity at pitch point $= \sqrt{V^2 + v^2}$

$$= \frac{Vv}{\cos A}.$$

$$\text{Torque transmitted} = \frac{63{,}024 \text{ h.p.}}{N'} \text{ lb. in.}$$

where N' = R.P.M. of worm shaft.

If P' = pitch of teeth on worm wheel:

Breadth of worm wheel = 2 to 2·5 P'.
Length of worm   = 3 to 4·5 P'.

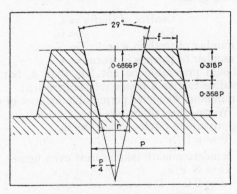

FIG. 34.—BROWN AND SHARPE 29° WORM.

Brown and Sharpe 29° Worm

The single-start Brown and Sharpe involute-thread worm is similar in proportions to the 29° involute rack used for spur gears or their generation. The tooth proportions (Fig. 34) are as follows:

Thread angle = 29°.
Addendum = 0·318 P.
Dedendum = 0·368 P.
Whole depth of tooth = 0·686 P.
Flat width on crest f = 0·335 P.
Flat width on root r = 0·31 P.

E.W.D.—9*

Distance, root centre to tooth on pitch line $= \dfrac{P}{4}$.

Diameter of rod or wire touching pitch line and flush with tops of teeth $\Big\} = \dfrac{1}{4P} \times$ secant $14\tfrac{1}{2}°$.

Distance of top of wire above pitch line $= \dfrac{P}{4} \tan 14\tfrac{1}{2}° + r$

where $r =$ radius of wire.

Worm-gear Calculations

The position of the pitch line in worm gearing is arbitrary, as there is no rolling circle. If it is assumed to be at the root of the worm and the throat of the worm wheel the calculations can be greatly simplified. The following is a method due to H. Kerr Thomas,* based upon the use of inch linear pitch, the following particulars being given :

Centres of shafts = C.

Ratio = G.

(*a*) Select number of teeth in wheel = N.

Select number of threads in worm = *n*.

(*n* should preferably be not less than 4, but as high as possible to give a reasonably large pitch).

(*b*) Select minimum diameter permissible for root of worm = *d*.

Worm-wheel diameter, $D = 2C - d$.   .   (1)

(*c*) Find approximate pitch of wheel teeth.

$P = \pi D/N$.   .   .   .   .   (2)

If P is indeterminate take nearest even figure :

(*d*) $D = N P/\pi$.   .   .   .   .   (3)

    $d = 2C - D$.   .   .   .   (4)

(*e*) The lead angle *a* is measured at the root diameter.

$\tan a = D/d\,G$.   .   .   .   (5)

(*f*) Cross-section of worm.

Circumferential pitch $= P_1 = P \cot a$.   (6)

Normal pitch $\quad = P_2 = P \cos a$.   (7)

The pressure-angle θ varies from 0 degrees at the root to about 45 degrees at the point; if on the axial section the worm tooth is flat-sided that of the worm wheel will be curved, and *vice versa*.

The power which can be transmitted depends upon the product of the tooth pressure in pounds $= p$, and the rubbing speed in feet per second $= v$. Unless the lubricant is artificially cooled the value of $p\,v$ should not exceed 100,000.

* Instit. of Autom. Engineers

If T = lb. torque at the assumed pitch line:

$p = $ T sec θ/sin a = lb. . . . . . . (8)

If r = revs. of worm per minute:

$v = \pi d$ sec a r/720 = ft. per sec. . . . . (9)

T = 63024 P/r × 0·5 d . . . . . . (10)

Substituting, $p v$ = 1100 P/sin 2 a cos θ . . . . (11)

It will be found that $p v$ varies with d/D in approximately linear ratio, hence the importance of keeping d as small as possible with respect to D.

David Brown and Sharpe (D.B.S.) Worm Gearing

This form of worm gearing bases its proportions on the module principle.

If M = module or circular pitch of the worm wheel divided by π:

Worm addendum   = 1·5 M cos A.
Worm dedendum   = 0·6 worm addendum = 0·9 M cos A.
Clearance   = 0·1 M cos A.
Wheel throat addendum = 0·75 M cos A.
Wheel overall addendum = 1·20 M cos A.
Normal module   = M cos A.

Efficiency of Worm Gearing

If p = pitch of single-start worm; d = worm-pitch diameter; A = lead angle or slope of helix; μ = coefficient of friction = tan ϕ (ϕ being the friction angle):

$$\tan A = \frac{p}{\pi d}$$

Efficiency $$= \frac{\tan A}{\tan (A + \phi)}.$$

Maximum efficiency occurs when A = $45° - \dfrac{\phi}{2}$ and its value is:

Maximum efficiency $$= \left(\frac{1 - \tan \frac{\phi}{2}}{1 + \tan \frac{\phi}{2}}\right)^2$$

For irreversibility the lead angle should be equal to the friction angle.

THE STRENGTH OF GEAR TEETH

The basis of most of the strength-calculation formulæ used for gears is that known as the *Lewis formula*, originated by W. Lewis of the Wm. Sellers Company, U.S.A. When gear teeth of suitable design roll together the line of action of the force W', acting on the driven tooth (Fig. 35), is at the pressure or obliquity angle. Where this line of action meets the centre line of the tooth a parabola is drawn, making a tangent to the sides of the tooth. This parabola is regarded as a beam of uniform strength equivalent to the effective

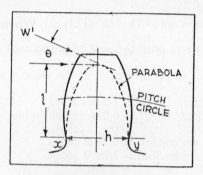

FIG. 35.—STRENGTH OF GEAR TEETH.

strength of the tooth. The line $x\,y$ represents the line of weakest section of the tooth and the equivalent force W acts at the distance l.

If f = maximum permissible stress for the gear-tooth material; b = face width of tooth:

Then moment $Wl = \dfrac{f\,b\,(2h)^2}{6}$

$$= \frac{2\,b\,.\,f\,(\text{C.P.})\,h^2}{3\,(\text{C.P.})}.$$

$$W = b\,f\,(\text{C.P.})\,.\left(\frac{2\,h^2}{3\,(\text{C.P.})\,l}\right)$$

Lewis formula $W = b\,.\,f\,.\,(\text{C.P.})\,y,$

where y is a variable factor depending upon the design of the tooth. This factor is practically independent of the pitch but is mainly dependent upon the number of teeth in the gear, and tabulated values for different designs of gear tooth are given in the following table :

VALUES FOR y IN LEWIS FORMULA

No. of Teeth	14½° Involute and 15° Cycloidal	20° Involute	20° Stub	Radial Flanks
10	0·056	0·064	0·083	0·050
11	·061	·072	·092	·051
12	·067	·078	·099	·052
13	·071	·083	·103	·053
14	·075	·088	·108	·054
15	·078	·092	·111	·055
16	·081	·094	·115	·056
17	·084	·096	·117	·057
18	·086	·098	·120	·058
19	·088	·100	·123	·059
20	·090	·102	·125	·060
21	·092	·104	·127	·061
23	·094	·106	·130	·062
25	·097	·108	·133	·063
27	·099	·111	·136	·064
30	·101	·114	·139	·065
34	·104	·118	·142	·066
38	·106	·122	·145	·067
43	·108	·126	·147	·068
50	·110	·130	·151	·069
60	·113	·134	·154	·070
75	·115	·138	·158	·071
100	·117	·142	·161	·072
150	·119	·146	·165	·073
300	·122	·150	·170	·074
Rack	·124	·154	·175	·075

The values of the safe working stress f depend upon the material and also the velocity of the teeth at the pitch circle or line. For velocities of 100 feet per minute, or less, the values of f are given in the following table :

VALUES OF f IN LEWIS FORMULA
(For gear-tooth velocities of 100 ft. per min.)

Material	Safe Working Stress f (lb. per sq. in.)
Wood (beech or maple) . . .	3,000
Rawhide	8,000
Fabroil	8,000
Bakelite laminated	8,000
Cast iron	8,000 to 10,000
Semi-steel	10,000
Bronze	11,500 to 15,000
Steel castings	18,000 to 20,000
Mild steel (unhardened) . .	25,000
Alloy steels (case-hardened) .	50,000
Nickel chrome steel (heat treated) .	100,000
Chrome vanadium steel (heat treated)	100,000
Cast steel (heat treated) . . .	50,000 to 70,000

Lewis Formulæ for Brown and Sharpe Gears

For $14\frac{1}{2}°$ involute and cycloidal teeth with generating circle of diameter equal to radius of the 12-tooth pinion :

$$W = b \cdot f \text{ (C.P.)} \left(0 \cdot 124 - \frac{0 \cdot 684}{N} \right) \text{ lb.}$$

where N = number of teeth. Inch units are used for b and C.P.

For the 20° standard Brown and Sharpe involute-gear teeth :

$$W = b \cdot f \text{ (C.P.)} \left(0 \cdot 154 - \frac{0 \cdot 912}{N} \right) \text{ lb.}$$

For cycloidal teeth with generating circle equal to radius of 15-tooth pinion with Brown and Sharpe standard proportions :

$$W = b \cdot f \text{ (C.P.)} \left(0 \cdot 106 - \frac{0 \cdot 678}{N} \right).$$

Speed Effect on Gear Strength.

The value of the working stress f decreases as the velocity of the gear teeth increases, in the general manner shown in the following table :

Effect of Gear-teeth Speed on Stress f

(Cast-steel gear)

Gear-teeth velocity (ft. per min.)	Up to 100	200	300	600	900	1,200	1,800	2,400
Safe stress f (lb. per sq. in.)	20,000	15,000	12,000	10,000	7,500	6,000	5,000	4,300

Strength of Brown and Sharpe Spur Gears

NOTATION

D.P. = diametral pitch.   C.P. = circular pitch.   F = width of face of gear.

V = velocity of pitch line in feet per minute ; this is the same for both meshing gears.

W = allowable load at pitch line in lb.

S = allowable stress for static load (V = 0).   Assuming 0·66 of ultimate strength for cast iron and steel, in lb. per sq. in.

Y = a factor for strength depending on pressure angle and number of teeth.

H.P. = horse power.

$\dfrac{600}{600 + V}$ = a factor to reduce S for metallic gears, as velocity V increases from zero speed.

$\dfrac{150}{200 + V} + 0.25$ = a factor to reduce S for non-metallic gears as V increases from zero speed.   Non-metallic materials include laminated phenolic materials, e.g. Bakelite laminated or rawhide.

FORMULÆ

$$W = \frac{600}{600 + V} \times S \times C.P. \times F \times Y$$

$$= \frac{600}{600 + V} \cdot \frac{SFY}{D.P.}$$

$$= \left(\frac{150}{200 + V} + 0.25 \right) \frac{SFY}{D.P.}$$

$$H.P. = \frac{WV}{33,000}.$$

Material	Safe Stress in lb. per sq. in. S
Phosphor bronze . .	12,000
Cast iron	8,000
Steel (carbon) . . .	20,000
Non-metallic . . .	6,000

For alloy and high-tensile steels in general the value of S is increased in proportion to the ratios of the ultimate or tensile strengths. Thus, for a 75-ton (tensile) alloy steel the value of S will be $\frac{75}{25}$ times that of mild steel (25 tons per sq. in.).

Speed Allowance in Brown and Sharpe Standard Gears

Referring to the gear formulæ given on page 271 the following table shows the velocity factors for the formulæ there given :

Velocity of Gears at Pitch Line (ft. per min.)	$\frac{600}{600 + V}$	$\frac{150}{200 + V} + 0.25$	Velocity of Gears at Pitch Line (ft. per min.)	$\frac{600}{600 + V}$	$\frac{150}{200 + V} + 0.25$
0	1·000	1·000	1,400	0·300	0·344
100	·857	·750	1,600	·272	·333
200	·750	·625	1,800	·250	·325
300	·666	·550	2,000	·230	·318
400	·600	·500	2,400	·200	·308
500	·545	·464	3,000	·167	·297
600	·500	·437	4,000	·130	·286
700	·462	·416	5,000	—	·279
800	·428	·400	6,000	—	·274
900	·400	·386	7,000	—	·271
1,000	·375	·375	8,000	—	·266
1,200	·333	·357	—	—	—

BRITISH STANDARD MACHINE-CUT GEARS

Gear-strength Formulæ

The British Standard Specification, B.S. No. 436—1940, for Machine-cut Gears (Helical and Spurs), covers machine-cut or ground-circular gears with either straight, single, or double helical, external or internal 20° full-depth involute gears, with a working height of twice the module, and comprises the following classes :

Class A1.—Precision-ground gears.

Class A2.—Precision-cut gears for peripheral speeds above 2,000 ft. per min.

Class B.—High-class cut gears, above 750 and below 3,000 ft. per min.

Class C.—Commercial-cut gears, below 1,200 ft. per min.

Class D.—Large internal gears.

The specification covers various gear-teeth proportions, clearances, tooth-thickness tolerances, pitch and profile tolerances, proportions of gear wheels of cast iron or cast steel, strength and horse-power capacity of gears, working temperatures, speed factors, gear-material hardness, surface stress and bending stress, etc. It gives worked-out examples of gear-proportion calculations, horse power, overload and intermittent ratings together with 15 charts or graphs used for gear calculations. The following formulæ are given in connection with the strengths of gears, etc.

Allowable Tangential Load

X_c = speed factor for wear. Z = zone factor. S_c = surface stress factor.

K = pitch factor.

Tangential load per inch face width for wear for suitably lubricated gears must not exceed the value obtained from the following :

$$\text{Tangential load} = \frac{X_c \, Z \, S_c}{K}.$$

Note.—Values of the factors mentioned are given in the charts (B.S. No. 436—1940).

Strength of Gears

The allowable tangential load per inch face width must not exceed :

$$\frac{X_b \, Y \, S_b}{P}$$

where X_b = speed factor for strength ; Y = strength factor ; S_b = bending-stress factor.

P = diametral pitch.

Note.—Values for these factors are given in the charts (B.S. No. 436—1940).

Horse Power Transmitted

$$\text{Horse power for wear} = \frac{X_c \, S_c \, Z \, FNT}{126,000 \, KP}$$

where F = face width; N = R.P.M. of gear wheel; T = number of teeth in gear wheel, then $K = P^{0\cdot8}$.

$$\text{Horse power for strength} = \frac{X_b \, S_b \, Y \, FNT}{126,000 \, P^2}.$$

Factor of Safety

$$\text{Factor of safety} = \frac{S_t \times Y \times F \times N \times T}{\text{Horse power transmitted} \times P^2 \times 126,000}$$

where S_t = ultimate tensile stress of gear material, in lb. per sq. in.

Automobile Gears

The British Standard formulæ for machine-cut gears used for industrial purposes can be modified so as to apply to automobile gear-box gears which are subjected to only occasional use instead of the continuous use assumed for the industrial gears.

This is effected by substituting for the speed factor the following value :

$$\text{Automobile-gear speed factor} = \frac{15 + G_1}{30} \text{ (forward gears)};$$

$$= \frac{15 + G_1}{25} \text{ (reverse gears)},$$

$$\text{where } G_1 = \frac{100 \, M \, R_a}{W_g \, r},$$

where
$\quad M$ = maximum engine torque, in lb. in.
$\quad R_a$ = overall reduction in gear considered

$$= \frac{\text{Engine r.p.m.}}{\text{Roadwheel r.p.m.}}.$$

$\quad W_g$ = gross laden weight of vehicle in lb.
$\quad r$ = rolling radius of tyre, in in.

SECTION 7

DRILLS AND DRILLING DATA

TWIST DRILL NOMENCLATURE *

Drill Diameter.—The diameter of the hole which a properly designed and ground drill will machine.

Overall Length.—The axial length from the drill point to the end of the shank.

Flute Length.—The axial length of the fluted portion.

Point of Drill.—The cone-shaped surface at the cutting end of drill.

Dead Centre.—The sharp edge at the extreme tip of drill formed by the intersection of the coned surfaces of the point ; it should lie on the axis of drill (Fig. 1).

Heel.—The portion of the drill point behind the cutting edges.

Cutting Lips or Edges.—The edges formed by the intersection of the flutes and the cone-shaped point (Fig. 1).

Lip Clearance.—The shape of the point in relation to the lip. The point is ground away behind the cutting edges to give proper

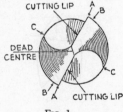

FIG. 1.

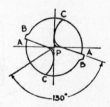

FIG. 2.

cutting-edge relief or clearance. The clearance angle (Fig. 5. R.H. Diagram) is usually 12° to 15°.

The Margin.—The narrow strip AB (Fig. 2) left after the outside diameter of the fluted portion has been ground away for relief purposes.

The Point Angle.—The conical angle of the drill point. In

* Based chiefly on Cleveland Twist Drill Co.'s recommendations.

standard twist drills for steel this angle is 118°, i.e. 59° on each side of the axis (Fig. 3).

Body Clearance.—The diameter of the portion of the drill from B to C (Fig. 2) provided for relief purposes ; it is of smaller diameter than the margin diameter of AB.

The Web.—The metal column which separates the flutes. It runs the complete fluted length of the drill and is the supporting

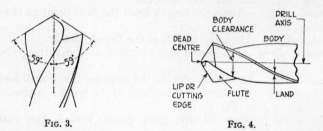

FIG. 3. FIG. 4.

section or backbone of the drill. The web tapers in thickness from the drill point to a maximum at the shank junction.

The Land.—The helical strips running down the fluted portion, corresponding to the margins (Fig. 4).

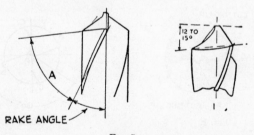

FIG. 5.

Rake Angle.—The inclination of the spiral fluting or groove (Fig. 5. L.H. Diagram). The rake angle + angle A is very nearly 90°.

The lip-clearance angle is gradually increased as the centre is approached until the line across the dead centre of the drill stands at an angle with the cutting edge of 120° to 135°. This angle is shown as 130° in Fig. 2.

NOTES ON DRILLS AND DRILLING

(1) The point angle of a twist drill should be varied to suit the material to be drilled. The following are typical point angles :

Materials to be Drilled	Point Angle Degrees	Remarks
Mild and Medium Steels . .	118	Lip clearance 12° to 15°.
Hard Steels. Manganese Steel .	140 to 150	Lip clearance 10°.
Heat-treated Steel, Drop Forgings, Connecting Rods . .	125	Lip clearance 12°.
Brass and Soft Bronze . .	118	Lip clearance 15°, with negative rake.
Copper and Copper Alloys .	100	Lip clearance 12°.
Cast Iron (softer grades) . .	90	Lip clearance 12°.
Hard Rubber, Fibre . . .	90	Lip clearance 12°. Slight negative rake. Slower helix.
Aluminium Alloys . . .	100 to 120	—
Wood, Ebonite, Vulcanite . .	60	Lip clearance 12°, with negative rake. Slower helix.
Bakelite and other plastics .	90	⎰ No rake or slight negative rake.
Bakelite Laminated . . .	50 to 60	⎱ Slower helix.
Stainless Steel (Staybrite) . .	118	Lip clearance 14° to 18°.
Magnesium Alloys . . .	130	Lip clearance 10° to 15°. Helix angle 10°.

(2) For drilling *Bakelite laminated,* in addition to a finer point angle of 50° to 60°, a slower helix or " twist " than for drills used on ordinary steels is recommended. Wider flutes and lips ground thin with little rake are necessary (Fig. 6).

FIG. 6.—DRILL FOR BAKELITE LAMINATED.

(3) For machining strong *magnesium alloys,* e.g. Elektron, use a medium-fluted drill, with show helix (10°) ; minimum land ; flutes as wide as possible ; cutting edges as keen as possible ; flutes must be polished ; dry cutting to be used.

(4) For drilling *stainless steels* use high-speed drills ; cutting lips ground with more back clearance than usual ; drill point must be thinned ; use turpentine as a cutting lubricant. These steels are liable to work-hardening effects.

Drilling Speeds and Feeds for Stainless Steels

Diameter of Drill (in.)	Drill Speed in R.P.M.	Feed per Revolution (in.)
$\frac{1}{16}$	2,050	Hand feed
$\frac{1}{8}$	1,450	Hand feed
$\frac{1}{4}$	830	·0045
$\frac{1}{2}$	400	·0070
$\frac{13}{16}$	225	·0095
1	185	·0110

For the Staybrite grade of stainless steels short stiff drills with keen cutting edges should be used. Centres should be heavily " centre-popped." Lip clearance angle 14° to 18°.

Drilling Speeds and Feeds for Staybrite Steels

Diameter of Drill (in.)	Drill Speed in R.P.M.	Feed per Revolution (in.)
$\frac{1}{16}$	1,200	Hand feed
$\frac{1}{8}$	850	Hand feed
$\frac{1}{4}$	460	·0045
$\frac{1}{2}$	260	·0070
$\frac{13}{16}$	200	·0095
1	170	·0110

(5) For drilling *manganese steel*, special high-speed alloy drills, e.g. Stag Major, * must be used. Best cutting speeds are 12 to 14 ft. per min., i.e. a 1-in. drill must rotate at 40 to 50 r.p.m. Lower or higher speeds give unsatisfactory results. Heavy feed pressures are required. The drill-point angle is made rather more acute than for ordinary steels.

Holes of depth equal to the drill diameter can be drilled satisfactorily with suitable drills, speeds and feed pressures.

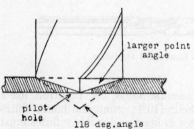

larger point angle

pilot hole

118 deg. angle

FIG. 7.—DRILLING SHEET METAL.

For drills of $\frac{3}{8}$-in. to $\frac{5}{8}$-in. diameter, a feed of 120 revolutions per in. is recommended.

(6) When *drilling relatively thin sheet steel*, in relation to the drill

* Edgar Allen Ltd., Sheffield.

diameter the drill-point angle should be increased with diminishing thickness of the steel plate (Fig. 7).

The use of a pilot drill hole is recommended in order to confine the cutting to the outer edges of drill. The drill point should be thinned as much as possible. The work should be well supported against spring effects.

(7) For drilling copper and its alloys the top rake should be reduced by grinding flats on the lips (Fig. 8). Alternatively small

As ground here

 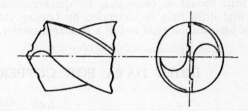

FIG. 8.   FIG. 9.—CHIP-BREAKER DRILL.

nicks may be ground in the cutting edges to act as *chip breakers*. This method is also generally used on drills for steel and aluminium to prevent formation of long spiral turnings which may become dangerous to operators (Fig. 9).

(8) Flat drills are useful for drilling sheet metals. The cutting edge should have the proper top rake and cutting angle for the metal to be drilled. The edges Y (Fig. 10) should be tapered towards X to provide clearance for the drill in its hole. The point should be kept thin.

Stepped flat drills are often used for brass, aluminium and non-metallic materials such as ebonite, erinoid, bakelite, etc. (Fig. 11).

(9) When drilling deep holes, special drills should be used. These have spiral lubricant holes in the flutes to convey the coolant to the cutting edges. Another type of drill has small-diameter copper pipes arranged along the flutes, to carry the coolant. The holes communicate with a hole drilled along the axis of the drill shank through which the

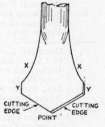

FIG. 10.—FLAT DRILL.

coolant is fed. Frequent removal of the drill from the hole during deep-drilling operation is recommended. High-speed steel

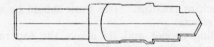

FIG. 11.—STEPPED DRILL.

drills should be employed, for quicker drilling results. Ordinary twist drills may be extended by brazing their shanks to lengths of high-carbon steel rod of a similar diameter.

DRILL DATA FOR COPPER ALLOYS

Group	Material	Helix Angle Recommended—Degrees	Approximate Feeds Permissible with 1-in. Diameter Drill at 880 r.p.m. (230 ft./min.)	
			Revs./in.	In./min.
A	Copper	40 (30)*	93	9½
	Cupro-nickel	40 (30)	93	9½
	Nickel Silver . . .	30	93	9½
	Phosphor Bronze (Wrought) .	10 (30)	52	17
	Silicon Bronze . . .	10 (30)	93	9½
B	Aluminium Bronze . . .	30	93	9½
	Aluminium-Nickel-Iron Bronze	30	93	9½
	Gunmetal (Cast) . . .	10 (30)	67	13
	Manganese Bronzes . . .	10 (30)	67	13
	Phosphor Bronze (Cast) . .	10 (30)	52	17
	Yellow Brass	10 (30)	67	13
C†	Gunmetal (Leaded) . .	0	52	17
	Hot Stamping Brass . .	0	52	17
	High-speed Screwing and Turning Brass	0	38	23
	Lead Bronze (Cast) . . .	0	38	23
	Nickel Brass (Leaded) . .	0	52	17
	Nickel Silver (Leaded) . .	0	38	23
	Selenium Copper . . .	0	38	23
	Tellurium Copper . . .	0	38	23

* Figures in brackets indicate the helix angle recommended where only standard or straight-fluted drills are available.

† All Group C materials drill extremely well with helix angles varying from 0 to 30 degrees.

Copper Devel. Assocn.]

TWIST DRILL TROUBLES, CAUSES AND REMEDIES

Symptom	Probable Cause	Remedy
BREAKING of drill.	Spring or backlash in press or work. Too little lip clearance. Too low speed in proportion to the feed. Improper cutting compound.	Test press and work for rigidity. Regrind properly. Increase speed. Use proper cutting compound.
BREAKING down of outer corner of cutting edges.	Material being drilled is hard or dirty. Too much speed.	Reduce speed and try turpentine.
BREAKING of drill when drilling brass or wood.	Chips clog up flutes.	Use " Cleveland " drills for brass and No. 113A for wood. In ordering specify " for brass " or " for wood."
BURNING of the heel of the drill.	No lip clearance on drill.	Regrind properly.
BROKEN TANG.	Too much feed or, more probably, imperfect fit of taper shank in the socket—due to nicks, dirt, burrs or worn-out socket.	Reduce feed—get a new socket or ream old one to prevent recurrence.
CHIPPING of lip or cutting edges.	Too much feed. Too much lip clearance.	Reduce feed—regrind properly.
CHIPPING or checking of a high-speed drill.	Heated and cooled too quickly while grinding or while operating.	Warm slowly before using. Do not throw cold water on hot drill while using or grinding.
CHANGE in character of chips while drilling.	Change in condition of the drill such as chipping of cutting edge, dulling, etc.	Regrind drill and correct the speed.
DRILL REFUSES to enter work.	Dull drill. Too little lip clearance.	Sharpen drill. Regrind properly.
HOLE larger than drill.	Unequal angle or length of the cutting edges—or both.	Regrind properly.
ONLY one lip cuts.	Unequal length or angle of cutting lips or both.	Regrind drill properly.
ROUGH HOLE.	Dull or improperly ground drill. Lack of lubricant or wrong lubricant.	Lubricate or change lubricant.
SPLITS up centre.	Too little lip clearance. Too much feed.	Regrind with proper clearance. Reduce feed.

DRILL-PERFORMANCE DATA

(Carbon-steel Drills)

Size Drill	*Thickness of Material*	*Rev. per Min.*	*Feed per Rev.*	*Peripheral Ft. per Min.*	*Cu. In. Removed per Min.*	*Weight Metal Removed per Min.*	*In. Drilled per Min.*
			Material : MACHINERY STEEL				
In.	*In.*		*In.*			*Oz.*	
⅝	½	870	·023	141	6·14	1·73	20·0
⅞	1½	655	·047	150	18·53	5·22	30·8
1	2	615	·0815	161	39·4	11·12	50·1
1¼	2	550	·0815	180	55·0	15·52	44·8
1½	3	380	·050	150	33·6	9·46	19·0
1¾	3	325	·061	150	47·7	13·45	19·8
2½	4	185	·061	120	55·4	15·6	11·3
3	4	155	·050	120	54·8	15·45	7·75
			Material : CAST IRON				
⅜	1½	1,010	·082	99	9·15	2·38	82·8
⅜	1½	1,010	·104	99	11·61	3·02	105·0
⅝	2	1,000	·082	163·6	25·2	6·54	82·0
⅞	2	816	·104	187·0	51·1	13·26	84·8
1	2½	800	·145	210·0	91·1	23·6	116·0
1¼	2	800	·145	260·0	142·2	37·0	116·0
1½	4	510	·120	200·0	108·0	28·1	61·2
1¾	4	435	·120	200·0	125·8	32·7	52·2
2½	4	300	·100	197·0	147·3	38·3	30·0
			Material : CHROME NICKEL STEEL—Brinell Hardness 250				
⅝	2	367	·011	60	1·24	·35	4·04
⅞	2	262	·015	60	2·36	·67	3·93
1	2	267	·019	70	3·98	1·12	5·07
1¼	3	215	·020	70	5·28	1·485	4·3
1½	3	153	·024	60	6·48	1·83	3·67
1¾	3	150	·020	60	7·22	2·04	3·0

[Cleveland Twist Drill Co.]

BRITISH STANDARD DRILL SPECIFICATIONS

The British Standard Specification for twist and straight-flute drills (B.S. No. 328—1928) illustrates and defines the different types of twist and straight-flute drills and their various designs of drill shanks. It gives tabular data on the diameter sizes and tolerances and markings. It also lays down a method of testing twist drills on billets of steel of 0·60 to 0·65 per cent. carbon content and Brinell hardness of 200 to 215. The billets are sufficiently thick to obviate the drill reaching and breaking through the opposite sides during the tests. The drills are flooded with lubricant during the tests. The latter are commenced with hand feed and the power feed is then engaged as soon as the lips of drill reach the surface of billet. The penetration per minute and depth of holes must be in accordance with the values given in the following table :

BRITISH STANDARD PERFORMANCE TEST FOR TWIST DRILLS FROM No. 60 TO 2 INCHES DIAMETER

Size	Decimal Equivalent	Penetration per Min.				Number of Holes to be Drilled	Depth of Holes to be Drilled *	
		Carbon		High Speed				
	In.	In.	Mm.	In.	Mm.		In.	Mm.
No. 60 Wire	0·0400	2·50	63·5	2·85	72·4	18	3/16	4·8
1/16	0·0625	2·75	69·9	3·65	92·7	24	9/32	7·1
No. 50 Wire	0·0700	2·83	71·9	4·00	101·6	28	19/64	7·5
3/32	0·0938	2·95	74·9	5·40	137·2	28	23/64	9·1
No. 40 Wire	0·0980	3·00	76·2	5·60	142·2	28	3/8	9·5
1/8	0·1250	3·10	78·7	6·70	170·2	24	7/16	11
No. 30 Wire	0·1285	3·12	79·2	6·80	172·7	24	29/64	12
No. 20 Wire	0·1610	3·22	81·8	7·40	188·0	24	33/64	13
3/16	0·1875	3·29	83·6	7·70	195·6	24	19/32	15
No. 10 Wire	0·1935	3·30	83·8	7·75	196·9	20	39/64	15
7/32	0·2188	3·35	85·1	7·90	200·7	20	43/64	17
No. 1 Wire	0·2280	3·33	84·6	7·90	200·7	20	11/16	17
1/4	0·2500	3·20	81·3	7·60	193·0	20	3/4	19
5/16	0·3125	2·88	73·2	7·00	177·8	20	29/32	23
3/8	0·3750	2·60	66·0	6·55	166·4	18	1 1/16	27
7/16	0·4375	2·30	58·4	6·05	153·7	18	1 7/32	31
1/2	0·5000	2·02	51·3	5·67	144·0	18	1 3/8	35
5/8	0·6250	1·70	43·2	5·00	127·0	15	1 11/16	43
3/4	0·7500	1·50	38·1	4·45	113·0	15	2	51
7/8	0·8750	1·40	35·6	4·00	101·6	14	2 5/16	59
1	1·0000	1·30	33·0	3·55	90·2	14	2 5/8	67
1 1/4	1·2500	1·10	27·9	2·83	71·9	9	3	76
1 1/2	1·5000	0·90	22·9	2·93	60·5	9	3	76
1 3/4	1·7500	0·80	20·3	2·07	52·6	8	3	76
2	2·0000	0·70	17·8	1·75	44·5	8	3	76

* I.e. From point of drill to surface of test billet.

DRILL CUTTING SPEEDS AND EQUIVALENT REVOLUTIONS PER MINUTE

Feet per Min.	5	10	20	30	40	50	60	70	80	90	100
Diam. (inch)					Revolutions per Minute						
1/16	305·7	611·4	1,223	1,834	2,445	3,057	3,668	4,280	4,891	5,502	6,114
1/8	152·8	305·6	611	917	1,222	1,528	1,834	2,139	2,445	2,750	3,056
3/16	101·9	203·8	408	611	815	1,019	1,222	1,426	1,630	1,834	2,038
1/4	76·4	152·8	306	458	611	764	917	1,070	1,222	1,376	1,528
5/16	61·1	122·2	245	367	489	611	733	856	978	1,100	1,222
3/8	50·9	101·8	204	306	408	509	611	713	815	916	1,018
7/16	43·7	87·4	175	262	349	437	524	611	699	786	874
1/2	38·2	76·4	153	229	306	382	459	535	611	688	764
9/16	34·0	67·9	136	204	272	340	407	475	543	611	679
5/8	30·6	61·2	123	184	245	306	367	428	489	552	612
11/16	27·3	55·5	111	167	222	273	333	389	444	500	555
3/4	25·4	50·8	102	153	203	254	306	357	408	458	508
13/16	23·7	47·4	94·8	142	190	237	284	332	379	427	474
7/8	21·9	43·8	87·3	131	175	219	262	306	349	392	438
15/16	20·4	40·7	81·4	122	163	204	244	285	326	366	407
1	19·1	38·2	76·4	115	153	191	229	267	306	344	382
1 1/16	18·0	35·9	71·8	108	144	180	215	251	287	323	359
1 1/8	17·0	34·0	68·0	102	136	170	204	238	272	306	340
1 3/16	16·1	32·2	64·4	96·6	129	161	193	225	258	290	322

D											
1¼	15·3	30·6	61·2	91·8	123	153	183	214	245	274	306
1 5/16	14·6	29·1	58·2	87·3	116	146	175	204	233	262	291
1⅜	13·9	27·8	55·6	83·3	111	139	167	195	222	250	278
1 7/16	13·3	26·5	53·0	79·5	106	133	159	186	212	239	265
1½	12·7	25·4	50·8	76·3	102	127	153	178	204	230	254
1 9/16	12·2	24·4	48·8	73·2	97·6	122	146	171	195	220	244
1⅝	11·7	23·4	47·0	70·5	93·9	117	141	165	188	212	234
1 11/16	11·3	22·6	45·2	67·8	90·4	113	136	158	181	203	226
1¾	10·9	21·8	43·6	65·5	87·3	109	131	153	175	196	218
1 13/16	10·6	21·1	42·2	63·3	84·4	106	127	148	169	190	211
1⅞	10·2	20·4	40·7	61·1	81·5	102	122	143	163	184	204
1 15/16	9·85	19·7	39·4	59·1	78·8	98·5	118	138	158	177	197
2	9·55	19·1	38·2	57·3	76·4	95·5	115	134	153	172	191

FORMULA FOR DRILL SPEEDS

D = diameter of drill in inches.   V = cutting speed in feet per minute.   N = revolutions per minute.

$$N = \frac{12\,V}{\pi D} \text{ where } \pi = 3.1416.$$

A feed per revolution of ·004 to ·007 for drills ¼ inch and smaller, and from ·007 to ·015 for larger, is recommended.

This feed is based on a peripheral speed of a drill equal to:

30 feet per minute for steel ; 35 feet per minute for iron ; 50 feet per minute for brass.

It may also be found advisable to vary the speed somewhat when the material to be drilled is more or less refractory.

DRILL LETTERS AND NUMBERS

Fractional Size Drills Inches	Wire Gauge Drills	Decimal Equivalent Inches	Fractional Size Drills Inches	Wire Gauge Drills	Decimal Equivalent Inches
	80	·0135		38	·1015
	79	·0145		37	·1040
1/64	....	·0156		36	·1065
	78	·0160	7/64	....	·1094
	77	·0180		35	·1100
	76	·0200		34	·1110
	75	·0210		33	·1130
	74	·0225		32	·1160
	73	·0240		31	·1200
	72	·0250			·1250
	71	·0260	1/8	....	
	70	·0280		30	·1285
	69	·0292		29	·1360
	68	·0310		28	·1405
1/32	....	·0312	9/64	....	·1406
	67	·0320		27	·1440
	66	·0330		26	·1470
	65	·0350		25	·1495
	64	·0360		24	·1520
	63	·0370		23	·1540
	62	·0380	5/32	....	·1562
	61	·0390		22	·1570
	60	·0400		21	·1590
	59	·0410		20	·1610
	58	·0420		19	·1660
	57	·0430		18	·1695
	56	·0465	11/64	....	·1719
3/64	....	·0469		17	·1730
	55	·0520		16	·1770
	54	·0550		15	·1800
	53	·0595		14	·1820
1/16	....	·0625		13	·1850
	52	·0635	3/16	....	·1875
	51	·0670		12	·1890
	50	·0700		11	·1910
	49	·0730		10	·1935
	48	·0760		9	·1960
5/64	....	·0781		8	·1990
	47	·0785		7	·2010
	46	·0810	13/64	....	·2031
	45	·0820		6	·2040
	44	·0860		5	·2055
	43	·0890		4	·2090
	42	·0935		3	·2130
3/32	....	·0937	7/32	....	·2187
	41	·0960		2	·2210
	40	·0980		1	·2280
	39	·0995			

DRILL LETTERS AND NUMBERS (contd.)

Fractional Size Drills Inches	Letter Size Drills	Decimal Equivalent Inches	Fractional Size Drills Inches	Letter Size Drills	Decimal Equivalent Inches
	A	·2340	7/16	....	·4375
15/64	....	·2344	29/64	....	·4531
	B	·2380	15/32	....	·4687
			31/64	....	·4844
	C	·2420			
	D	·2460	1/2	....	·5000
1/4	E	·2500			
	F	·2570	33/64	....	·5156
			17/32	....	·5312
	G	·2610	36/64	....	·5469
17/64	....	·2656			
	H	·2660	9/16	....	·5625
	I	·2720	37/64	....	·5781
			19/32	....	·5937
	J	·2770	39/64	....	·6094
	K	·2810			
9/32	....	·2812	5/8	....	·6250
	L	·2900	41/64	....	·6406
			21/32	....	·6562
	M	·2950	43/64	....	·6719
19/64	....	·2969			
	N	·3020	11/16	....	·6875
5/16	....	·3125	45/64	....	·7031
			23/32	....	·7187
	O	·3160	47/64	....	·7344
	P	·3230			
21/64	....	·3281	3/4	....	·7500
	Q	·3320	49/64	....	·7656
			25/32	....	·7812
	R	·3390	51/64	....	·7969
11/32	....	·3437			
	S	·3480	13/16	....	·8125
	T	·3580	53/64	....	·8281
			27/32	....	·8437
23/64	....	·3594	55/64	....	·8594
	U	·3680			
3/8	....	·3750	7/8	....	·8750
			57/64	....	·8906
	V	·3770	29/32	....	·9062
	W	·3860	59/64	....	·9219
25/64	....	·3906			
	X	·3970	15/16	....	·9375
			61/64	....	·9531
			31/32	....	·9687
	Y	·4040	63/64	....	·9844
13/32	....	·4062			
	Z	·4130			
27/64	....	·4219	1	....	1·0000

TAPPING DRILLS FOR BRITISH STANDARD WHITWORTH THREADS*

Nominal Diameter of Thread		Number of Threads per Inch	Minor Diameter of Nut		Stock Drills			
			Max.	Min.	In.	Mm.	Wire or Letter	Equivalent Diameter
in.	in.		in.	in.				in.
1/8	·1250	40	·1020	·0930	3/32		42	·0935
								·0938
							41	·0960
							40	·0980
						2·5		·0984
							39	0995
							38	·1015
3/16	·1875	24	·1474	·1341		3·5	29	·1360
								·1378
							28	·1405
					9/64			·1406
							27	·1440
							26	·1470
1/4	·2500	20	·2030	·1860	3/16			·1875
							12	·1890
							11	·1910
							10	·1935
							9	·1960
						5 0		·1969
							8	·1990
							7	·2010
					13/64			·2031
5/16	·3125	18	·2594	·2413			C	·2420
							D	·2460
					1/4		E	·2500
						6·5		·2559
							F	·2570
3/8	·3750	16	·3145	·2950		7·5	M	·2950
								·2953
					19/64			·2969
							N	·3020
					5/16			·3125
7/16	·4375	14	·3674	·3461		9·0	S	·3480
								·3543
							T	·3580
					23/64			·3594
1/2	·5000	12	·4169	·3922		10·0		·3937
							X	·3970
							Y	·4040
					13/32			·4063
							Z	·4130
						10·5		·4134

* Abstracted from British Standard Specification 1157—1944.

Tapping Drills for British Standard Whitworth Threads (*contd.*)

Nominal Diameter of Thread		Number of Threads per Inch	Minor Diameter of Nut		Stock Drills			
			Max.	Min.	In.	Mm.	Wire or Letter	Equivalent Diameter
in. $\frac{9}{16}$	in. ·5625	12	in. ·4794	in. ·4557	$\frac{15}{32}$	12·0		in. ·4688 ·4724
$\frac{5}{8}$	·6250	11	·5338	·5086	$\frac{33}{64}$ $\frac{17}{32}$	13·0 13·5		·5118 ·5156 ·5313 ·5315
$\frac{11}{16}$	·6875	11	·5963	·5711	$\frac{37}{64}$ $\frac{19}{32}$	15·0		·5781 ·5906 ·5938
$\frac{3}{4}$	·7500	10	·6490	·6220	$\frac{5}{8}$ $\frac{41}{64}$	16·0		·6250 ·6299 ·6406
$\frac{7}{8}$	·8750	9	·7620	·7328	$\frac{47}{64}$ $\frac{3}{4}$	19·0		·7344 ·7480 ·7500
1	1·0000	8	·8720	·8400	$\frac{27}{32}$ $\frac{55}{64}$	21·5 22·0		·8438 ·8465 ·8594 ·8661
$1\frac{1}{8}$	1·1250	7	·9776	·9420	$\frac{61}{64}$ $\frac{31}{32}$	24·0 24·5		·9449 ·9531 ·9646 ·9688
$1\frac{1}{4}$	1·2500	7	1·1026	1·0670	$1\frac{5}{64}$ $1\frac{3}{32}$	27·5 28·0		1·0780 1·0830 1·0940 1·1020
$1\frac{1}{2}$	1·5000	6	1·3269	1·2866	$1\frac{19}{64}$ $1\frac{5}{16}$	33·0 33·5		1·2970 1·2990 1·3130 1·3190
$1\frac{3}{4}$	1·7500	5	1·5408	1·4938	$1\frac{1}{2}$ $1\frac{33}{64}$ $1\frac{17}{32}$	38·0 38·5 39·0		1·4960 1·5000 1·5160 1·5310 1·5350
2	2·0000	4·5	1·7668	1·7154	$1\frac{23}{32}$ $1\frac{3}{4}$	44·0 44·5		1·7190 1·7320 1·7500 1·7520

E.W.D.—10

TAPPING DRILLS FOR BRITISH STANDARD FINE THREADS *

Nominal Diameter of Thread		Number of Threads per Inch	Minor Diameter of Nut		Stock Drills			
			Max.	Min.	In	Mm.	Wire or Letter	Equivalent Diameter
in. $\frac{3}{16}$	in. ·1875	32	in. ·1577	in. ·1475	$\frac{5}{32}$	4·0	25 24 23 22	in. ·1495 ·1520 ·1540 ·1563 ·1570 ·1575
$\frac{7}{32}$	·2188	28	·1841	·1730		4·5	17 16 15 14	·1730 ·1770 ·1772 ·1800 ·1820
$\frac{1}{4}$	·2500	26	·2125	·2008	$\frac{13}{64}$		7 6 5 4	·2010 ·2031 ·2040 ·2055 ·2090
$\frac{9}{32}$	·2812	26	·2437	·2320	$\frac{15}{64}$	6·0	A B C	·2340 ·2344 ·2362 ·2380 ·2420
$\frac{5}{16}$	·3125	22	·2684	·2543	$\frac{17}{64}$	6·5	F G H	·2559 ·2570 ·2610 ·2656 ·2660
$\frac{3}{8}$	·3750	20	·3280	·3110	$\frac{5}{16}$ $\frac{21}{64}$	8·0	O P	·3125 ·3150 ·3160 ·3230 ·3281
$\frac{7}{16}$	·4375	18	·3844	·3663	$\frac{3}{8}$	9·5	U V	·3680 ·3740 ·3750 ·3770
$\frac{1}{2}$	·5000	16	·4395	·4200	$\frac{27}{64}$ $\frac{7}{16}$	11·0		·4219 ·4331 ·4375
$\frac{9}{16}$	·5625	16	·5020	·4825	$\frac{31}{64}$ $\frac{1}{2}$	12·5		·4844 ·4921 ·5000

* Abstracted from British Standard Specification 1157—1944.

Tapping Drills for British Standard Fine Threads (*contd.*)

Nominal Diameter of Thread		Number of Threads per Inch	Minor Diameter of Nut		Stock Drills			
			Max.	Min.	In.	Mm.	Wire or Letter	Equivalent Diameter
in. $\frac{5}{8}$	in. ·6250	14	in. ·5549	in. ·5336	$\frac{35}{64}$	14·0		in. ·5469 ·5512
$\frac{11}{16}$	·6875	14	·6174	·5961	$\frac{39}{64}$	15·5		·6094 ·6102
$\frac{3}{4}$	·7500	12	·6669	·6432	$\frac{21}{32}$	16·5		·6496 ·6563
$\frac{13}{16}$	·8125	12	·7294	·7057	$\frac{23}{32}$	18·0 18·5		·7087 ·7188 ·7283
$\frac{7}{8}$	·8750	11	·7838	·7586	$\frac{49}{64}$ $\frac{25}{32}$	19·5		·7656 ·7677 ·7813
1	1·0000	10	·8990	·8720	$\frac{7}{8}$ $\frac{57}{64}$	22·5		·8750 ·8858 ·8906
$1\frac{1}{8}$	1·1250	9	1·0120	·9828	$\frac{63}{64}$ 1	25·0 25·5		·9843 ·9844 1·0000 1·0040
$1\frac{1}{4}$	1·2500	9	1·1370	1·1078	$1\frac{7}{64}$ $1\frac{1}{8}$	28·5		1·1090 1·1220 1·1250
$1\frac{3}{8}$	1·3750	8	1·2470	1·2150	$1\frac{7}{32}$ $1\frac{15}{64}$	31·0 31·5		1·2180 1·2200 1·2340 1·2400
$1\frac{1}{2}$	1·5000	8	1·3720	1·3400	$1\frac{11}{32}$ $1\frac{23}{64}$	34·5		1·3440 1·3580 1·3590

TAPPING DRILLS FOR BRITISH STANDARD PIPE THREADS (PARALLEL) *

B.S.P. Size	Nominal Diameter of Thread	Number of Threads per Inch	Minor Diameter of Nut		Stock Drills			
			Max.	Min.	In.	Mm.	Wire or Letter	Equivalent Diameter
in. $\frac{1}{8}$	in. ·3830	28	in. ·3483	in. ·3372	$\frac{11}{32}$		R S	in. ·3390 ·3438 ·3480
$\frac{1}{4}$	·5180	19	·4681	·4506	$\frac{22}{64}$	11·5		·4528 ·4531
$\frac{3}{8}$	·6560	19	·6061	·5886	$\frac{19}{32}$	15·0		·5906 ·5938
$\frac{1}{2}$	·8250	14	·7549	·7336	$\frac{47}{64}$ $\frac{3}{4}$	19·0		·7344 ·7480 ·7500
$\frac{5}{8}$	·9020	14	·8319	·8106	$\frac{13}{16}$ $\frac{53}{64}$	21·0		·8125 ·8268 ·8281
$\frac{3}{4}$	1·0110	14	·9709	·9496	$\frac{61}{64}$ $\frac{31}{32}$	24·5		·9531 ·9646 ·9688
$\frac{7}{8}$	1·1890	14	1·1189	1·0976	$1\frac{7}{64}$	28·0		1·1020 1·1090
1	1·3090	11	1·2178	1·1926	$1\frac{13}{64}$	30·5		1·2010 1·2030
$1\frac{1}{4}$	1·6500	11	1·5588	1·5336	$1\frac{35}{64}$	39·0 39·5		1·5350 1·5470 1·5550
$1\frac{1}{2}$	1·8820	11	1·7908	1·7656	$1\frac{25}{32}$	45·0		1·7720 1·7810

* Abstracted from British Standard Specification 1157—1944.

TAPPING DRILLS FOR BRITISH ASSOCIATION (B.A.) THREADS *

Designating Number	Nominal Diameter of Thread	Pitch	Minor Diameter of Nut		Stock Drills			
			Max.	Min.	In.	Mm.	Wire or Letter	Equivalent Diameter
	mm.	*mm.*	*mm.*	*mm.*				*in.*
No. 0	*6·000*	*1·000*	*5·150*	*4·800*			12	·1890
	(·2362 in.)	(·03937 in.)	(·2028 in.)	(·1890 in.)			11	·1910
							10	·1935
							9	·1960
						5·0		·1969
							8	·1990
							7	·2010
No. 1	*5·300*	*·900*	*4·535*	*4·22*			19	·1660
	(·2087 in.)	(·03543 in.)	(·1785 in.)	(·1661 in.)			18	·1695
					$\frac{11}{64}$			·1719
							17	·1730
							16	·1770
						4·5		·1772
No. 2	*4·700*	*·810*	*4·105*	*3·730*			26	·1470
	(·1850 in.)	(·0319 in.)	(·1580 in.)	(·1468 in.)			25	·1495
							24	·1520
							23	·1540
					$\frac{5}{32}$			·1563
							22	·1570
						4·0		·1575
No. 3	*4·100*	*·730*	*3·475*	*3·220*			30	·1285
	(·1614 in.)	(·02874 in.)	(·1368 in.)	(·1268 in.)				
No. 4	*3·600*	*·660*	*3·040*	*2·810*			34	·1110
	(·1417 in.)	(·0260 in.)	(·1197 in.)	(·1106 in.)			33	·1130
							32	·1160
						3·0		·1181
No. 5	*3·200*	*·590*	*2·695*	*2·490*			40	·0980
	(·1260 in.)	(·0232 in.)	(·1061 in.)	(·0980 in.)		2·5		·0984
							39	·0995
							38	·1015
							37	·1040
No. 6	*2·800*	*·530*	*2·345*	*2·160*			44	·0860
	(·1102 in.)	(·0209 in.)	(·0923 in.)	(·0850 in.)			43	·0890
No. 7	*2·500*	*·480*	*2·090*	*1·920*			48	·0760
	(·0984 in.)	(·0189 in.)	(·0823 in.)	(·0756 in.)	$\frac{5}{64}$			·0781
							47	·0785
						2·0		·0787
							46	·0810
							45	·0820
No. 8	*2·200*	*·430*	*1·830*	*1·680*			51	·0670
	(·0866 in.)	(·0169 in.)	(·0720 in.)	(·0661 in.)			50	·0700
No. 9	*1·900*	*·390*	*1·565*	*1·430*		1·5		·0591
	(·0748 in.)	(·0154 in.)	(·0616 in.)	(·0563 in.)			53	·0595
No. 10	*1·700*	*·350*	*1·400*	*1·280*			55	·0520
	(·0669 in.)	(·0138 in.)	(·0551 in.)	(·0504 in.)			54	·0550

* Abstracted from British Standard Specification 1157—1944.

TAPPING DRILLS FOR METRIC SCREW THREADS
(SYSTÈME INTERNATIONALE)*

Nominal Diameter of Thread	Pitch	Minor Diameter of Nut		Stock Drills			
		Max.	Min.	In.	Mm.	Wire or Letter	Equivalent Diameter
mm. 6 (·2362 in.)	mm. 1 (·03937 in.)	mm. 5·026 (·1979 in.)	mm. 4·863 (·1915 in.)		5·0	10 9	in. ·1935 ·1960 ·1969
7 (·2756 in.)	1 (·03937 in.)	6·026 (·0372 in.)	5·863 (·2308 in.)	$\frac{15}{64}$	6·0	A	·2340 ·2344 ·2362
8 (·3150 in.)	1·25 (·0492 in.)	6·782 (·0270 in.)	6·579 (·2590 in.)	$\frac{17}{64}$		G H	·2610 ·2656 ·2660
9 (·3543 in.)	1·25 (·0492 in.)	7·782 (·3064 in.)	7·579 (·2984 in.)			N	·3020
10 (·3937 in.)	1·5 (·0591 in.)	8·539 (·3362 in.)	8·295 (·3266 in.)	$\frac{21}{64}$	8·5	Q	·3281 ·3320 ·3346
11 (·4331 in.)	1·5 (·0591 in.)	9·295 (·3755 in.)	9·295 (·3659 in.)	$\frac{3}{8}$	9·5	U	·3680 ·3740 ·3750
12 (·4724 in.)	1·75 (·0689 in.)	10·295 (·4053 in.)	10·011 (·3941 in.)			X Y	·3970 ·4040
14 (·5512 in.)	2·0 (·0787 in.)	12·051 (·4745 in.)	11·727 (·4617 in.)	$\frac{15}{32}$	12·0		·4688 ·4724
16 (·6299 in.)	2·0 (·0787 in.)	14·051 (·5532 in.)	13·727 (·5404 in.)	$\frac{35}{64}$	14·0		·5469 ·5512
18 (·7087 in.)	2·5 (·0984 in.)	15·564 (·6128 in.)	15·158 (·5968 in.)	$\frac{39}{64}$	15·5		·6094 ·6102
20 (·7874 in.)	2·5 (·0984 in.)	17·564 (·6915 in.)	17·158 (·6755 in.)	$\frac{11}{16}$	17·5		·6875 ·6890
22 (·8661 in.)	2·5 (·0984 in.)	19·564 (·7702 in.)	19·158 (·7542 in.)	$\frac{49}{64}$	19·5		·7656 ·7677
24 (·9449 in.)	3·0 (·1181 in.)	21·077 (·8298 in.)	20·590 (·8106 in.)	$\frac{13}{16}$ $\frac{53}{64}$	21·0		·8125 ·8268 ·8281
27 (1·0630 in.)	3·0 (·1181 in.)	24·077 (·9479 in.)	23·590 (·9287 in.)	$\frac{15}{16}$	24·0		·9375 ·9449

* Abstracted from British Standard Specification 1157—1944.

Tapping Drills for Metric Screw Threads (Système Internationale) (*contd.*)

Nominal Diameter of Thread	Pitch	Minor Diameter of Nut		Stock Drills			
		Max.	Min.	In.	Mm.	Wire or Letter	Equivalent Diameter
mm. 30 (1·1811 in.)	mm. 3·5 (·1378 in.)	mm. 26·59 (1·0469 in.)	mm. 26·022 (1·0245 in.)	$1\frac{1}{32}$ $1\frac{3}{64}$	26·5		in. 1·0310 1·0430 1·0470
33 (1·2992 in.)	3·5 (·1378 in.)	29·59 (1·1650 in.)	29·022 (1·1426 in.)	$1\frac{5}{32}$	29·5		1·1560 1·1610
36 (1·4173 in.)	4·0 (·1575 in.)	32·103 (1·2639 in.)	31·453 (1·2383 in.)	$1\frac{1}{4}$	31·5 32·0		1·2400 1·2500 1·2600
39 (1·5354 in.)	4·0 (·1575 in.)	35·103 (1·3820 in.)	34·453 (1·3564 in.)	$1\frac{23}{64}$ $1\frac{3}{8}$	34·5 35·0		1·3580 1·3590 1·3750 1·3780
42 (1·6535 in.)	4·5 (·1772 in.)	37·616 (1·4809 in.)	36·885 (1·4521 in.)	$1\frac{29}{64}$ $1\frac{15}{32}$	37·0 37·5		1·4350 1·4570 1·4690 1·4760
45 (1 7717 in.)	4·5 (·1772 in.)	40·616 (1·5991 in.)	39·885 (1·5703 in.)	$1\frac{37}{64}$ $1\frac{19}{32}$	40·0 40·5		1·5750 1·5780 1·5940 1·5940
48 (1·8898 in.)	5·0 (·1968 in.)	43·128 (1·6980 in.)	42·316 (1·6660 in.)	$1\frac{11}{16}$	42·5 43·0		1·6730 1·6880 1·6930
52 (2·0473 in.)	5·0 (·1968 in.)	47·128 (1·8555 in.)	46·316 (1·8235 in.)	$1\frac{27}{32}$	46·5 47·0		1·8310 1·8440 1·8500

S.A.E. SCREW THREADS

Drills for Tapped Holes

GENERAL INFORMATION

The accompanying reference table for tap drills gives the thread depths in percentages for the basic minor-diameter limits for each thread size and pitch. The sizes, pitches and corresponding minor diameters are in agreement with the S.A.E. Standard for Screw Threads in Section 5 of the S.A.E. Handbook, except where shown in italics, the latter being included in the table to give it a wider range of usefulness. The drill sizes are standard up to and including ½-in. diameter, in accordance with the S.A.E. Standard in Section 8 of the Handbook, those shown in italics being larger than the range of standard diameters. Some drill sizes are included that are outside the ranges of the maximum and minimum minor diameters prescribed by the screw-thread standard, to provide thread depths suited to heavy-service requirements and to light-service applications.

Thread Size and T.P.I.	Minor Diam. Max.	Minor Diam. Min.	Drill Size	Thread Depth, per cent.	Thread Size and T.P.I.	Minor Diam. Max.	Minor Diam. Min.	Drill Size	Thread Depth, per cent.
No.	In.	In.			No.	In.	In.		
0—80	0·0514	0·0465	0·0453	91	3—48	0·0841	0·0764	0·0730	96
			0·0469	81				0·0760	85
			0·0492	68				0·0781	77
			0·0512	54				0·0810	66 +
			0·0531	42				0·0827	60
								0·0860	48
1—64	0·0623	0·0561	0·0531	98	3—56	0·0856	0·0797	0·0760	99
			0·0550	88 +				0·0781	90
			0·0571	78				0·0810	77 +
			0·0591	68				0·0827	70
			0·0610	59				0·0846	62
			0·0625	51				0·0860	56
1—72	0·0634	0·0580	0·0550	100	4—40	0·0893	0·0849	0·0810	95
			0·0571	88				0·0827	90
			0·0591	77				0·0860	80
			0·0610	66				0·0890	71
			0·0625	58				0·0906	66
			0·0629	55				0·0937	56
			0·0650	45				0·0960	49
2—56	0·0737	0·0667	0·0629	99	4—48	0·0960	0·0894	0·0860	96
			0·0650	90 +				0·0890	85
			0·0670	82				0·0906	79
			0·0700	69				0·0937	67
			0·0730	56				0·0960	59
			0·0760	43				0·0995	46
2—64	0·0746	0·0691	0·0670	94 −	5—40	0·1062	0·0979	0·0937	96
			0·0700	79				0·0960	89
			0·0730	64				0·0995	78
			0·0760	49				0·1024	70
								0·1040	65
								0·1065	57 +

Drills for Tapped Holes (*contd.*)

Thread Size and T.P.I.	Minor Diam.		Drill Size	Thread Depth, per cent.	Thread Size and T.P.I.	Minor Diam.		Drill Size	Thread Depth, per cent.
	Max.	Min.				Max.	Min.		
No. 5—44	In. 0·1068	In. 0·1004	0·0960	98	No. 10—40	In. 0·1673	In. 0·1629	0·1610	89
			0·0995	86				0·1660	74
			0·1024	76				0·1695	63
			0·1040	71				0·1719	56
			0·1065	63					
			0·1094	53	12—24	0·1801	0·1709	0·1660	92
								0·1695	86
6—32	0·1145	0·1042	0·0995	95				0·1719	81 +
			0·1024	87 +				0·1730	79
			0·1040	83 +				0·1770	72
			0·1065	78				0·1800	66 +
			0·1094	70 +				0·1850	57
			0·1130	62					
			0·1160	54	12—28	0·1835	0·1773	0·1695	100
								0·1719	95
6—40	0·1179	0·1109	0·1065	97 +				0·1730	92 +
			0·1094	88				0·1770	84
			0·1130	77				0·1800	77 +
			0·1160	68				0·1850	67
			0·1200	65				0·1875	61
8—32	0·1384	0·1302	0·1250	96	12—32	0·1868	0·1822	0·1770	96
			0·1285	87				0·1800	88 +
			0·1299	84				0·1850	76
			0·1339	74				0·1875	70
			0·1360	69					
			0·1378	64 +	$\frac{1}{4}$—20	0·2060	0·1959	0·1850	100
			0·1406	57 +				0·1875	96
								0·1910	91
8—36	0·1402	0·1339	0·1285	98				0·1935	87
			0·1299	94				0·1960	83
			0·1339	83 +				0·1990	78 +
			0·1360	77 +				0·2031	72
			0·1378	72 +				0·2090	63
			0·1406	65					
			0·1440	55	$\frac{1}{4}$—24	0·2114	0·2049	0·1960	100
								0·1990	94
10—24	0·1559	0·1449	0·1360	99 +				0·2031	86 +
			0·1378	96				0·2090	76 −
			0·1406	91				0·2130	68
			0·1440	85					
			0·1470	79					
			0·1520	70	$\frac{1}{4}$—28	0·2173	0·2113	0·2090	88
			0·1562	62				0·2130	80
								0·2187	67
10—32	0·1624	0·1562	0·1520	93 +					
			0·1562	83	$\frac{1}{4}$—32	0·2208	0·2162	0·2090	100
			0·1610	71				0·2130	91
			0·1660	59				0·2187	77
			0·1695	50				0·2244	63

Drills for Tapped Holes (*contd.*)

Thread Size and T.P.I.	Minor Diam.		Drill Size	Thread Depth, per cent.	Thread Size and T.P.I.	Minor Diam.		Drill Size	Thread Depth, per cent.
	Max.	Min.				Max.	Min.		
No.	In.	In.			No.	In.	In.		
¼—36	0·2247	0·2199	0·2187	87 −	⁷⁄₁₆—24	0·3985	0·3924	0·3860	95
			0·2244	71				0·3906	86 +
			0·2280	61				0·3970	74 +
								0·4062	58 −
¼—40	0·2273	0·2229	0·2187	96	⁷⁄₁₆—28	0·4041	0·3988	0·3970	87
			0·2244	79				0·4062	67
			0·2280	68 −					
⁵⁄₁₆—18	0·2630	0·2524	0·2460	92	½—12	0·4225	0·4098	0·3970	95
			0·2500	86 +				0·4062	86 +
			0·2520	84				0·4219	72
			0·2570	77				0·4375	58 −
			0·2610	71					
			0·2656	65	½—13	0·4290	0·4167	0·4062	94
⁵⁄₁₆—24	0·2739	0·2674	0·2610	95				0·4219	78
			0·2656	86 +				0·4375	62 +
			0·2720	75	½—16	0·4403	0·4323	0·4219	96
			0·2770	65 +				0·4375	77
⁵⁄₁₆—32	0·2833	0·2787	0·2720	99 +				0·4531	58 −
			0·2770	87	½—20	0·4531	0·4459	0·4375	96
			0·2812	77				0·4531	72
								0·4687	48
⅜—16	0·3184	0·3073	0·2969	96					
			0·3020	90	½—24	0·4610	0·4549	0·4531	86
			0·3071	83				0·4687	57 +
			0·3125	77					
			0·3160	72 +	½—28	0·4666	0·4613	0·4531	100 +
			0·3230	64				0·4687	67
⅜—24	0·3364	0·3299	0·3281	86 +	⁹⁄₁₆—12	0·4850	0·4723	0·4531	100 +
			0·3320	79				0·4687	86 +
			0·3390	66 +				0·4844	72
⅜—32	0·3458	0·3412	0·3390	88 +				0·5000	58
			0·3437	77	⁹⁄₁₆—16	0·5028	0·4948	0·4844	97
			0·3480	66 +				0·5000	77
⁷⁄₁₆—14	0·3721	0·3602	0·3480	96				0·5118	62
			0·3543	89 +				0·5156	57 +
			0·3594	84					
			0·3680	75	⁹⁄₁₆—18	0·5100	0·5024	0·5000	86 +
			0·3750	67				0·5118	70
⁷⁄₁₆—20	0·3906	0·3834	0·3750	96				0·5156	65
			0·3860	79	⁹⁄₁₆—24	0·5235	0·5174	0·5118	93 +
			0·3906	72				0·5126	86 +
			0·3970	62 +				0·5312	58 -

SLOCOMB OR CENTRE DRILLS

These drills are used for drilling centres in shafts that are to be turned between lathe centres or on cylindrical grinding machines.

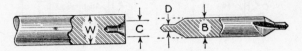

FIG. 12.—SLOCOMB CENTRE DRILL.

The corresponding sizes of the drills and drilled centres are given in the following table :

SLOCOMB OR CENTRE DRILL SIZES

Work		Centre Drill		
Diameter at W	Diameter at C	No.	Drill D	Body B
In.	In.	In.	In.	In.
$\frac{3}{16}$ to $\frac{5}{16}$	$\frac{1}{8}$	1	$\frac{1}{16}$	$\frac{3}{16}$
$\frac{3}{8}$ to 1	$\frac{3}{16}$	2	$\frac{3}{32}$	$\frac{5}{16}$
$1\frac{1}{4}$ to 2	$\frac{1}{4}$	3	$\frac{1}{8}$	$\frac{3}{10}$
$2\frac{1}{4}$ to 3	$\frac{5}{16}$	4	$\frac{5}{32}$	$\frac{7}{16}$

BRITISH STANDARD DRILLING-JIG BUSHES

Three types of drilling-jig bushes are specified in the British Standard Specification B.S. No. 1098—1943, viz. (a) Press-fit Bushes (Headless and Headed). (b) Renewable Bushes (Slip and Fixed). (c) Liners (Headless and Headed). The dimensions specified ensure interchangeability of the bushes. The following tables refer to Types (a) and (b).

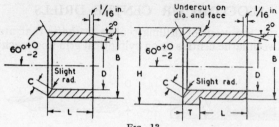

FIG. 13.

B.S. PRESS-FIT BUSHES : HEADLESS AND HEADED TYPES

1	2	3	4	5	6	7	8	9	10	11
	Hole Size				Body Diameter		Head		Length	
Group	D		Limits	B	Finish Size Limits	Un-finished Sizes	H Max.	T Max.	L $+0 \\ -\frac{1}{32}$	C
	Above	Up to and Inc.								
	In.	In.	In.	In.	In.	In.	In.	In.	In.	In.
1	$\frac{3}{64}$	$\frac{3}{32}$	$+0.0004$ $+0.0001$	$\frac{13}{64}$	$+0.0009$ $+0.0006$	0.218 0.213	$\frac{5}{16}$	$\frac{3}{32}$	$\frac{5}{16}, \frac{1}{2}$	$\frac{3}{32}$
2	$\frac{3}{32}$	$\frac{9}{64}$	$+0.0004$ $+0.0001$	$\frac{1}{4}$	$+0.0009$ $+0.0006$	0.270 0.265	$\frac{3}{8}$	$\frac{1}{8}$	$\frac{5}{16}, \frac{1}{2}$	$\frac{3}{64}$
3	$\frac{9}{64}$	$\frac{3}{16}$	$+0.0004$ $+0.0001$	$\frac{5}{16}$	$+0.0012$ $+0.0008$	0.332 0.327	$\frac{7}{16}$	$\frac{1}{8}$	$\frac{5}{16}, \frac{1}{2}, \frac{3}{4}$	$\frac{3}{64}$
4	$\frac{3}{16}$	$\frac{5}{16}$	$+0.0004$ $+0.0001$	$\frac{1}{2}$	$+0.0012$ $+0.0008$	0.520 0.515	$\frac{11}{16}$	$\frac{3}{16}$	$\frac{5}{16}, \frac{1}{2}, \frac{3}{4}$	$\frac{5}{64}$
5	$\frac{5}{16}$	$\frac{1}{2}$	$+0.0006$ $+0.0002$	$\frac{3}{4}$	$+0.0015$ $+0.0010$	0.770 0.765	$\frac{15}{16}$	$\frac{1}{4}$	$\frac{1}{2}, \frac{3}{4}, 1$	$\frac{7}{64}$
6	$\frac{1}{2}$	$\frac{3}{4}$	$+0.0007$ $+0.0002$	1	$+0.0018$ $+0.0012$	1.020 1.015	$1\frac{1}{4}$	$\frac{5}{16}$	$\frac{3}{4}, 1, 1\frac{3}{8}$	$\frac{7}{64}$
7	$\frac{3}{4}$	1	$+0.0007$ $+0.0002$	$1\frac{3}{8}$	$+0.0018$ $+0.0012$	1.395 1.390	$1\frac{5}{8}$	$\frac{5}{16}$	$\frac{3}{4}, 1, 1\frac{3}{8}$	$\frac{9}{64}$
8	1	$1\frac{3}{8}$	$+0.0009$ $+0.0003$	$1\frac{3}{4}$	$+0.0021$ $+0.0014$	1.770 1.765	2	$\frac{3}{8}$	$1, 1\frac{3}{8}, 1\frac{3}{4}$	$\frac{9}{64}$
9	$1\frac{3}{8}$	$1\frac{3}{4}$	$+0.0010$ $+0.0003$	$2\frac{1}{4}$	$+0.0024$ $+0.0016$	2.270 2.265	$2\frac{1}{2}$	$\frac{3}{8}$	$1, 1\frac{3}{8}, 1\frac{3}{4}$	$\frac{7}{32}$

Note.—The recommended limits on the holes in the jig plate are British Standard Units (B.S. 164).

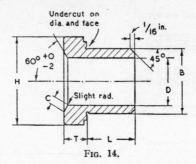

Fig. 14.

B.S. RENEWABLE BUSHES: SLIP AND FIXED SIZES

1	2	3	4	5	6	7	8	9	10	11	12
	Hole Size D					Body Diameter		Head		Length	C
Group	Slip Bushes		Fixed Bushes		Limits	B	Limits	H Max.	T Max.	L $+0$ $-\frac{1}{32}$	
	Above	Up to and Inc.	Above	Up to and Inc.							
	In.	In.	In.	In.	In.	In.	In.	In.	In.	In.	In.
1	0	$\frac{5}{32}$	0	$\frac{3}{16}$	$+0.0004$ $+0.0001$	$\frac{5}{16}$	$+0$ -0.0002	$\frac{5}{8}$	$\frac{3}{8}$	$\frac{5}{16}$, $\frac{1}{2}$, $\frac{3}{4}$	$\frac{1}{32}$
2	$\frac{9}{64}$	$\frac{11}{32}$	$\frac{3}{16}$	$\frac{5}{16}$	$+0.0004$ $+0.0001$	$\frac{1}{2}$	$+0$ -0.0002	$\frac{15}{16}$	$\frac{3}{8}$	$\frac{5}{16}$, $\frac{1}{2}$, $\frac{3}{4}$	$\frac{5}{64}$
3	$\frac{9}{32}$	$\frac{17}{32}$	$\frac{5}{16}$	$\frac{1}{2}$	$+0.0006$ $+0.0002$	$\frac{3}{4}$	$+0$ -0.0003	$1\frac{1}{4}$	$\frac{3}{8}$	$\frac{1}{2}$, $\frac{3}{4}$, 1	$\frac{7}{64}$
4	$\frac{15}{32}$	$\frac{25}{32}$	$\frac{1}{2}$	$\frac{3}{4}$	$+0.0007$ $+0.0002$	1	$+0$ -0.0003	$1\frac{5}{8}$	$\frac{7}{16}$	$\frac{3}{4}$, 1, $1\frac{3}{8}$	$\frac{7}{64}$
5	$\frac{23}{32}$	$1\frac{1}{32}$	$\frac{3}{4}$	1	$+0.0007$ $+0.0002$	$1\frac{3}{8}$	$+0$ -0.0003	2	$\frac{7}{16}$	$\frac{3}{4}$, 1, $1\frac{3}{8}$	$\frac{9}{64}$
6	$\frac{31}{32}$	$1\frac{13}{32}$	1	$1\frac{3}{8}$	$+0.0009$ $+0.0003$	$1\frac{3}{4}$	$+0$ -0.0004	$2\frac{1}{2}$	$\frac{1}{2}$	1, $1\frac{3}{8}$, $1\frac{3}{4}$	$\frac{9}{64}$
7	$1\frac{11}{32}$	$1\frac{25}{32}$	$1\frac{3}{8}$	$1\frac{3}{4}$	$+0.0010$ $+0.0003$	$2\frac{1}{4}$	$+0$ -0.0004	3	$\frac{1}{2}$	1, $1\frac{3}{8}$, $1\frac{3}{4}$	$\frac{7}{32}$

Note.—For slip bushes the maximum hole size in any one group is greater than the minimum hole size in the next larger group. This is to permit a hole, the diameter of which approaches the nominal transitional dimensions (col. 5) between any two groups, to be drilled and reamed through bushes from a common group.

MORSE TAPER SHANKS

(Dimensions in Inches)

No. of Taper	Plug Diameter at Small End *A*	Diameter at End of Socket *B*	Shank — Whole Length of Shank *C*	Shank Depth *D*	Depth of Hole *E*	Standard Plug Depth *F*	Thickness of Tongue *G*	Length of Tongue *H*	Radius of Mill for Tongue *J*	Diameter of Tongue *K*	Radius of Tongue *L*	Width of Keyway *M*	Length of Keyway *N*	End of Socket to Keyway *P*	Taper per Foot	Taper per Inch	No. of Key
0	·252	·356	2 11/32	2 7/32	2 15/32	2	5/32	1/4	5/32	·235	·04	·160	9/16	1 15/16	·6246	·05205	0
1	·369	·475	2 9/16	2 7/16	2 9/16	2 1/8	13/64	3/8	3/16	·343	·05	·213	3/4	2 1/16	·5986	·0498	1
2	·572	·700	3 1/16	2 15/16	3 1/16	2 9/16	1/4	7/16	1/4	17/32	·06	·260	7/8	2 1/16	·5994	·0499	2
3	·778	·938	3 7/8	3 11/16	3 13/16	3 3/16	5/16	9/16	3/8	23/32	·08	·322	1 3/16	3 1/16	·6023	·0502	3
4	1·020	1·231	4 7/8	4 5/8	4 3/4	4 1/16	15/32	5/8	9/16	31/32	·10	·478	1 1/4	4 1/16	·6233	·0519	4
5	1·475	1·748	6 1/8	5 7/8	6	5 3/16	5/8	3/4	3/4	1 13/32	·12	·625	1 1/2	5 3/16	·6315	·0526	5
6	2·116	2·494	8 9/16	8 1/4	8 1/4	7 1/4	3/4	1 1/8	1	2	·15	·760	1 3/4	7	·6256	·0521	6
7	2·750	3·270	11 5/8	11 1/4	10	10	1 1/8	1 3/8	1 1/4	2 5/8	·18	1·135	2 3/8	9 1/2	·6240	·0520	7

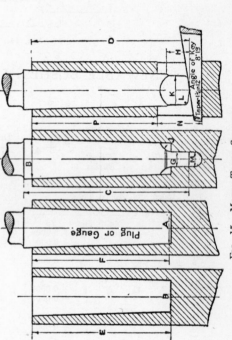

Fig. 15.—Morse Taper Shanks.

BROWN & SHARPE TAPERS

(Dimensions in Inches)

No. of Taper	Diam. of Plug at Small End	Plug Depth	Depth of Hole	Keyway from End of Spindle	Length of Keyway	Width of Keyway	Length of Arbor Tongue	Thickness of Arbor Tongue	Taper per Foot
	D	P	$P + \frac{1}{8}$	K	L	W	T	t	
1	·20	$\frac{15}{16}$	$1\frac{1}{16}$	$\frac{15}{16}$	$\frac{3}{8}$	·135	$\frac{3}{16}$	$\frac{1}{8}$	·500
2	·25	$1\frac{3}{16}$	$1\frac{5}{16}$	$1\frac{11}{64}$	$\frac{1}{2}$	·166	$\frac{1}{4}$	$\frac{5}{32}$	·500
3	·312	2	$2\frac{1}{8}$	$1\frac{31}{32}$	$\frac{5}{8}$	·197	$\frac{5}{16}$	$\frac{3}{16}$	·500
4	·35	$1\frac{1}{4}$	$1\frac{3}{8}$	$1\frac{13}{64}$	$\frac{11}{16}$	·228	$\frac{11}{32}$	$\frac{7}{32}$	·500
5	·45	$1\frac{3}{4}$	$1\frac{7}{8}$	$1\frac{11}{16}$	$\frac{3}{4}$	·260	$\frac{3}{8}$	$\frac{1}{4}$	·500
6	·50	$2\frac{3}{8}$	$2\frac{1}{4}$	$2\frac{15}{16}$	$\frac{7}{8}$	·291	$\frac{7}{16}$	$\frac{5}{32}$	·500
7	·60	3	$3\frac{1}{8}$	$2\frac{29}{32}$	$\frac{15}{16}$	·322	$\frac{15}{32}$	$\frac{6}{16}$	·500
8	·75	$3\frac{9}{16}$	$3\frac{11}{16}$	$3\frac{21}{32}$	1	·353	$\frac{1}{2}$	$\frac{11}{32}$	·500
9	·90	4	$4\frac{1}{8}$	$3\frac{7}{8}$	$1\frac{1}{8}$	·385	$\frac{9}{16}$	$\frac{3}{8}$	·500
9	·90	$4\frac{1}{4}$	$4\frac{3}{8}$	$4\frac{1}{8}$	$1\frac{1}{8}$	·385	$\frac{9}{16}$	$\frac{3}{8}$	·500
10	1·0446	5	$5\frac{1}{8}$	$4\frac{27}{32}$	$1\frac{5}{16}$	·447	$\frac{21}{32}$	$\frac{7}{16}$	·5161
10	1·0446	$5\frac{11}{16}$	$5\frac{13}{16}$	$5\frac{13}{32}$	$1\frac{5}{16}$	·447	$\frac{21}{32}$	$\frac{7}{16}$	·5161
11	1·25	$6\frac{3}{4}$	$6\frac{7}{8}$	$6\frac{19}{32}$	$1\frac{5}{8}$	·447	$\frac{21}{32}$	$\frac{7}{16}$	·500
12	1·50	$7\frac{3}{8}$	$7\frac{1}{2}$	$6\frac{1}{16}$	$1\frac{1}{2}$	·510	$\frac{3}{4}$	$\frac{1}{2}$	·500
13	1·75	$7\frac{3}{4}$	$7\frac{7}{8}$	$7\frac{9}{16}$	$1\frac{1}{2}$	·510	$\frac{3}{4}$	$\frac{1}{2}$	·500
14	2	$8\frac{1}{4}$	$8\frac{3}{8}$	$8\frac{1}{32}$	$1\frac{11}{16}$	·572	$\frac{27}{32}$	$\frac{9}{16}$	·500
15	2·25	$8\frac{3}{4}$	$8\frac{7}{8}$	$8\frac{17}{32}$	$1\frac{11}{16}$	·572	$\frac{27}{32}$	$\frac{9}{16}$	·500
16	2·50	$9\frac{1}{4}$	$9\frac{3}{8}$	9	$1\frac{7}{8}$	·635	$\frac{15}{16}$	$\frac{5}{8}$	·500
17	2·75	$9\frac{3}{4}$	$9\frac{7}{8}$	—	—	—	—	—	·500
18	3	$10\frac{1}{4}$	$10\frac{3}{8}$	—	—	—	—	—	·500

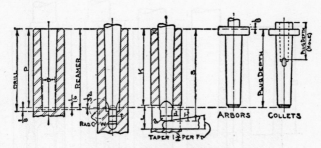

Fig. 16.—Brown & Sharpe Tapers.

THE CLEVELAND SYSTEM OF TAPERS

(Dimensions in Inches)

Number of Taper	Dia. of Plug at Small End	Standard Plug Depth	Depth of Hole	End of Socket to Keyway	Length of Keyway	Width of Keyway	Length of Tongue	Dia. of Shank at Small End	Thickness of Tongue	Radius of Mill for Tongue	Radius of Tongue "a"	Shank Depth	Whole Length of Shank	Taper per Foot	Dia. at End of Socket	Taper per Inch	No. of Key
	D	P	H	K	L	W	T	d	t	r	a	S	B		A		
0	·252	2	$2\frac{1}{32}$	$1\frac{15}{16}$	$\frac{9}{16}$	·160	$\frac{1}{4}$	·235	$\frac{5}{32}$	$\frac{5}{32}$	·04	$2\frac{7}{32}$	$2\frac{13}{32}$	·625	·356	·05208	
1	·369	$2\frac{1}{8}$	$2\frac{3}{16}$	$2\frac{1}{4}$	$\frac{3}{4}$	·213	$\frac{3}{8}$	·353	$\frac{13}{64}$	$\frac{3}{8}$	·05	$2\frac{7}{16}$	$2\frac{11}{16}$	·600	·475	·05	1
2	·572	$2\frac{9}{16}$	$2\frac{5}{8}$	2·488	$\frac{7}{8}$	·265	$\frac{7}{16}$	·553	$\frac{1}{4}$	$\frac{3}{8}$	$\frac{1}{16}$	$2\frac{15}{16}$	$3\frac{3}{16}$	·602	·700	·05017	2
3	·778	$3\frac{3}{16}$	$3\frac{1}{4}$	$3\frac{1}{16}$	$1\frac{1}{16}$	·330	$\frac{9}{16}$	·753	$\frac{5}{16}$	$\frac{7}{16}$	$\frac{3}{32}$	$3\frac{11}{16}$	$3\frac{15}{16}$	·602	·938	·05017	3
4	1·02	$4\frac{1}{16}$	$4\frac{1}{8}$	$3\frac{7}{8}$	$1\frac{1}{4}$	·490	$\frac{5}{8}$	·991	$\frac{15}{32}$	$\frac{7}{16}$	$\frac{3}{32}$	$4\frac{5}{8}$	$5\frac{1}{4}$	·623	1·231	·05191	4
5	1·475	$5\frac{3}{16}$	$5\frac{1}{4}$	$4\frac{15}{16}$	$1\frac{1}{2}$	·650	$\frac{3}{4}$	1·440	$\frac{5}{8}$	$\frac{1}{2}$	$\frac{1}{8}$	$5\frac{7}{8}$	$6\frac{3}{8}$	·630	1·748	·0525	4
6	2·116	$7\frac{1}{4}$	$7\frac{3}{8}$	7	$1\frac{3}{4}$	·780	1	2·064	$\frac{3}{4}$	$\frac{11}{16}$	$\frac{1}{8}$	$8\frac{1}{8}$	$8\frac{3}{4}$	·626	2·494	·05216	4
7	2·750	10	$10\frac{1}{8}$	$9\frac{1}{2}$	$2\frac{5}{8}$	1·135	$1\frac{3}{8}$	2·684	$1\frac{1}{8}$	$\frac{3}{4}$	·180	$11\frac{1}{4}$	$11\frac{5}{8}$	·625	3·270	·05208	

[Cleveland Twist Drill Co.]

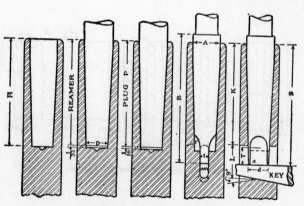

Fig. 17.—Cleveland System of Tapers.

THE JARNO TAPER

This system uses a taper of 0·05 in. per in. length, or 0·6 in. per ft.

$$\text{Diameter of large end} = \frac{\text{No. of taper}}{8}$$

$$\text{Diameter of small end} = \frac{\text{No. of taper}}{10}$$

$$\text{Length of taper} \qquad = \frac{\text{No. of taper}}{2}$$

In the Jarno system, the taper of which is 0·6 in. per ft. or 1 in 20, the number of the taper is the key by which all the dimensions are immediately determined. That is, the number of the taper is the number of tenths of an inch in diameter at the small end, the number of eighths of an inch at the large end, and the number of halves of an inch in length or depth. For example : the No. 6 taper is six-eighths (3/4) in. diameter at large end, six-tenths (6/10) in. diameter at the small end and six-halves (3) in. in length. Similarly, the No. 16 taper is sixteen-eighths or 2 in. diameter at the large end ; sixteen-tenths or $1\frac{6}{10}$ in. at the small end and sixteen-halves, i.e. 8 in., in length.

AMERICAN STANDARD TAPERS

Various systems of tapers were used in the United States up till about 1937, and many of these, such as the Brown & Sharpe, Cleveland, Morse, Jarno and Standard Tool Co. tapers, are still in use. In 1937 the American Standards Association published standard specifications for self-holding tapers. These comprised nineteen sizes, of which the first three were the same as the Brown & Sharpe series with a taper of $\frac{1}{2}$ in. per ft. The next six used the Morse taper of $\frac{5}{8}$ in. per ft., and the last ten, covering the largest sizes, employed a taper of $\frac{3}{4}$ in. per ft. The first thirteen sizes were driven by a tongue or tang.

SECTION 8

CUTTING ANGLES OF TOOLS

The terms generally employed to designate tool angles are shown in Fig. 1. The backing off of the front cutting face to afford relief to the tool, i.e. to enable the part below the cutting edge to clear the work, is termed the *front clearance angle* (B, in upper left-hand diagram, Fig. 1).

The side relief angle is termed the *side clearance angle* (B, in lower right-hand diagram, Fig. 1). A more detailed description of the

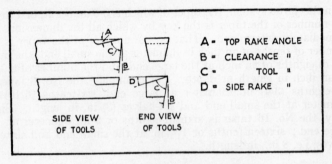

A = TOP RAKE ANGLE
B = CLEARANCE ″
C = TOOL ″
D = SIDE RAKE ″

SIDE VIEW OF TOOLS

END VIEW OF TOOLS

FIG. 1.—CUTTING TOOL NOMENCLATURE.

various terms employed in round-nosed cutting tools for turning, planing, shaping, etc., is given in Fig. 2. In this diagram the *side relief angle* is the same as the *side clearance angle* in Fig. 1.

Tool Materials

The materials used for machining tools are : (1) Carbon tool steel with 1·1 to 1·3 per cent. carbon, quenched and tempered to dark straw colour on cutting edge. (2) High-speed tool steel with 12 to 18 per cent. tungsten and smaller percentages of one or more of the following elements : molybdenum, cobalt, vanadium, chromium. (3) *Non-ferrous Alloys* or sintered carbides, such as tungsten carbide, tantalum and titanium carbides. Typical commercial cutting alloys of this group include Ardoloy, Wimet, Escaloy, Stellite and Carboloy.

With high-speed tool steels much higher cutting speeds can be used than with carbon tool steels, without the loss of cutting-edge temper. Tools of these steels will operate at a red heat satisfactorily, whereas carbon tool steels would immediately lose their cutting hardness and break down.

High-speed tool steels require special heat treatment, i.e. quenching and tempering temperatures and quenching media; the manufacturer's instructions for each type of steel should be adhered to.

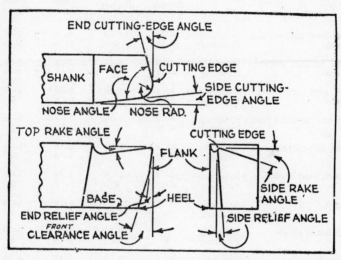

FIG. 2.—MORE DETAILED TOOL TERMS.

Cemented or sintered carbide tool materials are extremely hard, but somewhat brittle. They are relatively expensive and are brazed on ordinary steel shanks in the form of tool tips. The cutting speeds are $2\frac{1}{2}$ to $3\frac{1}{2}$ times those possible with high-speed steel tools at the same cuts and feeds.

TABLE OF CUTTING-TOOL ANGLES

Material to be Machined	Operation	Top Rake Angle. Degrees	Side Rake Angle. Degrees	Front Clearance Angle. Degrees	Side Clearance Angle. Degrees
Steel, low carbon and mild	Roughing	6–10	14–20	5– 8	5– 8
	Finishing	14–10	0	5– 8	0– 4
Steel, medium carbon, hard	Roughing	4– 8	8–14	5– 8	5– 8
	Finishing	8–14	0	5– 8	0– 4
Steel, high carbon, very hard	Roughing	3– 7	5–10	5– 8	5– 8
	Finishing	5–10	0	5– 8	0
Cast iron, medium hard	Roughing	6– 8	12–14	5– 8	5– 8
	Finishing	6–10	0	5– 8	0
Brass, free-cutting	Roughing	6– 8	4– 9	5– 8	5– 8
	Finishing	14–22	0	5– 8	0
Bronze, hard drawn	Roughing	5– 8	4– 8	5– 8	5– 8
	Finishing	5–10	0	5– 8	0
Copper	Roughing	8–12	14–24	5– 8	5– 8
	Finishing	8	14–24	5– 8	0
Aluminium alloys	Roughing	8	16–22	5– 8	5– 8
	Finishing	8	16–22	5– 8	0
Magnesium alloys	Roughing	5– 8	3– 5	6–10	6–10
	Finishing	10–14	0	6–10	0
Monel metal	Roughing	4– 8	10–14	5– 8	5– 8
	Finishing	14–22	0	5– 8	0

Note.—The top rake and front clearance angles for *parting tools* are usually the same as for the finishing-operation values given above. Side clearance angles are 1½° to 2°. For *forming tools* the top rake angle is usually a little greater than the value given for roughing operations. The front clearance angle is the same (5° to 8°) and both the side rake and side clearance angles are 0°.

MACHINING SPEEDS FOR VARIOUS MATERIALS AND TOOLS

Tool Material:	High-speed Steel		Carbon Steel	Tungsten Carbide	Stellite
Material Cut	Turning and Boring	Screwing and Reaming	Turning and Boring	Turning and Boring	Turning and Boring
	Ft. per min.	Ft. per min.	Ft. per min.	Ft. per min.	Ft. per min.
Mild steel . . .	150–200	20– 30	20–30	350– 600	250–300
0·5 carbon steel . .	65– 85	12– 16	14–18	200– 350	150–160
Hard steel (annealed) .	55– 65	12– 14	10–12	200– 300	140–150
Medium-hard cast iron	60– 80	10– 14	10–14	200– 250	100–130
Hard cast iron . .	30– 50	6– 10	9–11	100– 120	60– 80
Malleable iron . .	90–120	15– 20	13–16	200– 300	150–220
Brass rod . . .	240–400	90–120	30–60	500– 800	250–500
Aluminium-alloy castings . . .	250–450	90–130	30–60	500– 900	250–600
Magnesium-alloy castings . . .	350–800	120–180	40–70	500–1,000	300–600

Note.—The finishing speeds with very light cuts may be 50 per cent. higher than the values above given in most cases.

MACHINING SPECIAL MATERIALS

The following are the recommended cutting speeds, when using high-speed steel tools for plain turning of the materials mentioned:

Material	Cutting Speed in Feet per Min.
Ebonite and Vulcanite	300–600
Erinoid, Galalith	300–600
Plastics	250–550
Bakelite, Laminated	100–300
Porcelain (unglazed)	10– 20
Slate	20– 50
Marble	10– 20
Granite	5– 10
Rubber (Medium–Hard)	250–600

CUTTING SPEEDS, CLEARANCE AND RAKE ANGLES. ESCALOY SINTERED-CARBIDE TURNING TOOLS

Material	Cutting Speed Ft. per min.	Clearance Angle	Top Rake Angle
STEEL:			
28–35 tons tensile :			
Clean metal	300/1,200	4°/6°	8°
Castings	300/750	4°/6°	0°/3½°
Rough forgings—removing scale	300/400	4°/6°	0°/3½°
Black bar, stampings . .	300/750	4°/6°	0°
35–45 tons tensile :			
Clean metal	300/1,200	4°/6°	8°/13°
Castings	250/500	4°/6°	0°/3½°
Rough forgings—removing scale	300/400	4°/6°	0°/3½°
Black bar, stampings . .	300/750	4°/6°	3½°
40–45 tons tensile :			
Clean metal	300/750	4°/6°	3½°
Castings	200/350	4°/6°	0°
Rough forgings—removing scale	200/300	4°/6°	0°/3½°
Black bar, stampings . .	250/750	4°/6°	0°/3½°
55–65 tons tensile :			
Clean metal	300/1,000	4°/6°	0°/3½°
Rough forgings—removing scale	200/300	4°/6°	0°/3½°
Black bar, stampings . .	250/750	4°/6°	0°/3½°
High-speed steel—annealed . .	80/250	4°/6°	3½°
Chrome nickel—65–90 tons tensile :			
Clean metal	250/1,000	4°/6°	0°/3½°
Forgings	80/350	4°/6°	0°
Black bar, stampings . .	80/350	4°/6°	0°
Stainless steel :			
Bar	100/300	4°/6°	3½°
Castings	60/150	4°/6°	0°
Manganese steel—12 per cent. .	10/40	4°/6°	0°

Cutting Speeds, Clearance and Rake Angles.
Escaloy Sintered-Carbide Turning Tools (*contd.*)

Material	Cutting Speed Ft. per min.	Clearance Angle	Top Rake Angle
CAST IRON AND WROUGHT IRON :			
Cast iron—200 Brinell . . .	200/700	4°/6°	0°
Centrifugal castings . . .	120/350	4°/6°	3½°
Chilled-iron rolls	10/50	4°/6°	0°
Chromium iron	120/350	4°/6°	3½°
Close-grained iron . . .	150/400	4°/6°	3½°
Malleable iron	100/450	4°/6°	8°
10 per cent. nickel iron . .	20/45	4°/6°	0°
Pearlite iron	150/400	4°/6°	0°
White cast iron	10/30	4°/6°	0°
Wrought iron	250/600	4°/6°	8°
NON-FERROUS METALS :			
Admiralty bronze . . .	300/750	4°/6°	0°/3½°
Aluminium	1,000/2,000	4°/6°	13°/16°
Aluminium alloys . . .	300/750	4°/6°	13°/16°
Aluminium bronze . . .	300/750	4°/6°	0°/3½°
Bronze	400/1,000	4°/6°	0°/3½°
Soft brass	500/1,200	4°/6°	3½°
Hard-cast brass	400/1,000	4°/6°	0°
Copper	500/1,200	4°/6°	13°/16°
Cupro nickel	350/500	4°/6°	3½°
Duralumin	300/750	4°/6°	13°/16°
Gunmetal	400/1,000	4°/6°	0°/3½°
Manganese bronze . . .	300/750	4°/6°	0°
Silicon aluminium . . .	300/750	4°/6°	13°/16°
Zinc-base alloys	300/750	4°/6°	13°/16°
NON-METALLIC MATERIALS :			
Ebonite	500/1,000	20°	0°
Erinoid	500/1,000	20°	0°
Glass	30/70	4°/6°	3¼°
Hard Rubber	500/1,000	20°	0°
Plastics	500/1,000	20°	0°
Porcelain	10/65	4°/6°	0°
Marble	10/65	4°/6°	0°/3½°
Slate	50/100	4°/6°	3½°

[*English Steel Corporation*]

TUNGSTEN-CARBIDE TURNING TOOLS *

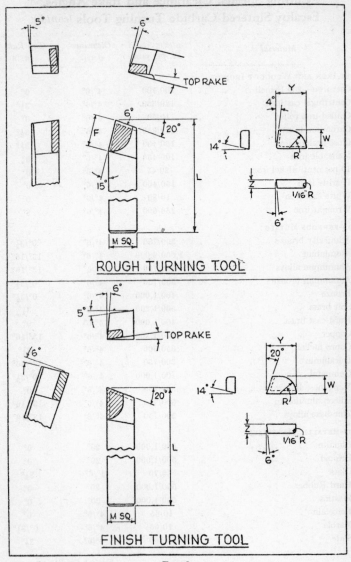

ROUGH TURNING TOOL

FINISH TURNING TOOL

Fig. 3.

* Ardoloy.

TUNGSTEN-CARBIDE TURNING TOOLS (*contd.*)

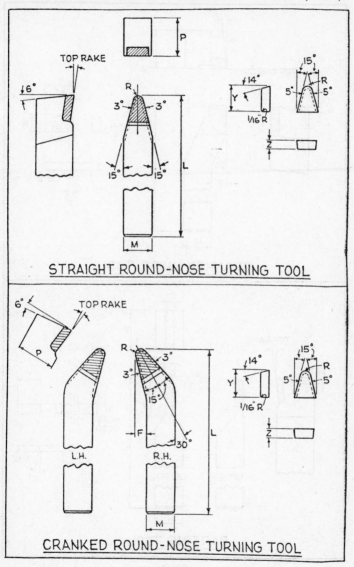

STRAIGHT ROUND-NOSE TURNING TOOL

CRANKED ROUND-NOSE TURNING TOOL

Fig. 4.

TUNGSTEN-CARBIDE TURNING TOOLS *(contd)*

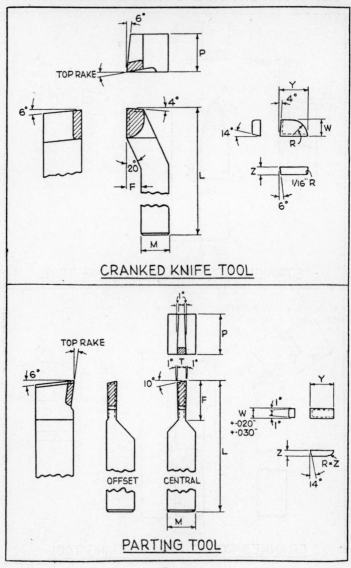

CRANKED KNIFE TOOL

PARTING TOOL

FIG. 5.

LATHE MACHINING DATA FOR TUNGSTEN-CARBIDE TOOLS

Material	Roughing			Finishing		
	Speed F.P.M.	Feed Cuts per In.	Depth of Cut In.	Speed F.P.M.	Feed Cuts per In.	Depth of Cut In.
STEEL						
BELOW 50 TONS TENSILE :						
Black stampings .	200– 250					
Rough forgings . .	200– 250	} 100	¼	600– 800	150	·02–·03
Clean metal . .	250– 350					
50–75 TONS TENSILE :						
Black stampings .	180– 200					
Rough forgings . .	180– 200	} 100	¼	600– 800	150	·02–·03
Clean metal . .	200– 250					
NICKEL-CHROME OVER 75 TONS						
Black stampings .	120– 160			250– 400		
Rough forgings . .	120– 160		} ¼	250– 400		} ·02–·03
Clean metal . .	150– 250			350– 500	} 150	
STEEL CASTINGS . .	150– 200	} 100	¼	300– 500		·02–·03
STAINLESS STEEL . .	100– 200		3⁄16	200– 300		·02–·03
MANGANESE STEEL 12 PER CENT. . . .	50– 70		⅛	80– 120	150	·01–·02
CAST IRON						
Below 200 Brinell . .	180– 220	100	¼	350– 450		} ·015–·03
Above 200 Brinell . .	160– 200	150	¼	200– 300		
Malleable iron . .	100– 160	150	¼	200– 300	} 100	
10 per cent. nickel iron .	20– 50	150	⅛	40– 70		·01–·02
Chilled C.I. . .	15– 20	300	¼	20– 40		·01–·02
NON-FERROUS						
Copper . . .	500– 800	50	¼	7,50–1000		
Soft brass . . .	200– 350	75	¼	300– 500		
Hard brass . . .	400– 600	100	¼	500– 800	} 100	·01–·02
Aluminium . . .	600–1,000	100	¼	Over 1,000		
Magnesium . . .	1,000–2,000	100	¼	Over 2,000		

[George Swift Ltd., Halifax]

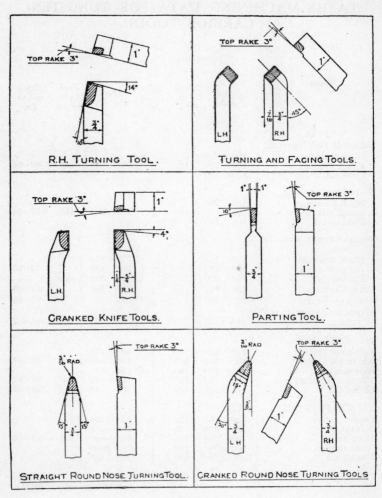

FIG. 6.

HORSE POWER FOR MACHINING METALS

Investigations have shown that the force required to machine a metal with well-designed tools having keen cutting edges and operated under the most efficient conditions of speed and feed depends upon the area and depth of the cut, the cutting speed and the cutting stress. The cutting stress has been found to be about 50 tons per square inch for soft cast iron ; 100 to 120 tons per square inch for mild steel ; 140 to 150 tons per square inch for medium-carbon steel, and 90 to 110 tons per square inch for hard cast iron.

If F = cutting stress in tons per square inch, V = cutting speed in feet per minute, and A = feed, in inches × depth of cut, in inches, then

$$\text{Horse power to machine metal} = \frac{FVA}{14\cdot7}$$

Example.—What is the H.P. required to machine mild steel at 150 feet per minute with a feed of $0\cdot05$ inches and cut of $\frac{1}{8}$ in. ?

$$\text{H.P.} = \frac{110 \times 150 \times 1 \times 0\cdot05}{14\cdot7 \times 8}$$
$$= 7\cdot0.$$

SINTERED-CARBIDE TOOLS

The results of tests made by the Carboloy Co. (Inc.), on a series of S.A.E. steels, cast irons and malleable irons, indicate that Carboloy, Ardoloy, etc., tools require an input horse power for machining different metals given by :

$$\text{H.P.} = A + B$$

where A = frictional H.P. lost in machine
B = H.P. of each tool
$= D \times F \times S \times C$

D = Depth of cut in in. S = Surface ft. per min.
F = Feed in in. per rev. C = Power constant (see following Tables, A and C).

Table A on p. 292 gives values of the " Power Constant " for Brinell hardness values up to 400, but the results of the limited number of tests that have been made on harder steels indicate that for steels of more than 400 Brinell the value of C should be doubled.

TABLE A.—POWER-CONSTANT VALUES FOR STEELS, ETC.

Material	Power Constant for Average Jobs	Power Constants							
		Brinell Hardness Numbers							
		100 to 125	126 to 150	151 to 175	176 to 200	201 to 250	251 to 300	301 to 350	351 to 400
S.A.E.									
1010– 1025	6·0	5·5	6·0	7·0	8·0	—	—	—	—
1030– 1055	8·0	—	6·0	7·0	8·0	9·5	11·5	—	—
1060– 1095	9·0	—	—	—	—	9·0	10·5	12·5	—
1112– 1120	6·0	4·0	5·0	6·0	—	—	—	—	—
X1314–X1340	5·0	—	4·5	5·0	5·5	6·0	—	—	—
T1330– T1350	9·0	—	—	—	8·0	9·0	11·0	13·0	—
2015– 2115	7·0	6·0	7·0	8·0	—	—	—	—	—
2315– 2335	7·5	—	—	6·5	7·0	7·5	9·0	11·0	—
2340– 2350	9·0	—	—	—	6·0	7·0	8·5	10·0	12·0
2512– 2515	8·0	—	—	6·0	7·0	8·0	9·5	11·0	—
3115– 3130	8·0	—	5·0	6·0	7·0	8·5	10·0	12·0	—
3140– 3450	9·0	—	—	—	6·0	7·5	9·0	10·5	12·5
4130– 4345	9·0	—	—	—	5·5	7·0	8·5	10·0	12·0
4615– 4820	9·0	—	—	5·5	6·0	7·0	8·5	10·0	11·5
5120– 5150	10·0	—	—	5·5	6·0	7·5	9·0	10·5	12·0
5210	10·0	—	—	—	7·0	8·0	10·0	12·0	—
6115– 6140	9·0	—	—	5·5	6·5	8·0	10·0	12·0	—
6145– 6195	12·0	—	—	—	8·5	10·0	12·0	14·0	16·0
Plain cast iron	4·0	—	3·0	3·5	4·0	5·0	6·0	—	—
Alloy cast iron	4·0	—	—	3·5	5·0	6·5	—	—	—
Malleable iron	4·0	3·0	4·0	5·0	—	—	—	—	—
Cast steel	9·0	—	—	7·5	8·0	9·5	—	—	—

[Carboloy Co. (Inc.)]

TABLE B.—MOTOR HORSE POWER FOR MULTI-TOOL MACHINES

Machine Motor H.P.

Machine	Cut
Power required to operate machine at starting speed with tools not cutting. Usually figured at 30 per cent. of cut.	Calculate H.P. required by each Tool, using formula given below : H.P. Tools cutting at same time : Tool No. 1 $(D \times F \times S \times C)$. = Tool No. 2 $(D \times F \times S \times C)$. = etc. . . . . = Total H.P. required by tools cutting =

TABLE C.—POWER CONSTANTS FOR NON-FERROUS METALS

Material	Power Constant
Brass:	
Hard	10
Medium	6
Soft	4
Lead-screw stock . .	3
Bronze:	
Hard	10
Medium	6
Soft	4
Aluminium:	
Cast	3
Hard (rolled) . . .	4
Monel (rolled) . . .	12
Zinc alloy (die cast) . .	3

CUTTING-POWER OF LATHES

Tests made upon lathes of various sizes (centre heights), using high-speed steel rough turning tools, properly sharpened to the correct angles, on 0·45 per cent. carbon-steel bar, as rolled, gave the following results :*

Lathes used in back gear in each case.
Cutting speed, 60 feet per minute in each case.
Feed used was 0·005 inch per revolution of work.

Size of Lathe (centre height)	Depth of Cut	Diameter Reduction per Cut
9-inch (Light). . .	$\frac{1}{8}$ in.	$\frac{1}{4}$ in.
9-inch (Toolmaker's) .	$\frac{5}{32}$ in.	$\frac{5}{16}$ in.
9-inch (Heavy) . .	$\frac{5}{32}$ in.	$\frac{5}{16}$ in.
11-inch	$\frac{3}{16}$ in.	$\frac{3}{8}$ in.
13-inch	$\frac{1}{4}$ in.	$\frac{1}{2}$ in.
15-inch	$\frac{3}{8}$ in.	$\frac{3}{4}$ in.

* South Bend Lathe Co.

CUTTING SPEEDS, ANGLES AND POWER CONSTANTS. ARDOLOY TURNING TOOLS

Material	Power Constant	Rough Turning. Ft. per min.	Finish Turning. Ft. per min.	Top Rake. Degrees	
GRADES OF STEEL *					
28–35 tons tensile . .	7				
Black bar, stampings .		250–300	400– 750	0°–10° negative	
Rough forgings—removing scale . .		200–300	300– 400	,,	,,
Clean metal . .		250–350	700– 800	,,	,,
Castings . .		250–300	400– 750	,,	,,
40–45 tons tensile . .	10				
Black bar, stampings .		200–250	500– 600	,,	,,
Rough forgings—removing scale . .		150–200	200– 300	,,	,,
Clean metal . .		200–300	500–1,000	,,	,,
Castings . .		150–250	250– 350	,,	,,
55–65 tons tensile . .	15				
Black bar, stampings .		200–250	300– 500	,,	,,
Rough forgings—removing scale . .		150–200	200– 300	,,	,,
Clean metal . .		200–300	500– 600	,,	,,
High-speed steel—annealed	10	60– 80	150– 250	,,	,,
Chrome nickel—65–90 tons tensile . .	17				
Black bar, stampings .		80–100	250– 350	,,	,,
Forgings . .		80–100	250– 350	,,	,,
Clean metal . .		200–300	500–1,000	,,	,,
Stainless steel . .	12				
Castings . .		60–100	100– 150	,,	,,
Bar . . .		100–150	200– 300	,,	,,
Manganese steel—12 per cent. . .		10– 20	30– 40	,,	,,
CAST IRON AND WROUGHT IRON					
Cast iron—200 Brinell .	4	150–200	300– 600	,,	,,
Close-grained iron .	4	150–200	250– 500	,,	,,
Centrifugal castings .	5	120–180	250– 350	,,	,,
Chromium iron . .	5	120–180	250– 350	,,	,,
Malleable iron . .	5	100–200	250– 400	,,	,,
10 per cent. nickel iron .	6	20– 30	30– 45	,,	,,
Pearlite iron . . .	4	150–250	250– 400	,,	,,
Wrought iron . . .	7	150–250	300– 500	,,	,,
White cast iron . .	6	10– 20	20– 30	,,	,,
Chilled-iron rolls . .	6	10– 20	30– 50	,,	,,

Notes.—Ardoloy is a sintered-carbide cutting alloy of hardness approaching that of the diamond. It is made by the British Thomson-Houston Co. Ltd., Rugby, and supplied by Alfred Herbert Ltd., Coventry.

Clearance angles of turning tools are from 4° to 6°, except for those materials marked with asterisk (*) when angle is 10°.

If negative-rake tools are used on machines of sufficient horse-power the speeds given in the table may be increased up to 100 per cent.

Cutting Speeds, Angles and Power Constants. Ardoloy Turning Tools (*contd.*)

Material	Power Constant	Rough Turning Ft. per min.	Finish Turning Ft. per min.	Top Rake. Degrees
NON-FERROUS METALS:				
Copper	4	500–800	800–1,200	13°–16°
Cupro nickel	10	350–450	400– 500	3½°
Soft brass	4	500–800	800–1,200	3½°
Hard brass	12	400–600	800–1,000	0°–10° negative
Bronze	8	400–600	800–1,000	,, ,,
Gunmetal	7	400–600	800–1,000	,, ,,
Aluminium bronze	12	300–500	600– 750	,, ,,
Admiralty bronze	7	300–500	600– 750	,, ,,
Manganese bronze	10	300–400	450– 650	,, ,,
Aluminium	3	Up to 1,000	Up to 2,000	13°–16°
Silicon aluminium	4	300–500	600– 750	13°–16°
Aluminium alloys	4	300–500	600– 750	13°–16°
Zinc-base alloys	3	300–500	600– 750	13°–16°
Duralumin	4	300–500	600– 750	13°–16°
NON-METALLIC MATERIALS:				
*Plastics		400–600	800–1,000	0°
*Erinoid		400–600	800–1,000	0°
*Ebonite		400–600	800–1,000	0°
*Hard rubber		400–600	800–1,000	0°
Porcelain		10– 30	40– 65	0°
Glass		30– 50	50– 70	3½°
Slate		50– 80	80– 100	3½°
Marble		10– 30	40– 65	0°–3½°

Nomogram for Determining Shank Size of Ardoloy and Similar Sintered-carbide Tools

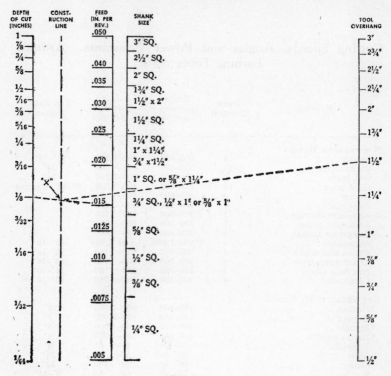

FIG. 7.

EXAMPLE OF USE OF NOMOGRAM

Assuming a feed of ·015 in., depth of cut ⅛ in. and overhang 1½ in., lay a straight-edge between the ⅛-in. and the ·015-in. point shown on the feed scale : this line crosses a construction line at a point "X." Join this point "X" with the scale for the tool overhang to be used ; in this example 1½ in. The point where this line crosses the shank-size line determines the recommended shank size to be used. The shank size is very nearly 1 sq. in.

CUTTING LUBRICANTS OR FLUIDS

The purpose of cutting lubricants is : (1) To cool the tool. (2) To cool the work. (3) To lubricate the surfaces between the tool and the work or chip as it is formed. (4) To improve the quality of the surface finish. The cutting lubricant also assists in washing away the swarf and reduces the pressure of the chip on the tool.

A cutting lubricant should have no corrosive action on the tool, work or the machine surfaces ; neither should it leave solid deposits.

The following table gives some recommended cutting lubricants for different metals and operations.

CUTTING LUBRICANTS FOR VARIOUS MATERIALS

Material	Turning	Chucking	Drilling	Reaming	Milling Tapping
Tool steel .	Dry or oil	Oil or soda water	Oil	Lard oil	Oil
Soft steel .	Dry or soda water	Soda water	Oil or soda water	Lard oil	Oil
Wrought iron	Ditto	Ditto	Soap or soda water	Lard oil	Oil
Aluminium .	Kerosene *				
Cast iron .	Dry				
Brass . .	Dry				
Copper .	Dry				
Babbitt .	Dry				
Glass . .	Turpentine or kerosene *				

* Paraffin.

A suitable cutting lubricant for *steel-turning purposes* consists of : soft soap, ½ pint ; sodium carbonate, 4 oz. ; lard oil, ½ pint ; water, 2 to 3 gallons. It is necessary to boil the solution. When cool it is ready for use.

For *turning, machine screw cutting and drilling steel,* a solution consisting of equal parts of paraffin and lard oil gives satisfactory results.

For *screw cutting and tapping,* a solution of ½ lb. of sodium carbonate in 1 gallon of hot water, to which is added 1½ pints of lard oil, is recommended.

For *wet grinding,* a solution of sodium carbonate in water can be used. Sufficient of the former should be added to the water to just prevent rusting of the work.

A lubricant suitable for *drilling hard steel or glass* consists of camphor dissolved in turpentine.

For lubricating drawing dies for brass a soapy-water solution can be used ; the addition of one-half the volume of lard oil gives rather better results.

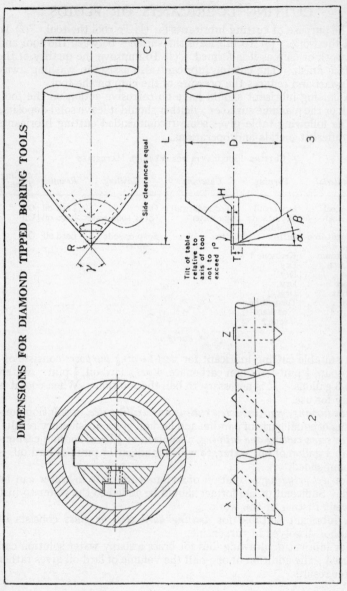

DIMENSIONS FOR DIAMOND TIPPED BORING TOOLS

Side clearances equal

Tilt of table relative to axis of tool not to exceed 1°

Fig. 8.

LUBRICANT FOR TAPS.—When tapping iron and steel a satisfactory lubricant to employ consists of a mixture of equal parts of sperm oil and white lead.

Another suitable lubricant consists of a mixture of 10 parts of powdered graphite; 30 parts of tallow; 40 parts of white lead; and 20 parts of lard oil (by weight).

For tapping cast iron the addition of a small proportion of paraffin will give improved results.

For tapping stainless steels neatsfoot oil alone or with the addition of white lead is recommended by the steel manufacturers. For machine tapping, a good flow of soluble oil or cutting lubricant should be used.

For tapping aluminium use beeswax or tallow.

For tapping Elektron and similar magnesium alloys a light smearing of the tap with tallow or engine oil will give improved results over dry cutting.

For tapping copper use lard oil, soluble oil or heavy machine oil.

DIAMOND-TIPPED TOOLS

Diamond-tipped tools are employed for rapid machining of many materials, such as non-ferrous alloys (aluminium, magnesium, white metals, etc.), and certain organic materials, e.g. plastics, ebonite, fibre, etc. They give high standards of finish, provided they are properly set and mounted, used on rigid mountings and machines and at the correct machining speeds. They are particularly applicable to machining aluminium-alloy pistons and petrol-engine white-metal and lead-bronze bearings.

The machining speeds (turning) vary, according to the nature of the work, from about 200 to 1,000 ft. per min., with feeds of 0·001 to 0·003 in. per revolution, and depths of cut of 0·015 to 0·025 in. for roughing and 0·004 to 0·010 in. for finishing.

Various designs of diamond tips are used to suit the particular application; information on this subject is given in Vol. I of *Engineering Workshop Practice* (Caxton Publishing Co., Ltd.).

The British Standards Institution has standardised diamond-tipped boring tools (B.S. 1120—1943), and the following is an abstract from the Specification:

" The tools are intended for mounting on the centre line of the boring bar as in Fig. (8) 1. They may be set at 45° to axis of boring bar for boring to a shoulder as shown at X (Fig. 8 (2)), or at any angle between 45° and 90° for through boring as shown at Y and Z (Fig 8 (2)).

(*Continued on page* 327).

DIMENSIONS FOR DIAMOND-TIPPED BORING TOOLS (See Fig. 8)

1	2	3	4	5	6	7	8	9	10	11	12 Overall Length of Tool, L — Suffix Letters for Type Code				
General Type	Range of Bore for which Tool is Suitable	Diameter of Tool Shank	Primary Clearance Angle	Secondary Clearance Angle	Included Angle of Nose	Height of Table above Centre Line	Radius of Nose	Maximum Stone Thickness	Chamfer on End of Shank	Recommended Diameter of Hole in Boring Bar	A	B	C	D	E
	In.	D	α	β	γ	H	R	T	C		In.	In.	In.	In.	In.
		In.	Deg.	Deg.	Deg.	In.	In.	In.	In. × Deg.	In.					
B1	3/8 – 1/2	3/16 −.0002 / −.0005	20° ±1°	25°	80° ±1°	+.002 / −.000	.015–.02	0.045	.01 × 45°	3/16 +.0003 / −.0000	5/16	3/8			
B2	1/2 – 3/4	1/4 −.0002 / −.0005	18° ±1°	23°	80° ±1°	+.003 / −.000	.015–.02	0.06	.015 × 45°	1/4 +.0003 / −.0000	3/8	1/2	5/8		
B3	3/4 – 1	5/16 −.0002 / −.0006	15° ±1°	20°	80° ±1°	+.004 / −.000	.015–.02	0.08	.02 × 45°	5/16 +.0004 / −.0000	1/2	5/8	3/4	7/8	
B4	1 – 1 1/2	5/16 −.0002 / −.0006	13° ±1°	18°	80° ±1°	+.006 / −.000	.015–.02	0.08	.02 × 45°	5/16 +.0004 / −.0000	5/8	7/8	1 1/8	1 3/8	
B5	1 1/2 – 2 1/2	5/16 −.0002 / −.0006	10° ±1°	None	80° ±1°	+.008 / −.000	.015–.02	0.10	.02 × 45°	5/16 +.0004 / −.0000	3/4	1	1 3/8	1 7/8	2 3/8
B6	Above 2 1/2	5/16 −.0002 / −.0006	7° ±1°	None	80° ±1°	+.01 / −.00	.015–.02	0.10	.02 × 45°	5/16 +.0004 / −.0000	3/4	1	2		
B7	Above 2 1/2	3/8 −.0002 / −.0006	7° ±1°	None	80° ±1°	+.01 / −.00	.015–.02	0.10	.02 × 45°	3/8 +.0004 / −.0000	2	2 3/8			

" Any tool is completely specified by quoting the General Type (column in the table on page 300) with a Suffix Letter (column 12) to indicate the required length. Thus, a B3C tool is suitable for boring any diameter between ¾ in. and 1 in., and has an overall length of ¾ in.

" Micrometer-type tools can be used in place of solid-shank type tools with respect to all dimensions, except the length.

" In specifying boring tools the diameter of the bore to be machined, and that of the boring bar, should be quoted; while the Suffix Letter (column 12) of the Type Code should be omitted."

MILLING-CUTTER CUTTING SPEEDS

Material to be Machined	High-speed Steel Cutter		Tungsten Carbide-tipped Cutter	
	Roughing	Finishing	Roughing	Finishing
	Ft. per min.	Ft. per min.	Ft. per min.	Ft. per min.
Mild steel	30– 50	100– 140	100– 200	400
Malleable iron . . .	60– 80	100– 130	150– 200	300– 450
Steel castings (sand) . .	30– 50	50– 70	75– 110	120– 180
,, ,, (electric) . .	40– 60	65– 85	90– 130	140– 220
Tool steel (annealed) . .	35– 50	60– 75	80– 120	150– 300
Steel forgings (hard alloy) .	25– 35	45– 60	70– 95	100– 150
,, ,, (annealed) .	40– 55	70– 85	100– 140	150– 220
,, ,, (low carbon) .	50– 70	75– 90	120– 160	180– 350
Cast iron (soft grade) 200 Brinell . .	60– 70	100– 130	130– 150	200– 350
,, ,, (medium) 220 Brinell	50– 60	85– 100	110– 130	180– 250
,, ,, (hard) over 230 Brinell	35– 45	60– 80	90– 110	150– 200
Stainless steel . . .	55– 65	85– 95	110– 130	200– 250
Brass (hard)	90– 100	180– 220	220– 250	300– 500
,, (soft)	180– 200	400– 500	500– 700	700– 800
Bronze	70– 85	110– 130	200– 350	300– 500
Aluminium castings . .	500– 600	800–1,000	700– 900	1,000–1,500
,, billets . .	350– 450	500– 700	600– 750	1,000–1,200
Magnesium castings . .	500– 800	1,000–2,000	800–1,000	1,200–1,800
Copper	120– 150	250– 300	300– 400	400– 500
Zinc alloys	1,500–2,000	2,000	2,000–2,500	2,000–2,500
Monel metal	50– 65	70– 85	100– 130	180– 250
Nickel-chrome steel . .	35– 45	70– 80	80– 110	120– 140

" Up " and " Down " Milling

Up Milling.—The cutter teeth move upwards and the work piece advances towards the cutter, i.e. the cutter rotates against the direction of the feed. Chip thickness increases from a minimum at beginning to maximum at end of cut.

Down Milling.—The cutter teeth move downwards and the work piece advances towards the cutter from the side where the cutter teeth are moving downwards. Chip thickness is a maximum at beginning of cut and a minimum at the end.

MILLING-CUTTER FEEDS

F = cutter feed, in inches per minute. T = thickness of cut, in inches.

n = number of teeth of milling cutter. N = R.P.M. of cutter.

D = diameter of cutter, in inches. S = cutting speed, in feet per minute.

$$\text{Thickness of cut } T = \frac{F}{Nn} \text{ inches}$$

$$\text{Cutting speed } S = \frac{3\cdot1416 \, DN}{12}$$

$$= 0\cdot2618 \, DN$$

$$N = \frac{12 \, S}{3\cdot1416 \, D}$$

$$= 3\cdot2806 \, \frac{S}{D}$$

$$\text{Number of chips per minute} = \frac{12 \, nS}{3\cdot1416 \, D}$$

$$= 3\cdot2806 \, \frac{S}{D}$$

$$\text{Also thickness of cut } T = \frac{3\cdot1416 \, FD}{12 \, Sn}$$

$$= 0\cdot2618 \, \frac{FD}{Sn}$$

Example.—Cutter diameter D = 3 in. No. of teeth, $n = 12$. Cutting speed S = 100 ft. per min. Required feed rate for chip of average thickness = 0·008 in.

$$T = 0.2618 \frac{FD}{Sn}$$

$$0.008 = \frac{0.2618 \times F \times 3}{100 \times 12}$$

$$F = \frac{100 \times 12 \times 0.008}{0.2618 \times 3}$$

$$= 12.23 \text{ in. per min.}$$

TABLE OF FEEDS FOR MILLING CUTTERS

Type of Milling Cutter	Feed in In. Advance per Tooth
Saws	0.002–0.004
Face mills	0.008–0.018
Shell-end mills . . .	0.007–0.016
End mills	0.005–0.010
Plain spiral mills . . .	0.010–0.016
Helical mills . . .	0.004–0.008
Form cutters . . .	0.004–0.007
Staggered-tooth side mills .	0.006–0.010

For carbon-steel cutters :

Roughing cuts in	cast iron,		40 linear ft. per min.	
,,	,,	medium steel,	60	,, ,,
,,	,,	annealed tool steel,	25	,, ,,
,,	,,	brass,	80	,, ,,
Finishing cuts in	cast iron,		60	,, ,,
,,	,,	medium steel,	80	,, ,,
,,	,,	annealed tool steel,	35	,, ,,
,,	,,	brass,	100	,, ,,

For *high-speed steel cutters,* the feeds for the same cutting speeds and depths of cut can be doubled.

For *tungsten-carbide cutters,* the feeds for the same cutting speeds and depths of cut can be multiplied by $2\frac{1}{2}$ to 3.

NUMBER OF TEETH IN MILLING CUTTERS

Milling cutters for roughing purposes have coarser-pitch teeth than those for normal or finish milling purposes.

Inserted teeth cutters usually have a greater pitch, i.e. smaller number of teeth than solid cutters of the same diameter.

E.W.D.—11*

Cutter teeth spacing of inserted-type cutters lies between $1\frac{1}{4}$ in. and $1\frac{1}{2}$ in., i.e. about 14 to 16 teeth for an 8-in. cutter.

For roughing purposes the number of teeth usually range from 8 for a 2-in. cutter to 16 for an 8-in. cutter.

For fine-finishing purposes the number of teeth for the same diameter of cutter is increased by about 60 per cent. In a typical range of fine finishing cutters the 2-in. cutter has 12 to 14 teeth, and the 8-in. cutter from 24 to 28 teeth.

For end mills with coarse-pitch teeth the 1-in. cutter has 4 teeth and the 2-in. cutter 8 teeth.

End mills for finishing purposes have 6 to 8 teeth for the 1-in. cutter and 12 to 16 for the 2-in. cutter.

For brass milling purposes the cutter usually has about 25 per cent. fewer teeth than in the plain end mill.

BRITISH STANDARD MILLING CUTTERS AND REAMERS

The shapes, names, dimensions and tolerances of milling cutters and reamers have been standardised in B.S. No. 122—1938. This specification illustrates each of the standard types and gives definitions of these. Tables showing the dimensions of the arbors, holes, keyways, with permitted tolerances and certain other dimensions, are given for four classes of cutters, viz. : (1) non-form relieved cutters ; (2) end mills ; (3) form-relieved cutters ; and (4) reamers. The numbers of teeth on individual cutters are not specified.

NEGATIVE-RAKE MILLING CUTTERS

In this method tungsten-carbide milling cutters, having negative, instead of the conventional positive, top rake are employed.

Fig. 9 (left) * shows the conventional positive-rake cutter and (right) the negative-rake cutter. In the latter type the tungsten-carbide tips are in compression and the cutting forces tend to hold the tip more firmly on its seating. The included cutting angle is greater than 90° for the negative-rake cutter, but is less than 90° for the positive-rake one.

In the positive-rake cutter the resultant cutting forces tend to pull the tip away from its seating.

* *Production and Engineering Bulletin.*

Similarly, in the case of *slotting cutters* (Fig. 10) the cutting forces tend to weaken the tip joint, whereas in the negative-rake cutter (on right) they hold the tip by compression firmly on its seating.

Tungsten-carbide tips will withstand heavier cuts and speeds with negative than with positive rake.

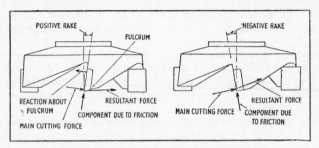

FIG. 9.—NEGATIVE-RAKE END MILLING CUTTER.

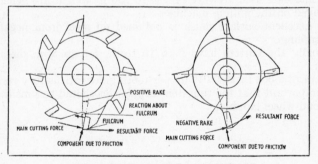

FIG. 10.—NEGATIVE-RAKE SLOTTING CUTTER.

NOTES ON NEGATIVE-RAKE MILLING

Much higher machining speeds and feeds can be used than with positive-rake cutters. Cutting speeds of 800 ft. per min. with a feed of 10 in. per min. have been used successfully on high-tensile steel forgings.

Aluminium alloys have been machined at speeds of 4,000 ft. per min. with a feed of 80 in. per min. These do not represent the maximum possible speeds and feeds.

The depth of cut that can be taken is limited only by the rigidity and available horse power of the milling machine.

With negative-rake cutters the initial point of impact of the tip with the work is at a greater distance from the cutting edge than with a positive-rake cutter, and the tip is thus protected ; this helps to build up the load more gradually. Much stronger clamping of tungsten-carbide blades is necessary in the case of negative-rake cutters.

No coolant is necessary when negative-rake cutters are employed. Owing to the cutting action there is no time for the heat generated to flow to the carbide tip or the work. The greater part of the heat is removed by the swarf, which frequently comes off white hot, or as a powder which " sparks."

Owing to the higher cutting speeds, feeds and depths of cut that can satisfactorily be employed, much greater rigidity is necessary in the milling machines used for negative-rake machining.

Appreciably more power is also required.

In order to obtain a uniform milling action at the high speeds, feeds and cuts used, flywheels of 80 to 250 lb. weight are generally employed on the milling machines.

An excellent surface finish is obtained on steel from negative-rake milling.

Usually the cutters have 6 to 10 teeth, for an 8-in. diameter cutter.

A cut of 0·003 in. to 0·010 in. per tooth gives satisfactory results. It is important that the tungsten-carbide tips should be finished by diamond-wheel lapping.

CUTTING PERFORMANCES

Tests made with negative-rake milling on 0·45 per cent. carbon steel on a surface measuring 8 × 5 in., with a cutter of 8-in. diameter, having 24 teeth tipped with tungsten carbide, showed that satisfactory results could be obtained with cutting speeds between 500 and 1,600 ft. per min. The depth of cut was 0·06 in. and feed 12 in. per min. The swarf came away in a white-hot condition.

Production Data for Carbide-tipped Negative-rake Cutters

Cutter	Cutting Speed Ft./min.	Feed. In./min.	Cut Depth × Width (in.)	Material	Remarks
10-in. diameter face mill: 12 teeth 5-degrees negative rake	1,633	12·5	$0{\cdot}030 \times 5$	Nickel-chrome steel forging 60-ton tensile	Finish approx 8 micro. in.
8-in. diameter face mill: 10 teeth	952	5·75	$\frac{3}{16} \times 2$	Do.	Still running after 3 hours' continuous duty
10-in. diameter face mill: 10 teeth	790	3·5	$\frac{1}{16}$ to $\frac{7}{16}$ $\frac{1}{8} \times 5$	Do.	
8-in. diameter face mill: 10 teeth	550	0·5	$\frac{1}{8} \times 5$	Steel 65-ton tensile	Chip volume 6·56 cu. in./ min. Good cutter life.
8-in. diameter face mill: 10 teeth	100	3·25	$\frac{1}{8} \times 5$	Do.	Chip volume 3·28 cu. in./ min.*

* By reducing the feed and using a higher speed less material was removed per minute, but the life of the cutter was shorter and there was no improvement in surface finish.

Approximate Cutting Speeds and Rate of Metal Removal with Negative-rake, Cemented Carbide-tipped Milling Cutters

Material	Tensile Strength. Tons/sq. in.	Suggested Cutting Speed. Ft./min.	Metal Removal. Cu. in./H.P./min.
Mild steel . .	30	900	3/4
,, ,, . .	35	850	3/4
Carbon steel .	40	800	7/8
High-tensile steel .	45	750	7/8
,, ,, ,, .	50	600	7/8
,, ,, ,, .	60	575	7/8
,, ,, ,, .	70	550	7/8
Cast iron grey . .	15–20	950	7/8
Cast iron inoculated	20–30	950	1

[Prod. and Eng. Bulletin]

SECTION 9

GRINDING WHEELS

The properties of artificial grinding wheels, as distinct from natural stone ones, depend upon: (1) the type of abrasive used; (2) the size of grain; and (3) the bonding medium.

TYPES OF ABRASIVE

The artificial grinding-wheel abrasives include: (1) *Silicon Carbide. Examples:* Carborundum and Crystolon. (2) *Aluminium Oxide. Examples:* Aloxite and Alundum. (3) *Diamond Impregnated.*

The silicon-carbide grains are much harder than those of aluminium oxide, but are more brittle. The grains of aluminium oxide, whilst not so hard, are tougher and, therefore, less liable to fracture.

Silicon-carbide abrasive wheels are used for grinding materials of *low-tensile* strength, e.g. brass, bronze, copper, tin, aluminium, magnesium, rubber, marble and stone.

Aluminium-oxide wheels are used for grinding materials of *high-tensile* strength and hardness, e.g. carbon and alloy steels, malleable iron, etc.

The Norton Company suggests the dividing line between the two abrasives as follows: above 50,000 lb. per sq. in., tensile strength Alundum; below this tensile strength, Crystolon.

STANDARD ABRASIVE GRAIN SIZES

Very Coarse	Coarse	Medium	Fine	Very Fine
6	12	30	70	150
8	14	36	80	180
10	16	40	90	220
	20	50	100	240*—1F
	24	60	120	280*
				320*—2F
				400*
				500*—3F
				600*—4F

[*The Carborundum Co. Ltd.*]

* The numerical grit sizes shown in this column are more accurately graded than those indicated by the suffix F.

Grain Size or Grit

The size of grain affects the kind of finish and rate of stock removal. The abrasive-material grains are graded by sieving through screens having a different number of holes or meshes to the linear inch. The grain sizes are indicated by standard numbers corresponding to the number of meshes in the sieve through which they pass, e.g. a 20 grit will pass through a sieve having 20 meshes per linear inch or 400 per sq. in. The range of grain sizes is from the coarsest, No. 6, to the finest, No. 600.

BONDS FOR GRINDING WHEELS

The abrasive grains are " cemented " or bonded together with various materials, and by different methods, according to the purpose of the wheel. The bonding materials include : (1) Ceramics ; (2) Silicate of Soda ; (3) Synthetic Resin ; (4) Rubber ; (5) Shellac. The grinding-wheel manufacturers employ certain letters in designating the type of wheel, to indicate the bond used.

(1) *Ceramics.*—*Vitrified* bonded wheels are made by mixing together the abrasive grains with ceramic materials and fusing them into a vitreous mass in suitable moulded shapes. This type is made in a much wider range of grades and structures than other bonded wheels.

(2) *Silicate-bonded Wheels.*—This type is quicker to make than the vitreous, cuts very much cooler and can be made in larger diameters. It is much used for cutlery and fine-edged instruments, e.g. knives.

(3) *Synthetic-resin Wheels.*—These employ artificial resins, e.g. bakelite, which are bonded in powder form with the abrasive grains, heated and subjected to a high pressure in the wheel moulds. They are very strong. Cut-off wheels, e.g. " Redmanol," can be made very thin and operated, with safety, at high speeds (10,000 to 16,000 surface ft. per min.). Wide-face wheels are used widely in the snagging of steel castings and malleable iron, at high speeds. Other applications include finishing rolls and cams, saw-gumming, cutting and shaping stone, marble and granite.

(4) *Rubber-bonded Wheels.*—Both silicon carbide and aluminium oxide can be bonded with rubber, and thin wheels used for cutting-off purposes are often made in this manner. This type of wheel is used for fine-finishing operations, for regulating wheels on centreless grinders, finishing ball races, saw-gumming, etc. They can be run at higher speeds than vitreous wheels.

(5) *Shellac-bonded Wheels.*—These wheels are suitable for finishing cast-iron rolls, chilled cast-iron rolls, cams, shafts, etc.

GRADES OF WHEELS

Grinding wheels are made in a wide range of grades from very soft to very hard. The grade is a measure of the strength with which the abrasive grains are held in position by the bond—as distinct from the actual hardness of the grains themselves. The ideal wheel is one which, for any particular operation, avoids excessive wear and blunting of the face, the material wearing at just the correct rate to expose the new abrasive grains.

Grinding-wheel manufacturers use certain symbols to designate the grade scales of their products. Those employed by the Carborundum and Norton companies are given herewith:

GRADE SCALE OF CARBORUNDUM AND ALOXITE BRAND WHEELS

	Vitrified	Silicate	Shellac	"Redmanol"	Rubber
Very hard .	D E	D E			A
Hard . .	F G H	F G H	1 2	3 4 5	B C D
Medium .	I J K L M	I J K L M	3 4 5	6 7 8 9 10	E F
Soft . .	N O P R S T	N O P R S T	6 7 8 9	11 12 13 14 15 16	
Very soft .	U V W	U V W	10	17	

GRADE SCALE OF NORTON ALUNDUM AND CRYSTOLON WHEELS

Very Soft	Soft	Medium	Hard	Very Hard
E, F, G	H, I, J, K	L, M, N, O	P, Q, R, S	T, U, W, Z

STRUCTURE, OR GRAIN SPACING

Variations in the structure are indicated in the wheel letter symbols by key numerals, representing the relative spacing of abrasive grains in the wheel. Thus Carborundum D3, D5, D7, denotes respectively, low, medium and high density. In the Norton wheels the structure numbers are as follows:

NORTON WHEEL-STRUCTURE NUMBERS

Structure Spacing:	Close Spacing	Medium Spacing	Wide Spacing
Structure number .	1, 2, 3	4, 5, 6	7, 8, 9, 10, 11, 12

DESIGNATIONS AND IDENTIFICATIONS OF GRINDING WHEELS

Grinding wheels are designated by letters or figures which enable the following essential characteristics to be identified: (a) abrasive type; (b) grain size; (c) grade; (d) structure, or grain spacing; (e) bond.

(A) CARBORUNDUM KEY SYMBOLS

Particulars of the designations have already been given, and it is usual to express the type of grinding wheel in the following manner:

Abrasive and Bond: Grit: Grade: Bond.

A letter " A " placed before the grit size indicates Aloxite " AA " or " White Aloxite."

Examples.—The materials or parts to be ground are indicated in heavier type on the left, in the following examples:

Agate—CARBORUNDUM VITRIFIED—60—K—E4.

  60—Indicates grit or size of abrasive grain.
  K— ,,   grade or degree of hardness.
  E4— ,,   bond and structure symbol.

Ball Bearings—ALOXITE RUBBER—100—VUL—KDN.

  100—Indicates grit or size of abrasive grain.
  VUL— ,,   the bond.
  KDN— ,,   the type of abrasive (K) and the grade (DN).

Bits, Auger—ALOXITE " REDMANOL "—E40—K6XQ.

  E—Indicates Process.
  40— ,,   grit or size of abrasive grain.
  K6XQ— ,,   abrasive (K), grade (6), bond (XQ).

(B) Norton Key Symbols

Standard grinding-wheel markings are arranged so that all of the five characteristics previously enumerated are indicated. A typical wheel marking is 3846—M5B.

Position	1	2	3	4	5
(a) Kind of abrasive . . .	38	—	—	—	—
(b) Grain (size of abrasive) . .		46	—	—	—
(c) Grade (strength of bond) .			M	—	—
(d) Structure (spacing of grains) .				5	—
(e) Kind of bond . . .					B

NORTON ABRASIVE DESIGNATIONS

Alundum brand of abrasive	(blank)
No. " 38 Alundum " brand of abrasive . . .	38
No. " 19 Alundum " brand of abrasive . . .	19
Crystolon brand of abrasive	37

NORTON GRAIN-SIZE DESIGNATION

Very Coarse	Coarse	Medium	Fine	Very Fine	Flour Sizes
8	12	30	70	150	280
10	14	36	80	180	320
	16	46	90	220	400
	20	60	100	240	500
	24	—	120	—	600

The Grade Scale and Structure Numbers have already been given for Norton wheels.

BOND OF NORTON WHEELS

The fifth and last symbol in the wheel designation indicates the kind of bond, as follows, with the exception of the standard vitrified bond, for which no letter is used :

Type of Bond	Designation
Standard vitrified bond	(blank)
" B " vitrified bond	B
Silicate bond	S
Standard shellac bond	L
" V " shellac bond	V
Bakelite bond	T
Rubber bond	R

EXAMPLES OF NORTON WHEEL DESIGNATIONS

(a) 3846—M5B. No " 38 Alundum " Abrasive. 46 Grain size. M Grade. 5 Structure. B Vitrified Bond.

(b) 16—P2T. Regular " Alundum " Abrasive. 16 Grain size. P Grade. 2 Structure. T Bakelite Bond.

SELECTION OF GRINDING WHEELS

The following is a summary of all the factors affecting the choice of a grinding wheel for any particular purpose, as recommended by the Norton Grinding Wheel Co. Ltd.

(1) Factors Affecting the Selection of the Abrasive

(A) Physical properties of material to be ground

{ Use grinding wheels made from " Alundum" for materials of high-tensile strength

- Carbon steels
- Alloy steels
- High-speed steel
- Annealed malleable iron
- Wrought iron
- Tough bronzes, etc.

Use grinding wheels made from " Crystolon " for materials of low-tensile strength

- Grey iron
- Chilled iron
- Brass and soft bronze
- Aluminium and copper
- Marble and other stone
- Rubber
- Leather
- Very hard alloys, as tungsten carbide, etc.

(2) Factors Affecting the Selection of Abrasive Grain Size

(A) Amount of material to be removed . . } Coarse wheel for fast cutting.*

(B) Finish desired . . Fine grain for fine finish.

(C) Physical properties of material to be ground { Coarse grain for soft ductile materials and fine grain for hard and brittle materials.

(3) Factors Affecting the Selection of Grade

(A) Physical properties of material to be ground { Hard wheels on soft materials, and vice-versa.

(B) Arc or area of contact { The smaller the area of contact, the harder the wheel should be.

(C) Wheel speed and work speed . . . { The higher the ratio of work speed to wheel speed, the harder the grade should be, and vice-versa.

(D) Condition of machine . { The presence of vibration and worn master parts of the machine usually necessitates using a harder wheel than would be required on a machine in good condition.

(4) Factors Affecting the Selection of Structure

Structure (grain spacing) refers to the number of cutting points per unit area of wheel face as well as the amount of clearance for chips between the abrasive particles.

(A) Physical properties of material . . { Soft, tough and ductile materials require a wheel with a wide spacing of abrasive grains. Hard and brittle materials require a wheel having a close spacing of abrasive grains.†

(B) Finish required . . { Fine finish requires the use of wheels having close spacing of abrasive particles of fine-grain size.

* Exception in case of very hard materials where depth of grain penetration is small.
† Exception—tungsten carbides.

(C) Nature of operation .

(a) Snagging and other operations with flexible application of pressure, require wide grain spacing.

(b) Surfacing operations require wide grain spacing.

(c) Cylindrical and centreless work, also tool and cutter grinding, are usually best performed with wheels of medium grain spacing.

(d) Heavy pressures which tend to destroy the form of shaped wheels require wheels with close grain spacing.

(5) Factors Affecting the Selection of Bond

The vitrified type of bond is most generally used. However, in some instances, unusual operating and performance requirements make the selection of other types advantageous.

(A) Dimensions of wheel .

Thin cutting-off wheels and others subjected to bending strains require bakelite, shellac or rubber bonds. Solid wheels over 36-in. diameter require silicate bond.

(B) Operating speed .

Vitrified wheels are best for speeds below 6,500 s.f.p.m. ; bakelite, shellac and rubber wheels are best for speeds above 6,500 s.f.p.m.

(C) Finish required . .

Shellac- or rubber-bonded wheels are best for high finish where production is not a factor.

Selection of Carborundum Wheels for Various Operations

The following classified particulars cover a wide range of grinding operations and types of materials to be ground, thus enabling a suitable grade of wheel to be selected for any special application.

GRINDING-WHEEL SELECTION TABLE

Class of Work	Abrasive and Bond	Grit	Grade	Bond
AGATE				
Offhand roughing .	Carborundum vitrified	60	K	E4
Offhand finishing . .	Carborundum vitrified	2F	J	E5G
AIR BAGS (rubber)				
Cleaning . . .	Carborundum " Redmanol "	E14		C12R
ALUMINIUM AND ALUMIN-IUM ALLOYS				
Cylindrical (between centres) .	Carborundum vitrified	365	M	E3
Surfacing (cups and cylinders) . .	Carborundum vitrified (*YT process*)	24	R	E1
Surfacing (Planitor machines) . .	Carborundum vitrified	24	M	E3
Internal . . .	Carborundum vitrified (*YT process*)	40	P	E1 +
Snagging				
Wheels operating at 5,000–6,500 s.f.p.m.	Carborundum vitrified (*YT process*)	16	H +	HD
Wheels operating at 8,000–9,500 s.f.p.m.	Carborundum " Redmanol "	E161		C11XQ/33
ARDOLOY (see Cemented Carbides, pp. 340, 341)				
ARMATURES (laminations)				
Cylindrical . . .	Aloxite vitrified	401	M	28
ARMOUR PLATE				
Surfacing . . .	Aloxite vitrified	16	K	30
Edge grinding (segments)	Aloxite " L "	20	M	L
AXES (soft steel)				
Siding. . . .	Aloxite vitrified	30	G	64
Edging . . .	Aloxite vitrified	20	G	64
AXLES (auto)				
Cylindrical				
Between centres .	Aloxite vitrified	40B	K	BLU/D5
Centreless . .	Aloxite vitrified	60	K	BLU/D5C
AXLES (railway)				
Cylindrical . . .	Aloxite vitrified	40B	K	BLU/D5
BALL BEARINGS (radial) (Soft steel)				
Rough surfacing (cups and cylinders) .	Aloxite " L " (*YL process*)	30	O	L
(Hardened steel)				
Finish surfacing (cups and cylinders) .	Aloxite " Redmanol "	E40		K16F

Grinding-wheel Selection Table (*contd.*)

Class of Work	Abrasive and Bond	Grit	Grade	Bond
BALL BEARINGS (radial)— (*contd.*)				
Centreless				
Small diameters .	Aloxite vitrified	60	O	BLU
Medium diameters .	Aloxite vitrified	603	R	BLU
Large diameters .	Aloxite vitrified	603	S	BLU
Rough grooving				
(Inner race) . .	Aloxite rubber	60	VUL	KDN
Finish grooving				
(Inner race) . .	Aloxite rubber	100	VUL	KDN
Rough and finish				
Grooving (inner race, one operation)				
Form grinding .	Aloxite rubber	100	VUL	KDN
Oscillating . .	Aloxite vitrified	100	L	29
By centreless method	Aloxite vitrified	603	J	BLU
Rough grooving				
(Outer race) . .	Aloxite vitrified	60	K	BLU
Finish grooving				
(Outer race) . .	Aloxite rubber	120	VUL	K2
Rough and finish				
Grooving (outer race, one operation) .	Aloxite rubber	100	VUL	K1
Internal . . .	Aloxite vitrified	603	K	BLU/P
BALL BEARINGS (thrust) (hardened)				
Surfacing (cups and cylinders) . .	Aloxite " Redmanol "	E40		K16F
Surfacing (cylinders— Blanchard high-speed machine) .	Aloxite " Redmanol "	E40		K16F
Grooving . . .	Aloxite rubber	100	VUL	KDN
BATH TUBS				
Snagging . . .	Carborundum vitrified	20	G +	VA
BILLETS (high-speed and high-carbon steel)				
Cleaning (swing frame)				
Wheels operating 5,000– 6,500 s.f.p.m. .	Aloxite vitrified	20	H	33
Wheels operating 8,000– 9,500 s.f.p.m. .	Aloxite " Redmanol "	E141		K10XQ/41
Cleaning (flexible shaft)				
Wheels operating 5,000– 6,500 s.f.p.m. .	Aloxite vitrified	24	G	64
Wheels operating 8,000– 9,500 s.f.p.m. .	Aloxite " Redmanol "	E141		K9XQ/43
BILLETS (alloy steel)				
Cleaning (swing frame)				
Wheels operating 5,000– 6,500 s.f.p.m. .	Aloxite vitrified	20	G	64

Grinding-wheel Selection Table (*contd.*)

Class of Work	Abrasive and Bond	Grit	Grade	Bond
BILLETS (alloy steel)— (*contd.*)				
Wheels operating 8,000– 9,500 s.f.p.m. .	Aloxite " Redmanol "	E141		K10XQ/41
Cleaning (flexible shaft)				
Wheels operating 5,000– 6,500 s.f.p.m. .	Aloxite vitrified	24	G	64
Wheels operating 8,000– 9,500 s.f.p.m. .	Aloxite " Redmanol "	E141		K9XQ/43
BITS (auger)				
Grinding throat . .	Aloxite rubber	40	VUL	K1
Fluting . . .	Aloxite " Redmanol "	E40		K6XQ
BOLTS (case-hardened steel) Cylindrical				
Between centres .	Aloxite vitrified	40B	M	BLU/D5
Centreless .	Aloxite vitrified	60	J	BLU/D5C
Centreless (dual wheel)	Aloxite vitrified			
Thick section		60	K	30C
Thin section		60	H	33C
BRAKE DRUMS (Chromidium, etc.) .	Carborundum vitrified	36	O	E2
BRAKE DRUMS (Pressed steel) . .	Aloxite vitrified	40	O	26
BRAKE LININGS (Ferodo)				
Wet grinding . .	Carborundum vitrified (*YT process*)	30	M	E3
BRAKE SHOES (chilled iron)				
Snagging . . .	Carborundum vitrified	20	G +	VA
BRASS Cylindrical				
Between centres .	Carborundum vitrified	36	M	E3
Centreless . .	Carborundum vitrified	50	M	E3
Internal . . .	Carborundum vitrified	40	P	E1 +
Surfacing (cups and cylinders) . .	Carborundum vitrified	30	P	E1 +
Segmental wheels .	Carborundum vitrified	30	P	E1 +
Snagging				
Over 12-in. diameter	Carborundum vitrified	20	H +	HD
Under 12-in. diameter	Carborundum vitrified	30	G +	VA
Cutting-off . . .	Carborundum " Redmanol "	E36		C8R
BRICK (vitrified)				
Snagging . . .	Carborundum vitrified	16	H +	HD
Surfacing (cups and cylinders) . .	Carborundum vitrified	16	M	E3
Cutting-off . . .	Carborundum " Redmanol "	E30		C8R
Cutting-off (steel centre)	Carborundum " Redmanol "	E201		C10

Grinding-wheel Selection Table (*contd.*)

Class of Work	Abrasive and Bond	Grit	Grade	Bond
BROACHES				
Sharpening . . .	Aloxite " AA " vitrified	A60	N	180
BRONZE (soft) (see Brass)				
BRONZE (hard)				
Cylindrical				
Between centres .	Aloxite vitrified	50	M	28
Centreless . .	Aloxite vitrified	60	K	30C
Internal . . .	Aloxite vitrified	50	M	BLU/P
Snagging				
Low speed . .	Carborundum vitrified	24	H +	HD
High speed . .	Aloxite " Redmanol "	E141		K9XQ/43
Cutting-off . . .	Aloxite " Redmanol "	E30		K4XQ
BUSHINGS (hardened steel)				
Cylindrical				
Between centres .	Aloxite vitrified	60	M	BLU/D5
Centreless . .	Aloxite vitrified	60	M	BLU/D5C
Internal . . .	Aloxite vitrified	60	M	BLU/P
BUSHINGS (cast iron)				
Cylindrical				
Between centres .	Carborundum vitrified	365	M	E3
Centreless . .	Carborundum vitrified	403	M	E3
Internal . . .	Carborundum vitrified	36	R	E1
BUTTONS (see Pearl)				
CAMS (rough forging)				
Roughing . . .	Aloxite vitrified	30	E	66
CAMS (hardened steel)				
Finishing (vitrified wheels) . .	Aloxite vitrified	401	P	BLU
Finishing (" Redmanol " wheels) . .	Aloxite " Redmanol "	E50		K12R/375
CAM ROLLERS (hardened steel)				
Cylindrical				
Between centres .	Aloxite vitrified	50	K	30
Internal . . .	Aloxite vitrified	60	M	BLU/P
CAM-SHAFT BEARINGS				
Cylindrical				
Between centres .	Aloxite vitrified	40B	L	BLU/D4
CAR WHEELS (chilled iron)				
Cylindrical . . .	Carborundum vitrified	20	H +	HD
CAR WHEELS (steel)				
Cylindrical				
Between centres .	Aloxite vitrified	20	H	33

Grinding-wheel Selection Table (*contd.*)

Class of Work	Abrasive and Bond	Grit	Grade	Bond
CAR WHEELS (manganese steel) Cylindrical				
Between centres .	Aloxite vitrified	16	G	64
CARBON (soft) Cutting-off . . .	Carborundum " Redmanol "	E30		C4XQ
CARBON (hard, round, small) Cutting-off . . .	Carborundum " Redmanol "	E40		C6XQ
CARBON (hard, round, large) Cutting-off . . .	Carborundum " Redmanol "	E50		C6XQ
CARBON (hard, plate) Stripping . . .	Carborundum " Redmanol "	E50		C4XQ
CARBON (metallic) Cutting-off . . .	Carborundum " Redmanol "	E40		C4XQ
CARBON Surfacing . . .	Carborundum vitrified	20	M	E3
Centreless . . .	Carborundum vitrified	365	K	E4
CARD CLOTHING Pointing tips . .	Aloxite rubber			V247
Cylindrical Between centres .	Carborundum vitrified	80	K	E4
CAST IRON Cutting-off . . .	Carborundum " Redmanol "	E30		C4XQ
Cylindrical Between centres .	Carborundum vitrified	403	M	E3
Centreless . .	Carborundum vitrified	365	K	E4
Internal . . .	Carborundum vitrified	40	P	E1 +
Surfacing (cups and cylinders) Vertical spindle .	Carborundum vitrified	24	R	E1
Surfacing (straight wheels)	Carborundum vitrified	36	R	E1
Surfacing (segmental wheels and cylinders)	Carborundum vitrified	24	P	E1 +
Snagging . . .	Carborundum vitrified	24	G +	VA
	Carborundum vitrified	24	F	CVR
Snagging (portable) Wheels operating at 5,000–6,500 s.f.p.m.	Carborundum vitrified	24	G +	VA
Wheels operating at 8,000–9,500 s.f.p.m.	Carborundum " Redmanol "	E161		C8XQ/35
CHAIN LINKS (malleable iron and steel) Snagging Wheels operating at 5,000–6,500 s.f.p.m.	Aloxite vitrified	30	F	65
Wheels operating at 8,000–9,500 s.f.p.m.	Aloxite " Redmanol "	E241		K9XQ/43

Grinding-wheel Selection Table (*contd.*)

Class of Work	Abrasive and Bond	Grit	Grade	Bond
CHAIN LINKS (unannealed malleable iron)				
Snagging . . .	Carborundum vitrified	30	G +	VA
CHAIN LINKS (manganese steel)				
Snagging . . .	Aloxite vitrified	30	F	65
CHASERS (thread)				
Surfacing . . .	Aloxite " AA " vitrified	A54	O	180
Grinding throats . .	Aloxite " Redmanol "	E60		K10R
Grinding threads . .	Aloxite " AA " vitrified	A220	P	600
CHILLED IRON				
Snagging . . .	Carborundum vitrified	24	G +	VA
Surfacing (cups and cylinders) . .	Carborundum vitrified	24	R	E1
Surfacing (straight wheels) . .	Carborundum vitrified	30	R	E1
Cylindrical (see Rolls)				
CHISELS				
Surfacing (cups and cylinders) . .	Aloxite " Redmanol "	E50		K8R
Edging (cups and cylinders) . .	Aloxite vitrified	60	M	28
Sharpening . . .	Aloxite vitrified	60	K	30
CLUTCH PLATES (cast iron)				
Surfacing . . .	Carborundum vitrified	40	R	E1
CLUTCH PLATES (hardened steel)				
Surfacing . . .	Aloxite vitrified	46	S	BLU
	Aloxite " AA " vitrified	A46	S	180
COMMUTATORS				
Roughing . . .	Carborundum vitrified	60	K	E4
Finishing . . .	Carborundum vitrified	150	M	E3
COMMUTATOR SPINDLES				
Cylindrical . . .	Aloxite vitrified	40B	L	BLU/D4
CONCRETE				
Surfacing (bricks by hand)	Carborundum vitrified	20		E5
Surfacing (bricks by machine)				
Roughing. . .	Carborundum vitrified	30		E6
Finishing. . .	Carborundum vitrified	80		E6
Surfacing (cup wheels) .	Carborundum vitrified	20	I	E6
CONNECTING RODS				
Internal . . .	Aloxite vitrified	603	M	BLU/P
Surfacing (cups and cylinders) . .	Aloxite " L "	24	S	L

Grinding-wheel Selection Table (*contd.*)

Class of Work	Abrasive and Bond	Grit	Grade	Bond
COPPER				
Cylindrical (tubes) .	Carborundum shellac	80		C4A
Cylindrical . . .	Carborundum shellac	60		C4A
(also see Rolls)	Carborundum vitrified	60	P	E1 +
Cutting-off . . .	Carborundum " Redmanol "	E30		C6XQ
Surfacing (cups and cylinders) . .	Carborundum vitrified	20	P	E1 +
COUPLERS AND DRAW BARS				
Snagging . . .	Aloxite vitrified	24	G	64
CRANKSHAFTS (Nitrided) . . .	Aloxite vitrified	40B	P	BLU/D5
CRANKSHAFTS (Diesel, large) . .	Aloxite vitrified	40	L	29
CRANKSHAFTS (Automobile) . .	Aloxite vitrified	366	J	31/D5
	Aloxite vitrified	40C	I	BLU/D6
Snagging (for balancing)				
Wheels operating 5,000–6,500 s.f.p.m.	Aloxite vitrified	24	I	32
Wheels operating 8,000–9,500 s.f.p.m.	Aloxite " Redmanol "	E141		K12XQ/42
CUTANIT (see Cemented Carbides, pp. 340, 341)				
CUTTERS (steel)				
Sharpening (machine) .	Aloxite vitrified	60	N	BLU
	Aloxite vitrified	A60	N	180
CUTTERS				
(Fellows gear) . .	Aloxite vitrified	80	R	BLU
(Gleason gear) . .	Aloxite vitrified	46	P	BLU
(Sunderland gear) .	Aloxite " AA " vitrified	A60	K	600
CUTTERS (moulding) .				
Sharpening (offhand) .	Aloxite vitrified	50	M	28
CYLINDERS (internal-combustion engines)				
Internal (new cylinders)	Carborundum vitrified	36	R	E1
Regrinding . . .	Carborundum vitrified	36	S	EO
Honing (stones) . .	Carborundum vitrified	120		G6H
Rehoning (stones) Roughing . .	Carborundum vitrified	80		G4H
Rehoning (stones) Finishing . .	Carborundum vitrified	180		G6H
Honing, after reboring (Stones) . . .	Carborundum vitrified	3F		WPH

Grinding-wheel Selection Table (*contd.*)

Class of Work	Abrasive and Bond	Grit	Grade	Bond
CYLINDERS (centrifugally cast iron)				
Internal . . .	Carborundum vitrified	40	T	T2L
Honing . . .	Carborundum vitrified	120		G6H
CYLINDERS (steel for aeroplanes)				
Internal . . .	Aloxite " AA " vitrified	A60	P	180/P
Honing . . .	Carborundum vitrified	180		G4H
Honing (mirror finish) .	Carborundum vitrified	3F		WPH
CYLINDER LINERS (nitralloy, etc.)				
Internal . . .	Carborundum vitrified	60	N	WNG
Honing . . .	Aloxite " AAL "	A180	N	LH
Honing (mirror finish) .	Carborundum vitrified	4F		WPH
DIES (forging)				
Cleaning				
Wheels operating from 5,000–6,500 s.f.p.m.	Aloxite vitrified	60	H	33
Wheels operating from 8,000–9,500 s.f.p.m.	Aloxite " Redmanol "	E40		K6XQ
DIES (threading)				
Chamfering				
(Cone wheel) . .	Aloxite vitrified	60	H	33
DIES (drawing)				
Cleaning . . .	Aloxite vitrified	60	H	33
Spindle-mounted wheels	Aloxite vitrified	80	M	28
Surfacing (cups and cylinders) . .	Aloxite " L "	30	S	L
	Aloxite " AAL "	A30	P	L
	Aloxite " Redmanol "	E30		K14F
Surfacing (straight wheels) . .	Aloxite " AA " vitrified	A54	P	180
	Aloxite vitrified	54	R	BLU
DRILLS				
Cutting-off . . .	Aloxite " Redmanol "	E30		K4XQ
Cylindrical				
Between centres .	Aloxite vitrified	60	K	BLU/D5
Centreless . .	Aloxite vitrified	60	K	BLU/D5C
Precision (sharpening side grinding) .	Aloxite vitrified	46	M	BLU
	Aloxite vitrified	50	M	28
Precision (periphery) .	Aloxite vitrified	36	P	25
Point thinning . .	Aloxite vitrified	60	K	30
	Aloxite " Redmanol "	E60		K6R
DRILLS (small)				
Fluting . . .	Aloxite rubber	80	VUL	KC
Offhand sharpening .	Aloxite vitrified	60	J	31

Grinding-wheel Selection Table (*contd.*)

Class of Work	Abrasive and Bond	Grit	Grade	Bond
DRILLS (large)				
Fluting . . .	Aloxite rubber	60	VUL	KC
Offhand sharpening .	Aloxite vitrified	40	J	31
EBONITE, ERINOID, ETC.				
Centreless . . .	Carborundum vitrified	365	K	B4
ESCALOY (see Cemented Carbides, pp. 366, 367)				
FIBRE RODS				
Centreless				
Roughing. . .	Carborundum vitrified	403	M	E3
Finishing . .	Carborundum vitrified	80	O	WOG
FILES				
Surfacing . . .	Aloxite vitrified	301	G	34
Edging . . .	Aloxite vitrified	30	G	64
Centreless . . .	Aloxite vitrified	60	I	32C
Re-cut (large wheels) .	Aloxite vitrified	306	G	50/T2
FIRTH BROWN CARBIDE (see Cemented Carbides, pp. 366, 367)				
FLAT IRONS				
Surfacing (cups, cylinders and segments) .	Carborundum vitrified	30	R	E1
	Aloxite " AAL "	A30	P	L
Surfacing (offhand) .	Carborundum vitrified	24	K	E4
Snagging				
Wheels operating at 5,000–6,500 s.f.p.m.	Carborundum vitrified	30	F	CVR
	Carborundum vitrified	24	G +	VA
Wheels operating at 8,000–9,500 s.f.p.m.	Carborundum " Redmanol "	E201		C10XQ/36
FORGINGS				
Snagging				
Wheels operating at 5,000–6,500 s.f.p.m.	Aloxite vitrified	20	F	65
Wheels operating at 8,000–9,500 s.f.p.m.	Aloxite " Redmanol "	E141		K9XQ/43
FORK TINES				
Offhand . . .	Aloxite vitrified	24	E	66
GAUGES (plug)				
Cylindrical				
Between centres .				
Roughing (unhardened)	Aloxite vitrified	401	M	28
Semi-finish (hardened) .	Aloxite " AA " vitrified	A100	M	180
Finish (hardened). .	Aloxite " Redmanol "	KHM		K8Y/385

Grinding-wheel Selection Table (*contd.*)

Class of Work	Abrasive and Bond	Grit	Grade	Bond
GAUGES (thread) Coarse pitch . .	Aloxite " AA " vitrified	A150	L	180
GAUGES (thread) Fine pitch . . .	Aloxite " AA " vitrified	A220	P	600
GEARS (cast iron) Cleaning between teeth (offhand) . .	Carborundum rubber	24	VUL	C1
GEARS (hardened steel) Form precision grinding and generative precision grinding Lees Bradner machine	Aloxite vitrified Aloxite " Redmanol " Aloxite " Redmanol "	54 E50 E50	P	BLU K10R/36 KA12R/36
Churchill machine .	Aloxite " AA " vitrified	A405	P	600
Maag machine . .	Aloxite " AA " vitrified	A60	M	180
Orcutt machine .	Aloxite " L "	60	O	L/D5
Internal . . .	Aloxite vitrified	60	M	BLU/P
Surfacing (cups and cylinders) . .	Aloxite " L " Aloxite " AAL "	24 A30	R P	L L
Surfacing (straight wheels) . .	Aloxite vitrified Aloxite " AA " vitrified	46 A54	R S	BLU 180
GLASS (cut) Puntying (concaving bottoms of glasses and tumblers) .	Aloxite vitrified	120	K	D1641
Puntying (beading, deep)	Aloxite vitrified	120	K	D1641
Puntying (beading, shallow) . .	Aloxite vitrified	F	N	D1640
Puntying (grapes, etc., on rich cut glass) .	Aloxite vitrified	F	N	D1640
Puntying (grapes, etc., on light ware) .	Aloxite vitrified	F	N	D1640
Puntying (petals, etc., on rich cut glass) .	Aloxite vitrified	120	K	D1641
Puntying (petals, etc., on light ware) . .	Aloxite vitrified	F	N	D1640
Edging (rich cut glass) .	Aloxite vitrified	180	L	D1640
Edging (light ware) .	Aloxite vitrified	180	L	D1640
Engraving (punties, flat eaves, etc.) . .	Aloxite vitrified	220	J	D1645
Engraving (edge cuts) .	Aloxite vitrified	F	N	D1640
Engraving (fine work) .	Aloxite vitrified	F	H	D1648
Fluting (rich cut glass) .	Aloxite vitrified	220	K	D1644
Fluting (light ware) .	Aloxite vitrified	220	K	D1644
Scalloping (rich cut glass)	Aloxite vitrified	F	N	D1640
Smoothing and flat work (rich cut glass) .	Aloxite vitrified	F	N	D1640
Mitre cutting (roughing)	Carborundum vitrified	80	H	E7G
Mitre cutting (finishing)	Aloxite vitrified	120	K	D1641

Grinding-wheel Selection Table (*contd.*)

Class of Work	Abrasive and Bond	Grit	Grade	Bond
GLASS (plate—table tops, windscreens, mirrors, etc.)				
Rough bevelling—				
Vertical spindle .	Carborundum vitrified	80	P	E1 + G
Finish bevelling—				
Vertical spindle .	Aloxite vitrified	180	M	D1639
Rough bevelling—				
Automatic machine on face of wheel .	Carborundum vitrified	70	N	E2 +
Finish bevelling—				
Automatic machine on face of wheel .	Aloxite vitrified	180	M	D1639
Edging . . .	Aloxite vitrified	220	K	D1644
Edging on roller-type machine .	Aloxite vitrified	180	P	D1636
Mitre cutting . .	Aloxite vitrified	220	K	D1644
Notching (roughing) .	Carborundum " Redmanol "	E60		C10R/32
Notching (finishing) .	Aloxite vitrified	220	K	D1644
Scroll work (roughing) .	Aloxite vitrified	120	K	D1641
Scroll work (finishing) .	Aloxite vitrified	3F	K	D1644
GLASS (lamp shades) .				
Grinding edges				
(Automatic) . .	Aloxite vitrified	150	P	25
(Hand) . . .	Aloxite vitrified	180	K	D1644
GLASS (lenses)				
Edging				
Roughing. . .	Aloxite vitrified	220	K	D1644
Finishing . . .	Aloxite vitrified	3F	K	D1644
GLASS (tubing)				
Cylindrical . . .	Carborundum vitrified	220	M	WMG
Internal . . .	Carborundum vitrified	220	P	WPG
Nicking . . .	Carborundum vitrified	220	H	E9
GLASS (tumblers)				
Edging . . .	Aloxite vitrified	150	P	25
GLASS (specials such as Marmarine, Opalite, Vitrolite, etc.)				
Edging				
Roughing. . .	Carborundum vitrified	100	J	E5
Finishing . . .	Aloxite vitrified	180	K	D1644
GRANITE				
Edging (with steel-centred wheel) . .	Carborundum " Redmanol "	E241		C8
Edging . . .	Carborundum " Redmanol "	E301		C8XQ
Grooving . . .	Carborundum " Redmanol "	E241		C8XQ
Moulding and surfacing	Carborundum vitrified	24	M	E3
Honing . . .	Carborundum shellac	1803		C6F

Grinding-wheel Selection Table (*contd.*)

Class of Work	Abrasive and Bond	Grit	Grade	Bond
GRANITE—(*contd.*)				
Rubbing (hand)				
Roughing. . .	Carborundum vitrified	30		E2
Finishing . .	Carborundum vitrified	180		E2
Honing . . .	Carborundum vitrified	3F	M	1209 (Special)
GUIDE BARS				
Surfacing (segments) .	Aloxite " L "	30	R	L
Surfacing (cylinders) .	Aloxite " L "	30	R	L
Surfacing (straight wheels) . . .	Aloxite vitrified	30	N	BLU
HAMMERS (claw)				
Grinding between claws	Aloxite rubber	50	VUL	KC
Other operations . .	Aloxite vitrified	30	H	33
HOBS (high-speed steel)				
Sharpening . . .	Aloxite vitrified	60	P	BLU
HOUSINGS (auto axle)				
Cylindrical				
Between centres .	Aloxite vitrified	40B	M	BLU/D5
Snagging . . .	Aloxite vitrified	24	G	64
Surfacing (segments) .	Aloxite " AAL "	A24	O	L
Surfacing (cylinders) .	Aloxite " L "	24	P	L
KNIVES (band)				
Sharpening . . .	Aloxite " AA " vitrified	A60	N	180
KNIVES (butcher)				
Machine surfacing .	Aloxite " Redmanol "	E50		K10R
Offhand surfacing .	Aloxite vitrified	50	K	30
KNIVES (Chipper and Barker)				
Sharpening . . .	Aloxite silicate	303	P	SP
KNIVES (cigarette)				
Sharpening . . .	Aloxite " L "	50	N	L
KNIVES (circular)				
Sharpening . . .	Aloxite vitrified	80	P	25
KNIVES (hog)				
Sharpening . . .	Aloxite silicate	303	P	SP
KNIVES (leather dehairing)				
Sharpening (bricks) .	Carborundum vitrified	20		HL
KNIVES (leather fleshing)				
Sharpening (bricks) .	Carborundum vitrified	20		HL

Grinding-wheel Selection Table (*contd.*)

Class of Work	Abrasive and Bond	Grit	Grade	Bond
KNIVES (leather shaving) Sharpening				
(Low-speed machines)	Aloxite vitrified	60	H	33
(High-speed machines)	Aloxite " Redmanol "	E693		K6R
KNIVES (leather skiving) Sharpening . . .	Aloxite vitrified	80	H	33
KNIVES (leather splitting) Sharpening . . .	Aloxite vitrified	24	K	30
	Aloxite " Redmanol "	E241		K14R
KNIVES (moulding) Offhand sharpening .	Aloxite vitrified	60	K	30
KNIVES (machine) . . Sharpening				
(Periphery) . .	Aloxite silicate	403	M	SM
(Cup wheel) . .	Aloxite silicate	403	P	SP
KNIVES (paper) Sharpening				
Periphery . .	Aloxite silicate	403	M	SM
	Aloxite " Redmanol "	E301		K14F
Cup wheel . .	Aloxite silicate	403	P	SP
KNIVES (pocket)				
Machine surfacing .	Aloxite " Redmanol "	E120		K8V
Offhand surfacing .	Aloxite " Redmanol "	E120		K9V
KNIVES (section)				
Bevelling . . .	Aloxite vitrified	40	M	28
Surfacing backs .	Aloxite silicate	403	P	SP
	Aloxite " AAL "	A36	P	L
KNIVES (sugar beet) Rooting . . .	Aloxite shellac	36		K4B
KNIVES (table—carbon steel)				
Roughing . . .	Aloxite " Redmanol "	E60		K8R
Finishing . . .	Aloxite " Redmanol "	E100		K8V
Rough and finish (one operation) .	Aloxite " Redmanol "	E60		K8R
Bolster grinding . .	Aloxite rubber	60		KBR
KNIVES (table—stainless steel)				
Roughing . . .	Aloxite " Redmanol "	E60		K11R
Finishing . . .	Aloxite " Redmanol "	E100		K10R
Bolster grinding . .	Aloxite rubber	60	VUL	KBR
KNIVES (tobacco) Sharpening . . .	Aloxite " L "	40	P	L

Grinding-wheel Selection Table (*contd.*)

Class of Work	Abrasive and Bond	Grit	Grade	Bond
KNIVES (veneer)				
Sharpening . . .	Aloxite silicate	403	M	SM
LATHE CENTRES . .	Aloxite vitrified	40B	M	BLU/D5
LAWN-MOWER BLADES				
Sharpening . . .	Aloxite vitrified	60	J	31
LEATHER (see Knives for leather-knife wheel recommendations)				
Finishing or napping chamois leather .	Carborundum vitrified	16	M	E3
Suèding (drum wheel) .	Carborundum vitrified	16	L	B3 +
LIMESTONE				
Sawing				
Inserted teeth . .	Carborundum shellac	141	2	A3M
Steel centres . .	Carborundum " Redmanol "	E201		C10
Surfacing . . .	Carborundum vitrified	30	M	E3
Moulding . . .	Carborundum vitrified	40	M	E3
Rubbing (hand) . .	Carborundum vitrified	180		E2
LINKS, MOTION (locomotive)				
Machine grinding .	Aloxite vitrified	40B	M	BLU/D5
LINKS (chain—malleable iron and steel)				
Snagging . . .	Aloxite vitrified	30	F	65
LINKS (chain—unannealed malleable iron)				
Snagging . . .	Aloxite vitrified	24	E	66
	Carborundum vitrified	20	G +	VA
LINKS (chain—manganese)				
Snagging . . .	Aloxite vitrified	24	F	65
MACHINE-SHOP GRINDING				
General offhand . .	Aloxite vitrified		H	33
MALLEABLE IRON ANNEALED				
Snagging				
Wheels operating 5,000–6,500 s.f.p.m.	Aloxite vitrified	24	F	65
Wheels operating 8,000–9,500 s.f.p.m.	Aloxite " Redmanol "	E141		K12XQ/46
MALLEABLE IRON UNANNEALED				
Snagging . . .	Aloxite vitrified (*YL process*)	20N7	F	65
	Carborundum vitrified	24	F	CVR

Grinding-wheel Selection Table (*contd.*)

Class of Work	Abrasive and Bond	Grit	Grade	Bond
MARBLE				
Coping (steel centres) .	Carborundum " Redmanol "	E201		C10
Mouldings (forming)				
Roughing . . .	Carborundum vitrified	30	M	E3
Finishing . . .	Carborundum vitrified	60	M	E3
Honing . . .	Carborundum shellac	2F		C6F
Balusters and columns (turning)				
Slotting (steel centres)	Carborundum " Redmanol "	E201		C10
Roughing . . .	Carborundum vitrified	30	M	E3
Finishing . . .	Carborundum vitrified	60	M	E3
Honing . . .	Carborundum shellac	2F		C6F
Slabs (polishing)				
First gritting . .	Carborundum vitrified	40		E2
Second gritting . .	Carborundum vitrified	120		E2
Third gritting . .	Carborundum vitrified	220		E2
Honing . . .	Carborundum shellac	2F		C6F
Honing edges of slabs .	Carborundum shellac	1803		C6F
MICROMETERS				
Grinding threads . .	Aloxite " AAL "	A1F	O	L/D5
MONEL METAL				
Cutting-off . . .	Aloxite " Redmanol "	E30		K4XQ
Surfacing . . .	Aloxite vitrified	46	R	BLU
Snagging . . .	Aloxite vitrified	20	G	64
NEEDLES (gramophone)				
Pointing . . .	Aloxite vitrified	40	G	74
	Carborundum vitrified	40	G	E8
NEEDLES (sewing)				
Pointing . . .	Carborundum vitrified	120	D	E14
NITRALLOY STEEL (Before nitriding)				
Cylindrical . .	Aloxite vitrified	401	M	28
Surfacing . .	Aloxite " AAL "	A30	O	L
Internal . . .	Aloxite vitrified	60	N	BLU/P
NITRALLOY STEEL (After nitriding)				
Cylindrical . .	Aloxite " AA " vitrified	A100	P	180
Surfacing . .	Carborundum vitrified	24	S	EOG
Internal . . .	Carborundum vitrified	60	N	WNG
PEARL				
Buttons (backing) .	Carborundum vitrified	60	J	E5
Buttons (surfacing) .	Carborundum vitrified	36	J	E5
Buttons (roughing blanks)	Carborundum vitrified	30	H +	HD
Buttons (slitting) .	Carborundum rubber	80	VUL	CB
Buttons (grooving) .	Carborundum vitrified	180	G	E10
	Carborundum rubber	40	VUL	CB

Grinding-wheel Selection Table (*contd.*)

Class of Work	Abrasive and Bond	Grit	Grade	Bond
PEARL—(*contd.*)				
Buttons (grinding fish eyes) . . .	Carborundum vitrified	120	H	E9
Novelties				
Offhand roughing .	Carborundum vitrified	100	H	E9
Offhand finishing .	Carborundum vitrified	220	H	E9
PINS				
Pointing . . .	Aloxite vitrified	120	G	D847
PIPE (soft steel)				
Cutting-off . . .	Aloxite " Redmanol "	E30		K4XQ
Internal . . .	Aloxite vitrified	24	J	31
PIPE BALLS (manganese steel)				
Cylindrical				
Roughing. . .	Aloxite vitrified	30	H	33
Re-grinding . .	Aloxite vitrified	36	K	30
Centreless . .				
Roughing. . .	Aloxite vitrified	40	H	33
Re-grinding . .	Aloxite vitrified	60	J	31C
PISTONS (aluminium)				
Cylindrical				
Between centres .	Carborundum vitrified (*YT process*)	365	N	E2 +
Centreless . .	Carborundum vitrified	50	T	T2L
PISTONS (cast iron)				
Cylindrical . . .	Carborundum vitrified	365	M	E3
Centreless . . .	Carborundum vitrified	40	P	E1 +
PISTONS (steel)				
Cylindrical . . .	Aloxite vitrified	50	P	BLU
Centreless . . .	Aloxite vitrified	50	P	25
Centreless (fine finishing)	Aloxite " Redmanol "	E150		K12R
Centreless (super-fine finishing) . .	Carborundum " Redmanol "	E500		C6Y/285
PISTON PINS				
Centreless				
Roughing. . .	Aloxite vitrified	60	K	BLU/D5C
Finishing . . .	Aloxite " Redmanol "	E150		K4R/35
Lapping . . .				
Roughing. . .	Aloxite vitrified	80	K	30
Finishing . . .	Carborundum " Redmanol "	E320		C8Y/29
PISTON RINGS (cast iron or semi-steel)				
Cylindrical roughing .	Carborundum vitrified	60	K	E4
Cylindrical finishing .	Carborundum vitrified	120	I	E6D
Surfacing (roughing cylinders). . .	Aloxite " AAL "	A30	S	L

Grinding-wheel Selection Table (*contd.*)

Class of Work	Abrasive and Bond	Grit	Grade	Bond
PISTON RINGS (cast iron or semi-steel)—(*contd.*)				
Surfacing (straight wheels)	Aloxite vitrified	60	J	31
Lapping (roughing) .	Carborundum vitrified	180	O	E2
Lapping (finishing) .	Carborundum vitrified	1F	P	E1 +
Lapping (super finishing)	Carborundum " Redmanol "	E600		C6Y
PISTON RODS (locomotive)				
Cylindrical . . .	Aloxite vitrified	401	M	28
PLOUGHS (steel)				
Surfacing . . .	Aloxite vitrified	20	G	64
Edging and jointing .	Aloxite vitrified	20	G	64
Fitting . . .	Aloxite vitrified	24	H	33
Re-sharpening points .	Aloxite vitrified	24	H	33
PLOUGHS (chilled iron)				
Surfacing . . .	Carborundum vitrified	20	G +	VA
Edging and jointing .	Carborundum vitrified	20	G +	VA
Fitting . . .	Carborundum vitrified	20	G +	VA
POINTS AND CROSSINGS (manganese steel)				
Hole grinding . .	Carborundum vitrified	24	M	E3
Offhand grooving				
Portable machine .	Aloxite vitrified	24	G	64
	Aloxite " Redmanol "	E141		K9XQ/45
Semi-precision grooving				
Planer-type machines	Aloxite vitrified	20	G	64
Snagging . . .	Aloxite vitrified	20	F	65
	Aloxite " Redmanol "	E141		K9XQ/45
Surfacing . . .	Aloxite vitrified	20	I	32
PORCELAIN				
Cutting-off . . .	Carborundum rubber	1F	VUL	CB
Cylindrical . . .	Carborundum vitrified	36	M	E3
Removing imperfections	Carborundum vitrified	60	H	E7
	Aloxite " AA " vitrified	A90	I	1675B
Surfacing (cylinder wheel)	Carborundum vitrified	20	R	E1
PULLEYS (cast iron)				
Cylindrical . . .	Carborundum vitrified	30	P	E1 +
Roughing with pulley grinder (cylinder wheel) . . .	Carborundum vitrified	24	K	E4
Finishing with pulley grinder (cylinder wheel) . . .	Carborundum " Redmanol "	E50		C10R
RAILS (welds)				
Surfacing				
Wheels . . .	Aloxite vitrified	24	G	64
Bricks . . .	Carborundum vitrified	121		HD
	Aloxite vitrified	16	I	32

Grinding-wheel Selection Table *(contd.)*

Class of Work	Abrasive and Bond	Grit	Grade	Bond
RAZORS				
Burring . . .	Aloxite vitrified	50	J	31
Side of tang . .	Aloxite vitrified	60	K	30
Concaving . . .	Aloxite vitrified	60	I	32
Shoulders (cutting-in) .	Aloxite vitrified	60	I	32
Shoulders (shaping after hardening) . .	Aloxite vitrified	120	H	33
Edging (roughing) .	Aloxite " AA " vitrified	A80	N	600
Edging (finishing) .	Aloxite shellac	2F		K4A
Point shaping . .	Aloxite vitrified	60	K	30
RAZOR BLADES (safety)				
Roughing . . .	Aloxite " Redmanol "	E180		K12R/31
Finishing . . .	Aloxite " Redmanol "	E600		K14Y/345
Honing . . .	Aloxite " Redmanol "	KAM		K6Y/37
REAMERS				
Backing off . .	Aloxite " AA " vitrified	A60	P	180
Cylindrical . . .	Aloxite vitrified	60	K	30
Fluting . . .	Aloxite rubber	60	VUL	KC
RIMS (automobile)				
Removing welds .	Aloxite vitrified	24	G	64
Grooving . . .	Aloxite rubber	24	VUL	KB
ROLLER BEARING CUPS				
Centreless				
Small diameters .	Aloxite vitrified	60	O	BLU/D5C
Medium diameters .	Aloxite vitrified	60	R	BLU/D5C
Large diameters .	Aloxite vitrified	60	S	BLU/D5C
Internal . . .	Aloxite vitrified	60	M	BLU/P
ROLLERS FOR BEARINGS				
Centreless (roughing) .	Aloxite vitrified	60	K	BLU/D5C
Centreless (finishing) .	Aloxite rubber	80	VUL	KC
ROLLS (brass)				
Cylindrical (roughing) .	Carborundum vitrified	40	N	E2 +
Cylindrical (finishing) .	Carborundum shellac	80		C4A/33
ROLLS (copper)				
Cylindrical (roughing) .	Carborundum vitrified	403	M	E3
Cylindrical (finishing) .	Carborundum vitrified	100	R	WR
	Carborundum shellac	80		C4A/33
ROLLS (granite)				
Roughing . . .	Carborundum vitrified	36	M	E3
Finishing . . .	Carborundum shellac	50		C4A
ROLLS (cast iron)				
Cylindrical (roughing) .	Carborundum vitrified	30	K	E4
Cylindrical (finishing) .	Carborundum shellac	40		C7A/33

Grinding-wheel Selection Table (*contd.*)

Class of Work	Abrasive and Bond	Grit	Grade	Bond
ROLLS (chilled iron)				
Cylindrical (hot plate rolls)	Carborundum vitrified	30	N	E2 +
Cylindrical (dryer rolls)	Carborundum " Redmanol "	E36		C12R/305
Cylindrical (rolls for cold rolling steel) . .	Carborundum shellac	80		C4A/33
ROLLS (hardened steel)				
Cylindrical . . .	Aloxite vitrified	401	O	26
Mirror finishing				
⌈ 1st roughing . .	Aloxite vitrified	50	S	23
2nd roughing . .	Aloxite vitrified	80	R	24
* ⎰ 1st finishing . .	Aloxite vitrified	150	R	24
2nd finishing . .	Aloxite vitrified	2F	P	D1638
⌊ Final finishing .	Aloxite " Redmanol "	KHM		K10Y
ROLLS (hard rubber)				
Cylindrical (roughing and finishing) . .	Carborundum vitrified	40	M	E3
ROLLS (medium hard rubber)				
Cylindrical (roughing and finishing) . .	Carborundum " Redmanol "	E36		C8R
ROLLS (soft rubber)				
Cylindrical (roughing) .	Carborundum " Redmanol "	E36		C8R
Cylindrical (finishing) .	Carborundum shellac	80		C4A/33
ROLL SCOURING (bricks)				
Cold rolls				
Roughing. . .	Carborundum vitrified	60		E3
Semi-finishing . .	Carborundum vitrified	120		E2
Finishing . .	Carborundum vitrified	1F		E4
Hot rolls				
Roughing. . .	Carborundum vitrified	70	S	T3L
Semi-finishing . .	Carborundum vitrified	90	S	T3L
Finishing . . .	Carborundum vitrified	120	S	T3L
RUBBER (hard)				
Cutting-off . . .	Carborundum " Redmanol "	E50		C8R
SANDSTONE				
Sawing				
Inserted tooth saw .	Carborundum shellac	141	2	A3M
Steel centre wheel .	Carborundum " Redmanol "	E201		C10
Surfacing . . .	Carborundum vitrified	24	M	E3
SAWS (woodcutting—band and circular)				
Gumming . . .	Aloxite vitrified	50	K	30
	Aloxite vitrified	50	K	D841
	Aloxite " Redmanol "	E36		K9R/38

* Sequence of wheels for built-up finish.

Grinding-wheel Selection Table (*contd.*)

Class of Work	Abrasive and Bond	Grit	Grade	Bond
SAWS (metal cutting—band)				
Gumming . . .	Aloxite rubber	80	VUL	K1
	Aloxite vitrified	80	G	34
SAWS (metal cutting—circular inserted tooth)				
High-speed steel				
Gumming . .	Aloxite " AA " vitrified	A54	N	180
SAWS (metal slitting)				
Gumming . . .	Aloxite rubber	80	VUL	K1
Surfacing (straight wheels) . .	Aloxite " AA " vitrified	A54	S	180
SCISSORS AND SHEARS (steel)				
Surfacing sides of blades				
Cylinders . .	Carborundum vitrified	40	H	E7
Offhand . . .	Aloxite vitrified	60	K	30
Grinding flash from bows	Aloxite vitrified	40	H	33
Pointing and shaping .	Aloxite vitrified	60	J	31
Grinding neck or corner	Aloxite vitrified	100	H	33
Striking cutting edges .	Aloxite vitrified	100	K	30
Re-sharpening . .	Aloxite vitrified	80	K	30
SHOVELS				
Edging . . .	Aloxite vitrified	24	F	65
SLATE				
Coping . . .	Carborundum " Redmanol "	E201		C10
Grooving . . .	Carborundum vitrified	40	M	E3
Surfacing . . .	Carborundum vitrified	40	P	E1 +
Finishing (blocks) .	Carborundum shellac	2F		C6F
SPLINE SHAFTS				
Cylindrical . . .	Aloxite vitrified	60	K	30
Surfacing splines				
Orcutt machine .	Aloxite " L "	60	O	L
Churchill machine .	Aloxite " AA " vitrified	A60	M	180
	Aloxite vitrified	60	M	BLU
SPRINGS (leaf)				
Grinding eyes . .	Aloxite vitrified	24	G	64
Chamfering . .	Aloxite vitrified	20	F	65
Cutting-off . . .	Aloxite " Redmanol "	E30		K4XQ4
SPRINGS (coil)				
Squaring ends . .	Aloxite vitrified	24	G	64
STAG ALLENITE (see Cemented Carbides, pp. 366, 367)				
STEATITE TUBES				
Cutting-off . . .	Carborundum " Redmanol "	E60		C4XQ

E.W.D.—12*

Grinding-wheel Selection Table (*contd.*)

Class of Work	Abrasive and Bond	Grit	Grade	Bond
STEEL CASTINGS (low carbon)				
Snagging (swing frame)				
Wheels operating at 5,000–6,500 s.f.p.m.	Aloxite vitrified	24	G	64
Wheels operating at 8,000–9,500 s.f.p.m.	Aloxite " Redmanol "	E141		K10XQ/43
Snagging (floor stand)				
Wheels operating at 5,000–6,500 s.f.p.m.	Aloxite vitrified	20	G	64
Wheels operating at 8,000–9,500 s.f.p.m.	Aloxite " Redmanol "	E141		K12XQ/45
Snagging (small bench stand)				
Wheels operating at 5,000–6,500 s.f.p.m.	Aloxite vitrified	24	G	64
Snagging (portable machine) . . .				
Wheels operating at 5,000–6,500 s.f.p.m.	Aloxite vitrified	24	G	64
Wheels operating at 8,000–9,500 s.f.p.m.	Aloxite " Redmanol "	E141		K9XQ/43
STEEL CASTINGS (manganese) (see also Points and Crossings)				
Snagging (swing frame)				
Wheels operating at 5,000–6,500 s.f.p.m.	Aloxite vitrified	20	F	65
Wheels operating at 8,000–9,500 s.f.p.m.	Aloxite " Redmanol "	E141		K10XQ/45
Snagging (floor stand)				
Wheels operating at 5,000–6,500 s.f.p.m.	Aloxite vitrified	20	F	65
Wheels operating at 8,000–9,500 s.f.p.m.	Aloxite " Redmanol "	ED121		K9RQ/45
STEEL (hardened)				
Cylindrical				
Between centres .	Aloxite vitrified	40B	N	BLU/D5
	Aloxite vitrified	603	N	BLU/D5
Centreless . . .	Aloxite vitrified	60	M	BLU/D5C
Surfacing (cups and cylinders). . .	Aloxite " L "	24	R	L
	Aloxite " AAL "	A30	P	L
	Aloxite " AA " " Redmanol "	E40		A16F
Surfacing (straight wheels) . .	Aloxite vitrified	46	R	BLU
	Aloxite " AA " vitrified	A54	S	180
Cutting-off . . .	Aloxite " Redmanol "	E30		K4XQ
Internal . . .	Aloxite vitrified	60	M	BLU/P
	Aloxite vitrified	603	M	BLU/P
	Aloxite " AA " vitrified	A60	M	180/P

Grinding-wheel Selection Table (*contd.*)

Class of Work	Abrasive and Bond	Grit	Grade	Bond
STEEL (soft)				
Cylindrical				
Between centres .	Aloxite vitrified	40B	M	BLU/D5
	Aloxite vitrified	60	K	BLU/D5
Centreless . . .	Aloxite vitrified	60	K	BLU/D5C
Surfacing (cups and cylinders) .	Aloxite " L "	24	. P	L
	Aloxite " AA " " Redmanol "	E40		A14F
Surfacing (segments) .	Aloxite " AAL "	A30	O	L
	Aloxite " AA " " Redmanol "	E30		A15F
Surfacing (straight wheels)	Aloxite vitrified	46	P	BLU
Cutting-off . . .	Aloxite " Redmanol "	E30		K2XQ2
Internal . . .	Aloxite vitrified	60	K	BLU/P
	Aloxite vitrified	603	K	BLU/P
STEEL (high-speed)				
Surfacing (cups and cylinders) .	Aloxite " AAL "	A30	S	L
	Aloxite " Redmanol "	E40		K14F
Surfacing (straight wheels) .	Aloxite " AA " vitrified	A46	S	180
Surfacing (segments) .	Aloxite " AAL "	A30	P	L/D5
	Aloxite " AA " " Redmanol "	E30		A16F
Cutting-off . . .	Aloxite " Redmanol "	E30		K4XQ
Internal . . .	Aloxite vitrified	60	N	BLU/P
	Aloxite " AA " vitrified	A60	N	180/P
Centreless . . .	Aloxite vitrified	60	N	BLU/D5C
STEEL (stainless)				
Cylindrical				
Between centres .	Carborundum vitrified	365	K	E4
Centreless . . .	Carborundum vitrified	365	M	E3
Surfacing (cups and cylinders) .	Aloxite " AAL "	A30	P	L
Surfacing (straight wheels) . .	Carborundum vitrified	40	P	E1 +
	Aloxite " AA " vitrified	A54	P	180
Cutting-off . . .	Aloxite " Redmanol "	E30		K4XQ
Internal . . .	Carborundum vitrified	60	M	E3
STELLITE				
Cylindrical . . .	Aloxite vitrified	40B	M	BLU/D5
Surfacing (cups and cylinders) .	Aloxite " AAL "	A36	P	L
Surfacing (straight wheels). .	Aloxite " AA " vitrified	A54	P	180
Cutting-off . . .	Aloxite " Redmanol "	E60		K6XQ
Internal . . .	Aloxite " AA " vitrified	A60	N	180
Offhand tool grinding .	Aloxite vitrified	40	I	32
Drills				
Pointing—machine .	Aloxite vitrified	46	N	BLU
Pointing—hand .	Aloxite vitrified	60	K	30

Grinding-wheel Selection Table (*contd.*)

Class of Work	Abrasive and Bond	Grit	Grade	Bond
STOVE PARTS (cast iron)				
Snagging . . .	Carborundum vitrified	24	G +	VA
	Carborundum vitrified	24	F	CVR
Fitting and mounting .	Carborundum vitrified	30	G +	VA
Surfacing tops (automatic machine)				
Roughing . . .	Carborundum vitrified	30	H +	HD
Finishing . . .	Carborundum vitrified	60	H	E7
TAPS				
Squaring ends . .	Aloxite vitrified	50	J	31
Grinding relief . .	Aloxite vitrified	60	P	BLU
Fluting . . .	Aloxite vitrified	60	K	30
	Aloxite " Redmanol "	E60		K8XQ
Threading . . .	Aloxite " AA " vitrified	A220	O	PH5
Grinding shanks (cylindrical) . . .	Aloxite vitrified	40B	M	BLU/D5
TILE				
Cutting-off . . .	Carborundum " Redmanol "	E36		C4XQ
TOOLS (lathe and planer)				
Light (offhand) . .	Aloxite vitrified	40	J	31
Heavy (offhand) . .	Aloxite vitrified	30	H	33
Automatic (cup wheel) .	Aloxite vitrified	24	K	30
Automatic (straight wheels) . .	Aloxite vitrified	40	J	31
TUBES (steel)				
Cutting-off . . .	Aloxite " Redmanol "	E100		K4V
TUBES (brass, aluminium, etc.)				
Cutting-off . . .	Carborundum " Redmanol "	E80		C4V
CEMENTED CARBIDES (see pp. 366, 367)				
TUNGSTEN RODS				
Surfacing . . .	Carborundum vitrified	100	P	WP
Cutting-off . . .	Aloxite rubber	80	VUL	KC
VALVES (automobile)				
Grinding faces . .	Aloxite vitrified	60	J	31
Stems (centreless) .	Aloxite vitrified	60	J	31C
Cutting-off . . .	Aloxite " Redmanol "	E30		K4XQ
VALVE TAPPETS				
Cylindrical				
Between centres .	Aloxite vitrified	40B	M	BLU/D5
Centreless . .	Aloxite vitrified	60	K	BLU/D5C
VITREOUS WARE				
Surfacing (segments or cylinders) . .	Carborundum vitrified	24	P	E1 +

Grinding-wheel Selection Table *(contd.)*

Class of Work	Abrasive and Bond	Grit	Grade	Bond
WELDS Cleaning (portable tool, air or electric) Wheel operating at 5,000–6,500 s.f.p.m.	Aloxite vitrified	24	G	64
Wheel operating at 8,000–9,500 s.f.p.m.	Aloxite " Redmanol "	E141		K9XQ/43
WIDIA OR WIMET METAL (see Cemented Carbides, pp. 366, 367)				
WORMS Grinding threads . .	Aloxite vitrified	46	P	BLU
WRENCHES Snagging . . .	Aloxite vitrified	20	G	64
Surfacing . . .	Aloxite vitrified	24	H	33
WROUGHT IRON Snagging . . .	Aloxite vitrified	24	G	64

SURFACE SPEED OF POLISHING MOPS IN FEET PER MINUTE

Speed of Spindle	Diameter of Mop (in inches)						
R.P.M.	6	8	10	12	14	16	18
800	1,250	1,680	2,150	2,500	2,900	3,250	3,700
900	1,400	1,900	2,400	2,800	3,250	3,700	4,100
1,000	1,575	2,100	2,600	3,100	3,600	4,100	4,550
1,200	1,950	2,550	3,200	3,750	4,400	5,000	5,550
1,400	2,250	2,950	3,650	4,400	5,100	5,800	6,500
1,600	2,550	3,400	4,200	5,000	5,900	6,600	7,500
1,800	2,900	3,800	4,750	5,650	6,600	7,500	8,500
2,000	3,200	4,200	5,250	6,250	7,300	8,400	9,300
2,200	3,450	4,550	5,750	6,900	8,000	9,100	10,300
2,400	3,750	5,000	6,300	7,500	8,800	10,000	11,200
2,600	4,100	5,450	6,800	8,200	9,600	10,900	12,200
2,800	4,400	5,900	7,400	8,900	11,000	11,500	13,200
3,000	4,700	6,250	7,900	9,400	11,400	12,500	14,100
3,200	5,000	6,650	8,400	10,000	11,800	13,400	15,100
3,400	5,250	7,000	8,900	10,600	12,500	14,300	16,000
3,600	5,600	7,500	9,500	11,300	13,200	15,100	17,000

[W. Canning & Co. Ltd.]

GRINDING AND LAPPING CEMENTED-CARBIDE TOOLS

The various makes of silicon carbide wheels given below are suitable for grinding tungsten carbide and similar cutting materials. It is, however, recommended that, wherever possible, diamond-impregnated wheels be used.

| Class of Work | Carborundum Green Grit Carborundum | | | Universal Unirundum Vitrified | | Norton Green Crystolon | | |
	Grit	Grade	Bond (vitri-fied)	Grit	Grade	Abrasive	Grit and Grade	Structure
TIPPED TOOLS								
Off-hand Grinding (Cup Wheels)								
Roughing (dry) . .	GC60	J5	VG	C46	LV	39	C60–I	7V
Roughing (wet) . .	GC60	J5	VG	C46	LV	39	C46–K	7V
Semi-finishing (wet) .				C60	JV	39	C90–L	7V
Finishing (dry) . .	GC120	J5	VG	C100	IV	39	C100–I	7V
Finishing (wet) . .	GC120	J5	VG	C100	IV	39	C220–I	9V
Off-hand Grinding (Peripheral)								
Roughing (dry) . .	GC60	K5	VG	C46	LV	39	C60–J	7V
Roughing (wet) . .	GC80	J + 5	VG	C46	LV	39	C70–K	7V
Finishing (dry) . .	GC120	J5	VG	C100	IV	39	C100–J	7V
Finishing (wet) . .	GC120	J5	VG	C100	IV	39	C120–K	7V
Machine Grinding (Tool and Cutter)								
Roughing (cup wheels) .	GC60	J5	VG	C46	KV	39	C60–J	7V
Roughing (peripheral) .	GC60	J5	VG	C46	LV	39	C60–K	7V
Finishing (cup wheels) .	GC120	J5	VG	C100	IV	39	C60–I	7V
Finishing (peripheral) .	GC120	J5	VG	C100	IV	39	C80–J	7V
Form Grinding .	GC120	J5	VG	C220	KV	39	C150–I	9V
Cylindrical Grinding								
Roughing . .	GC60	J5	VG	C46	LV	39	C80–K	7V
Finishing . .	GC120	J5	VG	C100	IV	39	C100–K	7V
Surface Grinding								
Roughing . .	GC60	J5	VG	C46	LV	39	C60–J	7V
Finishing . .	GC120	J5	VG	C100	IV	39	C90–J	7V

[Courtesy Jones & Shipman, Ltd.]

DIAMOND-IMPREGNATED WHEELS

These wheels are used for grinding sintered-carbide tools and parts; they are quicker and more accurate in action than special grit silicon-carbide wheels. The wheels are given a bonded-diamond abrasive face, the thickness of which is indicated by a number which expresses the number of thirty-seconds of an inch, e.g. No. 4 is $\frac{4}{32}$ or $\frac{1}{8}$-in. thick ; this is the maximum thickness of any layer.

Diamonds employed include the crushed South African diamonds properly sieved and graded into four standard grit sizes, viz. 100, 180, 240 and 400.

The percentage of diamonds present in the layer is termed the *diamond concentration*, and includes three groups, viz.: A—Low Concentration (25 per cent.); B—Medium Concentration (50 per cent.); C—High Concentration (maximum). The following table gives the applications and grades of Carborundum brand diamond wheels for various purposes (for grinding and lapping):

DIAMOND LAYER GRINDING AND LAPPING WHEELS

Type	Application	Roughing	Finishing	Ultra Finishing	Lapping
D50 DW }	Internal	100 C	100 C	{ 180 C 240 C	—
D51 D51E D51F D51FF }	Grooving Slotting Cut-off Form grinding Chip breaking {	100 2C 100 4C 100 8C	— 180 8C —	— — —	— — —
D51	Cut-off 1/64 in. wide	100 8C	—	—	—
D51	Cut-off 1/32 in. wide	100 8C	—	—	—
D51 {	Cylindrical Surface grinding }	100 2C	240 2C	—	400 2C
D51	Internal	100 2C	100 2C	(larger than 1/2 in. diam.)	
D51	Precision {	100 2C 100 2B	180 2B —		
D52	Offhand and precision {	100 4A 100 2C 100 2W 100 4W	180 2B 240 2B — —	400 1C — — —	400 2B — — —
D53 D53A D53B }	Precision {	100 4A 100 2B	180 2B 240 2B	400 1C —	400 2B —
D53 D53A D53B }	Milling cutters {	100 1C 180 2B	240 2B —	240 2B —	— —
D56	Milling cutters {	180 2B 180 2W	240 2B 240 2W	240 2B —	— —
D54	Reamers	180 2B	—	—	—
D55 D55A D60 D60A D61 D61A }	Tool and cutter Grinding {	100 1C 100 2B	240 1C 240 2B	— —	— —
D56	Offhand and precision {	100 4A 100 2W	240 2B —	400 1C —	400 2B —
D57	Lapping machine {	— —	240 2B 240 1B	400 2B 400 1B	400 2B 400 1B
D75	Petrographic	1B	—	—	—
DS25	Lapping stone	—	240 2C	—	—
DS26	Lapping stone	—	240 1C	—	—

Diamond wheels are made in a range of standard shapes and sizes.

GRINDING MILLING CUTTERS

Milling-cutter teeth are ground to give a primary clearance angle or land, and a secondary clearance angle (Fig. 1).

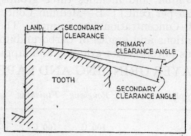

FIG. 1.—ILLUSTRATING PRIMARY AND SECONDARY CLEARANCES.

The values of these clearance angles are usually determined by experience, but the following table shows the values recommended as a general guide.

MILLING-CUTTER CLEARANCES

Material to be Machined	Clearance Angles
Mild and low-carbon steels . . .	$0° - 7°$
Hard steel (annealed) . . .	$2\frac{1}{2}° - 5°$
Steel castings	$6° - 7°$
Cast iron (fast feeds) . . .	$3° - 7°$
Bronze castings	$10° - 15°$
Hard bronze	$4° - 7°$
Copper	$12° - 15°$
Aluminium	$10° - 12°$

For large cutters the above values may be reduced a little, and for small cutters, increased.

Methods of Grinding

The two alternative methods of grinding cutters are shown in Figs. 2 and 3.*

In Fig. 2 the grinding wheel rotates from the body of the tooth off the cutting edge. The rotation of the wheel holds the cutter on the

* Carborundum Company Ltd.

tooth rest, but the wheel raises a burr on the cutting edge, which must be removed by stoning, and has a tendency to draw the temper of the steel. The other method (Fig. 3) rotates the wheel from the cutting edge toward the body of the tooth. It results in less danger of

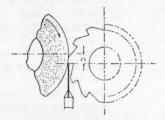

FIG. 2.—PLAIN-WHEEL CUTTER GRINDING.

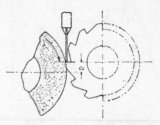

FIG. 3.—PLAIN-WHEEL CUTTER GRINDING (ALTERNATIVE METHOD).

burning the tooth, but great care must be used to hold the cutter on the tooth rest, since the rotation of the wheel tends to turn the cutter away from the rest. If the cutter turns while grinding, a ruined tooth results.

Cup wheels are also used for the grinding of cutters and reamers. The two methods of using cup wheels are similar to those used with plain wheels and are shown in Figs. 4 and 5.

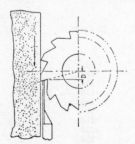

FIG. 4.—CUP-WHEEL CUTTER GRINDING.

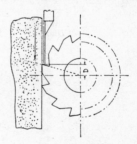

FIG. 5.—CUP-WHEEL CUTTER GRINDING (ALTERNATIVE METHOD).

The same methods are used for cup wheels. More care should, however, be taken with cup wheels, owing to the greater area of contact between the wheel and work.

Plain wheels are preferred on narrow lands and cup wheels for wide lands. A plain wheel may be tilted by swivelling the wheel

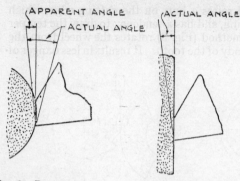

FIG. 6.—PLAIN-WHEEL
CUTTER CLEARANCE
GRINDING.

FIG. 7.— CUP-WHEEL
CUTTER CLEARANCE
GRINDING.

head to give an approximately straight-line cut. Plain wheels are often used for cutters up to 4 in. diameter, and cup wheels for larger sizes.

Figs. 6 and 7 show, exaggerated, the clearance obtained by plain and cup wheels. The plain wheel gives a greater actual cutting-edge angle than the apparent angle. The apparent angle should be large enough so that the heel of the tooth does not drag on the work when the cutter is in action.

TABLES FOR SETTING TOOTH REST
(A) Plain-wheel Clearance Table (Fig. 6)

For setting work centre and tooth rest below centre of wheel to obtain 5° and 7° clearance with wheels of different diameters when grinding on the periphery of the wheel.

Wheel Diameter	D. for 5°	D. for 7°
In.	In.	In.
2¼	·099	·139
2½	·110	·154
2¾	·121	·170
3	·132	·185
3¼	·143	·200
3½	·154	·216
3¾	·165	·231
4	·176	·246
4¼	·187	·262
4½	·198	·277
4¾	·209	·292
5	·220	·308
5¼	·231	·324
5½	·242	·339
5¾	·253	·354
6	·264	·370

Note.—If the grinding wheel is so large that it strikes the next tooth, a smaller wheel should be chosen and the centres readjusted so as to be correct for the new diameter.

(B) Cup-wheel Clearance Table (Fig. 7)

For setting tooth rest to obtain 5° and 7° clearance when grinding peripheral teeth of milling cutters with a cup wheel.

Cutter Diameter	D. for 5°	D. for 7°	Cutter Diameter	D. for 5°	D. for 7°
In.	In.	In.	In.	In.	In.
½	·022	·031	2¾	·121	·170
¾	·033	·046	3	·132	·185
1	·044	·062	3½	·154	·216
1¼	·055	·077	4	·176	·246
1½	·066	·092	4½	·198	·277
1¾	·077	·108	5	·220	·308
2	·088	·123	5½	·242	·339
2½	·110	·154	6	·264	·370

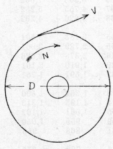

Fig. 8.

GRINDING-WHEEL SPEEDS

If D = diameter of wheel in inches, N = revolutions per minute, V = surface or grinding speed in feet per minute (Fig. 8):

$$V = \frac{\pi D}{12} \times N$$
$$= 0.2618 \, DN \text{ ft. per min.}$$

$$\text{and } D = \frac{12V}{\pi N}$$
$$= 3.8197 \frac{V}{N} \text{ in.}$$

$$\text{and } N = \frac{3.8197 \, V}{D} \text{ (r.p.m.).}$$

In the table that follows the corresponding revolutions per minute for the surface speeds given in the top line are shown opposite the diameters of wheel in the first column.

Dia-meter of Wheel in In.	Mm. about	Surface Speed of						
		4,000 ft. 1,200 m.	4,500 ft. 1,350 m.	5,000 ft. 1,500 m.	5,500 ft. 1,650 m.	6,000 ft. 1,800 m.	6,500 ft. 1,950 m.	7,000 ft. 2,135 m.
1/4	6	61,116	68,756	76,392	84,032	91,672	99,212	—
3/8	9	40,744	46,594	50,928	56,021	61,115	66,141	—
1/2	13	30,558	34,378	38,196	42,016	45,836	49,659	—
5/8	16	24,446	27,502	30,557	33,615	36,669	39,685	—
3/4	19	20,372	22,918	25,464	28,011	30,557	33,071	—
7/8	22	17,462	19,645	21,826	24,009	26,192	28,346	—
1	25	15,279	17,189	19,098	21,008	22,918	24,828	—
2	50	7,639	8,594	9,594	10,504	11,459	12,419	—
3	75	5,093	5,729	6,366	7,003	7,639	8,276	—
4	100	3,820	4,297	4,755	5,252	5,729	6,207	6,690
5	125	3,056	3,438	3,820	4,202	4,584	4,966	5,350
6	150	2,546	2,865	3,183	3,501	3,820	4,138	4,456
7	175	2,183	2,455	2,729	3,001	3,274	3,547	3,820
8	200	1,910	2,148	2,378	2,626	2,865	3,103	3,342
10	250	1,528	1,720	1,910	2,101	2,292	2,483	2,674
12	305	1,273	1,432	1,591	1,751	1,910	2,069	2,228
14	355	1,091	1,228	1,364	1,500	1,637	1,779	1,910
16	405	955	1,074	1,193	1,313	1,432	1,552	1,671
18	455	849	955	1,061	1,167	1,273	1,380	1,485
20	505	764	859	955	1,050	1,146	1,241	1,337
22	515	694	781	868	955	1,042	1,128	1,215
24	610	637	716	796	875	955	1,034	1,114
26	660	588	661	734	808	881	955	1,028
28	710	546	614	682	750	818	887	955
30	760	509	573	637	700	764	828	891
32	810	477	537	597	656	716	776	835
34	860	449	505	562	618	674	730	786
36	910	424	477	530	583	637	690	743
38	965	402	452	503	553	603	653	704
40	1,015	382	430	477	525	573	621	669
42	1,065	364	409	455	500	546	591	637
44	1,115	347	391	434	477	521	564	—
46	1,165	332	374	415	457	498	540	—
48	1,220	318	358	398	438	477	517	—
50	1,270	305	344	382	420	458	496	—
52	1,320	294	331	367	404	441	487	—
54	1,370	283	318	354	389	424	460	—
56	1,420	273	307	341	375	409	443	—
58	1,470	263	296	329	362	395	428	—
60	1,520	255	286	318	350	382	414	—

FACE SPEEDS AND R.P.M.

Wheel (per minute)								Dia-meter of Wheel in In.
8,000 ft. 2,435 m.	9,000 ft. 2,740 m.	9,500 ft. 2,890 m.	10,000 ft. 3,050 m.	12,000 ft. 3,650 m.	14,000 ft. 4,260 m.	16,000 ft. 4,870 m.	Mm. about	
—	—	—	—	—	—	—	6	$\frac{1}{4}$
—	—	—	—	—	—	—	9	$\frac{1}{3}$
—	—	—	—	—	—	—	13	$\frac{3}{8}$
—	—	—	—	—	—	—	16	$\frac{1}{2}$
—	—	—	—	—	—	—	19	$\frac{5}{8}$
—	—	—	—	—	—	—	22	$\frac{7}{8}$
—	—	—	—	—	—	—	25	1
—	—	—	—	—	—	—	50	2
—	—	—	—	—	—	—	75	3
7,640	8,606	9,085	9,570	11,470	—	—	100	4
6,112	6,880	7,260	7,650	9,180	—	—	125	5
5,092	5,730	6,048	6,366	7,639	—	—	150	6
4,366	4,910	5,184	5,457	6,548	—	—	175	7
3,820	4,296	4,536	4,775	5,730	—	—	200	8
3,056	3,438	3,629	3,820	4,584	—	—	250	10
2,456	2,864	3,024	3,183	3,819	4,456	5,092	305	12
2,183	2,456	2,592	2,728	3,274	3,820	4,366	355	14
1,910	2,148	2,268	2,387	2,865	3,342	3,820	405	16
1,698	1,910	2,016	2,122	2,547	2,970	3,396	455	18
1,528	1,718	1,814	1,910	2,296	2,674	3,056	505	20
1,389	1,562	1,649	—	—	—	—	515	22
1,273	1,532	1,512	—	—	—	—	610	24
1,175	1,322	1,396	—	—	—	—	660	26
1,091	1,228	1,296	—	—	—	—	710	28
1,018	1,146	1,209	—	—	—	—	760	30
955	1,074	1,134	—	—	—	—	810	32
899	1,010	1,067	—	—	—	—	860	34
849	955	1,008	—	—	—	—	910	36
806	905	955	—	—	—	—	965	38
764	859	907	—	—	—	—	1,015	40
729	818	866	—	—	—	—	1,065	42
—	—	—	—	—	—	—	1,115	44
—	—	—	—	—	—	—	1,165	46
—	—	—	—	—	—	—	1,220	48
—	—	—	—	—	—	—	1,270	50
—	—	—	—	—	—	—	1,320	52
—	—	—	—	—	—	—	1,370	54
—	—	—	—	—	—	—	1,420	56
—	—	—	—	—	—	—	1,470	58
—	—	—	—	—	—	—	1,520	60

CIRCUMFERENCES OF GRINDING WHEELS OF GIVEN DIAMETERS

The surface speed V = circumference of wheel × No. of revolutions per minute.

Diameter of Wheel in In.	Circumference of Wheel in Ft.	Diameter of Wheel in In.	Circumference of Wheel in Ft.	Diameter of Wheel in In.	Circumference of Wheel in Ft.
1	·262	25	6·546	49	12·828
2	·524	26	6·807	50	13·090
3	·785	27	7·069	51	13·352
4	1·047	28	7·330	52	13·613
5	1·309	29	7·592	53	13·875
6	1·571	30	7·854	54	14·137
7	1·833	31	8·116	55	14·499
8	2·094	32	8·377	56	14·661
9	2·356	33	8·639	57	14·923
10	2·618	34	8·901	58	15·184
11	2·880	35	9·163	59	15·446
12	3·142	36	9·425	60	15·708
13	3·403	37	9·687	61	15·970
14	3·665	38	9·948	62	16·232
15	3·927	39	10·210	63	16·493
16	4·189	40	10·472	64	16·755
17	4·451	41	10·734	65	17·016
18	4·712	42	10·996	66	17·274
19	4·974	43	11·257	67	17·541
20	5·236	44	11·519	68	17·802
21	5·498	45	11·781	69	18·064
22	5·760	46	12·043	70	18·326
23	6·021	47	12·305	71	18·588
24	6·283	48	12·566	72	18·850

GRINDING-WHEEL SPEEDS FOR DIFFERENT OPERATIONS

(Surface speeds)

	Ft. per min.
Cylindrical grinding	5,500– 6,500
Internal grinding	2,000– 6,000
Snagging, offhand grinding (vitrified wheels)	5,000– 6,000
Snagging (rubber and bakelite wheels)	7,000– 9,500 *
Surface grinding	4,000– 5,000
Knife grinding	3,500– 4,500
Hemming cylinders	2,100– 5,000 *
Wet tool grinding	5,000– 6,000
Cutlery wheels	4,000– 5,000
Rubber, shellac and bakelite cutting-off wheel	9,000–16,000 †

* This higher speed to be used only where suitable bearings are fitted.
† Higher speed recommended only where bearings, protection devices and suitable machine rigidity employed.

[*Norton Grinding Wheel Co.*]

WORK SPEED

For cylindrical grinding the wheel and work should revolve in directions shown (Fig. 9).

Wheel wear depends on ratio of wheel speed to work speed. The higher this ratio the lower the rate of wear of wheel.

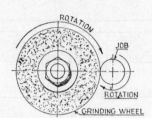

FIG. 9.

Work speed should usually be from 20 to 80 ft. per min. For roughing purposes slower work speeds, viz. 20 to 40 ft. per min., are used.

STANDARD GRINDING-WHEEL SHAPES

The standard shapes of grinding wheels are shown in Figs. 10, 11 and 12,* the following being a key to the letters indicating the dimensions of the wheels, as listed in tabular form by the manufacturers.

KEY TO LETTER DIMENSIONS

A—Flat spot of bevelled wall.
D—Diameter (overall).
E—Centre or back thickness.
F—Depth of recess.
G—Depth of recess.
H—Arbor-hole diameter.
J—Diameter of flat or small diameter.
K—Diameter of flat inside.
M—Large diameter of bevel.
P—Diameter of recess.
R—Radius.
T—Thickness (overall).
U—Width of face.
V—Angle of bevel.
W—Thickness of wall.

* Carborundum Co. Ltd

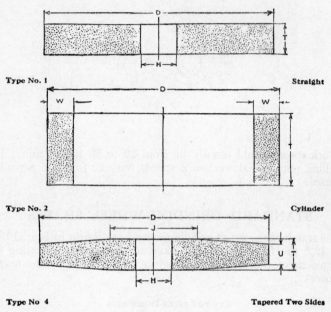

Type No. 1   Straight

Type No. 2   Cylinder

Type No 4   Tapered Two Sides

Fig. 10.

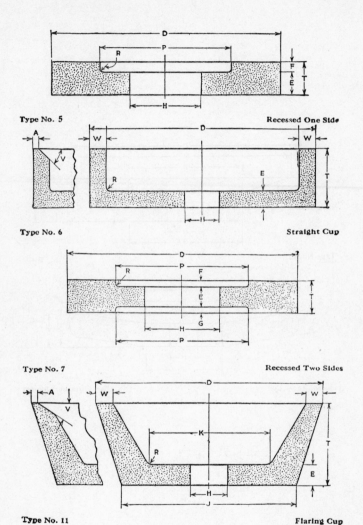

Type No. 5   Recessed One Side

Type No. 6   Straight Cup

Type No. 7   Recessed Two Sides

Type No. 11   Flaring Cup

FIG. 11.

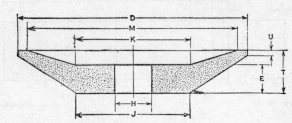

Type No. 12   Dish

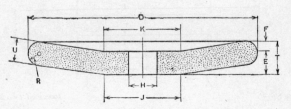

Type No. 13   (Saw Gummer) Saucer

FIG. 12.

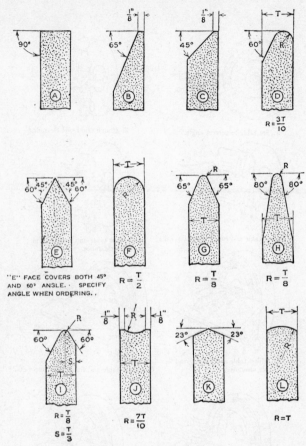

FIG. 13.—STANDARD SECTIONS OF GRINDING WHEELS.

GRINDING CEMENTED-CARBIDE TOOLS

Using Carborundum Green Grit wheels the grinding procedure is as shown in (1) to (8) (Fig. 14). Light pressures only should be used. The tool should be passed to and fro across the face. A large radius on the nose will require a rough grind. Grind against the cutting edge. Wet grinding prevents tool cracking due to overheating. The diagrams refer to right-hand tools.

380

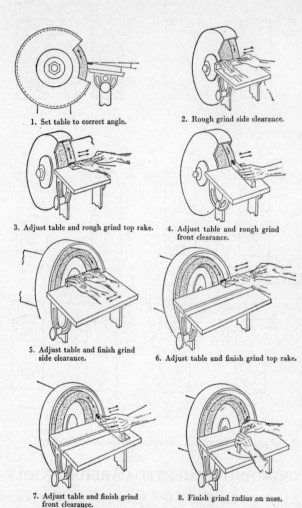

1. Set table to correct angle.

2. Rough grind side clearance.

3. Adjust table and rough grind top rake.

4. Adjust table and rough grind front clearance.

5. Adjust table and finish grind side clearance.

6. Adjust table and finish grind top rake.

7. Adjust table and finish grind front clearance.

8. Finish grind radius on nose.

FIG. 14.—GRINDING CEMENTED-CARBIDE TOOLS.

GRINDING FAULTS, CAUSES AND CURES*

The principal faults encountered in precision grinding of metals are as follows :

(1) *Out-of-Round* or *Tapered*, instead of parallel.

(2) *Surface Flaws*, such as holes, ridges, checks, cracks or scratches.

(3) *Wavy Surface*, i.e. surface left wavy or with spiral irregularities at a pitch of not less than 0·003 in. and height of a few thousandths inch.

(4) *Roughness*, i.e. very small wavy irregularities over the ground surface imposed on the latter. The pitch varies from 0·002 in. to 0·0001 in. and depth from surface from 0·000125 in. to 0·000003 in.

(1) A. Work Out-of-Round

CAUSES.—(*a*) Wheel too dense. (*b*) Faulty work centres. (*c*) Coolant supply inadequate. (*d*) Worn machine centres. (*e*) Driving pins not parallel to axis. (*f*) Uneven pressure on driving dog. (*g*) Centres shaky.

CURES.—(*a*) Change wheel or dress more open. (*b*) Clean centres. (*c*) Increase supply. (*d*) True centres. (*e*) True faceplate and pins. (*f*) Provide cushions between pin and dog, e.g. rubber or insulating tape. (*g*) Check tapers ; regrind if necessary.

(1) B. Work Tapered

CAUSES.—(*a*) Work springs under wheel pressure or spindle springs when internal grinding. (*b*) Expansion of work due to heat. (*c*) Excessive wheel wear during traverse. (*d*) Centres out of line with machine ways. (*e*) Worn spindle bearings. (*f*) Dressing tool set incorrectly.

CURES.—(*a*) Use correctly adjusted steadies ; reduce infeed or use narrower wheel. (*b*) Use more coolant ; reduce infeed ; use more open structure wheel. (*c*) Use harder wheel. (*d*) Re-align. (*e*) Check and rectify. (*f*) Reset tool correctly.

(2) Surface Flaws on Work

CAUSES.—(*a*) Wheel too coarse (narrow, deep and regular scratches). (*b*) Wheel too soft (wide, varying depth irregular scratches). (*c*)

* Courtesy, Messrs. Jones & Shipman, Ltd.

Loose grit (irregular marks). (*d*) Dirty coolant (irregular fish-tail scratches). (*e*) Blunt diamond (isolated deep marks). (*f*) Dirty wheel face (isolated deep marks).

CURES.—(*a*) Use finer grain wheel. (*b*) Use harder grade wheel, decrease workhead and traverse speeds, or increase spindle speed. (*c*) Keep air around machine clean or use dust collectors. (*d*) Clean tanks, filter and inside guard. (*e*) Turn in holder ; renew. (*f*) Dress wheel and remove loose grit with stiff bristle brush.

SOME OTHER CAUSES.—(*g*) Work springing. Wheel face not parallel to work, diamond faulty or wrongly located (fine spiral scratches). (*h*) Ragged wheel edges (wavy spiral lines). (*i*) Whipping belt (uneven scratches). (*j*) Unsuitable wheel (discoloured or burnt surface). (*k*) Local heating or wheel too wide (check marks).

CURES.—(*g*) Re-align headstock, wheelhead and tailstock ; replace diamond tool ; reduce infeed and provide extra work steadies. (*h*) Radius wheel edges. (*i*) Adjust for tension. (*j*) Use softer grade wheel. (*h*) Belt slipping ; examine and tighten.

(3) Wavy Surfaces

CAUSES.—(*a*) Too much clearance between spindle and bearing (short, close waves). (*b*) Wheel spindle warped or out-of-round (longer and more widely spaced waves). (*c*) General vibrations (regularly spaced waves). (*d*) Wheel out of balance (long checkerboard pattern marks). (*e*) Work centres or rests untrue (irregular marks). (*f*) Backlash in workhead gears (marks run full length of work, more prominent towards workhead). (*g*) Loose spindle pulley (regularly spaced waves). (*h*) Building vibrations (marks in phase with latter).

CURES.—(*a*) Allow bearings to attain working temperature, before commencing to grind. (*b*) Renew or re-grind and lap to new bearings. (*c*) Check machine rigidity, balance of motor and pulleys. (*d*) Re-balance. (*e*) Check condition and rectify as required. (*f*) Overhaul gears, spindles and replace belt ; check quantity of lubricant in gearbox. (*g*) Make tight. (*h*) Check nuts on foundation bolts or move machine to better position.

SPIRAL WAVES.—These are caused by the face of the wheel being convex or are due to misalignment of wheelhead and tailstocks, table setting and wheelhead setting. The waviness consists of traverse lines of the same pitch as the rate of traverse.

SECTION 10

PROPERTIES OF MATERIALS

HOOKE'S LAW

Within the elastic limits in tension and compression the strain is proportional to the stress producing it.

$$\text{If } p = \text{stress} = \frac{\text{load}}{\text{area}}. \quad x = \text{stretch}.$$

$$l = \text{original length of member}.$$

$$\text{Then } p = \frac{x}{l} \cdot E \quad \text{and } \frac{x}{l} = \text{tensile strain},$$

where E = modulus of elasticity (or Young's Modulus).

For iron and steel E is about 13,000 tons per sq. in., so that a stress of 1 ton per sq. in. produces an extension of $\frac{1}{13,000}$ the original length of the member stressed.

SHEAR STRESS WITHIN ELASTIC LIMIT

If q = shear stress. y = shear strain.
Then $q = y \cdot C$,
where C = modulus of rigidity.

VOLUMETRIC STRESS WITHIN ELASTIC LIMIT

When a solid is subjected to three forces or compressive stresses, p_1, of equal intensity, applied in three directions mutually at right angles, and if v = the change of volume, V = original volume, then

$$p_1 = \frac{v}{V} \cdot K,$$

where K = bulk, or volume modulus.

$$\text{The linear strain} = \frac{v}{3V} = \frac{p_1}{3K}$$

RELATION BETWEEN ELASTIC MODULI

$$\frac{1}{E} = \frac{1}{3C} + \frac{1}{9K}$$

$$E = \frac{9KC}{3K + C}$$

POISSON'S RATIO

The lateral or transverse strain when a member is stressed within the elastic limit is a definite proportion of the longitudinal strain.

$$\text{Poisson's ratio } \sigma = \frac{\text{transverse strain}}{\text{longitudinal strain}}.$$

Its values for metals lie between $\frac{1}{3}$ and $\frac{1}{4}$.

WORK DONE IN ELASTIC STRAIN

For simple tension and compression, within the elastic limit,

$$\text{Work per unit volume} = \frac{p}{2} \cdot \frac{x}{l} = \frac{p^2}{2E}$$

where p = stress, x = change of length, l = original length.
F = elastic modulus.

The term $\frac{p^2}{2E}$ is termed the resilience and it expresses the capacity of the material for storing work.

The best energy-storing metals are those with the highest elastic limits, or working stresses, such as the heat-treated alloy steels (spring steels, e.g. silico-chrome, chrome-vanadium and nickel chrome).

India-rubber, for its weight, can store up more energy than other material. Thus it has a resilience of 200 in.-lb., whilst the hardest cast steel gives 500 in.-lb., but weighs about eight times as much as rubber.

MODULI OF ELASTICITY AND RIGIDITY

	Modulus of Elasticity Tons per sq. in.	Modulus of Rigidity Tons per sq. in.
Wrought iron	12,000–13,000	5,000–6,000
Cast iron	6,000–8,500	2,250–3,500
Carbon steels	12,700–14,000	5,350–5,500
Nickel steels (3–4 per cent.) .	12,700	5,000
Nickel steels (30–35 per cent.). .	10,550	4,200
Copper (rolled)	6,700	2,500
Copper (annealed) . . .	7,150	2,700
Phosphor bronze . . .	6,700	2,500
Brass	5,000–6,000	2,000–3,000
Aluminium (rolled) . . .	4,000–4,500	1,700–1,800
Lead	1,120	390
Tin	3,500	1,340
Nickel	13,100	5,000
Monel metal	11,610	4,460
Glass (flint)	3,200–3,900	1,300–1,750

VALUES OF BULK MODULUS K

Material	K, in lb. per sq. in.
Water	320,000
Mercury	7,850,000
Glass (flint)	4,950,000–5,900,000
Brass	14,300,000–15,500,000
Copper	24,000,000
Cast iron	13,700,000
Wrought iron	20,700,000
Steel	25,200,000

VALUES FOR POISSON'S RATIO

Material	Value of Poisson's Ratio
Mild steel	0·29
Wrought iron	0·27
Cast iron	0·25
Brass (cast)	0·33
Copper (cast)	0·33
Glass (flint)	0·24

MODULI OF ELASTICITY FOR TIMBERS

Material	Modulus E Lb. per sq. in.
Ash	1,600,000
Beech	1,350,000
Birch	1,500,000
Cedar	500,000
Elm	700,000
Spruce	1,800,000
Larch	900,000
Honduras mahogany . . .	1,250,000
English oak	1,450,000
African oak	2,280,000
Pine :	
Red	1,850,000
Pitch	1,225,000
American	1,600,000
Yellow	1,600,000

COPPER AND COPPER ALLOYS (SHEET OR STRIP)

Physical and Mechanical Properties

	Copper	Gilding Metal 90 per cent. Cu 10 per cent. Zn	Cartridge Brass 70 per cent. Cu 30 per cent. Zn	Basis Brass 63 per cent. Cu 37 per cent. Zn	Yellow Metal 60 per cent. Cu 40 per cent. Zn	Phosphor Bronze 94-95 per cent. Cu 5-6 per cent. Sn	Nickel Silver 60-65 per cent. Cu 18 per cent. Ni 17-22 per cent. Zn	Aluminium Bronze 93-95 per cent. Cu 5-7 per cent. Al	Cupro-Nickel 80 per cent. Cu 20 per cent. Ni
Tensile strength: Annealed (tons/sq. in.)	15	18	22	23	26	25	25	26	22
Hard * (tons/sq. in.)	25	28	36	37	—	44	43	44	32
0·1 per cent. proof stress: Hard * (tons/sq. in.)	21	25	32	32	—	38	38	38	26
Modulus of elasticity ($\times 10^6$ lb./sq. in.)	18	17	15	15	14	19	19·5	18	19·5
Modulus of torsion ($\times 10^6$ lb./sq. in.)	6·5	—	4·8	—	—	6·5	6·5	—	—
Endurance limit for 50 million cycles: Annealed (tons/sq. in.)	4·5	7	8	—	10	10	10	—	8
Hard (tons/sq. in.)	8·5	—	10	—	12	11	—	—	—
Electrical conductivity (per cent. of I.E.C. standard)	100†	44	27	26	29	18	6·3	15-17	6·5
Thermal conductivity (calories per sq. cm./cm./sec./° C. at 20° C.)	0·92 †	0·45	0·29	0·285	0·30	0·195	0·06	0·17-0·19	0·087
Thermal expansion ($\times 10^6$ per ° C. in range 20°-110° C.)	16·6	17·5	19	19·5	20	17	14·8	17	15·5
Density	8·93	8·80	8·51	8·42	8·4	8·88	8·72	8·15	8·96
Melting point of range (° C.)	1,083	1,020-1,050	910-960	905-920	890-950	910-1,040	1,040-1,100	1,050-1,060	1,130-1,180

* Cold rolled 50 per cent. reduction of thickness.
† True only for high-conductivity copper as used for electrical purposes.

[*Copper Development Association*]

STRESS CONVERSION TABLE

(English to metric)

Tons per sq. in.	Lb. per sq. in.	Kilos per sq. mm.	Tons per sq. in.	Lb. per sq. in.	Kilos per sq. mm.
10·00	22,400	15·75	53	118,720	83·47
10·50	23,520	16·54	54	120,960	85·05
11·00	24,640	17·32	55	123,200	86·62
11·50	25,760	18·11	56	125,440	88·20
12·00	26,880	18·90	57	127,680	89·77
12·50	28,000	19·69	58	129,920	91·35
13·00	29,120	20·47	59	132,160	92·92
13·50	30,240	21·26	60	134,400	94·50
14·00	31,360	22·05	61	136,640	96·07
14·50	32,480	22·84	62	138,880	97·65
15·00	33,600	23·62	63	141,120	99·22
15·50	34,720	24·41	64	143,360	100·80
16·00	35,840	25·20	65	145,600	102·37
16·50	36,960	25·99	66	147,840	103·95
17·00	38,080	26·77	67	150,080	105·52
17·50	39,200	27·56	68	152,320	107·10
18·00	40,320	28·35	69	154,560	108·67
18·50	41,440	29·14	70	156,800	110·25
19·00	42,560	29·92	71	159,040	111·82
19·50	43,680	30·71	72	161,280	113·40
20·00	44,800	31·50	73	163,520	114·97
20·50	45,920	32·29	74	165,760	116·55
21·00	47,040	33·07	75	168,000	118·12
21·50	48,160	33·86	76	170,240	119·70
22·00	49,280	34·65	77	172,480	121·27
22·50	50,400	35·44	78	174,720	122·85
23·00	51,520	36·22	79	176,960	124·42
23·50	52,640	37·01	80	179,200	126·00
24·00	53,760	37·80	81	181,440	127·57
24·50	54,880	38·59	82	183,680	129·15
25	56,000	39·37	83	185,920	130·72
26	58,240	40·95	84	188,160	132·30
27	60,480	42·52	85	190,400	133·87
28	62,720	44·10	86	192,640	135·45
29	64,960	45·67	87	194,880	137·02
30	67,200	47·25	88	197,120	138·60
31	69,440	48·82	89	199,360	140·17
32	71,680	50·40	90	201,600	141·75
33	73,920	51·97	91	203,840	143·32
34	76,160	53·55	92	206,080	144·90
35	78,400	55·12	93	208,320	146·47
36	80,640	56·70	94	210,560	148·05
37	82,880	58·27	95	212,800	149·62
38	85,120	59·85	96	215,040	151·20
39	87,360	61·42	97	217,280	152·77
40	89,600	63·00	98	219,520	154·35
41	91,804	64·57	99	221,760	155·92
42	94,080	66·15	100	224,000	157·50
43	96,320	67·72	101	226,240	159·07
44	98,560	69·30	102	228,480	160·65
45	100,800	70·87	103	230,720	162·22
46	103,040	72·45	104	232,960	163·80
47	105,280	74·02	105	235,200	165·37
48	107,520	75·60	106	237,440	166·95
49	109,760	77·17	107	239,680	168·52
50	112,000	78·75	108	241,920	170·10
51	114,240	80·32	109	244,160	171·67
52	116,480	81·90	110	246,400	173·25

RESILIENCES OF DIFFERENT MATERIALS (Perry)

Material	Tension			Compression			Shear		
	f_t Lb. per Sq. In.	E × 10⁶ Lb. per Sq. In.	$f_t^2/2E$ In. Lb. per Cu. In.	f_e Lb. per Sq. In.	E × 10⁶ Lb. per Sq. In.	$f_e^2/2E$ In. Lb. per Cu. In.	f_s Lb. per Sq. In.	C × 10⁶ Lb. per Sq. In.	$f_s^2/2C$ In. Lb. per Cu. In.
Cast iron . .	3,500	14-23	3	10,500	14-23	12	2,700	5·0-7·6	5
Wrought iron .	24,000	29	10	24,000	21	10	20,000	10·5	19
Mild steel . .	35,000	30	20	35,000	21-25	15	26,500	11	32
Mild steel, hardened	70,500	30	83	—	—	83	53,000	11	128
Cast steel, un-hardened	80,000	30	107	—	—	—	64,000	11	186
Cast steel, hardened	190,000	36	501	—	—	—	145,000	13	809
Copper . .	4,300	15	0·62	4,000	17·1	0·5	2,900	5·6	0·75
Brass . .	6,950	9·2	2·62	6,500	15·3	1·23	5,200	3·4	4·00
Gunmetal . .	6,200	9·9	2·00	6,000	15·0	1·30	4,150	3·7	2·33
Phosphor bronze .	19,700	14	13·85	20,000	14·0	14·3	14,500	5·25	20·0
Glass . . .	4,500	8	1·26	10,000	5·8	8·6	—	3·3-3·9	—
Fir . . .	10,000	1·5	5	6,000	1·5	1·3	—	0·1-0·7	—
Oak . . .	14,500	1·3	4	10,000	1·3	3·85	—	—	—

Note.—f_t, f_e, and f_s are the tensile, compressive and shear stresses at the elastic limits.

STRENGTH PROPERTIES OF TIMBERS

Material	Tensile Strength: Lb. per Sq. In.		Shear Strength Lb. per Sq. In.	Compressive Strength Lb. per Sq. In.
	With Grain	Across Grain		
Ash	12,000–17,000	1,600–2,300	—	8,000–10,000
Beech	11,000–22,000	1,500–2,000	—	7,000–9,000
Birch	15,000	1,800	—	3,500
Cedar: West Indian	5,000	1,000–1,500	—	5,700
American	10,800	600–800	—	6,000
Lebanon	11,000	1,000–1,400	—	5,800
Elm: English	13,000–14,000	—	—	6,000–10,000
Canadian	13,000	—	—	7,000
Silver spruce	10,100	400–800	800–1,360 *	6,500
Greenheart	8,960	—	—	14,200
Larch	9,000–10,000	1,300–1,700	—	3,000–5,500
Mahogany: Honduras	16,000–20,000	1,800	—	8,000
Spanish	15,000	1,300	—	8,200
Maple	11,150	1,400–1,600	—	7,150
Oak: English	10,000	1,500	2,300	6,400
African	21,000	2,000–2,500	—	9,300
Pine: Red	12,000–14,000	1,200–1,400	—	5,500–7,500
White	8,700–11,000	1,100–1,300	—	4,000–6,500
Yellow	13,000	1,000–1,200	—	5,300
Dantzic	8,000	1,300–1,400	—	5,400
Riga	4,500	—	—	3,900
Pitch	12,600	1,200–1,400	650	8,000
Satinwood	10,000		—	7,000
Poplar	7,500	1,600	—	4,800
Hickory	15,000–18,000	2,200–2,500	—	9,000–11,000
Teak	7,000–15,000	2,200–2,300	—	8,000–12,000
Lancewood	20,000	2,200–2,600	—	7,000
Walnut: French	7,000–8,500	1,600	—	5,000–6,000

* Across grain.

DUCTILITY AND MALLEABILITY OF COMMON METALS

No.	Order of Ductility of Common Metals *	Order of Malleability of Common Metals †
1	Gold	Gold
2	Silver	Silver
3	Platinum	Copper
4	Iron	Tin
5	Nickel	Platinum
6	Copper	Lead
7	Zinc	Zinc
8	Tin	Iron
9	Lead	Nickel

* Ductility is the property which enables metals to be drawn out into wire.
† Malleability is the property of permanently extending, under pressure, in all directions, without rupture.

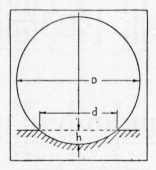

FIG. 1.—BRINELL HARDNESS METHOD.

HARDNESS OF METALS

Brinell Hardness Method

This consists in pressing a hardened steel ball of given diameter, with a specified load, into the surface of the metal, and measuring the depth of the impression made. Since the diameter of the impression is proportional to the depth it is usual to measure this diameter with a low-power microscope, instead of the depth. In the case of direct-reading hardness-testing instruments the depth of the impression is measured direct, using a magnifying system to give a high degree of accuracy in reading. The dial is graduated to read hardnesses.

Referring to Fig. 1, if D = diameter of steel ball, d = diameter of impression and h = depth of impression, in millimetres, then

$$h = \tfrac{1}{2} (D - \sqrt{D^2 - d^2}) \text{ mm.}$$

The *Brinell Hardness Number* is defined as the load P, in kilograms divided by the spherical area of impression.

Thus Brinell Hardness Number (B.H.N.)

$$= \frac{P}{\dfrac{\pi D}{2} (D - \sqrt{D^2 - d^2})}$$

$$= \frac{P}{1 \cdot 5708 \, D \, (D - \sqrt{D^2 - d^2})}$$

The British Standards Institution * has specified the relationship between P and D in four different groups, such that $\dfrac{P}{D^2} = 1$, 5, 10 and 20, respectively, in the case of all hardness tests on metals. It is necessary to state which value of $\dfrac{P}{D^2}$ is employed, in hardness tests.

For guidance in specifying an appropriate value for the ratio $\dfrac{P}{D^2}$ the approximate values for representative materials are as follows :

Steels, cast iron	30
Copper alloys, aluminium alloys . .	10
Copper, aluminium	5
Lead, tin and their alloys . . .	1

The load should be applied slowly to the specimen at right angles to the surface and the full load maintained for a period of 15 secs.

When a test has been made the usual procedure is to measure the diameter of the impression with a microscope fitted with a graticule scale and then to read off the corresponding Brinell hardness number from a set of tables, namely, the B.S.I. values given in the Specification mentioned in the footnote. These tables give the

* Method and Tables for Brinell Hardness Testing, B.S. No. 240, Part I, 1937.

Brinell hardness numbers for balls of 2-, 5- and 10-mm. diameter and loads of 4, 20, 25, 40, 100, 120, 250, 500, 750, 1,000 and 3,000 kg.

When testing *thin sheet metal*, the nature of the plastic flow is appreciably different from that obtained on thick parts, so that unreliable hardness numbers are given. It is therefore necessary to limit the thickness of the test specimen. Thus, the B.S.I. specifies the thickness to be at least ten times the depth of the impression as given by the following formula :

$$\text{Depth of impression (mm.)} = \frac{P}{\pi DH}$$

where P = load in kg., D = diameter of ball in mm., and H = Brinell hardness number.

Brinell Hardness and Tensile Strength

The tensile strength of a metal may be predicted with a fair degree of accuracy from its Brinell hardness number.

Thus : tensile strength = $k \times$ Brinell Hardness Number (tons per sq. in.),

where k is a constant which is 0·217 for plain carbon and alloy steels over the Brinell hardness range of 100 to 550. For other steels the following are typical values :

TENSILE STRENGTH FACTORS FOR ALLOY STEELS

Alloy Steel	k
Chrome steel	0·242
Nickel-chrome steel . . .	0·240
Nickel steel	0·239
Vanadium steel	0·235
Carbon steel	0·232

For *non-ferrous metals* :

$$\text{Tensile strength} = \frac{\text{Brinell Hardness Number}}{4} - 1 \text{ (tons per sq. in.)}.$$

BRINELL HARDNESSES AND TENSILE STRENGTH EQUIVALENTS

Load of 3,000 kg. on Ball 10-mm. diameter.

Diameter of Impression in Mm.	Brinell Figure	Equivalent Tensile Stress in Tons/Sq. In.			Diameter of Impression in Mm.	Brinell Figure	Equivalent Tensile Stress in Tons/Sq. In.		
		Factor 0·21	Factor 0·23	Factor 0·25			Factor 0·21	Factor 0·23	Factor 0·25
2·40	653	137	150	163	4·75	159	33	37	40
2·45	627	132	144	157	4·80	156	33	36	39
2·50	601	126	138	150	4·85	152	32	35	38
2·55	578	121	133	144	4·90	149	31	34	37
2·60	555	116	128	139	4·95	146	31	34	36
2·65	534	112	123	134	5·00	143	30	33	36
2·70	514	108	118	129	5·05	140	29	32	35
2·75	495	104	114	124	5·10	137	29	31	34
2·80	477	100	110	119	5·15	134	28	31	33
2·85	461	97	106	115	5·20	131	27	30	33
2·90	444	93	102	111	5·25	128	27	29	32
2·95	429	90	99	107	5·30	126	26	29	31
3·00	415	87	95	104	5·35	123	26	28	31
3·05	401	84	92	100	5·40	121	25	28	30
3·10	388	82	89	97	5·45	118	25	27	29
3·15	375	79	86	94	5·50	116	24	27	29
3·20	363	76	83	91	5·55	114	24	26	28
3·25	352	74	81	88	5·60	111	23	25	28
3·30	341	72	78	85	5·65	109	23	25	27
3·35	331	69	76	83	5·70	107	22	25	27
3·40	321	67	74	80	5·75	105	22	24	26
3·45	311	65	71	78	5·80	103	22	24	26
3·50	302	63	69	75	5·85	101	21	23	25
3·55	293	61	67	73	5·90	99	21	23	25
3·60	285	60	65	71	5·95	97	20	22	24
3·65	277	58	64	69	6·00	95	20	22	24
3·70	269	56	62	67	6·05	94	20	22	23
3·75	262	55	60	65	6·10	92	19	21	23
3·80	255	53	59	64	6·15	90	19	21	22
3·85	248	52	57	62	6·20	89	19	20	22
3·90	241	50	55	60	6·25	87	18	20	22
3·95	235	49	54	59	6·30	85	18	20	21
4·00	229	48	53	57	6·35	84	18	19	21
4·05	223	47	51	56	6·40	82	17	19	21
4·10	217	45	50	54	6·45	81	17	19	20
4·15	212	44	49	53	6·50	79	17	18	20
4·20	207	43	48	52	6·55	78	16	18	19
4·25	201	42	46	50	6·60	77	16	18	19
4·30	197	41	45	49	6·65	75	16	17	19
4·35	192	40	44	48	6·70	74	15	17	18
4·40	187	39	43	47	6·75	73	15	17	18
4·45	183	38	42	46	6·80	72	15	16	18
4·50	179	37	41	45	6·85	70	15	16	17
4·55	174	36	40	43	6·90	69	14	16	17
4·60	170	36	39	42	6·95	68	14	16	17
4·65	167	35	38	42	7·00	67	14	15	17
4·70	163	34	37	41					

[*Vickers, Ltd.*]

E.W.D.—13*

BRINELL HARDNESS OF DIFFERENT METALS AND ALLOYS *

Material	Brinell Number
Lead, cast	4–8
Babbitt metals	10–25 (cast)
Tin	15–25 (annealed or cast)
Zinc, sheet	25–40
Copper, sheet	30–60
Silver	40–70
Gold, 14–24 carat	50–140 (annealed)
Wrought iron	70–85
Bronze, phosphor, sand-cast	80–95
Mild steel	80–105 (as drawn or rolled)
Duralumin plate, medium	90–120
Brass, medium-drawn	100–150
Bronze, phosphor, chilled	100–180
Cast iron, grey, sand-cast	115–200
Brass, hard drawn	120–170
Bronze, manganese, drawn	120–220
Nickel steel	130–160 (annealed)
Duralumin plate, hard	140–160
High-speed steel	150–260
Vanadium steel	150–300 (annealed)
Nickel-chrome steel	175–300
Tool steel, annealed	200–275
Cast iron, grey, chilled	230–400
Nickel steel, hardened	300–600
High-speed steel, hardened . . .	450–700
Tool steel, tempered at 600° F. . . .	550–700 (glass hard at 625)
Nickel-chrome, air-hardened	600–700

* *Engineering Materials*, Vol. 3, A. W. Judge (Pitmans Ltd.).

MINIMUM THICKNESSES AND BRINELL NUMBERS

Brinell Hardness No.	Minimum Thickness (in decimals of an inch)	
	10-mm. Ball	5-mm. Ball
Above		
100	0·3125	0·1250
150	0·2500	0·0937
200	0·1875	0·0781
300	0·1250	0·0625
400	0·0937	0·0468
500	0·0625	0·0310

Brinell impressions cannot be made near to the edge of a specimen for a similar reason to that given in the case of thin sections ; thus it is necessary, for reliable readings, to arrange for *the centre of the impression to be not less than 2½ times the impression from the edge of the specimen.*

VICKERS' DIAMOND-PYRAMID HARDNESS

In this method a pyramidal diamond of 136° apex angle is used instead of the steel ball. It overcomes the objection to the use of

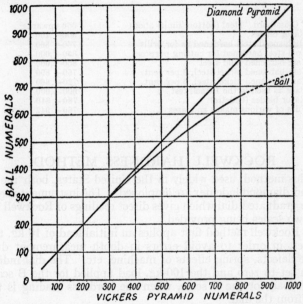

FIG. 2.—RELATION BETWEEN BRINELL AND VICKERS' HARDNESS NUMBERS.

the steel ball on hard materials, when the distortion of the ball gives erroneous readings.

The Vickers' pyramid numeral (V.P.N.) $= \dfrac{\text{Load, in kg.}}{\text{impressed area, in sq. mm.}}$

If $d = $ diagonal of the square-shaped impression made by the diamond indenter,

$$\text{Impressed area} = \frac{d^2}{1 \cdot 85436}$$

The V.P.N. values are the same as the Brinell hardness numbers up to 300, but are progressively higher above this value. The V.P.N. values obey a linear relation to the hardnesses and are independent of the loads applied.

DIAMOND HARDNESSES OF TYPICAL HARD STEELS

Description	Vickers' Pyramid Numeral
" Glass-hard " steel (bottom limit) about .	650 upwards
Razor blades	600– 700
High-speed steel hardened as for drills . .	760– 860
Tool steel hardened for cutting purposes .	850–1,000
Case-hardened mild steel	860–1,000
Case-hardened nickel steel, 3 per cent. . .	750– 890
Case-hardened nickel steel, 5 per cent. . .	720– 860
Balls as used in the Brinell test . . .	900–1,000
Razor blades (Gillette)	780– 840
Files of various makes and sizes . . .	760– 942

ROCKWELL HARDNESS METHOD

In this method, used widely in the United States, both the steel ball and diamond indenter are employed. The instrument used has a large graduated dial which gives direct readings of Rockwell hardness, two scales being provided.

The Rockwell method first applies an initial load of 10 kg. to the indenter, in order to avoid errors in depth measurement due to surface defects, spring effects of machine, etc. The dial indicator is then set to zero and the 100-kg. load applied for the B scale or 150-kg. load for the C scale, when the hardness reading is taken direct from the dial.

The B scale is used for tests on unhardened steels, phosphor bronze and other non-ferrous metals. For readings on this scale a $\frac{1}{16}$-in. diameter steel ball is employed in conjunction with a 100-kg. major load. For *very soft metals*, $\frac{1}{8}$-, $\frac{1}{4}$- and $\frac{1}{2}$-in. diameter balls are used.

The C scale is employed with a 120° cone angle diamond indenter, with a major load of 150 kg. It is used for all tests on the harder metals, such as hardened steels.

The scale ranges for both B and C on the Rockwell instrument dial are marked with red and black lettering respectively, and range from 0 to 100 divisions, but the useful part of the C scale is about

40 to 70, corresponding to the B.S. diamond-pyramid scale of 410 to 1,000.

A Rockwell scale A is also used in conjunction with a diamond indenter, and 60-kg. load for the hardest materials. Its readings range from about 43 to 90.

THE SHORE SCLEROSCOPE METHOD

The principle of this method is that of measuring the rebound height of a small diamond-tipped hammer dropped from a given vertical height on to the surface (horizontal) of the metal under test. The height of fall is 10 in., and the hammer falls down a glass tube. The vertical scale for measuring the rebound has 140 equal divisions and the 100 division represents the average hardness of martensitic high-carbon steel (quenched). The hammer measures $\frac{1}{4}$-in. diameter, is $\frac{3}{4}$ in. long, and weighs $\frac{1}{12}$ oz. The shape of the diamond indenter is slightly spherical.

HARDNESS VALUES OF METALS ON SHORE SCALE

Name of Metal	Annealed or Cast	Cold Worked	Chilled
Lead	2 – 4	3– 7	—
Aluminium	3½– 5	6–12	—
Gold, 24–14 carat . . .	5 –25	24–70	—
Silver	6½–14	20–37	—
Copper	6 – 8	14–20	—
Zinc	8 –10	18–20	—
Babbitt metal	4 – 9	—	—
Tin	8 – 9	12–14	—
Bismuth	8 – 9	—	—
Brass	7 –35	20–45	—
Platinum	10 –15	17–30	—
Bronze, phosphor . . .	12 –21	25–40	—
Bronze, manganese . . .	16 –21	25–40	—
Iron, wrought, pure . . .	16 –18	25–30	—
Nickel (cast)	13 –16	—	—
Nickel, wrought	17 –19	35–40	—
Mild steel, 0·05–0·15 carbon . .	18 –25	30–40	—
Iron, grey (sand cast). . .	25 –45	—	—
Tungsten (not ductile) . .	60 –70	—	60– 70
Iron, grey, chilled . . .	—	—	50– 90
Steel, tool, 1 per cent. carbon .	30 –35	40–50	90–105
Steel, tool, 1·65 per cent. carbon .	38 –45	—	90–105
Steel, vanadium . . .	30 –50	50–60	50–105
Steel, chrome nickel . . .	35 –50	40–60	60–105
Steel, nickel	25 –30	35–45	50– 90
Steel, high speed	30 –45	40–60	70–100

[*Engineering Materials*, Vol. 3, A. W. Judge (Pitmans Ltd.).]

APPROXIMATE COMPARISON OF HARDNESS SCALES †

Diamond-pyramid Scale (B.S. 427 —1931)	Brinell (Steel-ball) Scale (B.S. 240—1937)		Direct-reading Hardness Test (Rockwell Principle) (B.S. 891—1940)					
			C Scale 150-kg. Diamond Cone		A Scale 60-kg. Diamond Cone		B Scale 100-kg. $\frac{1}{16}$-in. Steel Ball	
	Variations *	Adopted Value	Variations *	Adopted Value	Variations *	Adopted Value	Variations *	Adopted Value
(1)	(2)	(3)	(4)	(5)	(6)	(7)	(8)	(9)
20	15– 25	20						
40		40						
60		55						
70		65						
80		75						
90		85						
100	80–100	95				43	47–61	54
120		115				47		65
140		135				50		77
160		155				53		83
180		175				56		89
200	175–205	195			58–60	59	93–95	94
220		215				60		97
240		235	18–23	20		61		100
260		255		24		63		
280		275		27		64		
300	280–300	295	27–33	30	65–68	66		
320		310		32		67		
340		325		34		68		
360		345		36		69		
380		360		39		70		

* I.e. range to be expected among individual cases. The variations given apply to the line on which they occur, and intermediate values may be estimated by considering the next set of variations in the same column.

† B.S.I. Specification No. 860—1939.

Approximate Comparison of Hardness Scales (*contd.*)

Diamond-pyramid Scale (B.S. 427—1931)	Brinell (Steel-ball) Scale (B.S. 240—1937)		Direct-reading Hardness Test (Rockwell Principle) (B.S. 891—1940)			
			C Scale 150-kg. Diamond Cone		A Scale 60-kg. Diamond Cone	
	Variations *	Adopted Value	Variations *	Adopted Value	Variations *	Adopted Value
(1)	(2)	(3)	(4)	(5)	(6)	(7)
400	370–395	380	38–42	40	70–72	71
420		395		42		72
440		415		44		73
460		430		45		73
480		445		47		74
500	445–480	460	46–50	48	73–76	75
520		475		49		75
540		499		50		76
560		505		51		76
580		520		52		77
600	515–550	535	52–56	54	75–79	77
620		545		55		78
640		560		56		78
660		570		57		79
680		585		57		79
700	580–602	595	57–61	58	76–80	80
725		605		59		81
750		630		61		81
800			60–64	62	77–83	82
850				63		82
900			63–67	65	78–84	83
950				66		83
1,000			65–69	68		84
1,100				69		85
1,200				70		87
1,250					87–90	88
1,400				71	90–93	91

* I.e. range to be expected among individual cases. The variations given apply to the line on which they occur, and intermediate values may be estimated by considering the next set of variations in the same column.

MOHS' SCALE OF HARDNESS

Mohs' method of determining the relative hardnesses of different materials is based on the principle of a harder metal or material being able to scratch a softer one. The relative hardness test proposed by Mohs * consists in selecting ten different minerals and arranging these in their relative order of scratching, the softest material having the lowest numerical value on the hardness scale. The following were the selected materials and their hardnesses, as previously defined :

Material	Order of Hardness	Material	Order of Hardness
Talc	1	Orthoclase . .	6
Gypsum . . .	2	Quartz . . .	7
Calcite . . .	3	Topaz . . .	8
Fluorspar . . .	4	Corundum . .	9
Apatite . . .	5	Diamond . . .	10

* Mohs, *Grundriss der Mineralogie*, 1822, Part I, p. 374.

SOFT SOLDERS

Composition (percentage)			Melting Point ° C.	Description and Application
Tin	Lead	Bismuth		
0	100	—	325	Pure lead.
10	90	—	305	High lead coarse solder.
20	80	—	280	Coarse plumber's solder.
30	70	—	260	} Fine plumber's solder for seams and angles.
40	60	—	237	
50	50	—	212	} Coarse tinman's solder for use with ordinary copper bit.
60	40	—	190	
66	34	—	180	Fine tinman's solder for blow-lamp use.
75	25	—	183	} Fine and hard solders for blow-pipe use.
80	20	—	186	
20	30	50	96	Pewter solder.

BRITISH STANDARD SOLDERS *

De-signa-tion	Application	Tin (percentage)			Antimony (percentage)		Lead
		Nom.	Min.	Max.	Min.	Max.	
A	Work requiring low melting point. Steel tube joints .	65	64	66	—	1	The Remainder
B	Tinsmiths' and coppersmiths' fine work. Hand soldering .	50	49	51	2·5	3	
C	General work and hand soldering	40	39	41	2	2·4	
D	Plumbers' wiped joints . .	30	29	31	1	1·7	
E	Special electrical purposes .	95	94·5	95·5	—	0·5	
F	Machine soldering. General electrical purposes. Zinc and galvanised ironwork . .	50	49	51	—	0·5	
G	Dipping baths. Zinc and galvanised iron. Tinned electrical joints	42	41	43	—	0·4	
H	Lead cable wiped joints . .	35	34	36	—	0·3	
J	Dipping baths . . .	30	29	31	—	0·3	
K	Special machine soldering .	60	59	61	—	0·5	

* B.S. No. 219—1942.

SOLDERING FLUXES

Fluxes used for soldering purposes may be (1) Protective, (2) Chemical. The former type, which includes resin, tallow, olive oil or vaseline, serve to protect the cleaned surface during heating

Fluxes for Soft-soldering Purposes

Metal to be Soldered	Flux
Aluminium	According to method. Stearin or Fry's zinc flux. In some cases no flux is needed.
Brass, copper, gunmetal or bronze .	Zinc chloride, resin,* tallow or sal ammoniac (ammonium chloride).
Steel	Zinc chloride or sal ammoniac.
Tinned steel	Zinc chloride or resin,* Alcho-re Oleic acid No. 9.
Lead	Tallow,* resin,* or vaseline.*
Galvanised iron or steel . .	Hydrochloric acid.
Zinc	Hydrochloric acid.
Pewter	Gallipoli oil * or Venice turpentine.*
Stainless steel . . .	Frysol S.S. soldering fluid, Fryolene (orthophosphoric flux).
Tin	Ammonium phosphate,* zinc chloride.
Cast iron	Fryolux compound.
Nickel, monel metal, chromium plate	Fryolene.

* Non-corrosive flux.

against surface corrosion. They are non-acid and the soldered joints are not attacked by these fluxes. Chemical fluxes remove oxides and other compounds caused by heating the metals for the "tinning" operation.

Self-fluxing Solders

These are mixtures of powdered solder and flux, e.g. lead-tin solder in powdered form, mixed with powdered sal ammoniac. They are applied by sprinkling on to the heated metal. Tinning is effectively accomplished with such fluxes, the surplus metal and dross being wiped off with a cloth.

Solder creams and pastes consist of similar mixtures held in a pasty mass with a suitable binding medium of a syrupy consistency. They are brushed on to the work, and the latter then heated until the solder content spreads over the surface.

Solder Flux Recipes

A useful general-purpose soldering paste can be made up by mixing petroleum jelly (or vaseline) with zinc chloride in the proportion of 1 lb. of the former to 1 fluid ounce of the latter. Another useful paste is made of starch and zinc chloride in suitable proportions to form the required pasty consistency. Petroleum jelly (or vaseline) mixed with powdered sal ammoniac makes a good soldering flux paste.

An acid-free soldering flux that will not attack metals can be made up as follows:

Zinc chloride	20 parts by weight
Ammonium chloride	10 ,, ,,
Boiling water	100 ,, ,,

The flux should be kept in a stoppered bottle.

A non-corrosive flux suitable for brass, copper and bronze is made by dissolving resin in alcohol so as to form a pasty liquid, which can be applied with a brush.

Zinc chloride flux is made by dissolving sufficient granulated zinc in hydrochloric acid until all effervescence ceases.

Notes on Silver Solders

Silver solders have a melting range of about 650° to 780° C. The British Standard Grade A and Grade B silver solders have melting ranges of 690°–735° C. and 700°–775° C., respectively.

The 50–50 silver copper alloy melts at 870° C.

SILVER (HARD) SOLDERS

Composition (percentages)			Applications
Silver	Copper	Zinc	
5–10	95–100	—	Thin iron and mild-steel plates.
45	55	—	Tough solder for instruments, very fluid.
30	50	20	Small brass work.
38·5	46	15·5	Bronze and nickel (German) silver.
9	43	48	General work on brass and copper alloys.
80	20	—	Hardest solder.
75	25	—	General high-grade purposes.
50	50	—	Softest solder. Resists burning.
60–62	27·5–29·5	9–11	British Standard Grade A silver solder.
42–44	36–38	18·5–21	British Standard Grade B silver solder.
60	27	17	Good general-purpose solder.

The fluxes used are of the borax class, e.g. borax and boracic acid. They are usually calcined, pulverised and made into a paste with water.

High melting-point solders are usually silver-copper alloys (780° to 1,000° C.), and nickel-copper alloys (780°–1,080° C.).

BRAZING ALLOYS

Composition (percentages)				Applications
Copper	Zinc	Tin	Nickel	
66	34	—	—	Hardest, suitable for iron and steel.
60	40	—	—	Hard, suitable for iron and copper.
50	50	—	—	Ordinary spelter. For brass and copper.
37·5	50	—	12·5	White alloys. For nickel silver and iron.
35	57	—	8·0	
57·5	25	17·5	—	White alloy for brass. More fusible than spelter.
43·4	6·6	50 ·	—	Whiter alloy. More fusible than spelter.

Notes on Brazing Alloys

These alloys have a higher melting-point range than silver solders, viz. from 850° to 1,080° C. They give stronger joints.

The common brazing alloy is Spelter (see table above), which melts at about 870° C. It is used for brazing steels and also brasses having melting points above 1,000° C. For higher melting-point brasses, the percentage of zinc is reduced below 40 per cent.

The melting point of the brazing alloy should be at least 150° C. below that of the metals to be brazed.

The colour of the brazing alloy should match that of the metal to be brazed. As the copper content is increased in the brazing alloy the colour changes from the golden shade of the 50/50 alloy to pale yellow for the 70/30 per cent. copper-zinc alloy ; then to a golden colour again for the 75 to 90 per cent. copper-zinc alloy. Above 95 per cent. the colour becomes similar to that of copper. Pure copper, which has a melting point of 1,083° C., is often used for brazing steel parts, such as high-speed tool steel tips, Stellite, etc. The use of a hydrogen atmosphere in brazing obviates the use of a brazing flux. Brazing fluxes are of the borax class, e.g. calcined borax.

HARDENING AND TEMPERING STEEL

Steels with more than 0·2 per cent. carbon are hardenable by rapid cooling, e.g. by quenching in water.

When a hardenable steel is heated to a temperature just above the upper critical point, viz. about 850° C. (bright cherry-red), and quenched in water, it attains its hardest and strongest condition throughout its mass. The steel is also in its most brittle condition.

The toughness of such a hardened steel is increased by reheating it to a lower temperature than the hardening one, followed by a further quenching. The ductility increases with the *tempering* temperature, but the hardness and tensile strength are at the same time reduced, progressively.

The *normal tempering temperature* for carbon tool steel, for edge-cutting tools for metals, e.g. lathe tools, corresponds to about 450° C.

For cutting-tool purposes only the portion of the tool near the cutting-edge end is usually hardened, the shank being left relatively soft, but tough.

Hardening and Tempering Alloy Steels

The strength and hardness properties of various high-tensile alloy steels, e.g. those containing small percentages of nickel, chromium, molybdenum, vanadium, etc., are superior to those of plain carbon steels, and by varying the tempering temperature of any given alloy steel a wide range of strength and hardness properties

can be obtained. The chart in Fig. 3 illustrates the tempering
curves for a nickel-chromium-molybdenum steel known as " 65-ton "
steel over a range of tempering temperatures from 700° C. down to

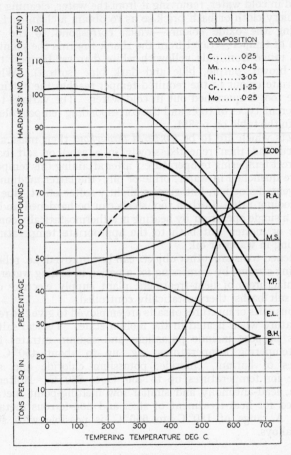

Fig. 3.—Effect of Tempering Temperature on Properties of Nickel-
Chromium-Molybdenum Steel.

0° C. (corresponding to the fully quenched untempered condition).
The tests were made on a 1⅛-in. diameter bar of the steel which
was hardened in oil from 830° C.

Edge Hardening

The process of *edge hardening and tempering* consists in heating the cutting end of the tool to a bright cherry-red, quickly quenching this end in cold water, removing it from the water, cleaning the end with emery cloth or bath brick so as to obtain a clean surface and observing the oxide colours—which correspond to the various degrees of temper—travel from the shank towards the point. The colours range from pale yellowish white (hardest temper) through straw, brown, purple, blue and dark blue (softest). When the appropriate colour to the required temper reaches the cutting-edge end the tool is quenched out in cold water. The various tempers for different types of tools and the corresponding temper colours are shown in the table on p. 381.

Objects which are to be *tempered throughout* their mass are first hardened and then reheated slowly in a sand or salt bath, to the correct tempering temperature ; after attaining this temperature they are quenched in water, brine or oil ; the latter medium tends to prevent distortion, but gives a slightly softer effect, due to the lower cooling rate. Carbon tool steels can be hardened and tempered in a single operation by heating in a thermostatically controlled furnace or molten salt bath to the appropriate temperature and quenching in water or oil.

Hardened tools and other objects can be improved, i.e. relieved of hardening strains, by immersing for a period in boiling water.

Manufacturers of heat-treatment plant supply electric- or gas-heated salt baths, thermostatically controlled.

Various salts or mixtures of salts are employed to give the required temperature when heated in the molten state. Typical salts used for this purpose include potassium and sodium nitrates for the lower tempering temperatures, e.g. up to about 450° C. ; and mixtures of barium, chloride, potassium chloride and sodium chloride for temperatures up to 750° C. to 850° C. Molten lead, lead-tin, lead-antimony and similar low melting-point metals are also used for heat-treatment of steel and non-ferrous metals and alloys. A range of 180° C. to 650° C. is possible with suitable fusible alloys.

Surface Hardening

The surface layer of steel of any carbon content, down to practically pure iron, can be given a hardness similar to that of quenched carbon tool steel (untempered), whilst leaving the core or interior mass relatively soft, by several alternative methods, as follows :

(1) CASE HARDENING.—The steels used for this method are low-carbon ones, including mild steel, low-carbon nickel, and low-carbon nickel-chrome steel. The process consists in packing the steel articles in a heat-resisting steel or nickel-chrome alloy sheet-metal container, together with the carburising material, e.g. wood charcoal, bone black, charred bone and similar carbonaceous materials. The box is then sealed with fireclay, to exclude air, and placed in a furnace, where it is heated to 850° to 950° C. for a few hours, after which the parts are removed and quenched.

This process increases the carbon content of the surface layer to about 0·9 to 1·1 per cent.

For small steel objects, a workshop method of case-hardening is to heat the parts to a bright cherry-red temperature, and then to sprinkle powdered potassium ferrocyanide on to the surface. The objects are then reheated in the furnace, removed and a further quantity of the salt sprinkled over it. Reheating follows this operation, after which the object is quenched in cold water. In the *cyanide process*, molten sodium cyanide is employed. The objects are heated for several hours in the molten salt to 900° to 950° C., and then quenched in water. The thickness of the case increases with the period of heating in the salt ; a minimum period of two hours is necessary.

Cyanide-hardened parts are extremely hard, uniformly case-hardened, and have a clean surface when quenched. The process is relatively quick and inexpensive. It is considered superior, commercially, to the pack-hardening method previously described.

Steel parts can also be surface-hardened by heating them to the appropriate temperature (above 850° C.), in an atmosphere of a carbon-containing gas, e.g. acetylene, coal-gas, hydrocarbon vapour.

(2) THE NITROGEN HARDENING PROCESS.—Known also as the nitriding method, this consists in heating the alloy-steel parts in contact with a stream of ammonia gas at a steady temperature of 500° C., for a period of 40 to 100 hours. The nitrogen of the ammonia enters into the composition of the steel to form an extremely hard surface layer. Special alloy steels are used for the nitriding method and are known as nitralloys. Special alloy cast irons, e.g. Nitricastiron, can also be surface-hardened by the same method ; these irons are much used for internal-combustion engine cylinder liners.

The advantages of the nitriding process are : (1) It gives a harder surface (up to 1,100 diamond-pyramid hardness) than case hardening. (2) Owing to the lower temperature (500° C. as compared with

850°–900° C. for case hardening) less distortion occurs ; moreover the core can be much harder on this account. (3) It shows a marked resistance to corrosion. (4) It has a high corrosion-fatigue resistance. (5) The treated steel parts have a clean finish and require no further treatment—as is necessary with the surface-carburation method.

The steels used for nitriding contain one or more of the following elements, viz. : aluminium, chromium, molybdenum, tungsten, titanium and vanadium. They are available, commercially, in a wide range of tensile strengths and maximum hardness values.

(3) FLAME HARDENING METHOD.—Essentially a local hardening process, this consists in the impingement of an oxy-acetylene or oxy-hydrogen flame on to the area to be surface hardened, followed by rapid cooling on removal of the flame. Normal air cooling is effective, but a cold-water spray gives better hardening results. The surface metal is heated above the critical temperature, followed by rapid cooling, thus converting the structure of the steel from the soft pearlitic to the very hard martensitic condition. Flame hardening is used for gear teeth, crankshaft journals, cam faces, etc., and special machines are available * for production hardening of similar parts, in quantity. Steels of initial hardness 200–250 Brinell are raised, superficially, to 600–650 Brinell by the flame-hardening process.

(4) INDUCTION HARDENING METHOD.—This is based upon the electric-induction heating of the surface layers of the steel parts to a

COLOURS AND TEMPERATURES OF HEATED STEEL

Colour	Temperature (approx.)	
	° C.	° F.
Faint red	516	960
Dull red	699	1,290
Brilliant red	743	1,470
Cherry red	900	1,650
Bright cherry red	1,000	1,830
Orange	1,100	2,010
Bright orange	1,200	2,190
Bright yellow white	1,300	2,370
Bright white	1,400	2,550
Intense white	1,540	2,800

temperature above the upper critical one, followed by rapid cooling —usually by water-spraying the heated surfaces. High-frequency electric current is employed in the plant used, e.g. the Tocco, and the induced current in the surface of the steel surrounded by the H.F. coil rapidly heats the surface. Immediately the current is switched off a water-spray is turned on to the heated surface.

This method is used for purposes such as crankshaft journal hardening, for camshafts, plain shafts, cylinder liners, etc.

The current frequency used is from 2,000 to 10,000 cycles per second. A similar degree and nature of surface hardness to that of the flame-hardening method is obtained.

STEEL TEMPERING OXIDE COLOURS AND TEMPERATURES *

Colour	Temperature		Suitable for Tempering
	° C.	° F.	
Dark blue . .	300	572	Springs, wood saws.
Full blue . .	295	563	Circular saws for metal, screw-drivers.
Very dark purple	290	554	Cold chisels for iron, needles.
Dark purple .	285	545	Moulding and planing cutters for soft wood, cold chisels for cast iron, firmer chisels.
Full purple .	280	536	Bone and ivory saws, cold chisels and setts, steel gimlets.
Light purple .	275	527	Axes, hot setts and adzes, dental and surgical instruments, pressing cutters.
Brown purple .	270	518	Augers, flat brass drills, twist drills, coopers' tools.
Reddish brown .	265	509	Wood-boring tools, stone-cutting tools.
Yellowish brown	260	500	Plane irons, gouges, planing and moulding cutters, punches and dies, cups, snaps, and shear blades.
Yellow brown .	255	491	Planing and moulding cutters for hard wood, penknives, chasers.
Very dark yellow	250	482	Taps, mill chisels and picks, screw-cutting dies, rock drills.
Dark yellow .	245	473	Boring cutters, leather-cutting dies, reamers.
Dark straw .	240	464	Milling cutters, bone-cutting tools, drills, wood-engraving tools.
Straw . .	235	455	Iron planers, paper cutters, ivory-cutting tools, steel planers, cold chisels, lathe tools, milling cutters.
Pale straw . .	230	446	Hammer faces, brass screwing dies.
Light straw .	225	437	Light turning tools, steel-engraving tools.
Very light straw .	220	428	Scrapers, lathe tools for brass.

* *Engineering Materials*, Vol. 1, A. W. Judge (Pitmans Ltd.).

ANNEALING AND NORMALISING OF METALS

Definitions

Annealing means reheating, followed by slow cooling, and its purposes may be to remove internal stresses or to induce softness, in which case the maximum annealing temperature may be chosen arbitrarily.

For steels the annealing temperatures should not be more than 50° C. above the Ac 3 critical point on the iron carbide diagram, e.g. 750° C. for 0·9 per cent. carbon steel.

Normalising means heating a steel to a temperature above its upper critical range, and allowing it to cool slowly in air. It is desirable that the temperature shall be maintained for about 15 minutes, and shall not exceed the critical range by more than 50° C.

Annealing takes longer than normalising, and is employed to refine the crystalline structure, and to remove internal stresses due to cold working, etc., e.g. rolling, hammering, pressing, forging and casting. Annealing leaves the metal in its softest condition. It gives a somewhat coarser structure than normalising.

Spheroidising, or sub-critical annealing, is the method of heating the steel for a prolonged period at a temperature below the lower critical point—usually between 670° and 680° C. for steel. The iron carbide becomes transformed into spheroids or balls of minute size, embedded in a matrix of nearly pure soft iron. Steel thus treated is able to withstand considerable deformation by cold working.

Annealing Steel Articles

Steel objects, e.g. castings or forgings, are annealed in a metal container, lined with firebrick, sealed against air ingress with asbestos or clay. The box and its contents are heated for 3 to 8 hours (the longer period for larger objects), to the annealing temperature (750° to 800° C.). The furnace heat is then shut off and the furnace allowed to cool down slowly. Small objects can be heated to the annealing temperature and then buried in sand, lime or fine ashes in order to cool slowly.

Annealing Cast Iron

The annealing process is similar to that for steel, very slow cooling being essential. To remove casting stresses and improve the structure good-quality cast irons should be heated to 450°–550° for

ANNEALING TEMPERATURES FOR TOOL STEELS

Type of Steel	Temperature of Annealing		Period	Remarks
	°C.	°F.	Hours	
No. 1 temper, 1½ per cent. carbon	720	1,328	1–4	These temperatures should not be exceeded, and tools should be box annealed.
No. 2 temper, 1¼ per cent. carbon	720	1,328	1–4	
No. 3 temper, 1⅛ per cent. carbon	720	1,328	1–4	
No. 4 temper, 1 per cent. carbon	720	1,328	1–4	
No. 5 temper, ⅞ per cent. carbon	750	1,382	1–4	
No. 6 temper, ¾ per cent. carbon	770	1,418	1–4	
High-speed Tool Steel				
Tungsten 8–18 per cent. Chromium 4–5½ per cent.	870	1,600–1,700	2–3	Heat slowly so that tools take from 1–2 hours to attain annealing temperature, then keep at same for 2–3 hours, and allow to cool in furnace, or bury in sawdust, lime, dry sand, etc.
Carbon 1·8–0·7 per cent. Vanadium 0–0·29 per cent.	928	1,600–1,700	2–3	

a period of 1 hour for each inch thickness of section. Different compositions of iron require different annealing temperatures. Full annealing pearlitic cast iron requires heating to 800°–900° C. for a short period ; this gives maximum machining qualities without marked loss of strength and hardness.

Local Annealing of Steel

The area to be annealed is heated with an electric arc or oxy-acetylene flame, and allowed to cool as slowly as possible, using a covering of a non-conductor of heat, e.g. sand, fine ashes, lime or asbestos.

Annealing Stainless Steels

Stampings and forgings are annealed before machining by heating in a furnace to 750°–800° C., followed by slow cooling. Stay-brite stainless steel is annealed to the same degree as mild steel by heating to 1,100°–1,200° C. and cooling in still air.

Annealing Manganese Steel

Although in its normal condition this steel is so hard that it cannot be machined with cutting tools, it is in its most ductile state when annealed at 1,000°–1,050° C. and quenched in water ; if allowed to cool in air it becomes comparatively brittle and very hard.

Annealing Copper

The important feature in annealing copper is the correct annealing temperature, this being from 200°–600° C., according to the impurities present and the amount of cold work that has been done on the metal. For most commercial coppers an annealing temperature of 500° C. is satisfactory. The mode of cooling, with copper, is immaterial ; either water quenching or air cooling is applicable, but quenching serves to remove dirt and scale.

Annealing Brass

Ordinary copper-zinc brasses are annealed by heating for about 15–30 minutes, at 600° C., and allowing to cool either in air or by water quenching.

Special brasses and bronzes of high-tensile strength require different annealing temperatures, e.g. for most bronzes, from 650°–800° C.

Annealing Nickel

The annealing temperature for nickel is between 750° and 850° C. The open annealing method is preferable to box annealing. Air cooling after heating to the annealing temperature gives satisfactory results.

Annealing Monel Metal

Monel metal consists of about 67 per cent. nickel, 28 per cent. copper, and 5 per cent. of other metals. It is as strong as medium carbon steel (30–45 tons per sq. in.), tough but ductile, and is strongly resistant to corrosion by impure atmospheres or waters.

Monel metal is annealed in a neutral atmosphere, to avoid oxidation. For this purpose the parts should be placed in an iron box, sealed with fireclay, and heated in a muffle to 840°–850° C. for a few minutes. The parts are then cooled rapidly in air or water.

Annealing Aluminium and Light Alloys

Aluminium which has become work-hardened by mechanical forming, rolling or pressing operations is annealed by heating to 350° C. and allowing to cool in water or air. Care is necessary to ensure that the metal is not overheated during annealing ; sometimes temperatures of 250°–300° C. are used. Aluminium alloys are annealed at specified temperatures for each alloy ; these generally range from 300°–380° C.

Duralumin—one of the age-hardening strong light aluminium alloys—is annealed by heating to 360°–380° C. and quenching in water. The metal should not be subjected to the annealing temperature for more than 2 or 3 minutes. It should be fabricated as soon as possible after annealing, since age-hardening occurs and eventually leaves the metal in too hard and brittle a condition for cold-working.

A rough indication of the annealing temperature for duralumin is that if a piece of white paper or a matchstick is held on to the surface it will commence to char, or turn brown.

Magnesium Alloys

The strong light alloys of magnesium, e.g. Elektron and Dowmetal, are not normally in a sufficiently ductile condition for cold working, e.g. bending, and any mechanical working must be carried out at temperatures between 220° and 300° C.

PUNCHES AND DIES

Punch and Die Clearances

In general, the amount of clearance between the punch and its die, when blanking sheet metal, depends upon the thickness and the kind of metal. The clearance increases almost in linear proportion to the thickness of metal. The clearance is greater for harder than for softer metals.

When blanking sheet brass (rolled), satisfactory results are obtained when the clearance between the punch and die is 5 per cent. of the thickness, e.g. for 16 S.W.G. sheet brass (0·064 in.) the clearance is 0·0032 in.

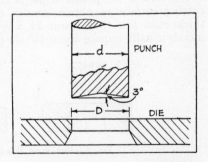

FIG. 4.—PUNCH AND DIE CLEARANCES.

For soft metals the clearance D — d (Fig. 4) is approximately 12½ per cent. of the thickness. For hard metals the clearance is approximately 10 per cent. of the thickness.

PUNCH AND DIE CLEARANCES

Thickness		Clearance Between Punch and Die *	
		Soft Metal	Hard Metal
S.W.G.	In.	In.	In.
4/0	0·400	0·040	0·049
2/0	·348	·035	·043
0	·324	·032	·039
2	·276	·028	·034
4	·232	·023	·028
6	·192	·019	·023
8	·160	·016	·020
10	·128	·013	·016
12	·104	·010	·0125
14	·080	·008	·0095
16	·064	·006	·0074
18	·048	·005	·0061
20	·036	·004	·0049
22	·028	·003	·0037
24	·022	·0025	·0031
26	·018	·0018	·0022
30	·0124	·0012	·0015

* Difference between diameters of die and punch.

SHEAR ON PUNCHES AND DIES

The face of the punch or die is given an angle or shear on the cutting surface to obtain greater cutting efficiency. Metals of thicknesses less than about 24 S.W.G. require no shear. Thick metals usually require about 10° shear.

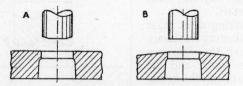

FIG. 5.—SHEAR ON PUNCHES AND DIES.

When the stock is to be left flat the shear is given to the punch, the die being left flat (Diagram A, Fig. 5).

When the punched part of the metal is to be left flat the shear is given to the die, the punch being left flat (Diagram B, Fig. 5).

BLANKING PRESSURES

The blanking pressure for cutting out discs of various shapes in different metals is calculated as follows :

P = pressure for blanking (tons). S = length of periphery of blank (in.). t = thickness of metal (in.). f_s = shear strength of metal (tons sq. in.).

$$P = Stf_s \text{ tons.}$$

In general the shear stress may be taken as 0·80 to 0·84 of the tensile strength for ductile metals. For hard and brittle materials the ratio is 0·85 to 0·90. It is assumed that the punch and die

SHEAR STRENGTHS OF MATERIALS

Material	Shear Stress (tons per sq. in.)
Mild-steel plate	20–22
Hard-steel plate	27–37
Spring steel	40–45
Rolled brass plate	12–15
Hard rolled aluminium plate . .	8–12
Gunmetal	14–16
Tinplate	20–25
Copper	10–12
Fibre sheet	7

edges are keen and that the proper clearance has been given. When proper shear is given to the punch or die the blanking pressure is reduced by about 10–15 per cent.

Example.—Required, the blanking pressure to produce a disc of 1-in. diameter in mild steel of ⅛-in. thickness. Shear stress $f_s = 20$ tons per sq. in.

$$
\begin{aligned}
P &= Stf_s \\
&= (\pi \times 1) \times \tfrac{1}{8} \times 20 \\
&= \frac{3 \cdot 1416 \times 1 \times 20}{8} \\
&= 7 \cdot 854 \text{ tons.}
\end{aligned}
$$

DETERMINATION OF SIZE OF BLANK

In sheet-metal drawing or cupping operations it is necessary to know the size and shape of the blank which, when pressed, will give the required size and shape of the drawn shell. Four alternative methods of finding the blank diameter for drawn cylindrical and other circular shapes are :

(1) Surface-area Method

The total external area of the drawn circular shell is calculated from a scale drawing by means of the usual mensuration formulæ. The blank diameter D is obtained from the formula :

$$D = \sqrt{\frac{4 \times \text{external area}}{\pi}}$$
$$= \sqrt{1 \cdot 272 \times \text{external area}}$$

For a drawn shell of diameter d and depth h,

$$\text{Diameter of blank D} = \sqrt{d^2 + 4dh}$$

Note.—This formula is applicable to thin pressings, no radiused corners, and no alteration in thickness of the drawn metal. If the metal thins in drawing, the blank size will be slightly larger than actually required.

(2) Equal-volume Method

The principle of this method is that the volume of the blank must be equal to that of the drawn shell. This takes account of the variation of thickness during drawing.

If T = thickness of blank ; A = area of blank ; t = mean thickness of drawn shell ; a = total area of drawn shell :

$$\text{Volume of blank} = \text{AT}$$
$$= at$$
$$\text{A} = \frac{at}{\text{T}}$$

It is necessary for complex shapes of drawn shell to split up the shell drawing into a number of individual sections and calculate the section volumes in order to arrive at the total shell volume.

(3) Equal-weight Method

From a knowledge of the weight of the drawn shell, the density of the stock metal and the thickness of the stock or blank the size of blank can be estimated.

If W = weight of drawn shell (lb.) ; T = stock thickness (in.) ; w = weight per cu. in. of the stock metal ; A = area of blank :

$$\text{AT}w = \text{W}$$

For a cylindrical shell of weight W lb., the diameter D of the blank is given by

$$D = 1 \cdot 13 \sqrt{\frac{W}{Tw}} \text{ in.}$$

(4) Mean-height Method

This method takes account of the different thicknesses of the stock and drawn shell walls.

If H = height of a shell of thickness equal to T, the thickness of the original stock; h = height of thinner shell of thickness t:

$$\text{Then } HT = ht$$

Then, for cylindrical shells the blank diameter is:

$$D = \sqrt{d^2 + 4dH}$$

where d = drawn shell diameter.   No thinning of metal is assumed.

The methods given are approximate only and usually satisfactory for trial purposes.   In practice the blank dimensions do not always agree with the theoretical ones due to: (1) Stretching or thinning of the metal at different parts of the drawn shell.   (2) Non-allowance for radii of corners.   (3) Tool design and condition.   (4) Condition of stock metal.   (5) The various shapes of shells required.   (6) Lubrication of the tools.

THINNING OF METAL IN DRAWING OPERATIONS

Variations in thickness of drawn shells from original stock thickness depend upon: (1) Depth of draw.   (2) Thickness of stock in relation to dimensions of drawn shell.   (3) Properties of metal used, i.e. degree of ductility.   (4) Design and degree of smoothness of the tools.   (5) Method of lubrication of work and tools.   (6) Pressure applied to prevent puckering.

The following table refers to measurements * made on a series of small cups as produced in a drawing press.

METAL THINNING IN DRAWING SHELLS

Initial Metal Thickness	Blank Diameter	Cup Diameter	Thickness of Base and Base of Skirt	Percentage Reduction
In.	In.	In.	In.	
·008	$1\frac{1}{2}$	$\frac{13}{16}$	·007	12·5
·015	$1\frac{9}{16}$	$\frac{7}{8}$	·014	7
·020	$1\frac{1}{16}$	$\frac{15}{16}$	·017	15
·024	$3\frac{1}{2}$	2	·020	17
·028	$2\frac{1}{8}$	$1\frac{1}{8}$	·023	18
·034	$2\frac{7}{8}$	$1\frac{11}{16}$	·031	9
·044	$1\frac{7}{8}$	$1\frac{1}{8}$	·040	9

* *Press Tool Practice*, P. S. Houghton (Chapman and Hall, Ltd.)

E.W.D.—14

Number of Operations in Drawing Circular Shells

The reductions in diameter of the successive drawing operations from a sheet-metal blank of ductile metal can be determined as follows :

D = diameter of blank ; d_1 = first operation diameter ; c = a constant.

$$d_1 = cD.$$

The value of c varies from about 0·55–0·63. For thin stock the former value is recommended, and for thick stock the latter. For soft metals, e.g. aluminium and annealed copper, a value of 0·50 may be used.

For thin stock each successive operation reduction in diameter is usually from 20 to 30 per cent. For soft metals, with occasional annealing as the metal hardens, a reduction of 30–40 per cent. is possible. For thick stock, in relation to the final drawn-cup dimensions, from 10 to 15 per cent. reduction per successive operation is usual.

In the case of an aluminium blank of diameter $4\frac{7}{8}$ in. and thickness 0·015 in., which was drawn into a cylindrical shell of $1\frac{7}{8}$-in. diameter with walls of (about) 0·010 in. thick, the following results were obtained : *

DRAWING OPERATIONS FOR ALUMINIUM CYLINDRICAL SHELL

Operation	Diameter	Per cent. of Previous Operation	Reduction of Diameter	Wall Thickness
	In.		In.	In.
Blank . .	$4\frac{7}{8}$	—	—	—
Cup . . .	$2\frac{3}{4}$	56·5	—	0·015
1st draw . .	$2\frac{1}{2}$	91·0	$\frac{1}{4}$	·014
2nd draw .	$2\frac{1}{4}$	90·0	$\frac{1}{4}$	·012
3rd draw . .	$2\frac{1}{16}$	91·7	$\frac{3}{16}$	·011
4th draw . .	$1\frac{7}{8}$	91·0	$\frac{3}{16}$	·010

DRAWING PRESSURES

For approximate purposes the drawing pressure required to produce a cylindrical flat-bottomed shell may be taken as that necessary to blank or shear through the bottom of the shell. For a

* See footnote on p. 417.

circular-base shell, if d = diameter of base (in.), t = thickness of base (in.), f_s = shearing stress (tons per sq. in.) :

$$\text{Maximum drawing pressure} = 3 \cdot 1416 dt f_s \text{ tons}$$

For shallow draws, i.e. depth less than 0·3 times shell diameter, the drawing pressure is usually much less, viz. from 25 to 35 per cent. of above value.

SHEET-METAL BENDING ALLOWANCES

(1) Sharp 90° Bends (Figs. 6 and 7)

A = outside dimension of bend (in.).   B = other outside dimension of bend (in.).   T = thickness of sheet metal (in.).

(*a*) *For Ductile Metals*, e.g. mild steel, copper, brass, aluminium, etc. :
Length of blank, before bending = A + B − 1·6T in.

(*b*) *Semi-ductile Metals*, e.g. hard steel, drawn brass, bronze, etc. :
Length of blank before bending = A + B − 1·3T in.

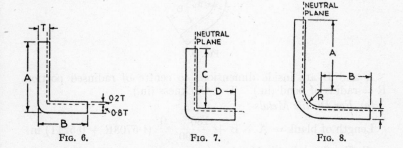

Fig. 6.   Fig. 7.   Fig. 8.

If C = inside dimension of bend (in.) ; D = other inside dimension of bend (in.) (Fig. 7) ; T = thickness of sheet metal (in.) :

(*a*) *For Ductile Metals :*
Length of Blank = C + D + 0·4T in.

(*b*) *For Semi-ductile Metals :*
Length of blank = C + D + 0·6T in.

(2) Curved Bends, 90° (Fig. 8)

A = inside dimensions of bend (in.).   B = other inside dimension of bend (in.).   R = inside radius of bend (in.).   T = thickness (in.).

(a) *For Ductile Metals :*

Length of blank $= A + B + \dfrac{\pi}{2}\left(R + \dfrac{T}{3}\right)$ in.

$$= A + B + 1{\cdot}5708R + 0{\cdot}524T \text{ in.}$$

(b) *For Semi-ductile Metals :*

Length of blank $= A + B + \dfrac{\pi}{2}\left(R + \dfrac{T}{4{\cdot}5}\right)$ in.

$$= A + B + 1{\cdot}5708R + 0{\cdot}35T \text{ in.}$$

(3) Curved Bends Through ($180° - \theta°$)

Note.—The actual angle of bend (Fig. 9) is $180° - \theta°$, and the included angle of bend is $\theta°$.

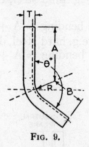

Fig. 9.

A and B are inside dimensions to centre of radiused portion. $R =$ radius of bend (in.). $T =$ thickness (in.).

(a) *For Ductile Metals :*

Length of blank $= A + B + \dfrac{180° - \theta°}{90°}\ (1{\cdot}5708R + 0{\cdot}524T)$ in.

(b) *For Semi-ductile Metals :*

Length of blank $= A + B + \dfrac{180° - \theta°}{90°}\ (1{\cdot}5708R + 0{\cdot}35T)$ in.

(4) Sharp Bends Through ($180 - \theta°$)

C and D $=$ inside dimensions to apex of angle (in.). Actual angle of bend $= 180° - \theta°$. Included angle $= \theta°$. $T =$ thickness (in.).

(a) *For Ductile Metals :*

Length of blank $= C + D + \dfrac{180° - \theta°}{90°}\ (0{\cdot}4T)$ in.

(b) For Semi-ductile Metals :

$$\text{Length of blank} = C + D + \frac{180° - θ°}{90°} (0.6T) \text{ in.}$$

(5) Metal Bent Through 180° (Fig. 10)

In this case the metal is bent back flat on itself.

M = outside dimension of one side (in.). N = outside dimension of other side (in.). T = thickness (in.).

Length of blank = M + N (in.).

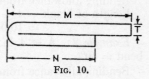

Fig. 10.

Note.—This formula applies to ductile metals bent back as shown, without cracking.

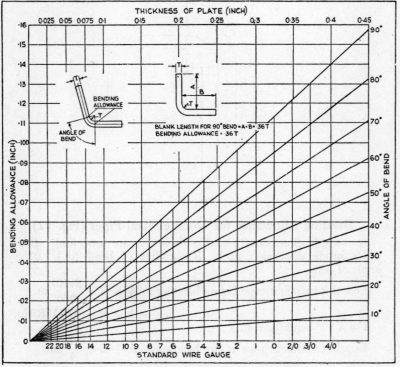

Fig. 11.—Sheet-metal Bending Allowances.

Sheet-metal Bending Allowance Chart

The chart shown in Fig. 11 gives the amounts to be added to the inside dimensions A and B (in.) to obtain the *length of blank* for 90°, and angular bends (sharp).

Example 1: A = 4 in. B = 6 in. T = 10 S.W.G. 90° bend.

Bending allowance from chart = 0·045 in.

Length of blank = 4 + 6 + 0·045 in.

$\qquad\qquad\qquad$ = 10·045 in.

Example 2: A = 4 in. B = 6 in. T = 5 S.W.G. Angle of bend = 50°.

Bending allowance from chart = 0·035 in.

Length of blank = 4 + 6 + 0·035 in.

$\qquad\qquad\qquad$ = 10·035 in.

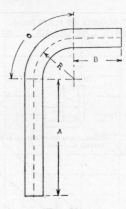

FIG. 12.

Bending Allowance for Ductile Metal Pipes (Fig. 12)

A = inside dimension to centre of circular arc bend (in.). B = other inside dimension (in.). R = radius of bend (in.). θ° = angle of bend.

Length of straight pipe before bending = $A + B + \dfrac{2\pi R\theta}{360}$ in.

$\qquad\qquad\qquad\qquad\qquad\qquad$ = A + B + 0·0175Rθ in.

For a 45° bend (θ = 45°).

Length of straight pipe before bending = $A + B + \dfrac{\pi R}{4}$ in.

$\qquad\qquad\qquad\qquad\qquad\qquad$ = A + B + 0·7854R in.

423

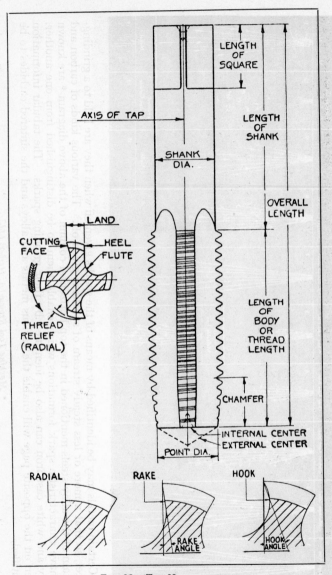

FIG. 13.—TAP NOMENCLATURE.

424

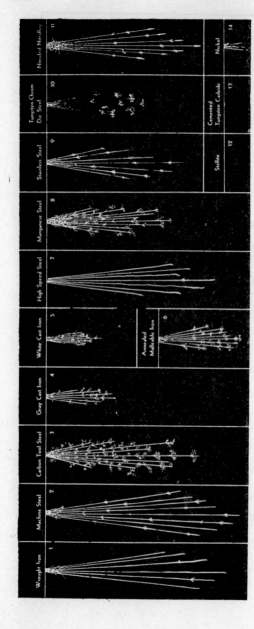

Certain metals may be identified by means of the sparks given off when they are held to a grinding-wheel, so that a more or less steady stream of sparks is given off. The various kinds of carbon and certain of the alloy steels mentioned in the top horizontal column of the above diagram * are known to have characteristic spark formations which enable them to be distinguished from one another. Grey and white cast iron can also be identified by their grinding sparks. The tabular information given on the opposite page will enable the various metals and alloys and the sintered carbides to be identified.

* *Machine Tool Review* [*A. Herbert Ltd.*].

CHARACTERISTICS OF SPARKS GENERATED BY THE GRINDING OF METALS

Metal	Volume of Stream	Relative Length of Stream, Inches*	Colour of Stream close to Wheel	Colour of Sparks near end of Stream	Quantity of Spurts	Nature of Spurts
1. Wrought iron . .	Large	65	Straw	White	Very few	Forked
2. Machine steel . .	Large	70	White	White	Few	Forked
3. Carbon tool steel .	Moderately large	55	White	White	Very many	Fine, repeating
4. Grey cast iron .	Small	25	Red	Straw	Many	Fine, repeating
5. White cast iron .	Very small	20	Red	Straw	Few	Fine, repeating
6. Annealed malleable iron	Moderate	30	Red	Straw	Many	Fine, repeating
7. High-speed steel .	Small	60	Red	Straw	Extremely few	Forked
8. Manganese steel .	Moderately large	45	White	White	Many	Fine, repeating
9. Stainless steel .	Moderate	50	Straw	White	Moderate	Forked
10. Tungsten-chromium die steel. .	Small	35	Red	Straw †	Many	Fine, repeating †
11. Nitrided Nitralloy. .	Large (curved)	55	White	White	Moderate	Forked
12. Stellite . .	Very small	10	Orange	Orange	None	—
13. Cemented tungsten carbide . .	Extremely small	2	Light Orange	Light Orange	None	—
14. Nickel . .	Very small ‡	10	Orange	Orange	None	—
15. Copper, brass, aluminium	None	—	—	—	None	—

* Figures obtained with 12-in. wheel on bench stand and are relative only.   Actual length in each instance will vary with grinding-wheel, pressure, etc.   † Blue-white spurts.   ‡ Some wavy streaks.

[*Machine Tool Review.*]

E.W.D.—14*

SPEEDS OF BELTS AND PULLEYS

If D = diameter of larger pulley (Fig. 14), d = diameter of smaller pulley, N = revolutions per minute (R.P.M.) of larger pulley and n = R.P.M. of smaller pulley

$$\text{Then } \frac{N}{n} = \frac{d}{D}.$$

Velocity of belt = $\pi DN = \pi dn$.

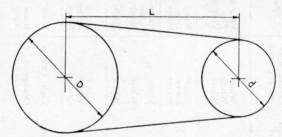

FIG. 14.

TRAIN OF BELT PULLEYS (Fig. 15)

If N_1, N_2, N_3, N_4, etc. be the R.P.M. of pulley, 1, 2, 3, 4, etc.

$$\text{Then } N_2 = \frac{D_1}{d_1} . N_1$$

$$N_3 = \frac{D_2}{d_2} . N_2 = \frac{D_1}{d_1} . \frac{D_2}{d_2} . N_1$$

$$N_4 = \frac{D_3}{d_3} . N_3 = \frac{D_1}{d_1} . \frac{D_2}{d_2} . \frac{D_3}{d_3} . N_1$$

$$N_n = \frac{D_1 \, D_2 \, D_3 \, \ldots \, Dn}{d_1 \, d_2 \, d_3 \, \ldots \, dn} \times N_1$$

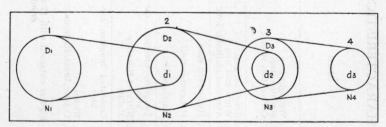

FIG. 15.

LENGTH OF BELTS

1. Open Belt (Fig. 14)

Let D and d = diameters of pulleys in inches, L = distance between centres in inches.

$$\text{Length of belt} = \frac{\pi}{2}(D + d) + \frac{(D - d)^2}{4L} + 2L \text{ (in.)}$$

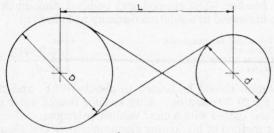

FIG. 16.

2. Cross Belt (Fig. 16)

$$\text{Length of belt} = \frac{\pi}{2}(D + d) + \frac{(D + d)^2}{4L} + 2L \text{ (in.)}$$

WORKSHOP METHODS AND RECIPES

ADHESIVES (SEE CEMENTS)

ALUMINIUM

(a) *To Blacken.*—The cleaned and polished aluminium articles should be immersed in a solution made up as follows :

Potassium permanganate	.	1½ oz.
Nitric acid	.	¼ oz. (weight)
Copper nitrate	.	4 oz.
Water	.	1 gallon

The solution should be heated to about 170° F. and the parts kept in it for 20–30 minutes. After washing in cold water the parts are dried and coated with a clear varnish or lacquer.

Another method of blackening aluminium after first cleaning and polishing it is to employ a solution made up as follows :

Dissolve 8 oz. of caustic soda in half a gallon of boiling water ; add 2 oz. of common salt and allow the solution to drop to about 200° F. The articles should then be immersed in this and withdrawn in about 20 seconds, when they should be quite black. Immediately rinse in clean cold water and dry out in a mixture of warm sawdust and powdered graphite, only as much of the latter as is required to blacken the sawdust. A transparent cold lacquer should then be applied. Ordinary arsenic black bronzing solution, consisting of hydrochloric acid 43 per cent., sulphate of iron 3 per cent., and white arsenic 4 per cent., to which is added the other 50 per cent. of water, is sometimes used. The colour appears quickly, but if not black enough a second immersion is preferable to a prolonged stay, on account of the hydrochloric acid. Another form of black finish can be obtained by dipping the aluminium articles after cleansing and frosting in hot linseed oil, allowing the excess oil to drain off, and finally heating to about 400° C. As aluminium after light frosting will hold a lacquer exceedingly well, an excellent black finish and one strongly adherent is readily obtained by using a matt black paint, such as Bates' dead-black paint.

(b) *To Anodise.*—Anodising consists in giving, by chemical methods, a protective surface layer of aluminium oxide or hydroxide, by making the aluminium (or its alloy) the anode in a bath of dilute chromic acid, using a carbon- or stainless-steel cathode. A

3 per cent. chromic acid solution, at 40° C., is used, with a current density of 3–3½ amperes (Bengough process). In the M.B.V. process the aluminium articles are immersed in a boiling solution, consisting of 5 per cent. sodium carbonate with 1·5 per cent. sodium chromate, for 3 minutes, followed by washing in water and drying.

Anodised surfaces may be dyed with aniline dyes of various colours and then lacquered with transparent cellulose or synthetic resin lacquers.

(c) *To Frost.*—Immerse in a hot solution of caustic soda for a few seconds, remove and wash thoroughly in hot water. Use 2 lb. of soda per gallon of water. Sand blasting of the previously cleaned surfaces also gives a frosted or matt surface. Scratch-brushing is another alternative.

Polishing.—First clean and degrease. For rough castings use canvas polishing wheels with emery or aluminium-oxide abrasives (60–100 grit), and a speed of 6,000 ft. per min. Then follow with another buffing wheel, using 180-grit abrasive with tallow or bees-wax. Final polishing can be done with a mop charged with tripoli in a grease binder. For sheet metal the latter operation only need be used. For a high degree of polish use a very soft wheel run dry with Vienna lime rouge, or similar abrasive, at 10,000 ft. per min.

Soldering.—Special solders requiring no fluxes are now available, e.g. Alunize, Fryal and Fry's L.M. The surface is heated until the solder melts on it. A scraper or scratch-wire brush is then applied to break up the aluminium oxide and allow the solder to unite with the aluminium (or its alloy). The surplus solder and disturbed oxide are wiped off with a rag, leaving a perfectly " tinned " surface. The joint can then be completed with more aluminium solder.

BELT DRESSINGS

For dressing leather belts, to preserve their flexibility and pulley-gripping qualities, they should be treated with collan oil ; although not so effective, castor or olive oil may be used. Allow the oil to soak well into the leather, after scraping off any hard surface deposits. About 12 hours is usually required. Do not use a mineral oil for dressing a leather belt.

A dressing to prevent belt slip consists of : tallow, 1 oz. ; lard oil, 2 oz. ; Venice turpentine, 16 oz. A mixture consisting of 2 oz. of beeswax in 1 pint of neatsfoot oil is also effective as a belt dress-ing. The beeswax should be melted first and the oil added gradually afterwards, stirring well until thoroughly mixed.

BELTS, TO PREVENT SLIPPING

To prevent leather belts from slipping on their pulleys, sprinkle powdered resin or Fuller's earth on the inside surfaces on advancing side of belt near the pulley.

BRASS

Cleaning.—Remove surplus grease or oil with caustic soda, paraffin or petrol. Wash in hot water and immerse in a 20 per cent. solution of hydrochloric or nitric acid for a minute or two. Remove from solution and wash well.

A quick and cheap method of cleaning brass and bronze parts is to rub them well with a mixture of salt and vinegar; oxalic-acid solution may be used instead of ordinary vinegar.

A good cleaning compound for brass and copper is made from oxalic acid, 1 oz., rottenstone 6 oz., and enough whale oil and spirits of turpentine (in equal parts) to mix into a soft paste.

Blackening.—Dissolve 1 part of natural malachite in 25 parts of liquid ammonia and place the brass in this solution, after first cleaning it. After a few minutes gradually warm the mixture. Examine the object from time to time until the desired black finish is seen to have been attained. Afterwards rinse in water and dry.

Another method is to immerse the brass article in a solution of chloride of antimony. Then remove and dry over a spirit lamp or bunsen flame. Finally, brush over with a blacklead brush.

Yet another method is to make up a solution consisting of 120 grains of silver nitrate in 5 oz. of water; then dissolve 120 grains of copper nitrate in 5 oz. of water. Take equal parts of these solutions and mix together. After cleaning the brass parts in hot soda water, they are dipped in the above solution. Finally they are removed and heated in an oven until the desired shade is attained.

As a final method, brush over with optical black or a syrupy solution of lampblack, oil varnish and methylated spirit. Very little varnish—just sufficient to fix the lampblack when the spirit evaporates—is required. Alternatively, immerse in a solution of platinum chloride and nitrate of tin.

Bronzing.—Apart from the use of bronze paints, brass can be given a bronze finish by chemical methods, of which the following is a typical one : immerse the clean polished article in a solution consisting of 2 parts potassium permanganate, 10 parts of iron sulphate and 1 part of hydrochloric acid in 200 parts of water. Allow it to remain in this solution for 30 seconds, then remove, wash in cold water, and dry in fine soft sawdust. Another bronzing solution consists of equal parts of copper sulphate and granulated tin. Stir well to precipitate the copper. Collect the latter, dry, grind very finely, and then add boiled linseed oil and turpentine. This gives a bronzing paint.

Yellow brass articles can be bronzed by first dipping them in boiling water and then in a solution consisting of equal parts of nitric and sulphuric acids and water. First mix the nitric acid and water together and then add, drop by drop, the sulphuric acid. Remove from the acid solution, dip quickly in boiling water once again, and then dry in pine sawdust.

Blue Colouring.—Immerse the parts in a solution consisting of antimony chloride, ½ oz. ; hydrochloric acid, 1½ oz. ; water, 10 oz. The warmed articles should be suspended in this solution, examined from time to time, and when of the desired blue shade removed, washed, and dried in sawdust.

Green Colouring.—Immerse in a boiling solution of copper acetate, 1 part ; copper sulphate, 1 part ; alum, 1 part ; and 10 parts of water.

Lacquering.—There are various kinds of lacquers used for preserving the polished appearance of brass. These depend upon the principle of forming a transparent protective coating, so that the surface of the brass cannot be attacked by the atmosphere.

Lacquers are of the hot- or cold-application type ; in the former variety it is necessary to heat the object before applying the lacquer. The simplest of the cold " lacquers " are the transparent cellulose or more recent synthetic resin, e.g. bakelite ones, sold for the purpose. When applying this kind of lacquer the temperature of the room in which the lacquering is done should be from 65°–70° F.

The other group of lacquers, as the name implies, contains lacs, or gum resins dissolved in alcohol ; other ingredients such as annatto, turmeric and colouring matter are also used.

The following is a typical composition : annatto, ½ oz. ; saffron, ½ oz. ; turmeric, 2 oz. ; seed-lac in coarse powder, 6 oz. ; alcohol, 2 pints. The first three ingredients should be digested in the alcohol for several days and the solution afterwards strained into a bottle containing the seed-lac. The bottle is then corked and agitated until the lac is all dissolved.

It is usual to add such substances as saffron, gamboge, dragon's blood and aniline colouring matters where coloured lacquers are required.

Lacquers are generally applied sparingly to the previously cleaned and well-polished surface of the brass, using a camel-hair brush for the purpose.

Tin Coating of.—Brass articles for electrical or decorative purposes can readily be given a uniform light tin coating as follows: place the previously cleaned and polished parts in an enamelled pot, such as a saucepan. Cover them with water and then add about 2 oz. of granulated tin and one tablespoonful of cream of tartar to each half-pint of water. Then heat the contents to the boiling point and maintain at this temperature for 20–30 minutes. The tinned surface obtained can readily be soldered.

Oxidised Finish on.—To oxidise brass, take some granulated tin or pieces of pure tin sheet clippings and place in a solution of 8 oz. of cream of tartar to 1 gallon of water.

If the brass articles are boiled in this for a few minutes, they will become coated with a bright film of tin. This may be improved if a piece of zinc is placed in contact with the brass. The brasswork must be cleaned free from all grease before placing in the above solution. Having got a white or silver-like appearance, proceed as follows: mix some blacklead with water, and with a soft brush apply to the main portions of the brass parts, omitting prominent portions or where a pattern is raised above the general surface. The omission is only to be on the most prominent parts of these, and should not leave large patches untouched. Allow the blacklead to dry, and then, with a clean soft brush, go briskly over the portions where black and white meet. This is to tone down the line of demarcation and allow the black and white to grade together. At the same time the brushing brightens the black portions, while the higher white relief may be polished a little with a clean soft leather. As the coating of tin is very thin, discretion will suggest very light handling in this process, or the brass may show through. When finished, lacquer with colourless lacquer. Failing the latter commodity, one may make a good protective by dissolving some white shellac in methylated spirit or alcohol.

Steel-blue Colour.—Immerse in a dilute solution of arsenic chloride maintained at boiling point until the colour appears. Remove and wash well.

CASTINGS

Filling Holes in.—Porous or blemished castings in steel, brass, aluminium, etc., can be filled by impregnation with plastic lacquers in closed chambers, under pressure, at a sufficiently high temperature. Usually lacquers in solvents are employed, the solvent evaporating at 80°–90° C. Polyvinylchloride and polystyrol plastics are used. After impregnation the plastic can be hardened by further heating.

Porous aluminium castings can be made watertight (under pressure) by impregnation with 1 part sodium silicate with 3 parts water, heated to 100° F., pressure being applied for about 20 minutes.

A putty-filler for holes or cracks is made by mixing together 6½ lb. iron filings ; 1 lb. plaster of Paris ; 4 oz. whiting ; 1½ oz. bone black ; 4 oz. gum arabic and 4 oz. Portland cement mixed to a paste with water. This sets hard in a short period.

For filling holes in *iron castings* several mixtures are available. The best known of these is, perhaps, the following : mix together 16 oz. of cast-iron filings, or turnings, 2 oz. of sal-ammoniac, and 1 oz. of powdered sulphur. Make into a fairly stiff paste with water and apply to the holes ; the mixture sets hard.

Another satisfactory filling composition is made by mixing 10 parts of manganese dioxide, 5 parts of zinc oxide and 1 part of borax to a paste with water-glass solution.

Where holes in castings have to be filled solely for the purpose of concealing them, but not from strength considerations, a suitable filler can be made by mixing equal parts of red lead and litharge with glycerine to the consistency of a dough.

Sand Removal.—This is usually effected by placing in a tumbling barrel with a mixture of sand, steel turnings, iron balls and small broken scrap-iron. Wire brushes, machine driven, can be used. For small work a tool made by clamping a number of hacksaw blades together, side by side, will be found effective for removing sand from brass and gunmetal castings.

CEMENTS AND ADHESIVES

(1) *Leather to Steel.*—(a) Dissolve 1 oz. of gum arabic in just sufficient water for this purpose and 1 oz. of isinglass in a similar amount of alcohol (or spirits of wine) and mix.

(b) Dissolve 8 oz. of fish glue and 4 oz. of ordinary glue in a mixture of equal parts of alcohol and water. Roughen the surface of the metal to be cemented by brushing it with acetic acid, or sand-blasting. The leather should be clamped to the metal and allowed to dry under pressure.

(2) *For Hydraulic Pipe Joints.*—Mix together 1 part of slaked lime, 2 parts of graphite and 3 parts of barium sulphate. Powder well and mix with 1 part of boiled linseed oil.

(3) *For Leather Belting.*—Mix together 8 parts of gutta-percha, 2 parts of pure white indiarubber, 1 part of pitch, 1 part of shellac and 1 part of boiled linseed oil.

(4) *For Metal to Glass.*—Boil together 2 oz. of thick glue, 1 oz. linseed oil and ½ oz. turpentine. This cement should be applied hot with a brush and the parts allowed from one to two days to dry under pressure. Cellulose cement, such as Durofix, is also suitable for this purpose.

(5) *For Glass Tubes in Brasswork.*—Mix together 10 oz. of resin, 2 oz. of beeswax and 1 oz. of powdered red ochre.

(6) *For Fixing Abrasive Powders to Wood or Metal.*—When making disc or cylindrical grinders by cementing emery, garnet, or carborundum powder to wood or metal forms, a good strong cement for the purpose can be made by melting together equal parts of shellac, white resin and phenol crystals.

(7) *Universal Cellulose Cement.*—This water-, oil-, and petrol-proof cement has a large number of useful applications for uniting various engineering materials. It is made by dissolving celluloid cuttings in one or more of the cellulose solvents, e.g. acetone, amyl acetate, sulphuric ether, benzine, etc. The following are typical recipes :

(*a*) Celluloid, 5 parts ; amyl acetate, 50 parts.

(*b*) Celluloid, 5 parts ; amyl acetate, 25 parts ; acetone, 25 parts.

(*c*) Celluloid, 5 parts ; alcohol, 50 parts ; camphor, 5 parts.

(*d*) Celluloid, 5 parts ; amyl acetate, 10 parts ; acetone, 16 parts ; sulphuric ether, 16 parts.

The surfaces to be united should be roughened, and the joint allowed to dry under pressure.

(8) *Rubber Cement.*—This can be made by dissolving pure or Para rubber in carbon disulphide, benzine or light petrol. Sufficient rubber clippings should be used to give a syrupy consistency.

(9) *Iron to Iron.*—A good cement for fastening iron or steel parts consists of the following : iron filings, 60 parts ; sal-ammoniac, 2 parts ; powdered sulphur, 1 part. Mix into a thick paste with water and use soon after making up.

(10) *Cloth to Metal.*—A simple adhesive for this purpose consists of red shellac. The metal surface is heated sufficiently to melt the shellac, the latter being distributed by brushing. The cloth should be pressed well down whilst the shellac is still melted.

Another recipe is as follows : melted Cologne glue is soaked and boiled down and sifted wood ashes then added until a thick treacly mass results. This adhesive should be used hot. For tinned-iron surfaces about 2 per cent. of boracic acid should be used instead of the wood ashes.

(11) *For Grinder Discs.*—Although the manufacturers supply special cements, the following are excellent substitutes : (*a*) Dissolve silicate of soda in water to a treacly consistency and use pressure whilst drying. (*b*) Resin, 1 part ; beeswax, 4 parts ; paraffin wax, 4 parts. Heat the disc and rub over with the mixture. Press the abrasive cloth or paper disc into place and dry under pressure.

(12) *Waterproof and Fireproof Glue.*—This is a useful glue for engineering purposes. It is made as follows : take several pieces of best carpenter's glue and soak well in water. Pour off the surplus water and melt under gentle heat. Then add white lead in equal proportions. Mix well and add acetic acid or carbolic acid in order to keep it fresh. This glue is useful for wood, leather and other flexible materials.

(13) *Iron to Concrete.*—A good cement for fastening iron parts into holes made in stone, brick or concrete can be made by mixing together 60 parts of plaster of Paris, 20 parts of iron filings or trimmings of suitable size, and 1 part by weight of sal-ammoniac.

The mixture should then be thinned down to make a paste by adding diluted vinegar or acetic acid.

(14) *Cement for Brass to Wood.*—Brass articles such as lettering or designs can be fastened to hard woods without screws or nails by using carpenter's glue made to double the usual consistency and adding 1 fluid oz. of glycerine and 1 oz. of slaked lime to every pound of the glue.

The brass should be dipped in a dilute solution of nitric acid, namely, 1 part of strong acid to 10 parts of water. The wood should be roughened with a coarse file or rasp in order to afford a better grip.

The metal should be warmed and smeared with the glue. After coating the wood with the same glue, press the parts together and allow to dry under pressure. The glue will not shrink when it dries, owing to the presence of the lime and glycerine.

(15) *Knife- and Tool-handle Cement.*—For fixing knife or tool handles in place, a mixture of 4 oz. resin, 1 oz. beeswax and 1 oz. fine brick dust or Portland cement, ground to a powder and then melted for pouring into the hole in the handle gives satisfactory results.

(16) *Fireproof Cement for Stonework.*—Mix together 10 parts silver sand, 1 part litharge and $\frac{1}{2}$ part quicklime, with sufficient boiled linseed oil to form a paste. This cement is suitable for concrete, stone, marble and granite.

(17) *Waterglass (sodium silicate) Cement.*—Various cements can be made using waterglass as a medium, with fillers such as man-

ganese, zinc white, Portland cement, plaster of Paris, powdered asbestos, etc.

A *heat-resistant cement* employs powdered asbestos and waterglass.

For *glass and porcelain* use 1 part of ground fluorspar, $\frac{1}{2}$ part of powdered glass and $\frac{1}{2}$ part of waterglass to form a thick syrupy mixture.

For stone and concrete joints use hydraulic cement and waterglass.

(18) *Fireproof Cement for Fixing Tiles.*—Powdered asbestos mixed with fireclay and water to form a putty.

(19) *Fire Cement.*—Mix 100 parts of wet fireclay, 3 parts black oxide of manganese, 3 parts silver sand and 1 part of powdered asbestos with water to make a paste or putty.

COPPER

Antique Finish on.—After degreasing and polishing, brush the surface with a solution of sulphide of ammonia.

Another method is to expose the cleaned copper surface to the fumes of a coke fire. To expedite the action, sprinkle sulphur on the burning coke.

Black Finish on.—After cleaning, heat over a gas or spirit stove flame and then immerse in a solution of copper nitrate. Remove and heat again. An alternative method is to immerse the copper article in a solution of $\frac{1}{4}$ oz. potassium sulphide in 1 gallon of boiling water to which a spoonful of ammonia has been added.

Blue Finish on.—Dip in a solution of $1\frac{1}{2}$ oz. sodium hyposulphite (photographic " hypo ") in 1 pint of water. If used hot, a deeper blue colour results.

Green Finish.—Clean thoroughly and immerse in a warm solution of 2 oz. sal-ammoniac, $1\frac{1}{2}$ oz. common salt and 1 gallon of water. Then wash, dry and immerse again until desired shade is obtained.

Grey Finish.—Warm the previously cleaned articles and immerse in a warm solution of 1 oz. sodium hyposulphite (photographic " hypo "), $\frac{1}{2}$ oz. sodium acetate and water, 1 pint. Remove from solution and hold over a gas or spirit flame. The procedure is repeated until the desired colour is obtained. Then wash well in warm water and dry.

Oxidising Copper.—Immerse the clean articles in a solution consisting of 2 oz. sodium hyposulphite, 2 oz. nitrate of iron and 1 pint of water until the desired shade is given. Then wash in water and dry.

Copper-plating Steel, Iron or Cast Iron.—All grease must be removed and the surfaces finished bright. Brush over with a concentrated solution of copper sulphate or moisten surface with water and rub well with a large crystal of copper sulphate. A *cast-iron surface* thus coppered can readily *be soft soldered.*

CRYSTALLINE FINISH ON METAL SURFACES

The crystalline finish, in black, brown or other plain colours, given to optical instruments, electrical apparatus containers, etc., can be obtained, using special enamels supplied by paint and enamel manufacturers for this purpose. One method is as follows : the work to be treated is first degreased with petrol or caustic soda solution. It is then polished to a bright appearance with emery cloth or other means. In order to provide a firm " key " for the enamel, the surface is next sand-blasted. It is then sprayed with a stoving enamel of the colour and tone required, and baked in the stove for two hours at a temperature of 240°–250° F. After this has hardened and cooled off, the work is again sprayed, but this time with a special clear frosting varnish, care being taken to get the coat on as evenly as possible.

The article is again baked, but this time at a much lower temperature, namely, 140°–150° F., for about half an hour, when the varnish cracks, producing the frosted appearance. The temperature is then raised to about 170° F. and baking continued for a further 1½ hours, this last hardening and setting the surface.

Over-heating when hardening-off causes the varnish to re-flow, spoiling the surface, and all must then be cleaned off and a fresh start made.

When in the stove, all large surfaces are preferably kept horizontal, as there is a tendency for the varnish to flow downwards, resulting in " fat " edges.

When used on colours other than black, a slight variation from the original shade results. A semi-glossy paint treated with frosting seems to give slightly better results than a dull matt paint. When applied with a brush, a very fine crystalline finish is produced, but the best results are undoubtedly obtained by spraying. A general rule seems to be that the thinner the coat of varnish applied, the finer the ultimate frosting.

DEGREASING METAL PARTS

The components of dismantled engines and machinery are degreased before inspection or measurement, or for repair purposes, by one of the following methods :

(*a*) By immersion in a paraffin bath and scrubbing with a plain bristle or wire brush ; for small parts an old toothbrush is satisfactory. After removal, drain and heat to get rid of traces of paraffin.

(*b*) By immersion in hot sodium carbonate (washing soda) solution, followed by a washing in hot water.

(*c*) By immersion in hot caustic soda solution of about 6–8 oz. per gallon. Care must be taken not to get any of the solution on the hands or clothes, as it has a strong caustic action. This solution is more effective than that given in (*b*).

(*d*) By the use of trichlorethylene. This is a rapid-action degreaser, and is generally used in the vapour form in special degreasing plant provided with heating coils in the liquid container or sump, and cooling coils above the trays containing the objects to be degreased. The vapour condenses on the latter coils and runs back into the sump. The liquid is relatively cheap and practically non-inflammable.

ETCHING METALS

Aluminium.—Use a solution of caustic soda in the proportion of 1 part of the fully saturated solution to 5 parts of water.

Brass.—To etch names or designs in brass plates, first coat the surface thinly with ordinary paraffin or candle wax ; the plates should be heated to allow the wax to spread evenly. When cool, write the name or design through the wax with a sharp metal tool and then gently pour on strong nitric acid ; use only sufficient acid to fill the recesses in the wax. Afterwards wash well with plenty of water.

A better etching fluid consists of 1 part nitric acid in 10 parts of water ; into this solution pour a hot solution of ½ part of potassium chlorate in 7 parts of water.

Copper.—Nitric acid alone or a mixture of 2 parts nitric acid and 1 part sulphuric acid. If the action is too rapid, dilute with water.

Glass.—Whenever possible the sand-blast method should be employed, using suitable metal stencils for masking the glass surface not required to be etched.

Chemical etching is done with hydrofluoric acid, or a fluoride mixture. As the former acid is a dangerous one, since it gives off a vapour which causes injury to the skin and is poisonous if inhaled, due precautions must be taken. The hands should be protected by rubber gloves and the etching done well away from the face.

Usually a salt mixture is employed for glass etching. A typical one is made up as follows : Dissolve about ¾ oz. of fluoride of soda with $\frac{1}{8}$ oz. of sulphate of potash in 1 pint of water. Make another solution of $\frac{1}{4}$ oz. chloride of zinc and $1\frac{1}{4}$ oz. hydrochloric acid in an equal quantity of water. Mix the solutions and apply to the glass surface with a brush ; in about 20–30 minutes the glass will be properly etched.

Lead.—A suitable etching solution is a 20–25 per cent. nitric acid solution.

Magnesium Alloys.—Weak acid solutions attack magnesium and its alloys. Ten to 15 per cent. solutions of nitric, hydrochloric or sulphuric acids can be used for etching purposes. Unlike aluminium, it is hardly affected by alkaline solutions. Common salt solutions attack the metal.

Steel.—A suitable etching solution for iron and soft steel consists of nitric acid, 1 part, and water, 3 to 4 parts.

For hard steel use nitric acid, 2 parts, and acetic acid, 1 part.

Another solution consists of hydrochloric acid, 5 parts ; water, 40 parts ; chlorate of potash, 1 part.

Zinc.—A 30–50 per cent. solution of hydrochloric acid is a good etching medium.

ETCHING RESIST

When metal surfaces are to be etched with letters or designs, they are first given a thin coating of an acid or etching-fluid resisting material. A widely used etching resist is ordinary candle or paraffin wax, which is melted on to the warmed metal surface so as to form a thin layer.

An etching wax which is rather better than paraffin is one consisting of asphalt, 4 parts, and beeswax, 3 parts. Beeswax alone is often used.

Another etching resist consists of 6 parts resin and 4 parts beeswax melted together. When in the melted condition, add 1 to 2 parts of olive oil and allow to cool in suitable " stick " moulds.

Another resist consists of 1 part pitch ; 2 parts paraffin wax ; $1\frac{1}{2}$ parts resin. These are melted together, and 1 part of turpentine is then added slowly, stirring all the time.

FILE CLEANING AND RE-SHARPENING

(1) *Cleaning.*—When aluminium or aluminium alloys are the metals to be removed from clogged files, the latter should be immersed in a strong solution of caustic soda for 5–10 minutes, after which the chips or particles can easily be brushed off. To prevent rusting after this treatment, wash in clean cold water and dry in warm sawdust.

If files are clogged with brass, bronze, copper or zinc, first immerse them in a strong solution of caustic soda, rinse in water, and dry quickly. Next immerse the files for 3–4 minutes in a solution consisting of nitric acid 1 gallon, hydrochloric acid $\frac{1}{2}$ gallon, water 2 gallons. To prevent rusting through acid treatment, the files should be immersed in a caustic-soda solution, well rinsed in running water, and dried in warm sawdust, afterwards wiping with an oily rag.

Paint, red or white lead, and substances of a similar nature can be removed from the file teeth by leaving the files in a paraffin-oil bath for 3–4 hours and then washing them thoroughly in very hot soda solution, brushing with a steel-bristled brush or file card. Solid lumps may have to be picked out by a sharp-pointed steel tool, such as a steel scriber.

Another general method of cleaning clogged files is to use a strip of rubber cut from an inner tube and rolled up tightly so as to form a cylinder about 1 in. in diameter ; it should be tied tightly at several places with fine wire. If pressed on the file teeth and drawn along them, the particles between the teeth will be forced out.

(2) *Resharpening.*—Worn files can be given a new lease of life by the chemical method of immersion in an acid solution which partly dissolves the metal, leaving sharp edges on the teeth. The file should be degreased and then, after washing in hot water, placed in a shallow tray containing a 10–20 per cent. solution of nitric acid in water. It should be removed and inspected from time to time with the aid of a magnifying lens. When the teeth are seen to be sharp, remove from the bath and wipe off the surplus acid from the tops of the teeth, using a piece of cloth stretched over a piece of wood. This leaves the acid in the file grooves to continue its action for a time. Afterwards, immerse in a strong washing-soda solution to neutralise the acid and then wash well in hot water.

A more effective solution consists of 1 volume sulphuric acid, $1\frac{1}{2}$ volumes of nitric acid and 8 volumes of water. If the files are immersed in a suitable container in a vertical position, the acid acts equally well on both sides.

FIRE EXTINGUISHER

In emergencies, where the usual chemical fire extinguishers are not available, small fires can be put out with ordinary sand or sawdust. A very effective fire-extinguishing mixture consists of 10 lb. of soda bicarbonate to every bushel of sawdust ; the former chemical gives off carbonic-acid gas, which prevents combustion.

Carbon tetrachloride is another efficacious liquid fire extinguisher ; it is often used in the spraying type of fire-extinguisher canister.

GLASS

Cleaning.—Solid or greasy deposits can be removed with a common soda-water solution, paraffin or petrol. A piece of chamois leather moistened with hot soda water or soapy solution is also effective. Equal parts of paraffin and carbon tetrachloride make an excellent cleaning and polishing solution.

Drilling Glass.—Glass cannot satisfactorily be drilled with ordinary metal drills or bits, on account of their unsuitable shapes and cutting angles and of the great hardness of glass.

By using special spade-pointed hardened-steel bits made for this purpose, however, it is possible to drill holes fairly quickly in plate glass. As an illustration, it may be mentioned that glass-boring drills of this type supplied by Messrs. Grayson Company, Sheffield, will drill holes of $\frac{1}{4}$-in. diameter through plate glass of $\frac{1}{4}$-in. thickness in $2\frac{1}{2}$ minutes.

Steel drills for this purpose should be worked at 80 r.p.m., using camphor dissolved in turpentine as a lubricant. Glass-boring drills of this type are of tapered shape, similar to flat, rectangular-section reamers, so that holes of different sizes can be drilled with the same drill. Thus for holes between $\frac{1}{4}$-in. and $\frac{3}{4}$-in. diameter only two sizes of the Grayson type of drill are required. As the hole obtained is tapered, it may be rendered more nearly parallel by drilling from opposite sides.

Another method of drilling a parallel hole through glass is by using as the drill a brass or copper tube of slightly smaller size than the required finished diameter. This tube is rotated in the drill chuck, the glass being clamped to the work-table. The end face of the tube is kept charged with a wetted mixture of diamond dust or carborundum powder. In its action the tube acts as an end grinder, the abrasive powder being held in the soft copper.

A hole can be made in a thin sheet of glass by first making a cylindrical mould of moist loam or clay on the upper surface, leaving the internal diameter the same size as that of the hole required. Then pour molten lead into the hole thus formed, when it will at once drop through the glass, leaving a hole of the required size.

Frosting Glass.—Sand-blasting is a quick and effective method. If a suitable hard metal stencil is placed over the glass, designs may be etched with a frosted effect.

Emery or carborundum powder with an oil binder can be used with a cork rubber to frost glass.

A frosted effect can be obtained by warming the cleaned glass and brushing over a saturated solution of Epsom-salt (magnesium sulphate).

Stippling with the end of a stout bristle brush charged with white paint or enamel also gives a frosted effect.

A frosting solution consists of 3 oz. magnesium sulphate, 1 oz. dextrine and 10 oz. of water.

Anti-dimming Solutions.—A 10 per cent. solution of medicinal glycerine in water makes an excellent non-steaming preparation for windscreens and windows. A piece of raw potato or soap rubbed over the glass and the latter wiped over with a clean cloth is also effective as a temporary measure.

A solution of 1 oz. of soft soap in 1 pint of methylated spirit is another good anti-dimming preparation.

Ink for Writing on Glass.—Shellac, 4 oz. ; Venice turpentine, 2 oz. ; Sandarac, ½ oz. ; oil of turpentine, 6 fluid oz. Dissolve by gentle heating and add 1 oz. of lampblack.

HOLES IN HARD METALS

Steels that have been hardened and tempered to a certain degree of hardness cannot generally be drilled by ordinary means. Tungsten-carbide-tipped drills are now available, and there is also a drill on the market, known as the Hardsteel Drill,* which will drill hardened steel, case-hardened and nitrided steels. It is of triangular section and extremely hard, and when used at the correct speed and feed pressure gives clean holes to within 0·001 in. ; it can also be used to reamer out holes in hardened steels. A copper rod or tube charged with fine carborundum powder or diamond dust, used as a drill, will make holes in hard steels and glass. A thick oil should be used.

If a few drops of nitric acid are used on the hard skin of a casting, the surface layer will be softened so that a hard alloy-steel type drill can then be used.

Spring steel can be perforated by placing it on a block of lead and punching with a centre punch so as to form a bulge ; the latter can then be ground off and the hole opened out with a reamer.

Holes can be " burnt " through hard steel plate using a carbon electric arc welding plant.

* Black Drill Co., Cleveland, Ohio., U.S.A. (British Agents, G. H. Alexander, Ltd., Birmingham).

LACQUERS

The lacquers used in engineering include those for brass instrument parts, aluminium and magnesium protective lacquers and polished or coloured steel components.

Brass Lacquers.—These are usually mixtures of natural gums or resins in alcohol. A typical lacquer for polished brass parts consists of 1 oz. shellac, 1 oz. seedlac, ½ oz. Venetian turpentine and 20 oz. alcohol. The work is heated before applying the lacquer, the latter being brushed or flowed over the surfaces. For microscopes and similar instruments a pale gold lacquer is used, the work being heated after lacquering. Special lacquers can be purchased for this purpose. In modern work the cellulose and synthetic resin lacquers (transparent) are used. These are equally applicable for all metals.

Lacquer for Drawings.—A suitable transparent lacquer consists of 4 parts of gum dammar, 18 parts acetone and 3 parts of thick fluid collodion.

Black Lacquer for Steel.—A glossy black lacquer is made by heating 10 parts of oil of turpentine with 1 part of sulphur to boiling point. The steel is coated with the preparation and held over the flame of a gas or spirit stove.

Gold Lacquer for Tinplate.—This consists of 6 parts of dried copal lacquer and 3 parts of linseed oil. This lacquer will not crack when the tinplate is bent.

MARKING MEDIUMS FOR STEEL

To prepare steel or iron surfaces for marking off centres, circles or straight lines, they may be well rubbed with ordinary chalk.

Whiting and white lead mixed to a thick paste with boiled linseed oil to which a little japan drier has been added makes another satisfactory marking mixture ; it should be thinned with petrol and applied with a brush. Any lines marked on the surface after it is dry show up distinctly.

Flat-machined or filed iron or steel surfaces can be prepared for marking by moistening them with water and rubbing over with a piece of copper sulphate ; this leaves a thin deposit of copper on the surface. Polished iron and steel parts can be marked by first rubbing them with a piece of rag or waste soaked in turpentine. Afterwards rub over the surfaces with ordinary indelible or copying pencil.

MARKING FOR BEARINGS AND SURFACE PLATES

The common marking material for testing high spots on shafts, bearings, flat surfaces, etc., when scraping engineering parts, consists of a mixture of powdered red lead and olive or linseed oil.

Artist's Prussian blue oil colour as supplied in lead tubes is a cleaner and more effective marking medium.

A more recent marking material consisting of a mixture of powdered anthracene in medicinal paraffin oil has been employed. The bearing when inspected under the rays of a G.E.C. Osira lamp shows up its high spots by fluorescent effects which are readily observed under daylight lighting conditions. The material is removed from the shaft with benzine.

RUST REMOVAL FROM STEEL AND IRON

Rust may be removed from iron and steel parts by two different methods, viz. (1) the use of abrasives, and (2) the use of chemicals.

The abrasives used with the first method include carborundum and emery powders, pumice, tripoli and rottenstone. They are applied dry, or mixed with lubricating oil, turpentine or paraffin oil, using a piece of cork, felt or cloth to hold the mixture. For very small steel parts, ordinary ink eraser cut to a suitable shape will be found effective for removing rust.

A paste made of carborundum or emery powder mixed with olive-oil, applied with a thick piece of cloth or felt, is useful for removal of heavy rust deposits.

If rusty steel parts are immersed in turpentine, naphtha or paraffin oil for about 12 hours, they can readily be cleaned with emery cloth or one of the abrasive mixtures previously mentioned.

A good chemical method is to immerse in a hot strong bath of caustic potash for about 30 minutes. Then immerse in a cold muriatic-acid pickling bath ; in a few minutes all of the rust will be removed or loosened sufficiently to be rubbed off readily with a cloth.

Another satisfactory method for steel tools is as follows : dissolve gradually, in one quart of distilled water, sufficient chloride of tin to make a saturated solution, i.e. until the water will not dissolve any more of this salt. Put the tools in a jar containing this solution and leave for about 10–15 hours. Then remove them from the solution and, after rinsing in hot water, dry with a cloth.

RUST PREVENTION

Apart from the well-known commercial methods for producing protective coatings on steel and iron articles, the following are typical workshop methods for preventing rusting :

(1) Brush the cleaned surfaces with a cellulose varnish. A simple composition is that obtained by dissolving celluloid chippings in acetone or amyl acetate until a thin-syrup consistency is obtained. Metal-protecting lacquers are also sold by hardware merchants.

(2) Dissolve 1 oz. of camphor in 2 lb. of melted lard. Skim the solution and mix with sufficient blacklead to give an iron colour. The metal parts should be smeared with this mixture.

(3) Dissolve 1 oz. of caoutchouc in 16 oz. of turpentine with a gentle heat. Then add 8 oz. of boiled linseed oil and mix well. This mixture should be applied with a brush.

(4) Melt 2 oz. of resin in 1 pint of linseed oil and then add to 1 gallon of paraffin oil. Apply with a brush.

(5) A satisfactory mixture for protecting machinery parts against rusting is made by mixing white lead and tallow in the proportions of 1 part of the former to 3 parts of the latter. Heat in a suitable receptacle and stir well. Then allow to cool a little and add 3 to 4 parts of linseed oil. Stir well until the mixture becomes quite cool; otherwise the white lead tends to settle at the bottom. This mixture retains its consistency all the year round.

(6) Red-lead, bituminous and chrome paints are well-known commercial substances for protecting iron and steel parts against rusting.

Commercial rust-prevention processes employ zinc, cadmium, lead, phosphate and other protective coatings obtained by chemical methods, usually involving the application of heat.

Coslettising.—This gives a matt black finish. It consists in boiling the steel parts in a solution of 1 oz. iron filings and 4 oz. phosphoric acid per gallon of water.

Sherardising.—The cleaned and pickled steel parts are heated in contact with zinc dust (usually with the addition of zinc oxide and powdered charcoal) in a metal container that is revolved during the process, at 300°–500° C. The surface obtained is a dull matt grey due to the zinc coating. The latter is of the order of a few thousandths inch thick.

Bower-Barff Process.—The steel parts are heated to about 900° C. in an airtight container in contact with superheated steam, followed by carbon monoxide gas. The coating obtained is one of mixed oxides of iron transformed finally into magnetic oxide of iron.

Parker Process.—The dry process consists in heating the steel parts at about 600° F., in contact with the fumes of acid metaphosphates of tungsten, strontium and molybdenum. The wet process consists in the immersion of the parts in a 1½ per cent. solution of the acid metaphosphates of tungsten and molybdenum.

Other commercial rust-proof coatings include Bonderising, the Gesner process, the plain Barff process, Bertrand's process and Hans Renold process.

Metallisation Process.—Based upon the original Schoop metalspraying process, this consists in spraying fine globules of molten metal on to the previously cleaned and sand-blasted surface. A special type of spraying pistol is used. The metal to be sprayed is fed, automatically, into the pistol, an air-driven turbine being provided inside the pistol for this purpose. As the wire enters the nozzle of the pistol it is melted by an oxy-gas flame and projected, by means of a compressed-air jet arranged at the nozzle, on to the surface.

Practically any metal can be sprayed in this manner, e.g. zinc, aluminium, copper, bronze, steels (stainless, high-carbon and alloy steels). Any desired thickness of coating can be provided. The metal is strongly adherent to the base metal (steel). The process is rapid and relatively inexpensive.

PLATING METALS WITHOUT ELECTRICITY

Small brass and gun-metal parts can be given a thin coating of certain metals such as nickel and chromium by boiling them in suitable solutions.

The following is a method of producing a sound coating of nickel and chromium with a small proportion of tin. The solution is made by adding granulated tin to hydrochloric acid until the latter will dissolve no more tin. Take 1 oz. of this solution and add to 5 oz. of distilled water in a glass or enamelled iron vessel and then heat to the boiling point.

When boiling, add ½ oz. of nickel sulphate and then ¼ oz. of chromium carbonate, followed by ¼ oz. of ammonium chloride.

The metal parts, after a thorough cleaning, should be immersed in the hot solution for 10–15 minutes and then removed and washed in warm soapy water or washing-soda solution. After rinsing in clean water and drying, the parts should be polished with a dry cloth.

In the case of steel articles it may be necessary to stir them about in the bath, using a piece of zinc in contact with the steel to enable the coating to form.

By altering the proportions of nickel and chromium salts the colour of the coating can be varied ; with the proportions stated a bluish-white colour is obtained.

SILVER-PLATING COMPOUNDS

There are several silver-plating compounds and solutions that may be used to give effective, but rather thin coatings.

(1) A solution can be made by grinding together 1 oz. dry chloride of silver, 2 oz. cream of tartar and 3 oz. common salt ; add enough water to obtain the desired consistency, and rub it on to the metal surface with a soft rag. This will give brass a dead-white silver coating. A coat of silver lacquer should be applied to the silvered surface to prevent the silver coating tarnishing.

(2) Use a paste made from chloride of silver and cream of tartar of equal quantities, together with a little powdered chalk. The paste may be rubbed on the surface with a rag or a piece of soft cork. The work should then be rinsed in clean water and dried out in clean hot boxwood sawdust.

For silvering small brass articles, make up the following solution : water 1 gallon, sodium cyanide 2 oz., silver cyanide 1 oz., caustic potash 3 oz. Prepare this by using one-third water, first at 160° F. to dissolve the sodium cyanide and silver cyanide, then add the balance of water and then the caustic potash. This solution can be used at 80° F., and higher temperatures as desired.

(3) Articles may be silver-coated by placing in a hot solution made up as follows :

Silver nitrate	9	grammes
Ammonia	9	,,
Sodium hyposulphite . .	15	,,
Finely powdered whiting . .	15	,,
Distilled water	150	,, (fluid)

The parts should first be cleaned thoroughly to remove all trace of grease, dust, oxide, etc., and afterwards polished.

Instead of immersing them in the solution they can be rubbed with a piece of cotton wool or a fine brush steeped in the solution.

After the coating has been obtained, wash well with water, dry, and polish with any non-abrasive silver-polishing preparation, such as prepared whiting.

NICKEL-PLATING COMPOUND

To nickel plate metal parts without the use of electricity they should be placed in a bath made up as follows :

Nickel ammonium sulphate .	.	.	.	45 grammes	
Nickel sulphate .	.	.	.	.	25 ,,
Tin chloride	.	.	.	.	20 ,,
Sodium chloride .	.	.	.	.	4 ,,
Cream of tartar .	.	.	.	.	18 ,,
Ammonium chloride .	.	.	.	10 oz.	
Water	.	.	.	.	900 grammes

STEEL

Blue or Gun-metal Coating on.—There are two principal methods of obtaining a blue finish on steel parts, namely, (1) the chemical, and (2) the heating methods. One recommended chemical method is to brush or sponge over the previously polished surface of the steel with a solution consisting of 2 parts of crystallised chloride of iron, 2 parts solid chloride of antimony, and 1 part of gallic acid in 4–5 parts of water. Allow the parts to dry in the air. This operation should be repeated two or three times. Afterwards wash well in water, dry, and rub with boiled linseed oil to deepen the shade.

The heating method consists in first giving the surfaces their final polish and then heating them uniformly until the original cold steely appearance gradually changes to the desired shade of blue. Then remove the source of heat and allow the articles to cool in air. Small objects may be heated in a sand bath, or in a mixture consisting of equal parts of fine sand and powdered charcoal.

Another method for small pieces is to place them on a flat bar of iron mounted over a bath of water or lubricating oil. The bar is heated from below with a gas flame until they start to colour. When they have become blue, the bar is tilted so as to upset the objects into the liquid below.

Black Coating.—If the steel articles are first heated, then dipped in engine lubricating oil and then heated in an oven for 5–10 minutes at 150°–180° C., a good adherent black skin is formed on the surface.

Another black-coating method for steel and iron is to immerse the parts in a warm solution consisting of $1\frac{1}{2}$ parts of caustic soda, 25–50 parts of sodium nitrate and 5 parts of tannic acid in enough water to dissolve these constituents.

Copper-plating Steel.—After degreasing and polishing, immerse in a solution made up of half a teaspoonful of sodium bisulphate and one teaspoonful of copper sulphate crystals to a tumbler of water. The coppering action is expedited by heating the solution.

Brown Finish.—This may be obtained by heating uniformly until the initial blue and purple colour changes to a brown ; then quench the article in cold water or oil.

The chemical method is, however, more generally employed. It consists in brushing the previously cleaned and finish-polished surface with a special bronzing solution, or solutions.

One satisfactory method is first to brush the polished-steel surface with a copper-sulphate solution. After a few minutes wipe the surface dry with a piece of clean cotton cloth. Then brush over with a solution of ammonium sulphide, taking care to apply the latter evenly over the previously coppered surface. After about 30 seconds, dry the surface with another clean cloth.

Another method is to give several brush coats with a solution made as follows : copper sulphate, 1 oz. ; sweet spirits of nitre, 1 oz. ; distilled water, 1 pint. An interval of a few hours should be allowed to elapse between each of the coats. Afterwards rub well with ordinary furniture polish used on a dry cloth.

Oxidised Finish.—To oxidise steel or iron take 2 parts of solid butter of antimony, 1 part of gallic acid and 5 parts of water, by volume, and make into a solution.

After cleaning the articles by washing in a hot solution of caustic soda or strong washing soda (soda carbonate), followed by a rinse in water, dip them into the solution until they are of the required colour and then remove and dip for a few seconds in hydrochloric or sulphuric acid.

Allow the parts to stand for about a day. Then remove the acid coating with a steel-wire brush. Repeat several times and, after dipping in linseed oil, heat to a red temperature and allow to cool slowly.

MOTTLED FINISH ON STEEL TOOLS

The parts are first degreased and polished. They are then suspended in a wire basket or on wire hooks in a molten salt mixture, consisting of 1 part by weight of sodium cyanide and 1 part of anhydrous sodium carbonate (soda ash). The temperature of the molten salts is maintained at 780°–800° C., the steel parts being then at a bright cherry-red heat. After attaining this temperature they are removed and quenched in cold water.

A rainbow mottled appearance is given by quenching the steel parts taken from the above mixture in a solution of 1 lb. sodium nitrate in 1 gallon of water. The parts should be quickly moved in and out of the solution during quenching.

PREVENTION OF SCALING AND PITTING OF STEEL PARTS

Heat-treated steel objects are often found to have a skin, scale or pitted appearance after hardening. In case-hardening, this does not occur if the cyanide or gas-carburising methods are employed. Similarly, parts hardened by the nitriding method have a clean smooth surface.

When scale or pitting occurs, this is due to oxidation by the furnace atmosphere and can be reduced or eliminated by arranging for a neutral or reducing atmosphere, such as nitrogen or excess of coal gas in the case of gas furnaces.

To prevent pitting of polished tools they may be coated with boric acid or painted over with a wet mixture of graphite or bone-black before placing in the furnace. When the tools are quenched in a salt bath, care should be exercised that the tongs used for removing the parts from the bath are not employed for introducing other tools into the furnace, as this will cause pitting.

Small steel tools are sometimes placed in air-tight steel boxes for heating in the furnace, in order to prevent scaling.

ZINC AND ZINC DIE CASTINGS

Black Finish on.—Zinc and zinc die-casting alloys can be given a satisfactory black coating by immersing the cleaned articles in a solution, maintained at 100° F., consisting of :

Nickel chloride	4 oz.
Ammonium chloride . . .	6 ,,
Sodium sulphocyanide . . .	2 ,,
Zinc chloride	2 ,,
Water	1 gallon

SECTION 12

MOMENTS OF INERTIA

1. The moment of inertia of any area A, about an axis such as XY, is the sum of all the extremely small areas a multiplied by the squares of their distances x from the axis.   (Fig. 1.)

Thus Moment of Inertia $I = \Sigma\, ax^2$.

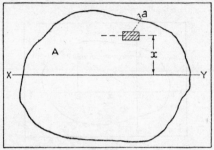

Fig. 1.

For complex areas the methods of integral calculus or graphical ones are used, but for simple geometrical shapes the moments of inertia can usually be obtained by straightforward calculation.

2. The radius of gyration k is the square root of the moment of inertia divided by the total area A.

Thus $I = Ak^2$ or $k = \sqrt{\dfrac{I}{A}}$

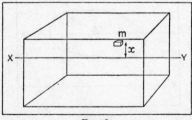

Fig. 2.

3. For solids the moment of inertia about an axis XY (Fig. 2) is the sum of the component small masses multiplied by the squares of their distances from the axis or axial plane.

Thus $I = \Sigma\, mx^2$.

4. The radius of gyration of a solid about a given axis is given by

$$k = \sqrt{\dfrac{I}{M}}$$

where M = mass of solid.

5. The polar moment of inertia of an area about an axis through O, perpendicular to its plane, is the sum of all the small areas p multiplied by the squares of their distances pr^2 from O. (Fig. 3.)

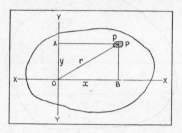

Fig. 3.

Thus $I_p = \Sigma pr^2$,
and since $r^2 = x^2 + y^2$
$$I_p = \Sigma px^2 + \Sigma py^2 = I_x + I_y.$$

The polar moment of inertia is, therefore, equal to the sum of the moments of inertia about two axes at right angles XX and YY passing through O.

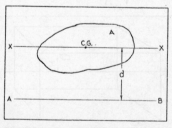

Fig. 4.

6. The moment of inertia of an area A about a parallel axis AB (Fig. 4) is given by the following relation :

$$I_{AB} = I_x + A \cdot d^2.$$

MOMENTS OF INERTIA

Section	Moment of Inertia about Axis XY	Radius of Gyration
	$\dfrac{a^4}{12}$	$0 \cdot 289a$
	$\dfrac{bd^3}{12}$	$0 \cdot 289d$
	$\dfrac{a_1^4 - a_2^4}{12}$	$0 \cdot 289 \sqrt{a_1^2 + a_2^2}$
	$\dfrac{1}{12}(b_1 d_1^3 - b_2 d_2^3)$	$0 \cdot 289 \sqrt{\dfrac{b_1 d_1^3 - b_2 d_2^3}{b_1 d_1 - b_2 d_2}}$
	$\dfrac{a^4}{12}$	$0 \cdot 289a$

Moments of Inertia (contd.)

Section	Moment of Inertia about Axis XY	Radius of Gyration
	$\dfrac{bd^3 - (b-t)d_1^3}{12}$	$0 \cdot 289 \sqrt{\dfrac{bd^3 - (b-t)\,d_1^3}{bd - (b-t)\,d_1}}$
	$\dfrac{bd^3 - (b-t)\,d_1^3}{12}$	$0 \cdot 289 \sqrt{\dfrac{bd^3 - (b-t)\,d_1^3}{bd - (b-t)\,d_1}}$
	$\dfrac{b_1 d^3 + 2bd_1^3}{12}$	$0 \cdot 289 \sqrt{\dfrac{b_1 d^3 + 2bd_1^3}{b_1 d + bd_1}}$
	$\dfrac{b_1 d^3 + 2bd_1^3}{12}$	$0 \cdot 289 \sqrt{\dfrac{b_1 d^3 + 2bd_1^3}{b_1 d + bd_1}}$
	$\tfrac{1}{2}\left[b\left(a_1^3 - x^3\right) + t\left(x^3 + a_2^3\right)\right]$ where $x = a_1 - t$ and $a_1 = \dfrac{bt^2 + td_1\,(d + b^3)}{2[bd - (b-t)d_1]}$	$\sqrt{\dfrac{\text{Moment of Inertia}}{\text{Area of Section}}}$

Moments of Inertia (*contd.*)

Section	Moment of Inertia about Axis XY	Radius of Gyration
	$0 \cdot 5412a^4$	$0 \cdot 456a$
	$\dfrac{bd^3}{36}$ $x = \dfrac{d}{3}$	$0 \cdot 2357d$
	$d^3\left(\dfrac{b^2 + 4ab + a^2}{36\,(a + b)}\right)$ where $x = \dfrac{d}{3}\left(\dfrac{b + 2a}{a + b}\right)$	$d\sqrt{\dfrac{b^2 + 4ab + a^2}{18\,(a + b)(2a + b)}}$
	$\dfrac{\pi d^4}{64}$	$0 \cdot 25d$
	$\dfrac{\pi}{64}\,(d^4 - d_1{}^4)$	$0 \cdot 25\sqrt{d^2 \times d_1{}^2}$

Moments of Inertia (*contd.*)

Section	Moment of Inertia about Axis XY	Radius of Gyration
	(Ellipse) $$\frac{\pi}{64} bd^3$$	$0 \cdot 25d$
	(Annular Ellipse) $$\frac{\pi}{64}(bd^3 - b_1 d_1^3)$$	$0 \cdot 25 \sqrt{\dfrac{bd^3 - b_1 d_1^3}{bd - b_1 d_1}}$
	$$\frac{d^4}{16}\left(\frac{\pi}{8} - \frac{8}{9\pi}\right)$$ $$= 0 \cdot 00686 d^4$$ $$x = \frac{2d}{3\pi} = 0 \cdot 212d$$	$0 \cdot 1327d$
	(Parabola) $0 \cdot 04571 bd^3$	$0 \cdot 2619d$
	(Parabola) $0 \cdot 03333 bd^3$	$0 \cdot 2236b$

SECTION 13

MENSURATION AND TRIGONOMETRY

RATIO OF CIRCUMFERENCE TO DIAMETER OF CIRCLE

This ratio is denoted by the Greek letter Pi, π, and its value is not an exact quantity, although it has been determined to several hundred places of decimals. Thus :

$$\pi = 3 \cdot 1415926535987 \ldots$$

For most engineering purposes the value of π may be taken as follows :

$$\pi = 3 \cdot 1416$$

and for approximate or rough calculations :

$$\pi = \frac{22}{7} \ (3 \cdot 1428 \ldots)$$

Functions of π.

$$\pi^2 = 9 \cdot 869604$$
$$\pi^3 = 31 \cdot 006277$$
$$\sqrt{\pi} = 1 \cdot 7724538$$
$$\frac{360}{\pi} = 114 \cdot 59156 \ \text{(or 2 radians)}$$
$$\frac{1}{\pi} = 0 \cdot 3183099$$
$$\log \pi = \cdot 4971499$$

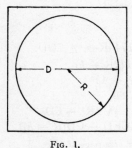

Fig. 1.

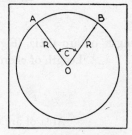

Fig. 2.

E.W.D.—15*

PROPERTIES OF CIRCLES

If R = radius of circle and D = diameter (= 2R) (Fig. 1)

$$\text{Circumference of circle} = 2\pi R$$
$$= \pi D \text{ where } \pi = 3\cdot1416^*$$
$$\text{Area of circle} = \pi R^2$$
$$= \pi \frac{D^2}{4} = 0\cdot7854D^2$$

Length of arc AB (Fig. 2) $= \dfrac{\pi CR}{180}$ where C = angle AOB in degrees.

$$C = \frac{180 \text{ AB}}{\pi R}$$
$$= \frac{57\cdot296 \text{ AB}}{R}$$

$$\text{Area of sector AOB} = \frac{\text{AB} \times \text{R}}{2}$$
$$= \frac{\pi CR^2}{360}$$
$$= 0\cdot008727CR^2$$

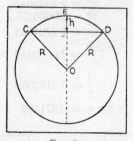

Fig. 3.

Length of arc CED (Fig. 3) $= 0\cdot01745R \times \angle \text{COD}.$

Length of chord CD $= 2\sqrt{h(2R - h)}$

$$R = \frac{CD^2 + 4h^2}{8h}$$

$$h = R - \tfrac{1}{2}\sqrt{4R^2 - CD^2}$$

Area of arc CED $= \tfrac{1}{2}[\text{RCED} - \text{CD}(R - h)]$

* For more accurate values of π *vide* page 457.

INSCRIBED SQUARES AND CIRCLES

1. Inscribed square in circle (Fig. 4).
   D = diameter of circle,   s = side of square.
   $$D^2 = 2s^2$$
   $$s = \frac{D}{\sqrt{2}} = 0.707107D.$$

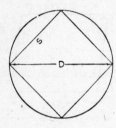

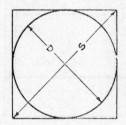

Fig. 4.   Fig. 5.

2. Square circumscribing circle (Fig. 5).
   D = diameter of circle,   S = diagonal of square.
   $$S^2 = 2D^2$$
   $$S = D\sqrt{2} = 1.4142D.$$

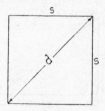

Fig. 6.

AREAS OF PLANE FIGURES

Square (Fig. 6).
     s = length of side,   d = diagonal.
$$s = \frac{d}{\sqrt{2}} = 0.707107d.$$

Area $= s^2 = \frac{d^2}{2}$, i.e. one-half the product of the diagonals.

Rectangle (Fig. 7).

    a = length of one side, b = length of other side.

    d = diagonal.

    $d = \sqrt{a^2 + b^2}.$

Area $= ab = a\sqrt{d^2 - a^2}.$

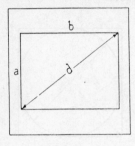

FIG. 7.

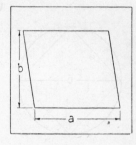

FIG. 8.

Parallelogram (Fig. 8).

    a = length of longer side, b = perpendicular distance to base.

Area $= ab.$

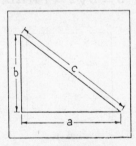

FIG. 9.

Right-angled Triangle (Fig. 9).

    Sides, a, b and c.

$$\text{Area} = \frac{ab}{2} = \frac{a}{2}\sqrt{c^2 - a^2}$$

$$= \frac{b}{2}\sqrt{c^2 - b^2}.$$

Acute-angled Triangle (Fig. 10).

$$\text{Area} = \frac{bh}{2} = \frac{b}{2}\sqrt{a^2 - \left(\frac{a^2 + b^2 - c^2}{2b}\right)^2}$$
$$= \sqrt{s(s-a)(s-b)(s-c)} \quad \text{where } s = \frac{a+b+c}{2}.$$

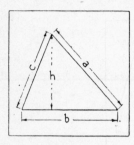

Fig. 10.

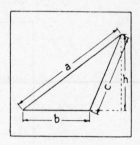

Fig. 11.

Obtuse-angled Triangle (Fig. 11).

$$\text{Area} = \frac{bh}{2} = \frac{b}{2}\sqrt{c^2 - \left(\frac{a^2 - c^2 - b^2}{2b}\right)^2}$$
$$= \sqrt{s(s-a)(s-b)(s-c)} \quad \text{where } s = \tfrac{1}{2}(a+b+c).$$

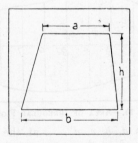

Fig. 12.

Trapezoid (Fig. 12).

$$\text{Area} = \frac{h}{2}(a+b).$$

Trapezium (Fig. 13).

Perpendicular heights from upper corners to base are h and l; base divided into three sections, a, b and c, by these perpendiculars.

$$\text{Area} = \frac{h(b + c) + l(a + b)}{2}$$
$$= \frac{(h + l)b + ch + al}{2}.$$

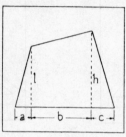

FIG. 13.

Areas of Irregular Figures.

Method 1 (Fig. 14).

Select the longer dimension and draw a line AB. Draw perpendiculars xx and yy to AB and tangential to the ends of curve. Divide the distance zz into a number of equal parts $z1, 12, 23 \ldots$

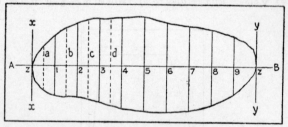

FIG. 14.—AREA OF IRREGULAR FIGURE.

Erect perpendiculars a, b, c, d . . . at the mid-points of these sections. Then, if a, b, c, d . . . represent the lengths of these ordinates intercepted by the curve, and $n =$ number of ordinates,

Area of curve = Mean height × distance zz
$$= \frac{(a + b + c + d + \ldots.)}{n} \times zz.$$

Method 2. Simpson's Rule for Areas (Fig. 15).

Divide the base into any even number of equal parts, i.e. there must be an odd number of ordinates.

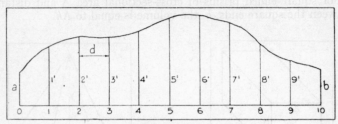

FIG. 15.—SIMPSON'S RULE FOR AREAS.

Let d = distance apart of ordinates.

  s = sum of all the even ordinate heights, $2'$, $4'$, $6'$ . . .
  n = sum of all the odd ordinate heights, $1'$, $3'$, $5'$ . . .
  e = sum of first and last, or end ordinates a and b.

Then Area = $\dfrac{e + 2n + 4s}{3} \times d$.

Rule.—Add together the first and last ordinate, twice the sum of the odd ordinates and four times the sum of the even ordinates, and multiply the result by one-third the distance between the ordinates.

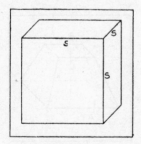

FIG. 16.

VOLUMES OF PLANE SOLIDS

Cube (Fig. 16).

  Length of side = s.
  Volume = s^3.

464

Parallelopiped or Square Prism (Fig. 17).

Lengths of three contiguous sides *a*, *b* and *c*, respectively.
Volume = $a \times b \times c$.

For square-ended prisms of cross-sectional area A and distance between the square ends, *h*, the volume is equal to A*h*.

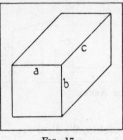

FIG. 17.

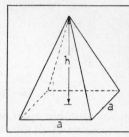

FIG. 18.

Pyramid (Fig. 18).

Sides of square base = *a*,   height = *h*.

Volume = $\dfrac{a^2 h}{3}$.

For pyramids with base of area A and height *h*, the volume is $\dfrac{Ah}{3}$.

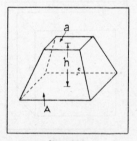

FIG. 19.

Volume of Frustum of Pyramid (Fig. 19).

A = area of base, *a* = area of top face,   *h* = height.

Volume = $\dfrac{h}{3}(A + a + \sqrt{A \times a})$.

Wedge (Fig. 20).   With parallel or square ends.

a and *b* are sides of base,   *h* = height.

Volume = $\dfrac{abh}{2}$.

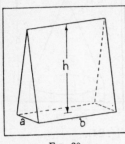

FIG. 20.

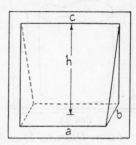

FIG. 21.

Wedge (Fig. 21).   With longer edge than base.

a and *b* are sides of base, *c* = length of edge, *h* = height.

Volume = $\dfrac{(2a + c)bh}{6}$.

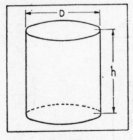

FIG. 22.

SURFACES AND VOLUMES OF SOLIDS

Cylinder of Diameter D *and Height* h (Fig. 22).

Area = $\dfrac{\pi D}{2}$ (D + 2*h*) = 1·5708D (D + 2*h*).

Volume = $\dfrac{\pi D^2 h}{4}$ = 0·7854D²*h*.

Cylinder of any Constant Cross Section (Fig. 23).
  Area = perimeter × height + 2 (area of cross section).
  Volume = area of cross section × height.

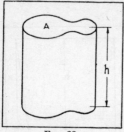

FIG. 23.

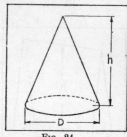

FIG. 24.

Cone of Base Diameter D *and Height* h (Fig. 24).

$$\text{Area of conical surface} = \frac{\pi D}{2} \sqrt{\frac{D^2}{4} + h^2}$$
$$= \frac{\pi D}{4} \sqrt{D^2 + 4h^2}$$
$$= 0 \cdot 7854\, D \sqrt{D^2 + 4h^2}.$$

$$\text{Volume} = \frac{\pi D^2 h}{12}$$
$$= 0 \cdot 2618 D^2 h.$$

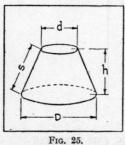

FIG. 25.

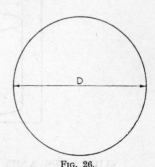

FIG. 26.

Frustum of Cone (Fig. 25).
  Larger diameter = D, smaller diameter = d, height = h.
  Area of conical surface $= \dfrac{\pi S}{2}\,(D+d)$ where $S = \frac{1}{2}\sqrt{(D-d)^2 + 4h^2}$
$$= 1 \cdot 5708 S\,(D + d).$$
  Volume $= 0 \cdot 2618 h\,(D^2 + Dd + d^2).$

Sphere (Fig. 26).
  Diameter $= D$.
  Area of surface $= \pi D^2 = 3{\cdot}1416D^2$.
  Volume of sphere $= \dfrac{\pi D^3}{6} = 0{\cdot}5236D^3$.

Spherical Sector (Fig. 27).
  Diameter $= D$,   height $= h$,   diameter of segment $= C$.
  Surface of sector $= \dfrac{\pi D}{2}\left(2h + \dfrac{C}{2}\right) = 1{\cdot}5708D\left(2h + \dfrac{C}{2}\right)$
    where $C = 2\sqrt{h(D - h)}$.
  Volume of sector $= \dfrac{\pi D^2 h}{6} = 0{\cdot}5236D^2 h$.

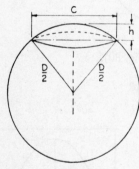

FIG. 27.

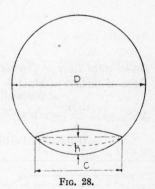

FIG. 28.

Spherical Segment (Fig. 28).
  Diameter $= D$,   height $= h$,   diameter of segment $= C$.
  Surface of segment $= \pi D h = 3{\cdot}1416D h$

$$= \pi\left(h^2 + \frac{C^2}{4}\right)$$
$$C^2 = 4\left(D h - h^2\right)$$
$$C = 2\sqrt{h\left(D - h\right)}.$$

  Volume of segment $= \pi h^2\left(\dfrac{D}{2} - \dfrac{h}{3}\right)$

$$= \frac{\pi h}{2}\left(\frac{C^2}{4} + \frac{h^2}{3}\right)$$

468

Torus, or Circular Section Ring (Fig. 29).

D = mean diameter,   d = diameter of section.

Area of surface = $\pi^2 dD = 9.8696dD$.

Volume = $\dfrac{\pi^2 d^2 D}{4} = 2.4674d^2 D$.

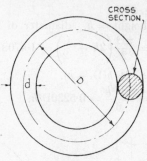

Fig. 29.

Parallel-sided Link of Circular Section (Fig. 30).

Area of surface = $\pi^2 dD + 2\pi lD$
$$= 9.8696dD + 6.2832ld.$$

Volume = $\dfrac{\pi d^2}{4}(\pi D + 2l)$
$$= 0.7854d^2(3.1416D + 2l).$$

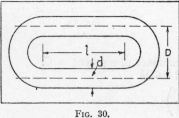

Fig. 30.

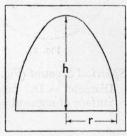

Fig. 31.

Paraboloid of Revolution (Fig. 31).

h = height,   r = radius.

Area of surface = $0.5236 \dfrac{r}{h^2} \{(4h^2 + r^2) = r^3\}$.

Volume = $\dfrac{\pi r^2 h}{2} = 1.5708r^2 h$.

THE ELLIPSE

Major axis AC $= 2a$. Minor axis BD $= 2b$.

Length of periphery ABCD $= \pi \sqrt{2(a^2 + b^2)}$ approximately. (Fig. 32).

Area $= \pi ab = 3.1416ab$.

Construction of Ellipse (Method 1). (Fig. 33.)

Given the lengths of the major and minor axes, $2a$ and $2b$, respectively.

Draw two lines AC and BD at right angles, intersecting at O.

Make OA $=$ OC $= a$, and OB $=$ OD $= b$.

With B as centre and length a as radius describe an arc to cut the major axis at E and F, respectively.

The two points E and F are the foci of the ellipse.

In OE take any convenient points, 1, 2, 3...

With A1 as radius describe arcs with centres E and F. Similarly with C1 as radius describe arcs with centres E and F. These arcs intersect at the four points 1′ which lie on the required ellipse.

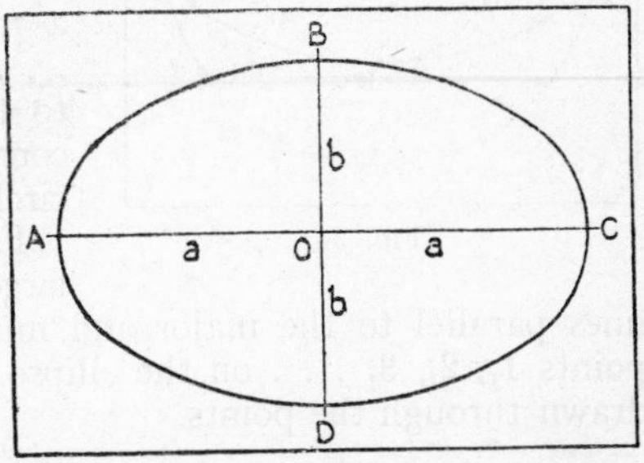

Fig. 32.

Repeat this construction for the points 2, 3 . . . to obtain the other points 2′, 3′ on the ellipse. A fair curve should then be drawn through the points.

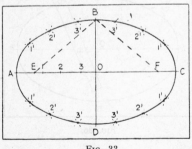

Fig. 33.

Method 2. Mechanical method of drawing ellipse (Fig. 33).

Find the focal points E and F as in Method 1.

Insert pins at E, F and B, and take a piece of fine cord and pass it fairly tightly around the pins at E, F and B so as to form the triangle EFB.

Next, remove the pin B and replace by a sharp pencil and, keeping the string taut all the time, trace out the ellipse.

470

The principle of this method depends upon the fact that in an ellipse the sum of the distances of any point on the ellipse, from the two focal points, is always the same, i.e. is equal to $EB + BF$.

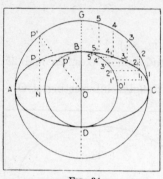

FIG. 34.

Method 3. Circle projection method (Fig. 34).

Given the major and minor axes, draw two concentric circles with centre O and radii a and b equal to one-half the major and minor axes, respectively.

Divide the circular arc GC into a number of equal parts 1, 2, 3 . . . Join these points 1, 2, 3 . . . to the centre O so as to cut the corresponding arc of the smaller circle in the points 1′, 2′, 3′ . . . From similar points on the larger and smaller circles draw lines parallel to the major and minor axes to give the required points 1_1, 2_1, 3_1 . . . on the ellipse. A fair curve should then be drawn through the points.

Method 4. Mechanical trammel method (Fig. 35).

Given the major and minor axes $2a$ and $2b$, respectively, draw two lines AC and BD at right angles, intersecting at O, making $OA = OC = a$ and $OB = OD = b$.

Take a strip of stiff sheet material, e.g. cardboard, with one edge straight, and mark off two distances along one edge, viz. $pm = b$ and $pn = a$. Then if the two points m and n are moved along the lines AC and BD, respectively, the point p will trace an ellipse and its positions can be marked with a sharp pencil point.

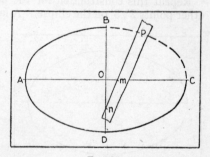

FIG. 35.

A piece of thin celluloid or Perspex with a central line and three short cross hair lines can be used instead of marks on the edge of a card. The elliptic chuck, based upon this principle, has a pair of tee-slots at right angles, and a bar *pn* with slider blocks at *m* and *n* is provided to slide in the tee-slots. At *m* and *n* the bar *pn* is provided with pins and bearings, so that as the blocks slide in the fixed chuck the pointer or tool *p* describes an ellipse. By means of screw adjustments the distances *pm* and *pn* can be varied, to cover a wide range of elliptical shapes and sizes.

MEASUREMENT OR SETTING OF TAPER ANGLES

1. *External Tapers.*

These may be checked with a " Go " and " Not Go " taper gauge as shown in Fig. 36. The semi-cylindrical projection on the left has two engraved lines, marked " N "
and " NG" respectively, and, to
pass inspection, the larger square
end of the taper under test should
lie between these two marks.

Another method is to employ a
works optical-projection apparatus
and to throw a much-enlarged image,
e.g. 10, 25 or 50 times, upon the

FIG. 36.—EXTERNAL TAPER GAUGE.

projection screen. A substantial part of the image is then measured, as shown in Fig. 37, namely, the diameters D and *d* and the axial distance L.

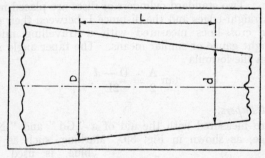

FIG. 37.

From these measurements the taper half-angle A is calculated as follows :

$$\tan \frac{A}{2} = \frac{D - d}{2L}.$$

472

For taper measurement, or taper-setting purposes, the adjustable gauge shown in Fig. 38* may be used. This is provided with a frame of any convenient shape carrying two accurate straight-edges E and F having slots for the clamping screws S. For setting

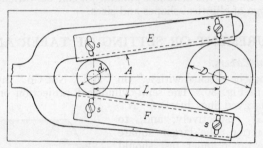

FIG. 38.—TAPER GAUGE.

purposes, standard cylinders or discs of diameters D and d are set at a certain distance apart L to give the taper angle A, as follows :

$$L = \frac{D - d}{2 \tan \dfrac{A}{2}}.$$

For checking the taper angle the straight-edges E and F are adjusted so as to lie flush with the taper under test and then locked in position. Two standard cylinders or discs are placed in contact with the straight-edges and the distance L between their engraved centres or cross-lines measured with a travelling microscope, vernier-height gauge or similar means. The taper angle A is estimated from the formula

$$\tan \frac{A}{2} = \frac{D - d}{2L}.$$

2. *Internal Tapers.*

These are measured with the aid of a " Go " and " Not Go " taper gauge, as shown in Fig. 39. Marking, such as Prussian

FIG. 39.—INTERNAL TAPER GAUGE.

blue, is used to indicate whether the gauge bears evenly all along the internal tapered surface.

* *Engineering Precision Measurements.* A. W. Judge (Chapman & Hall Ltd., London).

TRIGONOMETRICAL FORMULÆ

1. Right-angled Triangles (Fig. 40)

sine A $= \dfrac{BC}{AB} = \dfrac{a}{c}$ cosine A $= \dfrac{AC}{AB} = \dfrac{b}{c}$

tangent A $= \dfrac{BC}{AC} = \dfrac{a}{b}$ cotangent A $= \dfrac{AC}{BC} = \dfrac{b}{a} = \dfrac{1}{\text{tangent A}}$

secant A $= \dfrac{c}{b} = \dfrac{1}{\text{cosine A}}$ cosecant A $= \dfrac{c}{a} = \dfrac{1}{\text{sine A}}$

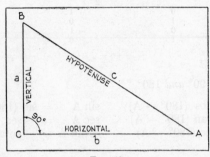

Fig. 40.

Abbreviations: sin = sine; cos = cosine; tan = tangent; cosec = cosecant; sec = secant; cotan = cotangent; versin = versed sine; coversin = versed cosine.

$$\text{versin A} = \frac{c - b}{c} = 1 - \cos A.$$

$$\text{coversin A} = \frac{c - a}{c} = 1 - \sin A.$$

Length of Sides

$$a = c \sin A \quad = b \tan A \quad = \sqrt{c^2 - b^2}$$
$$b = c \cos A \quad = a \cotan A \quad = \sqrt{c^2 - a^2}$$
$$c = a \cosec A \quad = b \sec A \quad = \sqrt{a^2 + b^2}$$

Angles

$$A + B = 90°. \qquad A = 90° - B. \qquad B = 90° - A.$$
$$\cos A = \sin (90° - A) \qquad \sin A \quad = \cos (90° - A)$$
$$\tan A = \cot (90° - A) \qquad \cotan A = \tan (90° - A)$$
$$\sec A = \cosec (90° - A) \qquad \cosec A = \sec (90° - A)$$

Trigonometrical Values of Special Angles

Angle	Cosine	Sine	Tangent
0°	1	0	0
30°	$\frac{\sqrt{3}}{2} = 0 \cdot 866025$	$\frac{1}{2} = 0 \cdot 5$	$\frac{1}{\sqrt{3}} = 0 \cdot 577350$
45°	$\frac{1}{\sqrt{2}} = 0 \cdot 707107$	$\frac{1}{\sqrt{2}} = 0 \cdot 707107$	1
60°	$\frac{1}{2} = 0 \cdot 5$	$\frac{\sqrt{3}}{2} = 0 \cdot 866025$	$\sqrt{3} = 1 \cdot 732051$
90°	0	1	∞ (infinity)
180°	− 1	0	0
270°	0	− 1	∞
360°	1	0	0

Angles between 90° *and* 180°.

$$\cos A = - \cos (180° - A) \qquad \sin A = \sin (180° - A);$$
$$\tan A = - \tan (180° - A) \qquad \sec A = - \sec (180° - A);$$
$$\operatorname{cosec} A = \operatorname{cosec} (180° - A) \qquad \operatorname{cotan} A = - \operatorname{cotan} (180° - A).$$

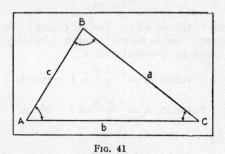

Fig. 41

2. Acute-angled Triangles (Fig. 41)

$$a^2 = b^2 + c^2 - 2bc \cos A$$
$$b^2 = a^2 + c^2 - 2ac \cos B$$
$$c^2 = a^2 + b^2 - 2ab \cos C$$

$$a = \frac{b \sin A}{\sin B} \quad b = \frac{c \sin B}{\sin C},$$

or $\dfrac{a}{\sin A} = \dfrac{b}{\sin B} = \dfrac{c}{\sin C}$

$$\cos A = \frac{b^2 + c^2 - a^2}{2bc}$$

$$\cos B = \frac{c^2 + a^2 - b^2}{2ac}$$

$$\cos C = \frac{a^2 + b^2 - c^2}{2ab}.$$

If perimeter $2s = a + b + c$, then:

$$\cos \frac{A}{2} = \sqrt{\frac{s(s-a)}{bc}}$$

$$\sin \frac{A}{2} = \sqrt{\frac{(s-b)(s-c)}{bc}}$$

$$\tan \frac{A}{2} = \sqrt{\frac{(s-b)(s-a)}{s(s-a)}}.$$

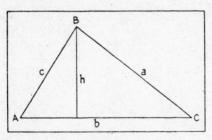

Fig. 42.

Area of triangle ABC $= \dfrac{a^2 \sin B \sin C}{2 \sin A}$

$\qquad\qquad\qquad = \frac{1}{2}\, ab \sin C$

$\qquad\qquad\qquad = \sqrt{s(s-a)(s-b)(s-c)}.$

In general. Area $= \frac{1}{2}$ base $\times$ perpendicular height

$\qquad\qquad = \frac{1}{2}\, bh$ (Fig. 42).

COMPOUND ANGLES

$$\sin (A + B) = \sin A \cos B + \cos A \sin B$$
$$\sin (A - B) = \sin A \cos B - \cos A \sin B$$
$$\cos (A + B) = \cos A \cos B - \sin A \sin B$$
$$\cos (A - B) = \cos A \cos B + \sin A \sin B$$

$$\tan (A + B) = \frac{\tan A + \tan B}{1 - \tan A \tan B}$$

$$\tan (A - B) = \frac{\tan A - \tan B}{1 + \tan A \tan B}.$$

ANGULAR MEASUREMENT

60 seconds (60″) = 1 minute.
60 minutes (60′) = 1 degree.
90 degrees (90°) = 1 right angle.

$$1 \text{ radian} = \frac{360}{2\pi} \text{ degrees} = 57{\cdot}295779 \text{ degrees}$$
$$= 57° \ 17′ \ 45″.$$

TRIGONOMETRICAL TABLES

Deg.	Min.	Sine	Cosine	Tangent	Cotangent	Secant	Cosecant		
0	0	·00000	1·00000	·00000	Infinity	1·00000	Infinity	90	0
	5	·00145	·99999	·00145	687·55	1·00000	687·55		55
	10	·00291	·99999	·00291	343·77	1·00000	343·77		50
	15	·00436	·99999	·00436	229·18	1·00001	229·18		45
	20	·00582	·99998	·00582	171·88	1·00002	171·89		40
	25	·00727	·99997	·00727	137·51	1·00003	137·51		35
	30	·00873	·99996	·00873	114·59	1·00004	114·59		30
	35	·01018	·99995	·01018	98·218	1·00005	98·223		25
	40	·01163	·99993	·01164	85·940	1·00007	85·946		20
	45	·01309	·99991	·01309	76·390	1·00009	76·400		15
	50	·01454	·99989	·01454	68·750	1·00011	68·757		10
	55	·01600	·99987	·01600	62·499	1·00013	62·507		5
1	0	·01745	·99984	·01745	57·290	1·00015	57·299	89	0
	5	·01891	·99982	·01891	52·882	1·00018	52·892		55
	10	·02036	·99979	·02036	49·104	1·00021	49·114		50
	15	·02181	·99976	·02182	45·829	1·00024	45·840		45
	20	·02327	·99973	·02327	42·964	1·00027	42·976		40
	25	·02472	·99969	·02473	40·436	1·00031	40·448		35
	30	·02618	·99966	·02619	38·188	1·00034	38·202		30
	35	·02763	·99962	·02764	36·178	1·00038	36·191		25
	40	·02908	·99957	·02910	34·368	1·00042	34·382		20
	45	·03054	·99953	·03055	32·730	1·00047	32·745		15
	50	·03199	·99950	·03201	31·242	1·00051	31·258		10
	55	·03345	·99944	·03346	29·882	1·00056	29·899		5
2	0	·03490	·99939	·03492	28·636	1·00061	28·654	88	0
	5	·03635	·99934	·03638	27·490	1·00066	27·508		55
	10	·03781	·99928	·03783	26·432	1·00072	26·450		50
	15	·03926	·99923	·03929	25·452	1·00077	25·471		45
	20	·04071	·99917	·04075	24·542	1·00083	24·562		40
	25	·04217	·99911	·04220	23·694	1·00089	23·716		35
	30	·04362	·99905	·04366	22·904	1·00095	22·926		30
	35	·04507	·99898	·04512	22·164	1·00102	22·186		25
	40	·04652	·99892	·04658	21·470	1·00108	21·494		20
	45	·04798	·99885	·04803	20·819	1·00115	20·843		15
	50	·04943	·99878	·04949	20·206	1·00122	20·230		10
	55	·05088	·99870	·05095	19·627	1·00130	19·653		5
		Cosine	Sine	Cotangent	Tangent	Cosecant	Secant	Deg.	Min.

Trigonometrical Tables (contd.)

Deg.	Min.	Sine	Cosine	Tangent	Cotangent	Secant	Cosecant		
3	0	·05234	·99863	·05241	19·081	1·0014	19·107	87	0
	5	·05379	·99855	·05387	18·564	1·0015	18·591		55
	10	·05524	·99847	·05532	18·075	1·0015	18·103		50
	15	·05669	·99839	·05678	17·611	1·0016	17·639		45
	20	·05814	·99831	·05824	17·169	1·0017	17·198		40
	25	·05960	·99822	·05970	16·750	1·0018	16·779		35
	30	·06105	·99813	·06116	16·350	1·0019	16·380		30
	35	·06250	·99804	·06262	15·969	1·0020	16·000		25
	40	·06395	·99795	·06408	15·605	1·0020	15·637		20
	45	·06540	·99786	·06554	15·257	1·0021	15·290		15
	50	·06685	·99776	·06700	14·924	1·0022	14·958		10
	55	·06831	·99766	·06846	14·606	1·0023	14·640		5
4	0	·06976	·99756	·06993	14·301	1·0024	14·336	86	0
	5	·07121	·99746	·07139	14·008	1·0025	14·043		55
	10	·07266	·99736	·07285	13·727	1·0026	13·763		50
	15	·07411	·99725	·07431	13·457	1·0028	13·494		45
	20	·07556	·99714	·07578	13·197	1·0029	13·235		40
	25	·07701	·99703	·07724	12·947	1·0030	12·985		35
	30	·07846	·99692	·07870	12·706	1·0031	12·745		30
	35	·07991	·99680	·08016	12·474	1·0032	12·514		25
	40	·08136	·99668	·08163	12·250	1·0033	12·291		20
	45	·08281	·99657	·08309	12·035	1·0034	12·076		15
	50	·08426	·99644	·08456	11·826	1·0036	11·868		10
	55	·08571	·99632	·08602	11·625	1·0037	11·668		5
5	0	·08716	·99619	·08749	11·430	1·0038	11·474	85	0
	5	·08860	·99607	·08895	11·242	1·0039	11·286		55
	10	·09005	·99594	·09042	11·059	1·0041	11·104		50
	15	·09150	·99580	·09189	10·883	1·0042	10·929		45
	20	·09295	·99567	·09335	10·712	1·0043	10·758		40
	25	·09440	·99553	·09482	10·546	1·0045	10·593		35
	30	·09585	·99540	·09629	10·385	1·0046	10·433		30
	35	·09729	·99526	·09776	10·229	1·0048	10·278		25
	40	·09874	·99511	·09923	10·078	1·0049	10·127		20
	45	·10019	·99497	·10069	9·9310	1·0051	9·9812		15
	50	·10163	·99482	·10216	9·7782	1·0052	9·8391		10
	55	·10308	·99467	·10363	9·6493	1·0054	9·7010		5
		Cosine	Sine	Cotangent	Tangent	Cosecant	Secant	Deg.	Min.

Trigonometrical Tables (*contd.*)

Deg.	Min.	Sine	Cosine	Tangent	Cotangent	Secant	Cosecant		
6	0	·10453	·99452	·10510	9·5144	1·0055	9·5668	84	0
	5	·10597	·99437	·10657	9·3831	1·0057	9·4362		55
	10	·10742	·99421	·10805	9·2553	1·0058	9·3092		50
	15	·10887	·99406	·10952	9·1309	1·0060	9·1855		45
	20	·11031	·99390	·11099	9·0098	1·0061	9·0651		40
	25	·11176	·99374	·11246	8·8918	1·0063	8·9479		35
	30	·11320	·99357	·11394	8·7769	1·0065	8·8337		30
	35	·11465	·99341	·11541	8·6648	1·0066	8·7223		25
	40	·11609	·99324	·11688	8·5555	1·0068	8·6138		20
	45	·11754	·99307	·11836	8·4490	1·0070	8·5079		15
	50	·11898	·99290	·11983	8·3450	1·0071	8·4047		10
	55	·12043	·99272	·12131	8·2434	1·0073	8·3039		5
7	0	·12187	·99255	·12278	8·1443	1·0075	8·2055	83	0
	5	·12331	·99237	·12426	8·0476	1·0077	8·1095		55
	10	·12476	·99219	·12574	7·9530	1·0079	8·0156		50
	15	·12620	·99200	·12722	7·8606	1·0081	7·9240		45
	20	·12764	·99182	·12869	7·7703	1·0082	7·8344		40
	25	·12908	·99163	·13017	7·6821	1·0084	7·7469		35
	30	·13053	·99144	·13165	7·5957	1·0086	7·6613		30
	35	·13197	·99125	·13313	7·5113	1·0088	7·5776		25
	40	·13341	·99106	·13461	7·4287	1·0090	7·4957		20
	45	·13485	·99087	·13609	7·3479	1·0092	7·4156		15
	50	·13629	·99067	·13758	7·2687	1·0094	7·3372		10
	55	·13773	·99047	·13906	7·1912	1·0096	7·2604		5
8	0	·13917	·99027	·14054	7·1154	1·0098	7·1853	82	0
	5	·14061	·99006	·14202	7·0410	1·0100	7·1117		55
	10	·14205	·98986	·14351	6·9682	1·0102	7·0396		50
	15	·14349	·98965	·14499	6·8970	1·0105	6·9690		45
	20	·14493	·98944	·14648	6·8269	1·0107	6·8998		40
	25	·14637	·98923	·14796	6·7584	1·0109	6·8320		35
	30	·14781	·98902	·14945	6·6912	1·0111	6·7655		30
	35	·14925	·98880	·15094	6·6252	1·0113	6·7003		25
	40	·15069	·98858	·15243	6·5605	1·0115	6·6363		20
	45	·15212	·98836	·15391	6·4971	1·0118	6·5736		15
	50	·15356	·98814	·15540	6·4348	1·0120	6·5121		10
	55	·15500	·98791	·15689	6·3737	1·0122	6·4517		5
		Cosine	Sine	Cotangent	Tangent	Cosecant	Secant	Deg.	Min.

Trigonometrical Tables (*contd.*)

Deg.	Min.	Sine	Cosine	Tangent	Cotangent	Secant	Cosecant		
9	0	·15643	·98769	·15838	6·3137	1·0125	6·3924	81	0
	5	·15787	·98746	·15988	6·2548	1·0127	6·3343		55
	10	·15931	·98723	·16137	6·1970	1·0129	6·2772		50
	15	·16074	·98700	·16286	6·1402	1·0132	6·2211		45
	20	·16218	·98676	·16435	6·0844	1·0134	6·1661		40
	25	·16361	·98652	·16585	6·0296	1·0137	6·1120		35
	30	·16505	·98629	·16734	5·9758	1·0139	6·0589		30
	35	·16648	·98604	·16884	5·9228	1·0141	6·0067		25
	40	·16792	·98580	·17033	5·8708	1·0144	5·9554		20
	45	·16935	·98556	·17183	5·8197	1·0147	5·9049		15
	50	·17078	·98531	·17333	5·7694	1·0149	5·8554		10
	55	·17222	·98506	·17483	5·7199	1·0152	5·8067		5
10	0	·17365	·98481	·17633	5·6713	1·0154	5·7588	80	0
	5	·17508	·98455	·17783	5·6234	1·0157	5·7117		55
	10	·17651	·98430	·17933	5·5764	1·0159	5·6653		50
	15	·17794	·98404	·18083	5·5301	1·0162	5·6198		45
	20	·17937	·98378	·18233	5·4845	1·0165	5·5749		40
	25	·18080	·98352	·18383	5·4397	1·0168	5·5308		35
	30	·18224	·98325	·18534	5·3955	1·0170	5·4874		30
	35	·18366	·98299	·18684	5·3521	1·0173	5·4447		25
	40	·18509	·98272	·18835	5·3093	1·0176	5·4026		20
	45	·18652	·98245	·18986	5·2671	1·0179	5·3612		15
	50	·18795	·98218	·19136	5·2257	1·0181	5·3205		10
	55	·18938	·98190	·19287	5·1848	1·0184	5·2804		5
11	0	·19081	·98163	·19438	5·1445	1·0187	5·2408	79	0
	5	·19224	·98135	·19589	5·1049	1·0190	5·2019		55
	10	·19366	·98107	·19740	5·0658	1·0193	5·1636		50
	15	·19509	·98078	·19891	5·0273	1·0196	5·1258		45
	20	·19652	·98050	·20042	4·9894	1·0199	5·0886		40
	25	·19794	·98021	·20194	4·9520	1·0202	5·0520		35
	30	·19937	·97992	·20345	4·9152	1·0205	5·0158		30
	35	·20079	·97963	·20497	4·8788	1·0208	4·9802		25
	40	·20222	·97934	·20648	4·8430	1·0211	4·9452		20
	45	·20364	·97905	·20800	4·8077	1·0214	4·9106		15
	50	·20507	·97875	·20952	4·7729	1·0217	4·8765		10
	55	·20649	·97845	·21104	4·7385	1·0220	4·8429		5
		Cosine	Sine	Cotangent	Tangent	Cosecant	Secant	Deg.	Min.

Trigonometrical Tables (*contd.*)

Deg.	Min.	Sine	Cosine	Tangent	Cotangent	Secant	Cosecant		
12	0	·20791	·97815	·21256	4·7046	1·0223	4·8097	78	0
	5	·20933	·97784	·21408	4·6712	1·0227	4·7770		55
	10	·21076	·97754	·21560	4·6382	1·0230	4·7448		50
	15	·21218	·97723	·21712	4·6057	1·0233	4·7130		45
	20	·21360	·97692	·21864	4·5736	1·0236	4·6817		40
	25	·21502	·97661	·22017	4·5420	1·0239	4·6507		35
	30	·21644	·97630	·22169	4·5107	1·0243	4·6202		30
	35	·21786	·97598	·22322	4·4799	1·0246	4·5901		25
	40	·21928	·97566	·22475	4·4494	1·0249	4·5604		20
	45	·22070	·97534	·22628	4·4194	1·0253	4·5311		15
	50	·22212	·97502	·22781	4·3897	1·0256	4·5022		10
	55	·22353	·97470	·22934	4·3604	1·0260	4·4736		5
13	0	·22495	·97437	·23087	4·3315	1·0263	4·4454	77	0
	5	·22637	·97404	·23240	4·3029	1·0266	4·4176		55
	10	·22778	·97371	·23393	4·2747	1·0270	4·3901		50
	15	·22920	·97338	·23547	4·2468	1·0273	4·3630		45
	20	·23062	·97304	·23700	4·2193	1·0277	4·3362		50
	25	·23203	·97271	·23854	4·1921	1·0281	4·3098		35
	30	·23344	·97237	·24008	4·1653	1·0284	4·2837		30
	35	·23486	·97203	·24162	4·1388	1·0288	4·2579		25
	40	·23627	·97169	·24316	4·1126	1·0291	4·2324		20
	45	·23769	·97134	·24470	4·0867	1·0295	4·2072		15
	50	·23910	·97099	·24624	4·0611	1·0299	4·1824		10
	55	·24051	·97065	·24778	4·0358	1·0302	4·1578		5
14	0	·24192	·97030	·24933	4·0108	1·0306	4·1336	76	0
	5	·24333	·96994	·25087	3·9861	1·0310	4·1096		55
	10	·24474	·96959	·25242	3·9616	1·0314	4·0859		50
	15	·24615	·96923	·25397	3·9375	1·0317	4·0625		45
	20	·24756	·96887	·25552	3·9136	1·0321	4·0394		40
	25	·24897	·96851	·25707	3·8900	1·0325	4·0165		35
	30	·25038	·96815	·25862	3·8667	1·0329	3·9939		30
	35	·25179	·96778	·26017	3·8436	1·0333	3·9716		25
	40	·25319	·96741	·26172	3·8208	1·0337	3·9495		20
	45	·25460	·96705	·26328	3·7983	1·0341	3·9277		15
	50	·25601	·96667	·26483	3·7759	1·0345	3·9061		10
	55	·25741	·96630	·26639	3·7539	1·0349	3·8848		5
		Cosine	Sine	Cotangent	Tangent	Cosecant	Secant	Deg.	Min.

E.W.D.—16

Trigonometrical Tables (*contd.*)

Deg.	Min.	Sine	Cosine	Tangent	Cotangent	Secant	Cosecant		
15	0	·25882	·96593	·26795	3·7320	1·0353	3·8637	**75**	**0**
	5	·26022	·96555	·26951	3·7105	1·0357	3·8428		55
	10	·26163	·96517	·27107	3·6891	1·0361	3·8222		50
	15	·26303	·96479	·27263	3·6680	1·0365	3·8018		45
	20	·26443	·96440	·27419	3·6470	1·0369	3·7817		40
	25	·26584	·96402	·27576	3·6264	1·0373	3·7617		35
	30	·26724	·96363	·27732	3·6059	1·0377	3·7420		30
	35	·26864	·96324	·27889	3·5856	1·0382	3·7225		25
	40	·27004	·96285	·28046	3·5656	1·0386	3·7031		20
	45	·27144	·96245	·28203	3·5457	1·0390	3·6840		15
	50	·27284	·96206	·28360	3·5261	1·0394	3·6651		10
	55	·27424	·96166	·28517	3·5067	1·0399	3·6464		5
16	0	·27564	·96126	·28674	3·4874	1·0403	3·6280	**74**	**0**
	5	·27703	·96086	·28832	3·4684	1·0407	3·6096		55
	10	·27843	·96046	·28990	3·4495	1·0412	3·5915		50
	15	·27983	·96005	·29147	3·4308	1·0416	3·5736		45
	20	·28122	·95964	·29305	3·4124	1·0421	3·5559		40
	25	·28262	·95923	·29463	3·3941	1·0425	3·5383		35
	30	·28401	·95882	·29621	3·3759	1·0429	3·5209		30
	35	·28541	·98841	·29780	3·3580	1·0434	3·5037		25
	40	·28680	·95799	·29938	3·3402	1·0438	3·4867		20
	45	·28820	·95757	·30097	3·3226	1·0443	3·4699		15
	50	·28959	·95715	·30255	3·3052	1·0448	3·4532		10
	55	·29098	·95673	·30414	3·2879	1·0452	3·4367		5
17	0	·29237	·95630	·30573	3·2708	1·0457	3·4203	**73**	**0**
	5	·29376	·95588	·30732	3·2539	1·0462	3·4041		55
	10	·29515	·95545	·30891	3·2371	1·0466	3·3881		50
	15	·29654	·95502	·31051	3·2205	1·0471	3·3722		45
	20	·29793	·95459	·31210	3·2041	1·0476	3·3565		40
	25	·29932	·95415	·31370	3·1877	1·0480	3·3409		35
	30	·30071	·95372	·31530	3·1716	1·0485	3·3255		30
	35	·30209	·95328	·31690	3·1556	1·0490	3·3102		25
	40	·30348	·95284	·31850	3·1397	1·0495	3·2951		20
	45	·30486	·95240	·32010	3·1240	1·0500	3·2801		15
	50	·30625	·95195	·32171	3·1084	1·0505	3·2653		10
	55	·30763	·95150	·32331	3·0930	1·0510	3·2506		5
		Cosine	Sine	Cotangent	Tangent	Cosecant	Secant	Deg.	Min.

Trigonometrical Tables (*contd.*)

Deg.	Min.	Sine	Cosine	Tangent	Cotangent	Secant	Cosecant		
18	0	·30902	·95106	·32492	3·0777	1·0515	3·2361	72	0
	5	·31040	·95061	·32653	3·0625	1·0519	3·2216		55
	10	·31178	·95015	·32814	3·0475	1·0525	3·2074		50
	15	·31316	·94970	·32975	3·0326	1·0530	3·1932		45
	20	·31454	·94924	·33136	3·0178	1·0535	3·1792		40
	25	·31592	·94878	·33298	3·0032	1·0540	3·1653		35
	30	·31730	·94832	·33459	2·9887	1·0545	3·1515		30
	35	·31868	·94786	·33621	2·9743	1·0550	3·1379		25
	40	·32006	·94740	·33783	2·9600	1·0555	3·1244		20
	45	·32144	·94693	·33945	2·9459	1·0560	3·1101		15
	50	·32282	·94646	·34108	2·9319	1·0566	3·0977		10
	55	·32419	·94599	·34270	2·9180	1·0571	3·0846		5
19	0	·32557	·94552	·34433	2·9042	1·0576	3·0715	71	0
	5	·32694	·94504	·34595	2·8905	1·0581	3·0586		55
	10	·32832	·94457	·34758	2·8770	1·0587	3·0458		50
	15	·32969	·94409	·34922	2·8636	1·0592	3·0331		45
	20	·33106	·94361	·35085	2·8502	1·0598	3·0206		40
	25	·33244	·94313	·35248	2·8370	1·0603	3·0081		35
	30	·33381	·94264	·35412	2·8239	1·0608	2·9957		30
	35	·33518	·94215	·35576	2·8109	1·0614	2·9835		25
	40	·33655	·94167	·35740	2·7980	1·0619	2·9713		20
	45	·33792	·94118	·35904	2·7852	1·0625	2·9593		15
	50	·33928	·94068	·36068	2·7725	1·0631	2·9474		10
	55	·34065	·94019	·36232	2·7599	1·0636	2·9355		5
20	0	·34202	·93969	·36397	2·7475	1·0642	2·9238	70	0
	5	·34338	·93919	·36562	2·7351	1·0647	2·9122		55
	10	·34475	·93869	·36727	2·7228	1·0653	2·9006		50
	15	·34612	·93819	·36892	2·7106	1·0659	2·8892		45
	20	·34748	·93769	·37057	2·6985	1·0664	2·8778		40
	25	·34884	·93718	·37223	2·6865	1·0670	2·8666		35
	30	·35021	·93667	·37388	2·6746	1·0676	2·8554		30
	35	·35157	·93616	·37554	2·6628	1·0682	2·8444		25
	40	·35293	·93565	·37720	2·6511	1·0688	2·8334		20
	45	·35429	·93513	·37887	2·6394	1·0694	2·8225		15
	50	·35565	·93462	·38053	2·6279	1·0699	2·8117		10
	55	·35701	·93410	·38220	2·6165	1·0705	2·8010		5
		Cosine	Sine	Cotangent	Tangent	Cosecant	Secant	Deg.	Min.

Trigonometrical Tables (*contd.*)

Deg.	Min.	Sine	Cosine	Tangent	Cotangent	Secant	Cosecant		
21	0	·35837	·93358	·38386	2·6051	1·0711	2·7904	69	0
	5	·35972	·93306	·38553	2·5938	1·0717	2·7799		55
	10	·36108	·93253	·38720	2·5826	1·0723	2·7694		50
	15	·36244	·93201	·38888	2·5715	1·0729	2·7591		45
	20	·36379	·93148	·39055	2·5605	1·0736	2·7488		40
	25	·36515	·93095	·39223	2·5495	1·0742	2·7386		35
	30	·36650	·93042	·39391	2·5386	1·0748	2·7285		30
	35	·36785	·92988	·39559	2·5279	1·0754	2·7185		25
	40	·36921	·92935	·39727	2·5171	1·0760	2·7085		20
	45	·37056	·92881	·39896	2·5065	1·0766	2·6986		15
	50	·37191	·92827	·40065	2·4960	1·0773	2·6888		10
	55	·37326	·92773	·40233	2·4855	1·0779	2·6791		5
22	0	·37461	·92718	·40403	2·4751	1·0785	2·6695	68	0
	5	·37595	·92664	·40572	2·4648	1·0792	2·6599		55
	10	·37730	·92609	·40741	2·4545	1·0798	2·6504		50
	15	·37865	·92554	·40911	2·4443	1·0804	2·6410		45
	20	·37999	·92499	·41081	2·4342	1·0811	2·6316		40
	25	·38134	·92443	·41251	2·4242	1·0817	2·6223		35
	30	·38268	·92388	·41421	2·4142	1·0824	2·6131		30
	35	·38403	·92332	·41592	2·4043	1·0830	2·6040		25
	40	·38537	·92276	·41762	2·3945	1·0837	2·5949		20
	45	·38671	·92220	·41933	2·3847	1·0844	2·5859		15
	50	·38805	·92164	·42105	2·3750	1·0850	2·5770		10
	55	·38939	·92107	·42276	2·3654	1·0857	2·5681		5
23	0	·39073	·92050	·42447	2·3558	1·0864	2·5593	67	0
	5	·39207	·91994	·42619	2·3464	1·0870	2·5506		55
	10	·39341	·91936	·42791	2·3369	1·0877	2·5419		50
	15	·39474	·91879	·42963	2·3276	1·0884	2·5333		45
	20	·39608	·91822	·43136	2·3183	1·0891	2·5247		40
	25	·39741	·91764	·43308	2·3090	1·0897	2·5163		35
	30	·39875	·91706	·43481	2·2998	1·0904	2·5078		30
	35	·40008	·91648	·43654	2·2907	1·0911	2·4995		25
	40	·40141	·91590	·43828	2·2817	1·0918	2·4912		20
	45	·40275	·91531	·44001	2·2727	1·0925	2·4829		15
	50	·40408	·91472	·44175	2·2637	1·0932	2·4748		10
	55	·40541	·91414	·44349	2·2549	1·0939	2·4666		5
		Cosine	Sine	Cotangent	Tangent	Cosecant	Secant	Deg.	Min.

Trigonometrical Tables (*contd.*)

Deg.	Min.	Sine	Cosine	Tangent	Cotangent	Secant	Cosecant		
24	0	·40674	·91355	·44523	2·2460	1·0946	2·4586	66	0
	5	·40806	·91295	·44697	2·2373	1·0953	2·4506		55
	10	·40939	·91236	·44872	2·2286	1·0961	2·4426		50
	15	·41072	·91176	·45047	2·2199	1·0968	2·4348		45
	20	·41204	·91116	·45222	2·2113	1·0975	2·4269		40
	25	·41337	·91056	·45397	2·2028	1·0982	2·4191		35
	30	·41469	·90996	·45573	2·1943	1·0989	2·4114		30
	35	·41602	·90936	·45748	2·1859	1·0997	2·4037		25
	40	·41734	·90875	·45924	2·1775	1·1004	2·3961		20
	45	·41866	·90814	·46101	2·1692	1·1011	2·3886		15
	50	·41998	·90753	·46277	2·1609	1·1019	2·3811		10
	55	·42130	·90692	·46454	2·1527	1·1026	2·3736		5
25	0	·42262	·90631	·46631	2·1445	1·1034	2·3662	65	0
	5	·42394	·90569	·46808	2·1364	1·1041	2·3588		55
	10	·42525	·90507	·46985	2·1283	1·1049	2·3515		50
	15	·42657	·90445	·47163	2·1203	1·1056	2·3443		45
	20	·42788	·90383	·47341	2·1123	1·1064	2·3371		40
	25	·42920	·90321	·47519	2·1044	1·1072	2·3299		35
	30	·43051	·90258	·47697	2·0965	1·1079	2·3228		30
	35	·43182	·90196	·47876	2·0887	1·1087	2·3158		25
	40	·43313	·90133	·48055	2·0809	1·1095	2·3087		20
	45	·43444	·90070	·48234	2·0732	1·1102	2·3018		15
	50	·43575	·90006	·48414	2·0655	1·1110	2·2949		10
	55	·43706	·89943	·48593	2·0579	1·1118	2·2880		5
26	0	·43837	·89879	·48773	2·0503	1·1126	2·2812	64	0
	5	·43968	·89816	·48953	2·0427	1·1134	2·2744		55
	10	·44098	·89751	·49134	2·0353	1·1142	2·2677		50
	15	·44229	·89687	·49314	2·0278	1·1150	2·2610		45
	20	·44359	·89623	·49495	2·0204	1·1158	2·2543		40
	25	·44490	·89558	·49677	2·0130	1·1166	2·2477		35
	30	·44620	·89493	·49858	2·0057	1·1174	2·2412		30
	35	·44750	·89428	·50040	1·9984	1·1182	2·2346		25
	40	·44880	·89363	·50222	1·9912	1·1190	2·2282		20
	45	·45010	·89298	·50404	1·9840	1·1198	2·2217		15
	50	·45140	·89232	·50587	1·9768	1·1207	2·2153		10
	55	·45269	·89167	·50769	1·9697	1·1215	2·2090		5
		Cosine	Sine	Cotangent	Tangent	Cosecant	Secant	Deg.	Min.

Trigonometrical Tables (*contd.*)

Deg.	Min.	Sine	Cosine	Tangent	Cotangent	Secant	Cosecant		
27	0	·45399	·89101	·50952	1·9626	1·1223	2·2027	63	0
	5	·45529	·89034	·51136	1·9556	1·1232	2·1964		55
	10	·45658	·88968	·51319	1·9486	1·1240	2·1902		50
	15	·45787	·88902	·51503	1·9416	1·1248	2·1840		45
	20	·45917	·88835	·51688	1·9347	1·1257	2·1779		40
	25	·46046	·88768	·51872	1·9278	1·1265	2·1717		35
	30	·46175	·88701	·52057	1·9210	1·1274	2·1657		30
	35	·46304	·88634	·52242	1·9142	1·1282	2·1596		25
	40	·46433	·88566	·52427	1·9074	1·1291	2·1537		20
	45	·46561	·88500	·52613	1·9007	1·1300	2·1477		15
	50	·46690	·88431	·52798	1·8940	1·1308	2·1418		10
	55	·46819	·88363	·52984	1·8873	1·1317	2·1359		5
28	0	·46947	·88295	·53171	1·8807	1·1326	2·1300	62	0
	5	·47075	·88226	·53358	1·8741	1·1334	2·1242		55
	10	·47204	·88158	·53545	1·8676	1·1343	2·1185		50
	15	·47332	·88089	·53732	1·8611	1·1352	2·1127		45
	20	·47460	·88020	·53919	1·8546	1·1361	2·1070		40
	25	·47588	·87951	·54107	1·8482	1·1370	2·1014		35
	30	·47716	·87882	·54296	1·8418	1·1379	2·0957		30
	35	·47844	·87812	·54484	1·8354	1·1388	2·0901		25
	40	·47971	·87742	·54673	1·8291	1·1397	2·0846		20
	45	·48099	·87673	·54862	1·8228	1·1406	2·0790		15
	50	·48226	·87603	·55051	1·8165	1·1415	2·0736		10
	55	·48354	·87532	·55241	1·8102	1·1424	2·0681		5
29	0	·48481	·87462	·55431	1·8040	1·1433	2·0627	61	0
	5	·48608	·87391	·55621	1·7979	1·1443	2·0573		55
	10	·48735	·87321	·55812	1·7917	1·1452	2·0519		50
	15	·48862	·87250	·56003	1·7856	1·1461	2·0466		45
	20	·48989	·87178	·56194	1·7795	1·1471	2·0413		40
	25	·49116	·87107	·56385	1·7735	1·1480	2·0360		35
	30	·49242	·87036	·56577	1·7675	1·1490	2·0308		30
	35	·49369	·86964	·56769	1·7615	1·1499	2·0256		25
	40	·49495	·86892	·56962	1·7556	1·1508	2·0204		20
	45	·49622	·86820	·57155	1·7496	1·1518	2·0152		15
	50	·49748	·86748	·57348	1·7437	1·1528	2·0101		10
	55	·49874	·86675	·57541	1·7379	1·1537	2·0050		5
		Cosine	Sine	Cotangent	Tangent	Cosecant	Secant	Deg.	Min.

Trigonometrical Tables (*contd.*)

Deg.	Min.	Sine	Cosine	Tangent	Cotangent	Secant	Cosecant		
30	0	·50000	·86602	·57735	1·7320	1·1547	2·0000	60	0
	5	·50126	·86530	·57929	1·7262	1·1557	1·9950		55
	10	·50252	·86457	·58123	1·7205	1·1566	1·9900		50
	15	·50377	·86384	·58318	1·7147	1·1576	1·9850		45
	20	·50503	·86310	·58513	1·7090	1·1586	1·9801		40
	25	·50628	·86237	·58709	1·7033	1·1596	1·9752		35
	30	·50754	·86163	·58904	1·6977	1·1606	1·9703		30
	35	·50879	·86089	·59101	1·6920	1·1616	1·9654		25
	40	·51004	·86015	·59300	1·6864	1·1626	1·9606		20
	45	·51129	·85941	·59494	1·6808	1·1636	1·9558		15
	50	·51254	·85866	·59691	1·6753	1·1646	1·9511		10
	55	·51379	·85792	·59888	1·6698	1·1656	1·9463		5
31	0	·51504	·85717	·60086	1·6643	1·1666	1·9416	59	0
	5	·51628	·85642	·60284	1·6588	1·1677	1·9369		55
	10	·51753	·85567	·60483	1·6534	1·1687	1·9323		50
	15	·51877	·85491	·60681	1·6479	1·1697	1·9276		45
	20	·52002	·85416	·60881	1·6426	1·1707	1·9230		40
	25	·52126	·85340	·61080	1·6372	1·1718	1·9184		35
	30	·52250	·85264	·61280	1·6318	1·1728	1·9139		30
	35	·52374	·85188	·61480	1·6265	1·1739	1·9093		25
	40	·52498	·85112	·61681	1·6212	1·1749	1·9048		20
	45	·52621	·85035	·61882	1·6160	1·1760	1·9004		15
	50	·52745	·84959	·62083	1·6107	1·1770	1·8959		10
	55	·52868	·84882	·62285	1·6055	1·1781	1·8915		5
32	0	·52992	·84805	·62487	1·6003	1·1792	1·8871	58	0
	5	·53115	·84728	·62689	1·5952	1·1802	1·8827		55
	10	·53238	·84650	·62892	1·5900	1·1813	1·8783		50
	15	·53361	·84573	·63095	1·5849	1·1824	1·8740		45
	20	·53484	·84495	·63299	1·5798	1·1835	1·8697		40
	25	·53607	·84417	·63503	1·5747	1·1846	1·8654		35
	30	·53730	·84339	·63707	1·5697	1·1857	1·8612		30
	35	·53852	·84261	·63912	1·5647	1·1868	1·8569		25
	40	·53975	·84182	·64117	1·5597	1·1879	1·8527		20
	45	·54097	·84104	·64322	1·5547	1·1890	1·8485		15
	50	·54220	·84025	·64528	1·5497	1·1901	1·8443		10
	55	·54342	·83946	·64734	1·5448	1·1912	1·8402		5
		Cosine	Sine	Cotangent	Tangent	Cosecant	Secant	Deg.	Min.

Trigonometrical Tables (*contd.*)

Deg.	Min.	Sine	Cosine	Tangent	Cotangent	Secant	Cosecant		
33	0	·54464	·83867	·64941	1·5399	1·1924	1·8361	57	0
	5	·54586	·83788	·65148	1·5350	1·1935	1·8320		55
	10	·54708	·83708	·65355	1·5301	1·1946	1·8279		50
	15	·54829	·83629	·65563	1·5252	1·1958	1·8238		45
	20	·54951	·83549	·65771	1·5204	1·1969	1·8198		40
	25	·55072	·83469	·65980	1·5156	1·1980	1·8158		35
	30	·55194	·83389	·66189	1·5108	1·1992	1·8118		30
	35	·55315	·83308	·66398	1·5061	1·2004	1·8078		25
	40	·55436	·83228	·66608	1·5013	1·2015	1·8039		20
	45	·55557	·83147	·66818	1·4966	1·2027	1·7999		15
	50	·55678	·83066	·67028	1·4919	1·2039	1·7960		10
	55	·55799	·82985	·67239	1·4872	1·2050	1·7922		5
34	0	·55919	·82904	·67451	1·4826	1·2062	1·7883	56	0
	5	·56040	·82822	·67663	1·4779	1·2074	1·7844		55
	10	·56160	·82741	·67875	1·4733	1·2086	1·7806		50
	15	·56280	·82659	·68088	1·4687	1·2098	1·7768		45
	20	·56401	·82577	·68301	1·4641	1·2110	1·7730		40
	25	·56521	·82495	·68514	1·4595	1·2122	1·7693		35
	30	·56641	·82413	·68728	1·4550	1·2134	1·7655		30
	35	·56760	·82330	·68942	1·4505	1·2146	1·7618		25
	40	·56880	·82247	·69157	1·4460	1·2158	1·7581		20
	45	·57000	·82165	·69372	1·4415	1·2171	1·7544		15
	50	·57119	·82082	·69588	1·4370	1·2183	1·7507		10
	55	·57238	·81998	·69804	1·4326	1·2195	1·7471		5
35	0	·57358	·81915	·70021	1·4281	1·2208	1·7434	55	0
	5	·57477	·81832	·70238	1·4237	1·2220	1·7398		55
	10	·57596	·81748	·70455	1·4193	1·2233	1·7362		50
	15	·57714	·81664	·70673	1·4150	1·2245	1·7327		45
	20	·57833	·81580	·70891	1·4106	1·2258	1·7291		40
	25	·57952	·81496	·71110	1·4063	1·2271	1·7256		35
	30	·58070	·81412	·71329	1·4019	1·2283	1·7220		30
	35	·58189	·81327	·71549	1·3976	1·2296	1·7185		25
	40	·58307	·81242	·71769	1·3934	1·2309	1·7151		20
	45	·58425	·81157	·71990	1·3891	1·2322	1·7116		15
	50	·58543	·81072	·72211	1·3848	1·2335	1·7081		10
	55	·58661	·80987	·72432	1·3806	1·2348	1·7047		5
		Cosine	Sine	Cotangent	Tangent	Cosecant	Secant	Deg.	Min.

Trigonometrical Tables (*contd.*)

Deg.	Min.	Sine	Cosine	Tangent	Cotangent	Secant	Cosecant		
36	**0**	·58778	·80902	·72654	1·3764	1·2361	1·7013	**54**	**0**
	5	·58896	·80816	·72877	1·3722	1·2374	1·6979		55
	10	·59014	·80730	·73099	1·3680	1·2387	1·6945		50
	15	·59131	·80644	·73323	1·3638	1·2400	1·6912		45
	20	·59248	·80558	·73547	1·3597	1·2413	1·6878		40
	25	·59365	·80472	·73771	1·3555	1·2427	1·6845		35
	30	·59482	·80386	·73996	1·3514	1·2440	1·6812		30
	35	·59599	·80299	·74221	1·3473	1·2453	1·6779		25
	40	·59716	·80212	·74447	1·3432	1·2467	1·6746		20
	45	·59832	·80125	·74673	1·3392	1·2480	1·6713		15
	50	·59949	·80038	·74900	1·3351	1·2494	1·6681		10
	55	·60065	·79951	·75128	1·3311	1·2508	1·6649		5
37	**0**	·60181	·79864	·75355	1·3270	1·2521	1·6616	**53**	**0**
	5	·60298	·79776	·75584	1·3230	1·2535	1·6584		55
	10	·60414	·79688	·75812	1·3190	1·2549	1·6553		50
	15	·60529	·79600	·76042	1·3151	1·2563	1·6521		45
	20	·60645	·79512	·76272	1·3111	1·2577	1·6489		40
	25	·60761	·79424	·76502	1·3072	1·2591	1·6458		35
	30	·60876	·79335	·76733	1·3032	1·2605	1·6427		30
	35	·60991	·79247	·76964	1·2993	1·2619	1·6396		25
	40	·61107	·79158	·77196	1·2954	1·2633	1·6365		20
	45	·61222	·79069	·77428	1·2915	1·2647	1·6334		15
	50	·61337	·78980	·77661	1·2876	1·2661	1·6303		10
	55	·61451	·78890	·77895	1·2838	1·2676	1·6273		5
38	**0**	·61566	·78801	·78129	1·2799	1·2690	1·6243	**52**	**0**
	5	·61681	·78711	·78363	1·2761	1·2705	1·6212		55
	10	·61795	·78622	·78598	1·2723	1·2719	1·6182		50
	15	·61909	·78532	·78834	1·2685	1·2734	1·6153		45
	20	·62024	·78442	·79070	1·2647	1·2748	1·6123		40
	25	·62138	·78351	·79306	1·2609	1·2763	1·6093		35
	30	·62251	·78261	·79544	1·2572	1·2778	1·6064		30
	35	·62365	·78170	·79781	1·2534	1·2793	1·6035		25
	40	·62479	·78079	·80020	1·2497	1·2807	1·6005		20
	45	·62592	·77988	·80258	1·2460	1·2822	1·5976		15
	50	·62706	·77897	·80498	1·2423	1·2837	1·5947		10
	55	·62819	·77806	·80738	1·2386	1·2852	1·5919		5
		Cosine	Sine	Cotangent	Tangent	Cosecant	Secant	Deg.	Min.

E.W.D.—16*

Trigonometrical Tables (*contd.*)

Deg.	Min.	Sine	Cosine	Tangent	Cotangent	Secant	Cosecant		
39	0	·62932	·77715	·80978	1·2349	1·2868	1·5890	51	0
	5	·63045	·77623	·81219	1·2312	1·2883	1·5862		55
	10	·63158	·77531	·81461	1·2276	1·2898	1·5833		50
	15	·63270	·77439	·81703	1·2239	1·2913	1·5805		45
	20	·63383	·77347	·81946	1·2203	1·2929	1·5777		40
	25	·63495	·77255	·82190	1·2167	1·2944	1·5749		35
	30	·63608	·77162	·82434	1·2131	1·2960	1·5721		30
	35	·63720	·77070	·82678	1·2095	1·2975	1·5694		25
	40	·63832	·76977	·82923	1·2059	1·2991	1·5666		20
	45	·63944	·76884	·83169	1·2024	1·3007	1·5639		15
	50	·64056	·76791	·83415	1·1988	1·3022	1·5611		10
	55	·64167	·76698	·83662	1·1953	1·3038	1·5584		5
40	0	·64279	·76604	·83910	1·1917	1·3054	1·5557	50	0
	5	·64390	·76511	·84158	1·1882	1·3070	1·5530		55
	10	·64501	·76417	·84407	1·1847	1·3086	1·5504		50
	15	·64612	·76323	·84656	1·1812	1·3102	1·5477		45
	20	·64723	·76229	·84906	1·1778	1·3118	1·5450		40
	25	·64834	·76135	·85157	1·1743	1·3135	1·5424		35
	30	·64945	·76041	·85408	1·1708	1·3151	1·5398		30
	35	·65055	·75946	·85660	1·1674	1·3167	1·5371		25
	40	·65166	·75851	·85912	1·1640	1·3184	1·5345		20
	45	·65276	·75756	·86165	1·1606	1·3200	1·5320		15
	50	·65386	·75661	·86419	1·1571	1·3217	1·5294		10
	55	·65496	·75566	·86674	1·1537	1·3233	1·5268		5
41	0	·65606	·75471	·86929	1·1504	1·3250	1·5242	49	0
	5	·65716	·75375	·87184	1·1470	1·3267	1·5217		55
	10	·65825	·75280	·87441	1·1436	1·3284	1·5192		50
	15	·65935	·75184	·87698	1·1403	1·3301	1·5166		45
	20	·66044	·75088	·87955	1·1369	1·3318	1·5141		40
	25	·66153	·74992	·88214	1·1336	1·3335	1·5116		35
	30	·66262	·74896	·88472	1·1303	1·3352	1·5092		30
	35	·66371	·74799	·88732	1·1270	1·3369	1·5067		25
	40	·66480	·74702	·88992	1·1237	1·3386	1·5042		20
	45	·66588	·74606	·89253	1·1204	1·3404	1·5018		15
	50	·66697	·74509	·89515	1·1171	1·3421	1·4993		10
	55	·66805	·74412	·89777	1·1139	1·3439	1·4969		5
		Cosine	Sine	Cotangent	Tangent	Cosecant	Secant	Deg.	Min.

Trigonometrical Tables (*contd.*)

Deg.	Min.	Sine	Cosine	Tangent	Cotangent	Secant	Cosecant		
42	0	·66913	·74314	·90040	1·1106	1·3456	1·4945	48	0
	5	·67021	·74217	·90304	1·1074	1·3474	1·4921		55
	10	·67129	·74119	·90568	1·1041	1·3492	1·4897		50
	15	·67237	·74022	·90834	1·1009	1·3509	1·4873		45
	20	·67344	·73924	·91099	1·0977	1·3527	1·4849		40
	25	·67452	·73826	·91366	1·0945	1·3545	1·4825		35
	30	·67559	·73728	·91663	1·0913	1·3563	1·4802		30
	35	·67666	·73629	·91901	1·0881	1·3581	1·4778		25
	40	·67773	·73531	·92170	1·0850	1·3600	1·4755		20
	45	·67880	·73432	·92439	1·0818	1·3618	1·4732		15
	50	·67987	·73333	·92709	1·0786	1·3636	1·4709		10
	55	·68093	·73234	·92980	1·0755	1·3655	1·4686		5
43	0	·68200	·73135	·93251	1·0724	1·3673	1·4663	47	0
	5	·68306	·73036	·93524	1·0692	1·3692	1·4640		55
	10	·68412	·72937	·93797	1·0661	1·3710	1·4617		50
	15	·68518	·72837	·94071	1·0630	1·3729	1·4595		45
	20	·68624	·72737	·94345	1·0599	1·3748	1·4572		40
	25	·68730	·72637	·94620	1·0568	1·3767	1·4550		35
	30	·68835	·72537	·94896	1·0538	1·3786	1·4527		30
	35	·68941	·72437	·95173	1·0507	1·3805	1·4505		25
	40	·69046	·72337	·95451	1·0477	1·3824	1·4483		20
	45	·69151	·72236	·95729	1·0446	1·3843	1·4461		15
	50	·69256	·72136	·96008	1·0416	1·3863	1·4439		10
	55	·69361	·72035	·96288	1·0385	1·3882	1·4417		5
44	0	·69466	·71934	·96569	1·0355	1·3902	1·4396	46	0
	5	·69570	·71833	·96850	1·0325	1·3921	1·4374		55
	10	·69675	·71732	·97133	1·0295	1·3941	1·4352		50
	15	·69779	·71630	·97416	1·0265	1·3961	1·4331		45
	20	·69883	·71529	·97700	1·0235	1·3980	1·4310		40
	25	·69987	·71427	·97984	1·0206	1·4000	1·4288		35
	30	·70091	·71325	·98270	1·0176	1·4020	1·4267		30
	35	·70195	·71223	·98556	1·0146	1·4040	1·4246		25
	40	·70298	·71121	·98843	1·0117	1·4061	1·4225		20
	45	·70401	·71018	·99131	1·0088	1·4081	1·4204		15
	50	·70505	·70916	·99420	1·0058	1·4101	1·4183		10
	55	·70608	·70813	·99709	1·0029	1·4122	1·4163		5
45	0	·70711	·70711	1·00000	1·00000	1·4142	1·4142	45	0
		Cosine	Sine	Cotangent	Tangent	Cosecant	Secant	Deg.	Min.

SECTION 14

TABLES OF LOGARITHMS AND ANTILOGARITHMS

The following tables of five-figure logarithms enable operations, such as multiplication, division, squares and cubes, square and cube roots, etc., to be performed in a simple and accurate manner, by processes of addition and subtraction, only. The logarithmic values are calculated to the base 10.

If any two numbers be represented by the letters N and M, then the following relations hold :

$$\log (N \times M) = \log N + \log M$$

$$\log \left(\frac{N}{M}\right) = \log N - \log M$$

$$\log N^n = n \log N \text{ where } n \text{ is any integer}$$

$$\log \sqrt[n]{N} = \frac{1}{n} \log N.$$

It is also useful to know that :

$$\log 1 = 0$$
$$\log 10 = 1.$$

Hence the logarithms of numbers less than 10 will be less than 1, i.e. will be decimals.

Similarly, since $\log 100 = 2$ and $\log 1000 = 3$, it follows that logarithms of numbers between 10 and 100 will be (1 plus a decimal number) ; between 100 and 1000 will be (2 plus a decimal number) and so on.

In the case of any logarithm of a number greater than 10, the whole number or integral part is termed its *characteristic* and the decimal part its *mantissa*.

The logarithms of all fractions (or decimals) have *negative* characteristics, but the mantissa is *positive* in each case.

Examples.
$\log 56432 = 4 \cdot 751525$
$\log 5643 \cdot 2 = 3 \cdot 751525$
$\log 564 \cdot 32 = 2 \cdot 751525$
$\log 56 \cdot 432 = 1 \cdot 751525$
$\log 5 \cdot 6432 = 0 \cdot 751525$
$\log 0 \cdot 56432 = \bar{1} \cdot 751525$
$\log 0 \cdot 056432 = \bar{2} \cdot 751525.$

In the following logarithmic tables the mantissæ of the numbers only are given, since these are the same for given numbers, irrespective of their characteristics.

To find the characteristic of the logarithm of a given number take one less than the number of integral figures in the number.

In the case of a number which is a decimal the negative characteristic is the same as the position from the decimal point at which the first significant figure appears in the decimal.

USING THE LOGARITHMIC TABLES

With the aid of the logarithmic tables, logarithms of numbers of five figures can be found, to six decimal places, in the following manner :

For numbers up to three integers the first column is used.

Thus log 5   = 0·69897
    log 555 = 2·74429.

For numbers with four integers the logarithm will be found under the number in the vertical column corresponding to the last integer, in line with the three remaining figures, in the first column.

Thus log 3567 = 3·55230
    log 29·48 = 1·46953.

For numbers with five integers, use is made of the table of mean log differences.

Thus log 35678 = 4·55230 + difference 98
             = 4·552398
    log 106·75 = 2·02816 + difference 206
             = 2·028366
    log 9·8763 = 0·99458 + difference 13
             = 0·994593.

It is important to note that if the difference is a *single* integer, it becomes the sixth decimal figure. If it is a *double* integer, it becomes the fifth and sixth decimal figures to be added to the logarithm under the number in the vertical column. If it is a *three-figure* integer, it becomes the fourth, fifth and sixth decimal figures to be added to the logarithm under the vertical column figure. The last or sixth decimal place thus obtained is approximate only.

ANTILOGARITHMS

It is frequently necessary to ascertain the actual numbers corresponding to given logarithmic values. Thus, in all calculations, e.g. multiplication, division and the evaluation of various roots, the first result obtained is in the form of a logarithm. It is therefore necessary to find the value of the corresponding number for the final result.

Whilst the Table of Logarithms that follows can be employed for this purpose, it is more convenient, and quicker, to use the Table of Antilogarithms given at the end of this volume.

These Tables give the values of all numbers between 00000 to 99999, whose logarithms are given.

Examples.—The method of using the Table is best illustrated by three typical examples, as follows :

(1) Find the number whose logarithm is 0·23940. From the Antilogarithm Table, the first three figures, viz. 0·239 are given in the extreme left-hand column, and under the column 4 we find the number 17354, so that the actual number whose logarithm is 0·23940 will be 1·7354.

(2) Find the antilogarithm of $\bar{3}$·57565.

From the Table, for 0·5756 the Antilog is	37636
and for 0·00005 the difference is	43
The final result is then	3764·03

(3) Find the antilogarithm of 0·86448.

From the Table, for 0·8644 the Antilog is	·73181
and for 0·00008 the difference is	135
The final result is then	7·31945

Multiplication of Numbers.

To multiply two or more numbers, add the logarithms and look up the value of the number of which the sum is the logarithm.

Example.

$$24·46 \times 1·038$$
$$\log 24·46 = 1·38846$$
$$\log 1·038 = 0·01620$$

Sum 1·40466.

From the tables this is the logarithm of 25·39.

Division of Numbers.

To divide one number by another subtract the logarithm of the divisor from that of the dividend and find the value of the number thus obtained.

Example.   Divide 764·35 by 1576·3

log 764·35 = 2·883289
log 1576·3 = 3·197643
_____

Difference $\bar{1}$·685646.

This is the logarithm of the number 0·48490.

Square Roots.

Find the logarithm of the number, divide this by 2 and find the number of which the result is the logarithm.

Example.   Find the square root of 59763.

log 59763 = 4·776432
½ log = 2·388216.

This is the logarithm of 244·46.

Cube Roots.

Find the logarithm of the number, divide this by 3 and find the number of which the result is the logarithm.

Example.   Find the cube root of 12457.

log 12457 = 4·095414
⅓ log = 1·365138.

This is the logarithm of 23·181.

Powers of Numbers.

Find the logarithm of the number, multiply this by the exponent of the power and find the number of which the result is the logarithm.

Example.   Find the value of 27·49⁴

log 2749 = 1·43917
multiply by 4 = 5·75668.

This is the logarithm of the number 571,040.

TABLE OF

	0	1	2	3	4	5	6
100	00000	00043	00087	00130	00173	00217	00260
101	00432	00475	00518	00561	00604	00647	00689
102	00860	00903	00945	00988	01030	01072	01115
103	01284	01326	01368	01410	01452	01494	01536
104	01703	01745	01787	01828	01870	01912	01953
105	02119	02160	02202	02243	02284	02325	02366
106	02531	02571	02612	02653	02694	02735	02776
107	02938	02979	03019	03060	03100	03141	03181
108	03342	03383	03423	03463	03503	03543	03583
109	03743	03782	03822	03862	03902	03941	03981
110	04139	04179	04218	04258	04297	04336	04375
111	04532	04571	04610	04649	04688	04727	04766
112	04922	04961	04999	05038	05077	05115	05154
113	05308	05346	05385	05423	05461	05500	05538
114	05690	05729	05767	05805	05843	05880	05918
115	06070	06107	06145	06183	06221	06258	06296
116	06446	06483	06521	06558	06595	06633	06670
117	06819	06856	06893	06930	06967	07004	07041
118	07188	07225	07262	07298	07335	07372	07408
119	07555	07591	07628	07664	07700	07737	07773
120	07918	07954	07990	08027	08063	08099	08135
121	08278	08314	08350	08386	08422	08458	08493
122	08636	08672	08707	08743	08778	08814	08849
123	08990	09026	09061	09096	09131	09167	09202
124	09342	09377	09412	09447	09482	09517	09552
125	09691	09726	09760	09795	09830	09864	09899
126	10037	10071	10106	10140	10175	10209	10243
127	10380	10415	10449	10483	10517	10551	10585
128	10721	10755	10789	10823	10856	10890	10924
129	11059	11093	11126	11160	11193	11227	11260
130	11394	11428	11461	11494	11528	11561	11594
131	11727	11760	11793	11826	11859	11893	11926
132	12057	12090	12123	12156	12189	12222	12254
133	12385	12418	12450	12483	12515	12548	12581
134	12710	12743	12775	12808	12840	12872	12904
135	13033	13065	13098	13130	13162	13194	13226
136	13354	13386	13418	13450	13481	13513	13545
137	13672	13704	13735	13767	13799	13830	13862
138	13988	14019	14051	14082	14114	14145	14176
139	14301	14333	14364	14395	14426	14457	14488
140	14613	14644	14675	14706	14737	14768	14798
141	14922	14953	14983	15014	15045	15076	15106
142	15229	15259	15290	15320	15351	15381	15412
143	15534	15564	15594	15625	15655	15685	15715
144	15836	15866	15896	15927	15957	15987	16017
145	16137	16167	16197	16227	16256	16286	16316
146	16435	16465	16495	16524	16554	16584	16613
147	16732	16761	16791	16820	16850	16879	16909
148	17026	17055	17085	17114	17143	17173	17202
149	17319	17348	17377	17406	17435	17464	17493
150	17609	17638	17667	17696	17725	17754	17782

LOGARITHMS

	7	8	9	Mean Log. Differences								
				1	2	3	4	5	6	7	8	9
100	00303	00346	00389	43	86	130	173	216	259	303	346	389
101	00732	00775	00817									
102	01157	01199	01242	42	85	127	169	212	254	297	339	381
103	01578	01620	01661									
104	01995	02036	02077	42	83	125	166	208	249	291	332	374
105	02407	02449	02490	41	82	123	165	206	247	288	329	370
106	02816	02857	02898									
107	03222	03262	03302	40	81	121	162	202	243	283	323	364
108	03623	03663	03703									
109	04021	04060	04100	40	79	119	159	198	238	278	317	357
110	04415	04454	04493	39	79	118	157	197	236	275	314	354
111	04805	04844	04883									
112	05192	05231	05269	39	77	116	154	193	232	270	309	347
113	05576	05614	05652									
114	05956	05994	06032	38	76	114	152	190	228	266	303	341
115	06333	06371	06408	38	75	113	150	188	226	263	301	338
116	06707	06744	06781									
117	07078	07114	07151	37	74	111	148	185	222	259	296	333
118	07445	07482	07518									
119	07809	07846	07882	36	73	109	145	182	218	254	291	327
120	08171	08207	08243	36	72	108	144	180	216	252	288	324
121	08529	08565	08600									
122	08884	08920	08955	35	71	107	142	178	213	248	284	319
123	09237	09272	09307									
124	09587	09621	09656	35	70	105	140	174	209	244	279	314
125	09933	09968	10003	35	69	104	138	173	208	242	277	311
126	10278	10312	10346									
127	10619	10653	10687	34	68	102	136	170	204	238	273	307
128	10958	10992	11025									
129	11294	11327	11361	34	67	100	134	168	201	235	268	302
130	11628	11661	11694	33	67	100	133	166	200	233	266	300
131	11959	11991	12024									
132	12287	12320	12352	33	66	98	131	164	197	229	262	295
133	12613	12646	12678									
134	12937	12969	13001	32	65	97	129	161	194	226	258	291
135	13258	13290	13322	32	64	96	128	160	192	224	256	288
136	13577	13609	13640									
137	13893	13925	13956	32	63	95	126	158	190	221	253	284
138	14208	14239	14270									
139	14520	14551	14582	31	62	93	125	156	187	218	249	280
140	14829	14860	14891	31	62	93	124	155	185	216	247	278
141	15137	15168	15198									
142	15442	15473	15503	30	61	91	122	152	183	213	244	274
143	15746	15776	15806									
144	16047	16077	16107	30	60	90	120	150	180	210	241	271
145	16346	16376	16405	30	60	90	119	149	179	209	239	269
146	16643	16673	16702									
147	16938	16967	16997	29	59	88	118	147	177	206	236	265
148	17231	17260	17289									
149	17522	17551	17580	29	58	87	116	145	174	203	232	261
150	17811	17840	17869	29	58	87	115	144	173	202	231	260

150—200

	0	1	2	3	4	5	6
150	17609	17638	17667	17696	17725	17754	17782
151	17898	17926	17955	17984	18013	18041	18070
152	18184	18213	18241	18270	18298	18327	18355
153	18469	18497	18526	18554	18582	18611	18639
154	18752	18780	18808	18837	18865	18893	18921
155	19033	19061	19089	19117	19145	19173	19201
156	19312	19340	19368	19396	19424	19451	19479
157	19590	19618	19645	19673	19700	19728	19756
158	19866	19893	19921	19948	19975	20003	20030
159	20140	20167	20194	20222	20249	20276	20303
160	20412	20439	20466	20493	20520	20547	20575
161	20683	20710	20736	20763	20790	20817	20844
162	20951	20978	21005	21032	21059	21085	21112
163	21219	21245	21272	21299	21335	21352	21378
164	21484	21511	21537	21564	21590	21617	21643
165	21748	21775	21801	21827	21854	21880	21906
166	22011	22037	22063	22089	22115	22141	22167
167	22272	22298	22324	22350	22375	22401	22427
168	22531	22557	22583	22608	22634	22660	22686
169	22789	22814	22840	22866	22891	22917	22943
170	23045	23070	23096	23121	23147	23172	23198
171	23299	23325	23350	23376	23401	23426	23451
172	23553	23578	23603	23628	23654	23679	23704
173	23805	23830	23855	23880	23905	23930	23955
174	24055	24080	24105	24130	24155	24179	24204
175	24304	24329	24353	24378	24403	24428	24452
176	24551	24576	24601	24625	24650	24674	24699
177	24797	24822	24846	24871	24895	24920	24944
178	25042	25066	25091	25115	25139	25164	25188
179	25285	25309	25334	25358	25382	25406	25431
180	25527	25551	25575	25600	25624	25648	25672
181	25768	25792	25816	25840	25864	25888	25912
182	26007	26031	26055	26079	26102	26126	26150
183	26245	26269	26292	26316	26340	26364	26387
184	26482	26505	26529	26552	26576	26600	26623
185	26717	26741	26764	26787	26811	26835	26858
186	26951	26975	26998	27021	27045	27068	27091
187	27184	27207	27231	27253	27277	27300	27323
188	27416	27439	27462	27485	27508	27531	27554
189	27646	27669	27692	27715	27738	27761	27784
190	27875	27898	27921	27944	27967	27989	28012
191	28103	28126	28149	28171	28194	28217	28240
192	28330	28353	28375	28398	28420	28443	28466
193	28556	28578	28601	28623	28646	28668	28690
194	28780	28803	28825	28847	28870	28892	28914
195	29003	29026	29048	29070	29092	29115	29137
196	29226	29248	29270	29292	29314	29336	29358
197	29447	29469	29491	29513	29535	29557	29579
198	29666	29688	29710	29732	29754	29776	29798
199	29885	29907	29929	29951	29972	29994	30016
200	30103	30125	30146	30168	30190	30211	30233

Logarithms (*contd.*)

	7	8	9	Mean Log. Differences								
				1	2	3	4	5	6	7	8	9
150	17811	17840	17869	29	58	87	115	144	173	202	231	260
151	18099	18127	18156									
152	18384	18412	18441	28	57	85	114	142	171	199	228	256
153	18667	18696	18724									
154	18949	18977	19005	28	56	84	112	141	169	197	225	253
155	19229	19257	19285	28	56	84	112	140	168	196	223	251
156	19507	19535	19562									
157	19783	19811	19838	28	55	83	110	138	165	193	221	248
158	20058	20085	20112									
159	20330	20358	20385	27	54	82	109	136	163	191	218	245
160	20602	20629	20656	27	54	81	108	135	162	189	216	244
161	20871	20898	20925									
162	21139	21165	21192	27	53	80	107	134	160	187	214	241
163	21405	21431	21458									
164	21669	21696	21722	26	53	79	106	132	158	185	211	238
165	21932	21958	21985	26	52	79	105	131	157	184	210	236
166	22194	22220	22246									
167	22453	22479	22505	26	52	78	104	130	156	181	207	233
168	22711	22737	22763									
169	22968	22994	23019	26	51	77	102	128	154	179	205	231
170	23223	23249	23274	25	51	76	102	127	153	178	204	229
171	23477	23502	23528									
172	23729	23754	23779	25	50	76	101	126	151	176	201	227
173	23980	24005	24030									
174	24229	24254	24279	25	50	75	100	124	149	174	199	224
175	24477	24502	24527	25	49	74	99	124	148	173	198	223
176	24724	24748	24773									
177	24969	24993	25018	24	49	73	98	122	147	171	196	220
178	25212	25237	25261									
179	25455	25479	25503	24	48	72	97	121	145	169	194	218
180	25696	25720	25744	24	48	72	96	120	144	168	192	217
181	25935	25959	25983									
182	26174	26198	26221	24	48	71	95	119	143	167	190	214
183	26410	26435	26458									
184	26647	26670	26694	24	47	71	94	118	141	165	188	212
185	26881	26905	26928	23	47	70	94	117	140	164	187	211
186	27114	27138	27161									
187	27346	27369	27393	23	46	69	93	116	139	162	185	208
188	27577	27600	27623									
189	27807	27830	27852	23	46	69	92	115	138	160	183	206
190	28035	28058	28081	23	46	68	91	114	137	160	182	205
191	28262	28285	28307									
192	28488	28510	28533	23	45	68	90	113	135	158	180	203
193	28713	28735	28758									
194	28937	28959	28981	22	45	67	89	112	134	156	179	201
195	29159	29181	29203	22	44	67	89	111	133	156	178	200
196	29380	29402	29425									
197	29601	29623	29645	22	44	66	88	110	132	154	176	198
198	29820	29842	29863									
199	30038	30059	30081	22	44	65	87	109	131	152	174	196
200	30255	30276	30298	22	43	65	87	108	130	152	173	195

Table of

	0	1	2	3	4	5	6
200	30103	30125	30146	30168	30190	30211	30233
201	30320	30341	30363	30384	30406	30427	30449
202	30535	30557	30578	30600	30621	30642	30664
203	30750	30771	30792	30814	30835	30856	30878
204	30963	30984	31006	31027	31048	31069	31091
205	31175	31197	31218	31239	31260	31281	31302
206	31387	31408	31429	31450	31471	31492	31513
207	31597	31618	31639	31660	31681	31702	31723
208	31806	31827	31848	31869	31890	31911	31931
209	32015	32035	32056	32077	32098	32118	32139
210	32222	32243	32263	32284	32305	32325	32346
211	32428	32449	32469	32490	32510	32531	32552
212	32634	32654	32674	32695	32715	32736	32756
213	32838	32858	32879	32899	32919	32940	32960
214	33041	33062	33082	33102	33122	33143	33163
215	33244	33264	33284	33304	33325	33345	33365
216	33445	33465	33486	33506	33526	33546	33566
217	33646	33666	33686	33706	33726	33746	33766
218	33846	33866	33885	33905	33925	33945	33965
219	34044	34064	34084	34104	34124	34143	34163
220	34242	34262	34282	34301	34321	34341	34361
221	34439	34459	34478	34498	34518	34537	34557
222	34635	34655	34674	34694	34713	34733	34752
223	34830	34850	34869	34889	34908	34928	34947
224	35025	35044	35064	35083	35102	35122	35141
225	35218	35237	35257	35276	35295	35315	35334
226	35411	35430	35449	35468	35488	35507	35526
227	35603	35622	35641	35660	35679	35698	35717
228	35793	35812	35832	35851	35870	35889	35908
229	35983	36002	36021	36040	36059	36078	36097
230	36173	36192	36210	36229	36248	36267	36286
231	36361	36380	36399	36418	36436	36455	36474
232	36549	36567	36586	36605	36624	36642	36661
233	36736	36754	36773	36791	36810	36829	36847
234	36922	36940	36959	36977	36996	37014	37033
235	37107	37125	37144	37162	37181	37199	37217
236	37291	37309	37328	37346	37365	37383	37401
237	37475	37493	37511	37530	37548	37566	37585
238	37658	37676	37694	37712	37731	37749	37767
239	37840	37858	37876	37894	37912	37931	37949
240	38021	38039	38057	38075	38093	38111	38130
241	38202	38220	38238	38256	38274	38292	38310
242	38381	38399	38417	38435	38453	38471	38489
243	38561	38578	38596	38614	38632	38650	38668
244	38739	38757	38775	38792	38810	38828	38846
245	38917	38934	38952	38970	38987	39005	39023
246	39093	39111	39129	39146	39164	39182	39199
247	39270	39287	39305	39322	39340	39357	39375
248	39445	39463	39480	39498	39515	39533	39550
249	39620	39637	39655	39672	39690	39707	39724
250	39794	39811	39829	39846	39863	39881	39898

Logarithms (*contd.*)

	7	8	9	Mean Log. Differences								
				1	2	3	4	5	6	7	8	9
200	30255	30276	30298	22	43	65	87	108	130	152	173	195
201	30471	30492	30514									
202	30685	30707	30728	21	43	64	86	107	129	150	172	193
203	30899	30920	30942									
204	31112	31133	31154	21	42	64	85	106	127	149	170	191
205	31323	31344	31366	21	42	63	85	106	127	148	169	190
206	31534	31555	31576									
207	31744	31765	31785	21	42	63	84	105	126	147	167	188
208	31952	31973	31994									
209	32160	32180	32201	21	41	62	83	104	124	145	166	186
210	32366	32387	32408	21	41	62	83	103	124	145	165	185
211	32572	32593	32613									
212	32777	32797	32818	20	41	61	82	102	123	143	163	184
213	32980	33001	33021									
214	33183	33203	33224	20	40	61	81	101	121	142	162	182
215	33385	33405	33425	20	40	60	81	101	121	141	161	181
216	33586	33606	33626									
217	33786	33806	33826	20	40	60	80	100	120	140	160	180
218	33985	34005	34025									
219	34183	34203	34222	20	40	59	79	99	119	138	158	178
220	34380	34400	34420	20	39	59	79	98	118	138	158	177
221	34577	34596	34616									
222	34772	34791	34811	20	39	59	78	98	117	137	156	176
223	34967	34986	35005									
224	35160	35180	35199	19	39	58	77	97	116	135	155	174
225	35353	35372	35392	19	39	58	77	96	116	135	154	173
226	35545	35564	35583									
227	35736	35755	35774	19	38	57	76	95	115	134	153	172
228	35927	35946	35965									
229	36116	36135	36154	19	38	57	76	95	114	132	151	170
230	36305	36324	36342	19	38	57	75	94	113	132	151	170
231	36492	36511	36530									
232	36680	36698	36717	19	37	56	75	93	112	131	149	168
233	36866	36884	36903									
234	37051	37070	37088	19	37	56	74	93	111	130	148	167
235	37236	37254	37273	18	37	55	74	92	111	129	148	166
236	37420	37438	37456									
237	37603	37621	37639	18	37	55	73	91	110	128	146	165
238	37785	37803	37822									
239	37967	37985	38003	18	36	54	73	91	109	127	145	163
240	38148	38166	38184	18	36	54	72	90	108	126	144	163
241	38328	38346	38364									
242	38507	38525	38543	18	36	54	72	90	107	125	143	162
243	38686	38703	38721									
244	38863	38881	38899	18	36	53	71	89	107	124	142	161
245	39040	39058	39076	18	35	53	71	88	106	124	142	160
246	39217	39234	39252									
247	39393	39410	39428	18	35	53	70	87	105	123	140	159
248	39568	39585	39602									
249	39742	39759	39777	17	35	52	70	87	104	122	139	157
250	39915	39933	39950	17	35	52	69	87	104	121	139	157

250—300

	0	1	2	3	4	5	6
250	39794	39811	39829	39846	39863	39881	39898
251	39967	39985	40002	40019	40036	40054	40071
252	40140	40157	40174	40192	40209	40226	40243
253	40312	40329	40346	40363	40381	40398	40415
254	40483	40500	40518	40535	40552	40569	40586
255	40654	40671	40688	40705	40722	40739	40756
256	40824	40841	40858	40875	40892	40909	40926
257	40993	41010	41027	41044	41061	41078	41095
258	41162	41179	41196	41212	41229	41246	41263
259	41330	41347	41363	41380	41397	41414	41430
260	41497	41514	41531	41547	41564	41581	41597
261	41664	41681	41697	41714	41731	41747	41764
262	41830	41847	41863	41880	41896	41913	41929
263	41996	42012	42029	42045	42062	42078	42094
264	42160	42177	42193	42210	42226	42243	42259
265	42325	42341	42357	42374	42390	42406	42423
266	42488	42504	42521	42537	42553	42570	42586
267	42651	42667	42684	42700	42716	42732	42749
268	42813	42830	42846	42862	42878	42894	42911
269	42975	42991	43007	43024	43040	43056	43072
270	43136	43152	43168	43185	43201	43217	43233
271	43297	43313	43329	43345	43361	43377	43393
272	43457	43473	43489	43505	43521	43537	43553
273	43616	43632	43648	43664	43680	43696	43712
274	43775	43791	43807	43823	43838	43854	43870
275	43933	43949	43965	43981	43996	44012	44028
276	44091	44107	44122	44138	44154	44169	44185
277	44248	44264	44279	44295	44311	44326	44342
278	44404	44420	44436	44451	44467	44482	44498
279	44560	44576	44591	44607	44623	44638	44654
280	44716	44731	44747	44762	44778	44793	44809
281	44871	44886	44901	44917	44932	44948	44963
282	45025	45040	45056	45071	45086	45102	45117
283	45179	45194	45209	45225	45240	45255	45271
284	45332	45347	45362	45378	45393	45408	45423
285	45484	45500	45515	45530	45545	45561	45576
286	45637	45652	45667	45682	45697	45712	45728
287	45788	45803	45818	45834	45849	45864	45879
288	45939	45954	45969	45984	45999	46015	46030
289	46090	46105	46120	46135	46150	46165	46180
290	46240	46255	46270	46285	46300	46315	46330
291	46389	46404	46419	46434	46449	46464	46479
292	46538	46553	46568	46583	46598	46613	46627
293	46687	46702	46716	46731	46746	46761	46776
294	46835	46849	46864	46879	46894	46908	46923
295	46982	46997	47012	47026	47041	47056	47070
296	47129	47144	47158	47173	47188	47202	47217
297	47276	47290	47305	47319	47334	47349	47363
298	47422	47436	47451	47465	47480	47494	47509
299	47567	47582	47596	47611	47625	47640	47654
300	47712	47727	47741	47755	47770	47784	47799

Logarithms (*contd.*)

	7	8	9	Mean Log. Differences								
				1	2	3	4	5	6	7	8	9
250	39915	39933	39950	17	35	52	69	87	104	121	139	157
251	40088	40106	40123									
252	40260	40278	40295	17	34	52	69	86	103	120	138	155
253	40432	40449	40466									
254	40603	40620	40637	17	34	51	68	85	102	119	137	154
255	40773	40790	40807	17	34	51	68	85	102	119	136	153
256	40943	40959	40976									
257	41111	41128	41145	17	34	50	67	. 84	101	118	135	152
258	41280	41296	41313									
259	41447	41464	41481	17	33	50	67	84	100	117	134	151
260	41614	41631	41647	17	33	50	67	83	100	117	133	150
261	41780	41797	41813									
262	41946	41962	41979	17	33	50	66	83	99	116	132	149
263	42111	42127	42144									
264	42275	42292	42308	16	33	49	66	82	99	115	131	148
265	42439	42455	42472	16	33	49	65	82	98	115	131	147
266	42602	42619	42635									
267	42765	42781	42797	16	32	49	65	81	97	114	130	146
268	42927	42943	42959									
269	43088	43104	43120	16	32	48	64	81	97	113	129	145
270	43249	43265	43281	16	32	48	64	80	96	112	128	144
271	43409	43425	43441									
272	43568	43584	43600	16	32	48	64	80	96	112	127	143
273	43727	43743	43759									
274	43886	43902	43917	16	32	47	63	79	95	111	127	142
275	44044	44059	44075	16	32	47	63	79	95	110	126	142
276	44201	44217	44232									
277	44358	44373	44389	16	31	47	63	78	94	110	125	141
278	44514	44529	44545									
279	44669	44685	44700	16	31	47	62	78	93	109	124	140
280	44824	44840	44855	15	31	46	62	77	93	108	124	139
281	44979	44994	45009									
282	45133	45148	45163	15	31	46	61	77	92	108	123	138
283	45286	45301	45316									
284	45439	45454	45469	15	31	46	61	76	92	107	122	137
285	45591	45606	45621	15	30	46	61	76	91	106	122	137
286	45743	45758	45773									
287	45894	45909	45924	15	30	45	60	76	91	106	121	136
288	46045	46060	46075									
289	46195	46210	46225	15	30	45	60	75	90	105	120	135
290	46344	46359	46374	15	30	45	60	75	90	105	120	135
291	46494	46508	46523									
292	46642	46657	46672	15	30	45	59	74	89	104	119	134
293	46790	46805	46820									
294	46938	46953	46967	15	29	44	59	74	88	103	118	133
295	47085	47100	47114	15	29	44	59	73	88	103	118	132
296	47232	47246	47261									
297	47378	47392	47407	15	29	44	58	73	88	102	117	131
298	47523	47538	47553									
299	47669	47683	47698	15	29	44	58	73	87	102	116	131
300	47813	47828	47842	14	29	43	58	72	87	101	116	130

Table of

	0	1	2	3	4	5	6
300	47712	47727	47741	47755	47770	47784	47799
301	47857	47871	47885	47900	47914	47929	47943
302	48001	48015	48029	48044	48058	48072	48087
303	48144	48159	48173	48187	48202	48216	48230
304	48287	48302	48316	48330	48344	48359	48373
305	48430	48444	48458	48473	48487	48501	48515
306	48572	48586	48600	48615	48629	48643	48657
307	48714	48728	48742	48756	48770	48784	48799
308	48855	48869	48883	48897	48911	48925	48940
309	48996	49010	49024	49038	49052	49066	49080
310	49136	49150	49164	49178	49192	49206	49220
311	49276	49290	49304	49318	49332	49346	49360
312	49415	49429	49443	49457	49471	49485	49499
313	49554	49568	49582	49596	49610	49624	49638
314	49693	49707	49721	49734	49748	49762	49776
315	49831	49845	49859	49872	49886	49900	49914
316	49969	49982	49996	50010	50024	50037	50051
317	50106	50119	50133	50147	50161	50174	50188
318	50243	50256	50270	50284	50297	50311	50325
319	50379	50393	50406	50420	50433	50447	50460
320	50515	50529	50542	50556	50569	50583	50596
321	50650	50664	50678	50691	50705	50718	50732
322	50786	50799	50813	50826	50839	50853	50866
323	50920	50934	50947	50961	50974	50987	51001
324	51054	51068	51081	51095	51108	51121	51135
325	51188	51202	51215	51228	51242	51255	51268
326	51322	51335	51348	51362	51375	51388	51402
327	51455	51468	51481	51495	51508	51521	51534
328	51587	51601	51614	51627	51640	51653	51667
329	51719	51733	51746	51759	51772	51785	51799
330	51851	51865	51878	51891	51904	51917	51930
331	51983	51996	52009	52022	52035	52048	52061
332	52114	52127	52140	52153	52166	52179	52192
333	52244	52257	52270	52283	52297	52310	52323
334	52375	52388	52401	52414	52427	52440	52453
335	52504	52517	52530	52543	52556	52569	52582
336	52633	52647	52660	52673	52686	52698	52711
337	52764	52776	52789	52802	52814	52827	52840
338	52891	52904	52917	52930	52943	52956	52969
339	53020	53033	53046	53058	53071	53084	53097
340	53148	53161	53173	53186	53199	53211	53224
341	53275	53288	53301	53314	53326	53339	53351
342	53403	53415	53428	53441	53453	53466	53479
343	53529	53542	53555	53567	53580	53593	53605
344	53656	53668	53681	53694	53706	53719	53731
345	53782	53794	53807	53820	53832	53845	53857
346	53908	53920	53933	53945	53958	53970	53983
347	54033	54045	54058	54070	54083	54095	54108
348	54158	54170	54183	54195	54208	54220	54233
349	54282	54295	54307	54320	54332	54345	54357
350	54407	54419	54432	54444	54456	54469	54481

Logarithms (*contd.*)

	7	8	9	Mean Log. Differences								
				1	2	3	4	5	6	7	8	9
300	47813	47828	47842	14	29	43	58	72	87	101	116	130
301	47957	47972	47986									
302	48101	48116	48130	14	29	43	57	72	86	101	115	129
303	48244	48259	48273									
304	48387	48401	48416	14	29	43	57	71	86	100	114	128
305	48529	48544	48558	14	28	43	57	71	85	100	114	128
306	48671	48685	48700									
307	48813	48827	48841	14	28	42	56	71	85	99	113	127
308	48954	48968	48982									
309	49094	49108	49122	14	28	42	56	70	84	98	112	126
310	49234	49248	49262	14	28	42	56	70	84	98	112	126
311	49374	49388	49401									
312	49513	49527	49541	14	28	42	56	69	83	97	111	125
313	49651	49665	49679									
314	49790	49803	49817	14	28	41	55	69	83	97	110	124
315	49927	49941	49955	14	28	41	55	69	83	96	110	124
316	50065	50078	50092									
317	50202	50215	50229	14	27	41	55	68	82	96	109	123
318	50338	50352	50365									
319	50474	50488	50501	14	27	41	54	68	82	95	109	122
320	50610	50623	50637	14	27	41	54	68	81	95	108	122
321	50745	50759	50772									
322	50880	50893	50907	13	27	40	54	67	81	94	108	121
323	51014	51028	51041									
324	51148	51162	51175	13	27	40	54	67	80	94	107	120
325	51282	51295	51308	13	27	40	53	67	80	93	107	120
326	51415	51428	51441									
327	51548	51561	51574	13	27	40	53	66	80	93	106	119
328	51680	51693	51706									
329	51812	51825	51838	13	26	40	53	66	79	92	105	119
330	51943	51957	51970	13	26	39	53	66	79	92	105	118
331	52074	52088	52101									
332	52205	52218	52231	13	26	39	52	65	78	91	104	117
333	52336	52349	52362									
334	52466	52478	52491	13	26	39	52	65	78	91	104	117
335	52595	52608	52621	13	26	39	52	65	78	91	104	117
336	52724	52737	52750									
337	52853	52866	52879	13	26	39	51	64	77	90	103	116
338	52981	52994	53007									
339	53110	53122	53135	13	26	38	51	64	77	90	102	115
340	53237	53250	53263	13	26	38	51	64	76	89	102	115
341	53364	53377	53390									
342	53491	53504	53517	13	25	38	51	63	76	89	101	114
343	53618	53631	53643									
344	53744	53757	53769	13	25	38	50	63	76	88	101	113
345	53870	53882	53895	13	25	38	50	63	75	88	101	113
346	53995	54008	54020									
347	54120	54133	54145	12	25	37	50	62	75	87	100	112
348	54245	54258	54270									
349	54370	54382	54394	12	25	37	50	62	75	87	99	112
350	54494	54506	54518	12	25	37	50	62	74	87	99	112

506

	0	1	2	3	4	5	6
350	54407	54419	54432	54444	54456	54469	54481
351	54531	54543	54555	54568	54580	54592	54605
352	54654	54667	54679	54691	54704	54716	54728
353	54777	54790	54802	54814	54827	54839	54851
354	54900	54913	54925	54937	54949	54962	54974
355	55023	55035	55047	55059	55072	55084	55096
356	55145	55157	55169	55182	55194	55206	55218
357	55267	55279	55291	55303	55315	55328	55340
358	55388	55400	55413	55425	55437	55449	55461
359	55509	55521	55534	55546	55558	55570	55582
360	55630	55642	55654	55666	55678	55690	55703
361	55751	55763	55775	55787	55799	55811	55823
362	55871	55883	55895	55907	55919	55931	55943
363	55991	56003	56015	56026	56038	56050	56062
364	56110	56122	56134	56145	56158	56170	56182
365	56229	56241	56253	56265	56277	56289	56301
366	56348	56360	56372	56384	56395	56407	56419
367	56467	56478	56490	56502	56514	56526	56538
368	56585	56597	56608	56620	56632	56644	56655
369	56703	56714	56726	56738	56750	56761	56773
370	56820	56832	56844	56855	56867	56879	56890
371	56937	56949	56961	56972	56984	56996	57008
372	57054	57066	57078	57089	57101	57113	57124
373	57171	57182	57194	57206	57217	57229	57241
374	57287	57299	57310	57322	57334	57345	57357
375	57403	57415	57426	57438	57449	57461	57473
376	57519	57530	57542	57553	57565	57576	57588
377	57634	57646	57657	57669	57680	57692	57703
378	57749	57761	57772	57784	57795	57807	57818
379	57864	57875	57887	57898	57910	57921	57933
380	57978	57990	58001	58013	58024	58035	58047
381	58092	58104	58115	58127	58138	58149	58161
382	58206	58218	58229	58240	58252	58263	58274
383	58320	58331	58343	58354	58365	58376	58388
384	58433	58444	58456	58467	58478	58490	58501
385	58546	58557	58569	58580	58591	58602	58614
386	58659	58670	58681	58692	58704	58715	58726
387	58771	58782	58793	58805	58816	58827	58838
388	58883	58894	58906	58917	58928	58939	58950
389	58995	59006	59017	59028	59040	59051	59062
390	59106	59118	59129	59140	59151	59162	59173
391	59218	59229	59240	59251	59262	59273	59284
392	59329	59340	59351	59362	59373	59384	59395
393	59439	59450	59461	59472	59483	59494	59505
394	59550	59561	59572	59583	59594	59605	59616
395	59660	59671	59682	59693	59704	59715	59726
396	59770	59780	59791	59802	59813	59824	59835
397	59879	59890	59901	59912	59923	59934	59945
398	59988	59999	60010	60021	60031	60043	60054
399	60097	60108	60119	60130	60141	60152	60162
400	60206	60217	60228	60239	60249	60260	60271

Logarithms (*contd.*)

	7	8	9	Mean Log. Differences								
				1	2	3	4	5	6	7	8	9
350	54494	54506	54518	12	25	37	50	62	74	87	99	112
351	54617	54630	54642									
352	54740	54753	54765	12	25	37	49	62	74	86	99	111
353	54863	54876	54888									
354	54986	54998	55011	12	25	37	49	61	74	86	98	110
355	55108	55121	55133	12	24	37	49	61	73	86	98	110
356	55230	55242	55255									
357	55352	55364	55376	12	24	36	49	61	73	85	97	109
358	55473	55485	55497									
359	55594	55606	55618	12	24	36	48	60	72	85	97	109
360	55715	55727	55739	12	24	36	48	60	72	84	96	108
361	55835	55847	55859									
362	55955	55967	55979	12	24	36	48	60	72	84	96	108
363	56074	56086	56098									
364	56194	56205	56217	12	24	36	48	59	71	83	95	107
365	56312	56324	56336	12	24	36	48	59	71	83	95	107
366	56431	56443	56455									
367	56549	56561	56573	12	24	35	47	59	71	83	95	106
368	56667	56679	56691									
369	56785	56797	56808	12	24	35	47	59	71	82	94	106
370	56902	56914	56926	12	23	35	47	59	70	82	94	105
371	57019	57031	57043									
372	57136	57148	57159	12	23	35	47	58	70	82	93	105
373	57252	57264	57275									
374	57368	57380	57391	12	23	35	46	58	70	81	93	104
375	57484	57496	57507	12	23	35	46	58	69	81	93	104
376	57600	57611	57623									
377	57715	57726	57738	12	23	34	46	58	69	81	92	104
378	57829	57841	57852									
379	57944	57955	57967	11	23	34	46	57	69	80	92	103
380	58058	58070	58081	11	23	34	46	57	68	80	91	103
381	58172	58184	58195									
382	58285	58297	58308	11	23	34	45	57	68	79	91	102
383	58399	58410	58422									
384	58512	58523	58535	11	23	34	45	56	68	79	90	102
385	58625	58636	58647	11	23	34	45	56	68	79	90	101
386	58737	58749	58760									
387	58850	58861	58872	11	22	34	45	56	67	78	90	101
388	58961	58973	58984									
389	59073	59084	59095	11	22	33	44	56	67	78	89	100
390	59184	59195	59207	11	22	33	44	56	67	78	89	100
391	59295	59306	59317									
392	59406	59417	59428	11	22	33	44	55	66	77	89	100
393	59516	59528	59539									
394	59627	59638	59649	11	22	33	44	55	66	77	88	99
395	59737	59747	59759	11	22	33	44	55	66	77	88	99
396	59846	59857	59868									
397	59956	59966	59977	11	22	33	44	55	66	76	87	98
398	60065	60075	60086									
399	60173	60184	60195	11	22	33	43	54	65	76	87	98
400	60282	60293	60304	11	22	33	43	54	65	76	87	98

Table of

	0	1	2	3	4	5	6
400	60206	60217	60228	60239	60249	60260	60271
401	60314	60325	60336	60347	60358	60368	60379
402	60423	60433	60444	60455	60466	60476	60487
403	60530	60541	60552	60563	60574	60584	60595
404	60638	60649	60660	60670	60681	60691	60703
405	60745	60756	60767	60778	60788	60799	60810
406	60853	60863	60874	60885	60895	60906	60917
407	60959	60970	60981	60991	61002	61012	61023
408	61066	61077	61087	61098	61109	61119	61130
409	61172	61183	61194	61204	61215	61225	61236
410	61278	61289	61300	61310	61321	61331	61342
411	61384	61395	61405	61416	61426	61437	61447
412	61490	61500	61511	61521	61532	61542	61553
413	61595	61605	61616	61626	61637	61647	61658
414	61700	61710	61721	61731	61742	61752	61763
415	61805	61815	61826	61836	61847	61857	61868
416	61909	61920	61930	61941	61951	61961	61972
417	62014	62024	62034	62045	62055	62065	62076
418	62118	62128	62138	62149	62159	62169	62180
419	62221	62232	62242	62252	62263	62273	62283
420	62325	62335	62346	62356	62366	62376	62387
421	62428	62438	62449	62459	62469	62479	62490
422	62531	62541	62552	62562	62572	62582	62593
423	62634	62644	62655	62665	62675	62685	62696
424	62737	62747	62757	62767	62777	62787	62798
425	62839	62849	62859	62869	62880	62890	62900
426	62941	62951	62961	62971	62981	62991	63002
427	63043	63053	63063	63073	63083	63093	63104
428	63144	63154	63165	63175	63185	63195	63205
429	63246	63256	63266	63276	63286	63296	63306
430	63347	63357	63367	63377	63387	63397	63407
431	63448	63458	63468	63478	63488	63498	63508
432	63548	63558	63568	63578	63589	63599	63609
433	63649	63659	63669	63679	63689	63699	63709
434	63749	63759	63769	63779	63789	63799	63809
435	63849	63859	63869	63879	63889	63898	63909
436	63949	63959	63969	63978	63988	63998	64008
437	64048	64058	64068	64078	64088	64098	64108
438	64147	64157	64167	64177	64187	64197	64207
439	64246	64256	64266	64276	64286	64295	64306
440	64345	64355	64365	64375	64385	64394	64404
441	64444	64454	64463	64473	64483	64493	64503
442	64542	64552	64562	64571	64581	64591	64601
443	64640	64650	64660	64670	64680	64689	64699
444	64738	64748	64758	64768	64777	64787	64797
445	64836	64846	64855	64865	64875	64884	64894
446	64933	64943	64953	64963	64972	64982	64992
447	65031	65040	65050	65060	65070	65079	65089
448	65128	65137	65147	65157	65166	65177	65186
449	65225	65234	65244	65254	65263	65273	65283
450	65321	65331	65340	65350	65360	65369	65379

Logarithms (*contd.*)

| | 7 | 8 | 9 | Mean Log. Differences |||||||||
				1	2	3	4	5	6	7	8	9
400	60282	60293	60304	11	22	33	43	54	65	76	87	98
401	60390	60401	60412									
402	60498	60509	60520	11	22	32	43	54	65	76	86	97
403	60606	60617	60627									
404	60713	60724	60735	11	21	32	43	54	64	75	86	97
405	60820	60831	60842	11	21	32	43	54	64	75	86	96
406	60927	60938	60949									
407	61034	61045	61055	11	21	32	43	53	64	75	85	96
408	61140	61151	61162									
409	61247	61257	61268	11	21	32	42	53	64	74	85	95
410	61352	61363	61374	11	21	32	42	53	63	74	85	95
411	61458	61469	61479									
412	61563	61574	61584	11	21	32	42	53	63	74	84	95
413	61669	61679	61689									
414	61773	61784	61794	10	21	31	42	52	63	73	84	94
415	61878	61888	61899	10	21	31	42	52	63	73	84	94
416	61982	61993	62003									
417	62086	62097	62107	10	21	31	42	52	62	73	83	94
418	62190	62201	62211									
419	62294	62304	62315	10	21	31	41	52	62	72	83	93
420	62397	62408	62418	10	21	31	41	52	62	72	83	93
421	62500	62511	62521									
422	62603	62613	62624	10	21	31	41	51	62	72	82	93
423	62706	62716	62726									
424	62808	62818	62829	10	20	31	41	51	61	72	82	92
425	62910	62921	62931	10	20	31	41	51	61	71	82	92
426	63012	63022	63032									
427	63114	63124	63134	10	20	30	41	51	61	71	81	91
428	63215	63225	63236									
429	63316	63327	63337	10	20	30	40	51	61	71	81	91
430	63417	63428	63438	10	20	30	40	50	61	71	81	91
431	63518	63528	63538									
432	63619	63629	63639	10	20	30	40	50	60	70	80	90
433	63719	63729	63739									
434	63819	63829	63839	10	20	30	40	50	60	70	80	90
435	63919	63929	63939	10	20	30	40	50	60	70	80	90
436	64018	64028	64038									
437	64118	64128	64137	10	20	30	40	50	60	69	79	89
438	64217	64227	64237									
439	64316	64325	64335	10	20	30	40	49	59	69	79	89
440	64414	64424	64434	10	20	30	39	49	59	69	79	89
441	64513	64523	64532									
442	64611	64621	64631	10	20	29	39	49	59	69	79	88
443	64709	64719	64728									
444	64807	64816	64826	10	20	29	39	49	59	68	78	88
445	64904	64914	64924	10	19	29	39	49	58	68	78	88
446	65002	65011	65021									
447	65099	65108	65118	10	19	29	39	49	58	68	78	87
448	65196	65205	65215									
449	65292	65302	65312	10	19	29	39	48	58	68	77	87
450	65389	65398	65408	10	19	29	39	48	58	67	77	87

510

Table of

	0	1	2	3	4	5	6
450	65321	65331	65340	65350	65360	65369	65379
451	65418	65427	65437	65446	65456	65466	65475
452	65514	65523	65533	65543	65552	65562	65571
453	65610	65619	65629	65639	65648	65658	65667
454	65706	65715	65725	65734	65744	65753	65763
455	65801	65811	65820	65830	65839	65849	65858
456	65896	65906	65915	65925	65935	65944	65954
457	65992	66001	66011	66020	66030	66039	66049
458	66086	66096	66105	66115	66124	66134	66143
459	66181	66191	66200	66210	66219	66229	66238
460	66276	66285	66295	66304	66313	66323	66332
461	66370	66379	66389	66398	66408	66417	66427
462	66464	66474	66483	66492	66502	66511	66521
463	66558	66567	66577	66586	66596	66605	66614
464	66652	66661	66670	66680	66689	66699	66708
465	66745	66755	66764	66773	66783	66792	66801
466	66839	66848	66857	66866	66876	66885	66894
467	66932	66941	66950	66960	66969	66978	66987
468	67025	67034	67043	67052	67062	67071	67080
469	67117	67126	67136	67145	67154	67164	67173
470	67210	67219	67228	67237	67247	67256	67265
471	67302	67311	67320	67330	67339	67348	67357
472	67394	67403	67413	67422	67431	67440	67449
473	67486	67495	67504	67514	67523	67532	67541
474	67578	67587	67596	67605	67614	67624	67633
475	67669	67678	67688	67697	67706	67715	67724
476	67761	67770	67779	67788	67797	67806	67815
477	67852	67861	67870	67879	67888	67897	67906
478	67943	67952	67961	67970	67979	67988	67997
479	68034	68043	68052	68061	68070	68079	68088
480	68124	68133	68142	68151	68160	68169	68178
481	68214	68223	68233	68242	68251	68260	68269
482	68305	68314	68323	68332	68341	68350	68359
483	68395	68404	68413	68422	68431	68440	68449
484	68484	68493	68502	68511	68520	68529	68538
485	68574	68583	68592	68601	68610	68619	68628
486	68664	68673	68681	68690	68699	68708	68717
487	68753	68762	68771	68780	68789	68797	68806
488	68842	68851	68860	68869	68878	68886	68895
489	68931	68940	68949	68957	68966	68975	68984
490	69020	69028	69037	69046	69055	69064	69073
491	69108	69117	69126	69135	69143	69152	69161
492	69196	69205	69214	69223	69232	69241	69249
493	69285	69293	69302	69311	69320	69329	69337
494	69373	69381	69390	69399	69408	69417	69425
495	69460	69469	69478	69487	69496	69504	69513
496	69548	69557	69566	69574	69583	69592	69601
497	69636	69644	69653	69662	69671	69679	69688
498	69723	69732	69740	69749	69758	69766	69775
499	69810	69819	69827	69836	69845	69853	69862
500	69897	69906	69914	69923	69932	69940	69949

Logarithms (contd.)

	7	8	9	Mean Log. Differences								
				1	2	3	4	5	6	7	8	9
450	65389	65398	65408	10	19	29	39	48	58	67	77	87
451	65485	65495	65504									
452	65581	65591	65600	10	19	29	38	48	58	67	77	86
453	65677	65686	65696									
454	65772	65782	65792	10	19	29	38	48	57	67	76	86
455	65868	65877	65887	10	19	29	38	48	57	67	76	86
456	65963	65973	65982									
457	66058	66068	66077	9	19	28	38	47	57	66	76	85
458	66153	66162	66172									
459	66247	66257	66266	9	19	28	38	47	57	66	76	85
460	66342	66351	66361	9	19	28	38	47	57	66	75	85
461	66436	66445	66455									
462	66530	66539	66549	9	19	28	38	47	56	66	75	85
463	66624	66633	66642									
464	66717	66727	66736	9	19	28	37	47	56	65	75	84
465	66811	66820	66829	9	19	28	37	47	56	65	75	84
466	66904	66913	66922									
467	66997	67006	67015	9	19	28	37	46	56	65	74	84
468	67089	67099	67108									
469	67182	67191	67200	9	19	28	37	46	56	65	74	83
470	67274	67284	67293	9	18	28	37	46	55	65	74	83
471	67367	67376	67385									
472	67459	67468	67477	9	18	28	37	46	55	64	74	83
473	67550	67559	67569									
474	67642	67651	67660	9	18	27	37	46	55	64	73	82
475	67733	67742	67752	9	18	27	37	46	55	64	73	82
476	67824	67834	67843									
477	67915	67925	67934	9	18	27	36	45	55	64	73	82
478	68006	68015	68024									
479	68097	68106	68115	9	18	27	36	45	54	63	72	82
480	68187	68196	68205	9	18	27	36	45	54	63	72	81
481	68278	68287	68296									
482	68368	68377	68386	9	18	27	36	45	54	63	72	81
483	68458	68467	68476									
484	68547	68556	68565	9	18	27	36	45	54	63	72	81
485	68637	68646	68655	9	18	27	36	45	54	63	72	81
486	68726	68735	68744									
487	68815	68824	68833	9	18	27	36	45	53	62	71	80
488	68904	68913	68922									
489	68993	69002	69011	9	18	27	35	44	53	62	71	80
490	69082	69090	69099	9	18	27	35	44	53	62	71	80
491	69170	69179	69188									
492	69258	69267	69276	9	18	26	35	44	53	62	71	79
493	69346	69355	69364									
494	69434	69443	69452	9	18	26	35	44	53	61	70	79
495	69522	69531	69539	9	18	26	35	44	53	61	70	79
496	69609	69618	69627									
497	69697	69705	69714	9	17	26	35	44	52	61	70	79
498	69784	69793	69801									
499	69871	69880	69888	9	17	26	35	43	52	61	70	78
500	69958	69966	69975	9	17	26	35	43	52	61	69	78

	0	1	2	3	4	5	6
500	69897	69906	69914	69923	69932	69940	69949
501	69984	69992	70001	70010	70018	70027	70035
502	70070	70079	70088	70096	70105	70113	70122
503	70157	70165	70174	70183	70191	70200	70209
504	70243	70252	70260	70269	70277	70286	70295
505	70329	70338	70346	70355	70363	70372	70381
506	70415	70424	70432	70441	70449	70458	70466
507	70501	70509	70518	70526	70535	70544	70552
508	70586	70595	70603	70612	70621	70629	70638
509	70672	70680	70689	70697	70706	70714	70723
510	70757	70765	70774	70783	70791	70800	70808
511	70842	70851	70859	70868	70876	70885	70893
512	70927	70935	70944	70952	70961	70969	70978
513	71012	71020	71029	71037	71046	71054	71062
514	71096	71105	71113	71122	71130	71138	71147
515	71181	71189	71198	71206	71214	71223	71231
516	71265	71273	71281	71290	71299	71307	71315
517	71349	71357	71366	71374	71383	71391	71399
518	71433	71441	71450	71458	71466	71475	71483
519	71517	71525	71533	71542	71550	71559	71567
520	71600	71609	71617	71625	71634	71642	71650
521	71684	71692	71700	71709	71717	71725	71734
522	71767	71775	71784	71792	71800	71809	71817
523	71850	71858	71867	71875	71883	71892	71900
524	71933	71941	71950	71958	71966	71974	71983
525	72016	72024	72032	72041	72049	72057	72065
526	72099	72107	72115	72123	72132	72140	72148
527	72181	72189	72197	72206	72214	72222	72230
528	72263	72272	72280	72288	72296	72304	72313
529	72346	72354	72362	72370	72378	72387	72395
530	72428	72436	72444	72452	72460	72468	72477
531	72509	72518	72526	72534	72542	72550	72558
532	72591	72599	72607	72616	72624	72632	72640
533	72673	72681	72689	72697	72705	72713	72722
534	72754	72762	72770	72778	72787	72795	72803
535	72835	72843	72852	72860	72868	72876	72884
536	72916	72925	72933	72941	72949	72957	72965
537	72997	73005	73014	73022	73030	73038	73046
538	73078	73086	73094	73102	73110	73119	73127
539	73159	73167	73175	73183	73191	73199	73207
540	73239	73247	73255	73263	73271	73280	73288
541	73320	73328	73336	73344	73352	73360	73368
542	73400	73408	73416	73424	73432	73440	73448
543	73480	73488	73496	73504	73512	73520	73528
544	73560	73568	73576	73584	73592	73600	73608
545	73640	73648	73656	73663	73671	73679	73687
546	73719	73727	73735	73743	73751	73759	73767
547	73799	73806	73815	73822	73830	73838	73846
548	73878	73886	73894	73902	73910	73918	73926
549	73957	73965	73973	73981	73989	73997	74005
550	74036	74044	74052	74060	74068	74076	74084

Logarithms (*contd.*)

	7	8	9	Mean Log. Differences								
				1	2	3	4	5	6	7	8	9
500	69958	69966	69975	9	17	26	35	43	52	61	69	78
501	70044	70053	70062									
502	70131	70139	70148	9	17	26	35	43	52	60	69	78
503	70217	70226	70234									
504	70303	70312	70320	9	17	26	34	43	52	60	69	77
505	70389	70398	70406	9	17	26	34	43	52	60	69	77
506	70475	70484	70492									
507	70561	70569	70578	9	17	26	34	43	51	60	68	77
508	70646	70655	70663									
509	70731	70740	70748	9	17	26	34	43	51	60	68	77
510	70817	70825	70834	9	17	26	34	43	51	60	68	77
511	70901	70910	70918									
512	70986	70995	71003	8	17	25	34	42	51	59	68	76
513	71071	71079	71088									
514	71155	71164	71172	8	17	25	34	42	51	59	68	76
515	71240	71248	71257	8	17	25	34	42	51	59	67	76
516	71324	71332	71341									
517	71408	71416	71425	8	17	25	34	42	50	59	67	76
518	71492	71500	71508									
519	71575	71584	71592	8	17	25	33	42	50	59	67	75
520	71659	71667	71675	8	17	25	33	42	50	58	67	75
521	71742	71750	71759									
522	71825	71834	71842	8	17	25	33	42	50	58	66	75
523	71908	71916	71925									
524	71991	71999	72008	8	17	25	33	41	50	58	66	75
525	72074	72082	72090	8	17	25	33	41	50	58	66	74
526	72156	72165	72173									
527	72239	72247	72255	8	16	25	33	41	49	58	66	74
528	72321	72329	72337									
529	72403	72411	72419	8	16	25	33	41	49	57	66	74
530	72485	72493	72501	8	16	25	33	41	49	57	65	74
531	72567	72575	72583									
532	72648	72656	72665	8	16	24	33	41	49	57	65	73
533	72730	72738	72746									
534	72811	72819	72827	8	16	24	33	41	49	57	65	73
535	72892	72900	72908	8	16	24	32	41	49	57	65	73
536	72973	72981	72989									
537	73054	73062	73070	8	16	24	32	40	48	57	65	73
538	73135	73143	73151									
539	73215	73223	73231	8	16	24	32	40	48	56	64	72
540	73296	73304	73312	8	16	24	32	40	48	56	64	72
541	73376	73384	73392									
542	73456	73464	73472	8	16	24	32	40	48	56	64	72
543	73536	73544	73552									
544	73616	73624	73632	8	16	24	32	40	48	56	64	72
545	73695	73703	73711	8	16	24	32	40	48	56	64	72
546	73775	73783	73791									
547	73854	73862	73870	8	16	24	32	40	48	56	63	71
548	73933	73941	73949									
549	74013	74020	74028	8	16	24	32	40	47	55	63	71
550	74091	74099	74107	8	16	24	32	39	47	55	63	71

E.W.D.— 17

	0	1	2	3	4	5	6
550	74036	74044	74052	74060	74068	74076	74084
551	74115	74123	74131	74139	74147	74155	74162
552	74194	74202	74210	74217	74225	74233	74241
553	74272	74280	74288	74296	74304	74312	74320
554	74351	74359	74367	74374	74382	74390	74398
555	74429	74437	74445	74453	74461	74468	74476
556	74507	74515	74523	74531	74539	74546	74554
557	74585	74593	74601	74609	74617	74624	74632
558	74663	74671	74679	74687	74694	74702	74710
559	74741	74749	74757	74764	74772	74780	74788
560	74819	74827	74834	74842	74850	74858	74865
561	74896	74904	74912	74919	74927	74935	74943
562	74974	74981	74989	74997	75004	75012	75020
563	75051	75059	75066	75074	75082	75089	75097
564	75128	75136	75143	75151	75159	75166	75174
565	75205	75212	75220	75228	75236	75243	75251
566	75282	75289	75297	75305	75312	75320	75328
567	75358	75366	75374	75381	75389	75397	75404
568	75435	75442	75450	75458	75465	75473	75481
569	75511	75519	75526	75534	75542	75549	75557
570	75587	75595	75603	75610	75618	75626	75633
571	75664	75671	75679	75686	75694	75702	75709
572	75740	75747	75755	75762	75770	75777	75785
573	75815	75823	75831	75838	75846	75853	75861
574	75891	75899	75906	75914	75921	75929	75937
575	75967	75974	75982	75989	75997	76004	76012
576	76042	76050	76057	76065	76072	76080	76087
577	76118	76125	76133	76140	76148	76155	76163
578	76193	76200	76208	76215	76223	76230	76238
579	76268	76275	76283	76290	76298	76305	76313
580	76343	76350	76358	76365	76373	76380	76388
581	76418	76425	76433	76440	76447	76455	76462
582	76492	76500	76507	76515	76522	76530	76537
583	76567	76574	76582	76589	76597	76604	76611
584	76641	76649	76656	76664	76671	76678	76686
585	76716	76723	76730	76738	76745	76753	76760
586	76790	76797	76805	76812	76819	76827	76834
587	76864	76871	76879	76886	76893	76901	76908
588	76938	76945	76952	76960	76967	76975	76982
589	77011	77019	77026	77034	77041	77048	77056
590	77085	77093	77100	77107	77115	77122	77129
591	77159	77166	77173	77181	77188	77195	77203
592	77232	77239	77247	77254	77261	77269	77276
593	77305	77313	77320	77327	77335	77342	77349
594	77379	77386	77393	77401	77408	77415	77422
595	77452	77459	77466	77474	77481	77488	77495
596	77525	77532	77539	77546	77554	77561	77568
597	77597	77605	77612	77619	77626	77634	77641
598	77670	77677	77685	77692	77699	77706	77714
599	77743	77750	77757	77764	77772	77779	77786
600	77815	77822	77830	77837	77844	77851	77858

Logarithms (*contd.*)

	7	8	9	Mean Log. Differences								
				1	2	3	4	5	6	7	8	9
550	74091	74099	74107	8	16	24	32	39	47	55	63	71
551	74170	74178	74186									
552	74249	74257	74265									
553	74327	74335	74343									
554	74406	74414	74421									
555	74484	74492	74500	8	16	23	31	39	47	55	63	70
556	74562	74570	74578									
557	74640	74648	74656									
558	74718	74726	74733									
559	74795	74803	74811									
560	74873	74881	74888	8	15	23	31	39	46	54	62	70
561	74950	74958	74966									
562	75028	75035	75043									
563	75105	75112	75120									
564	75182	75189	75197									
565	75259	75266	75274	8	15	23	31	38	46	54	61	69
566	75335	75343	75351									
567	75412	75419	75427									
568	75488	75496	75504									
569	75565	75572	75580									
570	75641	75648	75656	8	15	23	30	38	46	53	61	69
571	75717	75724	75732									
572	75793	75800	75808									
573	75868	75876	75884									
574	75944	75952	75959									
575	76020	76027	76035	8	15	23	30	38	45	53	60	68
576	76095	76102	76110									
577	76170	76178	76185									
578	76245	76253	76260									
579	76320	76328	76335									
580	76395	76403	76410	7	15	22	30	37	45	52	60	67
581	76470	76477	76485									
582	76544	76552	76559									
583	76619	76626	76634									
584	76693	76701	76708									
585	76767	76775	76782	7	15	22	30	37	45	52	59	67
586	76842	76849	76856									
587	76916	76923	76930									
588	76989	76997	77004									
589	77063	77070	77078									
590	77137	77144	77151	7	15	22	29	37	44	51	59	66
591	77210	77217	77225									
592	77283	77291	77298									
593	77357	77364	77371									
594	77430	77437	77444									
595	77503	77510	77517	7	15	22	29	36	44	51	58	66
596	77576	77583	77590									
597	77648	77656	77663									
598	77721	77728	77735									
599	77793	77801	77808									
600	77866	77873	77880	7	14	22	29	36	43	51	58	65

	0	1	2	3	4	5	6
600	77815	77822	77830	77837	77844	77851	77858
601	77887	77895	77902	77909	77916	77924	77931
602	77960	77967	77974	77981	77988	77996	78003
603	78032	78039	78046	78053	78060	78068	78075
604	78104	78111	78118	78125	78132	78140	78147
605	78175	78183	78190	78197	78204	78211	78219
606	78247	78254	78262	78269	78276	78283	78290
607	78319	78326	78333	78340	78347	78355	78362
608	78390	78397	78404	78412	78419	78426	78433
609	78462	78469	78476	78483	78490	78497	78504
610	78533	78540	78547	78554	78561	78569	78576
611	78604	78611	78618	78625	78632	78640	78647
612	78675	78682	78689	78696	78703	78711	78718
613	78746	78753	78760	78767	78774	78781	78788
614	78817	78824	78831	78838	78845	78852	78859
615	78887	78895	78902	78909	78916	78923	78930
616	78958	78965	78972	78979	78986	78993	79000
617	79028	79036	79043	79050	79057	79064	79071
618	79099	79106	79113	79120	79127	79134	79141
619	79169	79176	79183	79190	79197	79204	79211
620	79239	79246	79253	79260	79267	79274	79281
621	79309	79316	79323	79330	79337	79344	79351
622	79379	79386	79393	79400	79407	79414	79421
623	79449	79456	79463	79470	79477	79484	79491
624	79518	79525	79532	79539	79546	79553	79560
625	79588	79595	79602	79609	79616	79623	79630
626	79657	79664	79671	79678	79685	79692	79699
627	79727	79734	79741	79747	79754	79761	79768
628	79796	79803	79810	79817	79824	79830	79837
629	79865	79872	79879	79886	79893	79900	79906
630	79934	79941	79948	79955	79962	79968	79975
631	80003	80010	80017	80024	80030	80037	80044
632	80072	80079	80085	80092	80099	80106	80113
633	80140	80147	80154	80161	80168	80175	80181
634	80209	80216	80223	80229	80236	80243	80250
635	80277	80284	80291	80298	80305	80312	80318
636	80346	80352	80359	80366	80373	80380	80387
637	80414	80421	80428	80434	80441	80448	80455
638	80482	80489	80496	80502	80509	80516	80523
639	80550	80557	80564	80570	80577	80584	80591
640	80618	80625	80632	80638	80645	80652	80659
641	80686	80693	80699	80706	80713	80720	80726
642	80753	80760	80767	80774	80781	80787	80794
643	80821	80828	80835	80841	80848	80855	80862
644	80889	80895	80902	80909	80916	80922	80929
645	80956	80963	80969	80976	80983	80990	80996
646	81023	81030	81037	81043	81050	81057	81064
647	81090	81097	81104	81111	81117	81124	81131
648	81157	81164	81171	81178	81184	81191	81198
649	81224	81231	81238	81244	81251	81258	81265
650	81291	81298	81305	81311	81318	81325	81331

Logarithms (*contd.*)

	7	8	9	Mean Log. Differences								
				1	2	3	4	5	6	7	8	9
600	77866	77873	77880	7	14	22	29	36	43	51	58	65
601	77938	77945	77952									
602	78010	78017	78024									
603	78082	78089	78096									
604	78154	78161	78168									
605	78226	78233	78240	7	14	22	29	36	43	50	57	65
606	78297	78305	78312									
607	78369	78376	78383									
608	78440	78447	78455									
609	78512	78519	78526									
610	78583	78590	78597	7	14	21	28	36	43	50	57	64
611	78654	78661	78668									
612	78725	78732	78739									
613	78796	78803	78810									
614	78866	78873	78880									
615	78937	78944	78951	7	14	21	28	35	42	49	56	64
616	79007	79014	79021									
617	79078	79085	79092									
618	79148	79155	79162									
619	79218	79225	79232									
620	79288	79295	79302	7	14	21	28	35	42	49	56	63
621	79358	79365	79372									
622	79428	79435	79442									
623	79498	79504	79511									
624	79567	79574	79581									
625	79637	79644	79650	7	14	21	28	35	42	49	56	62
626	79706	79713	79720									
627	79775	79782	79789									
628	79844	79851	79858									
629	79913	79920	79927									
630	79982	79989	79996	7	14	21	28	34	41	48	55	62
631	80051	80058	80065									
632	80120	80127	80133									
633	80188	80195	80202									
634	80257	80264	80270									
635	80325	80332	80339	7	14	21	27	34	41	48	55	62
636	80393	80400	80407									
637	80462	80468	80475									
638	80530	80536	80543									
639	80598	80604	80611									
640	80665	80672	80679	7	14	20	27	34	41	47	54	61
641	80733	80740	80747									
642	80801	80808	80814									
643	80868	80875	80882									
644	80936	80942	80949									
645	81003	81010	81016	7	13	20	27	34	40	47	54	61
646	81070	81077	81084									
647	81137	81144	81151									
648	81204	81211	81218									
649	81271	81278	81285									
650	81338	81345	81351	7	13	20	27	33	40	47	53	60

	0	1	2	3	4	5	6
650	81291	81298	81305	81311	81318	81325	81331
651	81358	81365	81371	81379	81385	81391	81398
652	81425	81431	81438	81444	81451	81458	81465
653	81491	81498	81505	81511	81518	81525	81531
654	81558	81564	81571	81578	81584	81591	81598
655	81624	81631	81637	81644	81651	81657	81664
656	81690	81697	81704	81710	81717	81723	81730
657	81756	81763	81770	81776	81783	81790	81796
658	81823	81829	81836	81842	81849	81856	81862
659	81888	81895	81902	81908	81915	81921	81928
660	81954	81961	81968	81974	81981	81987	81994
661	82020	82027	82033	82040	82046	82053	82059
662	82086	82092	82099	82105	82112	82119	82125
663	82151	82158	82164	82171	82177	82184	82191
664	82217	82223	82230	82236	82243	82249	82256
665	82282	82289	82295	82302	82308	82315	82321
666	82347	82354	82360	82367	82373	82380	82386
667	82413	82419	82426	82432	82439	82445	82452
668	82478	82484	82491	82497	82504	82510	82517
669	82543	82549	82556	82562	82569	82575	82581
670	82607	82614	82620	82627	82633	82640	82646
671	82672	82679	82685	82692	82698	82705	82711
672	82737	82743	82750	82756	82763	82769	82776
673	82801	82808	82814	82821	82827	82834	82840
674	82866	82872	82879	82885	82892	82898	82905
675	82930	82937	82943	82950	82956	82962	82969
676	82995	83001	83007	83014	83020	83027	83033
677	83059	83065	83072	83078	83084	83091	83097
678	83123	83129	83136	83142	83149	83155	83161
679	83187	83193	83200	83206	83213	83219	83225
680	83251	83257	83264	83270	83276	83283	83289
681	83315	83321	83327	83334	83340	83347	83353
682	83378	83385	83391	83397	83404	83410	83417
683	83442	83448	83455	83461	83467	83474	83480
684	83506	83512	83518	83525	83531	83537	83544
685	83569	83575	83582	83588	83594	83601	83607
686	83632	83639	83645	83651	83658	83664	83670
687	83696	83702	83708	83715	83721	83727	83734
688	83759	83765	83771	83778	83784	83790	83797
689	83822	83828	83834	83841	83847	83853	83860
690	83885	83891	83897	83904	83910	83916	83923
691	83948	83954	83960	83967	83973	83979	83985
692	84011	84017	84023	84029	84036	84042	84048
693	84073	84080	84086	84092	84098	84105	84111
694	84136	84142	84148	84155	84161	84167	84173
695	84198	84205	84211	84217	84223	84230	84236
696	84261	84267	84273	84280	84286	84292	84298
697	84323	84329	84336	84342	84348	84354	84361
698	84385	84392	84398	84404	84410	84417	84423
699	84448	84454	84460	84466	84473	84479	84485
700	84510	84516	84522	84528	84535	84541	84547

Logarithms *(contd.)*

	7	8	9	Mean Log. Differences								
				1	2	3	4	5	6	7	8	9
650	81338	81345	81351	7	13	20	27	33	40	47	53	60
651	81405	81411	81418									
652	81471	81478	81485									
653	81538	81544	81551									
654	81604	81611	81617									
655	81670	81677	81684	7	13	20	27	33	40	46	53	60
656	81737	81743	81750									
657	81803	81809	81816									
658	81869	81875	81882									
659	81935	81941	81948									
660	82000	82007	82014	7	13	20	26	33	39	46	53	59
661	82066	82073	82079									
662	82132	82138	82145									
663	82197	82204	82210									
664	82263	82269	82276									
665	82328	82334	82341	7	13	20	26	33	39	46	52	59
666	82393	82400	82406									
667	82458	82465	82471									
668	82523	82530	82536									
669	82588	82594	82601									
670	82653	82659	82666	6	13	19	26	32	39	45	52	58
671	82717	82724	82730									
672	82782	82789	82795									
673	82847	82853	82859									
674	82911	82917	82924									
675	82975	82982	82988	6	13	19	26	32	39	45	51	58
676	83040	83046	83052									
677	83104	83110	83117									
678	83168	83174	83181									
679	83232	83238	83244									
680	83296	83302	83308	6	13	19	26	32	38	45	51	57
681	83359	83366	83372									
682	83423	83429	83436									
683	83487	83493	83499									
684	83550	83556	83563									
685	83613	83620	83626	6	13	19	25	32	38	44	51	57
686	83677	83683	83689									
687	83740	83746	83752									
688	83803	83809	83816									
689	83866	83872	83879									
690	83929	83935	83941	6	13	19	25	31	38	44	50	57
691	83992	83998	84004									
692	84054	84061	84067									
693	84117	84123	84130									
694	84180	84186	84192									
695	84242	84248	84255	6	12	19	25	31	37	44	50	56
696	84305	84311	84317									
697	84367	84373	84379									
698	84429	84435	84441									
699	84491	84497	84504									
700	84553	84559	84566	6	12	19	25	31	37	43	50	56

	0	1	2	3	4	5	6
700	84510	84516	84522	84528	84535	84541	84547
701	84572	84578	84584	84590	84597	84603	84609
702	84634	84640	84646	84652	84658	84665	84671
703	84695	84702	84708	84714	84720	84726	84733
704	84757	84763	84770	84776	84782	84788	84794
705	84819	84825	84831	84837	84843	84850	84856
706	84880	84887	84893	84899	84905	84911	84917
707	84942	84948	84954	84960	84966	84973	84979
708	85003	85009	85016	85022	85028	85034	85040
709	85065	85071	85077	85083	85089	85095	85101
710	85126	85132	85138	85144	85150	85156	85162
711	85187	85193	85199	85205	85211	85217	85224
712	85248	85254	85260	85266	85272	85278	85285
713	85309	85315	85321	85327	85333	85339	85345
714	85370	85376	85382	85388	85394	85400	85406
715	85431	85437	85443	85449	85455	85461	85467
716	85491	85497	85503	85509	85516	85522	85528
717	85552	85558	85564	85570	85576	85582	85588
718	85612	85618	85624	85631	85637	85643	85649
719	85673	85679	85685	85691	85697	85703	85709
720	85733	85739	85745	85751	85757	85763	85769
721	85793	85799	85806	85812	85818	85824	85830
722	85854	85860	85866	85872	85878	85884	85890
723	85914	85920	85926	85932	85938	85944	85950
724	85974	85980	85986	85992	85998	86004	86010
725	86034	86040	86046	86052	86058	86064	86070
726	86094	86100	86106	86112	86118	86124	86129
727	86153	86160	86165	86171	86177	86183	86189
728	86213	86219	86225	86231	86237	86243	86249
729	86273	86279	86285	86291	86297	86302	86308
730	86332	86338	86344	86350	86356	86362	86368
731	86392	86398	86404	86410	86415	86421	86427
732	86451	86457	86463	86469	86475	86481	86487
733	86510	86516	86522	86528	86534	86540	86546
734	86570	86575	86581	86587	86593	86599	86605
735	86629	86634	86640	86646	86652	86658	86664
736	86688	86694	86700	86705	86711	86717	86723
737	86747	86753	86758	86764	86770	86776	86782
738	86806	86811	86817	86823	86829	86835	86841
739	86864	86870	86876	86882	86888	86894	86900
740	86923	86929	86935	86941	86947	86952	86958
741	86982	86988	86993	86999	87005	87011	87017
742	87040	87046	87052	87058	87063	87070	87075
743	87099	87105	87111	87116	87122	87128	87134
744	87157	87163	87169	87174	87181	87186	87192
745	87216	87221	87227	87233	87239	87245	87251
746	87274	87280	87285	87291	87297	87303	87309
747	87332	87338	87344	87349	87355	87361	87367
748	87390	87396	87402	87408	87413	87419	87425
749	87443	87454	87460	87466	87471	87477	87483
750	87506	87512	87518	87523	87529	87535	87541

Logarithms (*contd.*)

	7	8	9	Mean Log. Differences								
				1	2	3	4	5	6	7	8	9
700	84553	84559	84566	6	12	19	25	31	37	43	50	56
701	84615	84621	84627									
702	84677	84683	84689									
703	84739	84745	84751									
704	84800	84807	84813									
705	84862	84868	84874	6	12	18	25	31	37	43	49	55
706	84923	84930	84936									
707	84985	84991	84997									
708	85046	85052	85058									
709	85107	85114	85120									
710	85169	85175	85181	6	12	18	24	31	37	43	49	55
711	85230	85236	85242									
712	85291	85297	85303									
713	85352	85358	85364									
714	85412	85418	85424									
715	85473	85479	85485	6	12	18	24	30	36	42	49	55
716	85534	85540	85546									
717	85594	85600	85606									
718	85655	85661	85667									
719	85715	85721	85727									
720	85775	85781	85787	6	12	18	24	30	36	42	48	54
721	85836	85842	85848									
722	85896	85902	85908									
723	85956	85962	85968									
724	86016	86022	86028									
725	86076	86082	86088	6	12	18	24	30	36	42	48	54
726	86135	86141	86147									
727	86195	86201	86207									
728	86255	86261	86267									
729	86314	86320	86326									
730	86374	86380	86386	6	12	18	24	30	36	42	48	54
731	86433	86439	86445									
732	86493	86498	86504									
733	86552	86558	86564									
734	86611	86617	86623									
735	86670	86676	86682	6	12	18	24	30	35	41	47	53
736	86729	86735	86741									
737	86788	86794	86800									
738	86847	86853	86859									
739	86906	86911	86917									
740	86964	86970	86976	6	12	18	23	29	35	41	47	53
741	87023	87029	87034									
742	87081	87087	87093									
743	87140	87146	87151									
744	87198	87204	87210									
745	87256	87262	87268	6	12	17	23	29	35	41	47	52
746	87315	87320	87326									
747	87373	87378	87384									
748	87431	87437	87442									
749	87489	87494	87500									
750	87547	87552	87558	6	12	17	23	29	35	41	46	52

	0	1	2	3	4	5	6
750	87506	87512	87518	87523	87529	87535	87541
751	87564	87570	87576	87581	87587	87593	87599
752	87622	87628	87633	87639	87645	87651	87656
753	87679	87685	87691	87697	87703	87708	87714
754	87737	87743	87749	87754	87760	87766	87772
755	87795	87800	87806	87812	87818	87823	87829
756	87852	87858	87864	87869	87875	87881	87887
757	87910	87915	87921	87927	87932	87938	87944
758	87967	87972	87978	87984	87990	87996	88001
759	88024	88030	88036	88041	88047	88052	88058
760	88081	88087	88093	88098	88104	88110	88116
761	88138	88144	88150	88156	88161	88167	88173
762	88195	88201	88207	88213	88218	88224	88230
763	88252	88258	88264	88269	88275	88281	88287
764	88309	88315	88321	88326	88332	88338	88343
765	88366	88372	88377	88383	88389	88394	88400
766	88423	88428	88434	88440	88445	88451	88457
767	88479	88485	88491	88496	88502	88508	88513
768	88536	88542	88547	88553	88559	88564	88570
769	88593	88598	88604	88610	88615	88621	88626
770	88649	88655	88660	88666	88672	88677	88683
771	88705	88711	88717	88722	88728	88734	88739
772	88761	88767	88773	88779	88784	88790	88795
773	88818	88824	88829	88835	88840	88846	88852
774	88874	88880	88885	88891	88896	88902	88908
775	88930	88936	88941	88947	88953	88958	88964
776	88986	88992	88997	89003	89009	89014	89020
777	89042	89048	89053	89059	89064	89070	89076
778	89098	89103	89109	89115	89120	89126	89131
779	89154	89159	89165	89170	89176	89182	89187
780	89209	89215	89221	89226	89232	89237	89243
781	89265	89271	89276	89282	89287	89293	89298
782	89321	89326	89332	89337	89342	89348	89354
783	89376	89382	89387	89393	89398	89404	89409
784	89432	89437	89443	89448	89454	89459	89465
785	89487	89492	89498	89504	89509	89515	89520
786	89542	89548	89553	89559	89564	89570	89575
787	89597	89603	89608	89614	89619	89625	89631
788	89653	89658	89664	89669	89675	89680	89686
789	89708	89713	89719	89724	89730	89735	89741
790	89763	89768	89774	89779	89785	89790	89796
791	89818	89823	89829	89834	89840	89845	89851
792	89872	89878	89883	89889	89894	89900	89905
793	89927	89933	89938	89944	89949	89955	89960
794	89982	89987	89993	89998	90004	90009	90015
795	90037	90042	90048	90053	90059	90064	90069
796	90091	90097	90102	90108	90113	90119	90124
797	90146	90151	90157	90162	90168	90173	90178
798	90200	90206	90211	90217	90222	90227	90233
799	90255	90260	90265	90271	90276	90282	90287
800	90309	90314	90320	90325	90331	90336	90342

Logarithms (*contd.*)

	7	8	9	Mean Log. Differences								
				1	2	3	4	5	6	7	8	9
750	87547	87552	87558	6	12	17	23	29	35	41	46	52
751	87604	87610	87616									
752	87662	87668	87674									
753	87720	87726	87731									
754	87777	87783	87789									
755	87835	87841	87846	6	11	17	23	29	34	40	46	52
756	87892	87898	87904									
757	87950	87955	87961									
758	88007	88013	88018									
759	88064	88070	88076									
760	88121	88127	88133	6	11	17	23	29	34	40	46	51
761	88178	88184	88190									
762	88235	88241	88247									
763	88292	88298	88304									
764	88349	88355	88360									
765	88406	88411	88417	6	11	17	23	28	34	40	45	51
766	88462	88468	88474									
767	88519	88525	88530									
768	88576	88581	88587									
769	88632	88638	88643									
770	88688	88694	88700	6	11	17	23	28	34	39	45	51
771	88745	88750	88756									
772	88801	88807	88812									
773	88857	88863	88868									
774	88913	88919	88925									
775	88969	88975	88981	6	11	17	22	28	34	39	45	50
776	89025	89031	89036									
777	89081	89087	89092									
778	89137	89142	89148									
779	89193	89198	89204									
780	89248	89254	89259	6	11	17	22	28	33	39	45	50
781	89304	89310	89315									
782	89359	89365	89371									
783	89415	89420	89426									
784	89470	89476	89481									
785	89526	89531	89537	6	11	17	22	28	33	39	44	50
786	89581	89586	89592									
787	89636	89642	89647									
788	89691	89697	89702									
789	89746	89752	89757									
790	89801	89807	89812	5	11	16	22	27	33	38	44	49
791	89856	89861	89867									
792	89911	89916	89922									
793	89966	89971	89977									
794	90020	90026	90031									
795	90075	90080	90086	5	11	16	22	27	33	38	44	49
796	90129	90135	90140									
797	90184	90189	90195									
798	90238	90244	90249									
799	90293	90298	90304									
800	90347	90352	90358	5	11	16	22	27	33	38	43	49

Table of

	0	1	2	3	4	5	6
800	90309	90314	90320	90325	90331	90336	90342
801	90363	90369	90374	90379	90385	90390	90396
802	90417	90423	90428	90437	90439	90444	90450
803	90472	90477	90482	90488	90493	90499	90504
804	90526	90531	90536	90542	90547	90553	90558
805	90580	90585	90590	90596	90601	90607	90612
806	90633	90639	90644	90650	90655	90660	90666
807	90687	90693	90698	90703	90709	90714	90720
808	90741	90746	90752	90757	90763	90768	90773
809	90795	90800	90806	90811	90816	90822	90827
810	90848	90854	90859	90865	90870	90875	90881
811	90902	90907	90913	90918	90923	90929	90934
812	90956	90961	90966	90972	90977	90982	90988
813	91009	91014	91020	91025	91030	91036	91041
814	91062	91068	91073	91078	91084	91089	91094
815	91116	91121	91126	91132	91137	91142	91148
816	91169	91174	91180	91185	91190	91196	91201
817	91222	91227	91233	91238	91243	91249	91254
818	91275	91281	91286	91291	91297	91302	91307
819	91328	91334	91339	91344	91350	91355	91360
820	91381	91387	91392	91397	91403	91408	91413
821	91434	91440	91445	91450	91455	91461	91466
822	91487	91492	91498	91503	91508	91514	91519
823	91540	91545	91550	91556	91561	91566	91572
824	91593	91598	91603	91608	91614	91619	91624
825	91645	91651	91656	91661	91666	91672	91677
826	91698	91703	91708	91714	91719	91724	91729
827	91751	91756	91761	91766	91772	91777	91782
828	91803	91808	91813	91819	91824	91829	91834
829	91855	91861	91866	91871	91876	91882	91887
830	91908	91913	91918	91923	91929	91934	91939
831	91960	91965	91971	91976	91981	91986	91991
832	92012	92018	92023	92028	92033	92038	92044
833	92064	92070	92075	92080	92085	92091	92096
834	92117	92122	92127	92132	92137	92143	92148
835	92169	92174	92179	92184	92189	92195	92200
836	92221	92226	92231	92236	92241	92247	92252
837	92272	92278	92283	92288	92293	92298	92304
838	92324	92330	92335	92340	92345	92350	92355
839	92376	92381	92386	92392	92397	92402	92407
840	92428	92433	92438	92443	92449	92454	92459
841	92480	92485	92490	92495	92500	92505	92511
842	92531	92536	92541	92547	92552	92557	92562
843	92583	92588	92593	92598	92603	92608	92614
844	92634	92639	92644	92650	92655	92660	92665
845	92686	92691	92696	92701	92706	92711	92716
846	92737	92742	92747	92752	92758	92763	92768
847	92788	92793	92799	92804	92809	92814	92819
848	92840	92845	92850	92855	92860	92865	92870
849	92891	92896	92901	92906	92911	92916	92921
850	92942	92947	92952	92957	92962	92967	92972

Logarithms (contd.)

	7	8	9	Mean Log. Differences								
				1	2	3	4	5	6	7	8	9
800	90347	90352	90358	5	11	16	22	27	33	38	43	49
801	90401	90407	90412									
802	90455	90461	90466									
803	90509	90515	90520									
804	90563	90569	90574									
805	90617	90623	90628	5	11	16	22	27	32	38	43	49
806	90671	90676	90682									
807	90725	90730	90736									
808	90779	90784	90789									
809	90832	90838	90843									
810	90886	90891	90897	5	11	16	21	27	32	38	43	48
811	90940	90945	90950									
812	90993	90998	91004									
813	91046	91052	91057									
814	91100	91105	91110									
815	91153	91158	91164	5	11	16	21	27	32	37	43	48
816	91206	91212	91217									
817	91259	91265	91270									
818	91312	91318	91323									
819	91365	91371	91376									
820	91418	91424	91429	5	11	16	21	26	32	37	42	48
821	91471	91477	91482									
822	91524	91529	91535									
823	91577	91582	91587									
824	91630	91635	91640									
825	91682	91687	91693	5	11	16	21	26	32	37	42	47
826	91735	91740	91745									
827	91787	91792	91798									
828	91840	91845	91850									
829	91892	91897	91903									
830	91944	91950	91955	5	10	16	21	26	31	37	42	47
831	91997	92002	92007									
832	92049	92054	92059									
833	92101	92106	92111									
834	92153	92158	92163									
835	92205	92210	92215	5	10	16	21	26	31	36	42	47
836	92257	92262	92267									
837	92309	92314	92319									
838	92361	92366	92371									
839	92412	92418	92423									
840	92464	92469	92474	5	10	16	21	26	31	36	41	47
841	92516	92521	92526									
842	92567	92572	92578									
843	92619	92624	92629									
844	92670	92675	92680									
845	92722	92727	92732	5	10	15	21	26	31	36	41	46
846	92773	92778	92783									
847	92824	92829	92834									
848	92875	92880	92886									
849	92927	92932	92937									
850	92978	92983	92988	5	10	15	20	26	31	36	41	46

526

Table of

	0	1	2	3	4	5	6
850	92942	92947	92952	92957	92962	92967	92972
851	92993	92998	93003	93008	93013	93018	93024
852	93044	93049	93054	93059	93064	93069	93074
853	93095	93100	93105	93110	93115	93120	93125
854	93146	93151	93156	93161	93166	93171	93176
855	93197	93202	93207	93212	93217	93222	93227
856	93247	93252	93257	93263	93268	93273	93278
857	93298	93303	93308	93313	93318	93323	93328
858	93349	93354	93359	93364	93369	93374	93379
859	93399	93404	93409	93414	93419	93425	93430
860	93450	93455	93460	93465	93470	93475	93480
861	93500	93505	93510	93515	93520	93525	93531
862	93551	93556	93561	93566	93571	93576	93581
863	93601	93606	93611	93616	93621	93626	93631
864	93651	93656	93661	93666	93671	93676	93681
865	93702	93707	93712	93717	93722	93727	93732
866	93752	93757	93762	93767	93772	93777	93782
867	93802	93807	93812	93817	93822	93827	93832
868	93852	93857	93862	93867	93872	93877	93882
869	93902	93907	93912	93917	93922	93927	93932
870	93952	93957	93962	93967	93972	93977	93982
871	94002	94007	94012	94017	94022	94027	94032
872	94052	94057	94062	94067	94072	94076	94081
873	94101	94106	94111	94116	94121	94126	94131
874	94151	94156	94161	94166	94171	94176	94181
875	94201	94206	94211	94216	94221	94226	94231
876	94250	94255	94260	94265	94270	94275	94280
877	94300	94305	94310	94315	94320	94325	94330
878	94349	94354	94359	94364	94369	94374	94379
879	94399	94404	94409	94414	94419	94424	94428
880	94448	94453	94458	94463	94468	94473	94478
881	94498	94502	94507	94512	94517	94522	94527
882	94547	94552	94557	94562	94566	94571	94576
883	94596	94601	94606	94611	94616	94621	94626
884	94645	94650	94655	94660	94665	94670	94675
885	94694	94699	94704	94709	94714	94719	94724
886	94743	94748	94753	94758	94763	94768	94773
887	94792	94797	94802	94807	94812	94817	94822
888	94841	94846	94851	94856	94861	94866	94871
889	94890	94895	94900	94905	94910	94915	94919
890	94939	94944	94949	94954	94958	94963	94968
891	94988	94993	94997	95002	95007	95012	95017
892	95036	95041	95046	95051	95056	95061	95066
893	95085	95090	95095	95100	95105	95109	95114
894	95134	95139	95143	95148	95153	95158	95162
895	95182	95187	95192	95197	95202	95207	95211
896	95231	95236	95240	95245	95250	95255	95260
897	95279	95284	95289	95294	95299	95303	95308
898	95328	95332	95337	95342	95347	95352	95357
899	95376	95381	95386	95390	95395	95400	95405
900	95424	95429	95434	95439	95443	95448	95453

Logarithms (*contd.*)

	7	8	9	Mean Log. Differences								
				1	2	3	4	5	6	7	8	9
850	92978	92983	92988	5	10	15	20	26	31	36	41	46
851	93029	93034	93039									
852	93080	93085	93090									
853	93130	93136	93141									
854	93181	93186	93191									
855	93232	93237	93242	5	10	15	20	25	30	36	41	46
856	93283	93288	93293									
857	93333	93339	93344									
858	93384	93389	93394									
859	93435	93440	93445									
860	93485	93490	93495	5	10	15	20	25	30	35	40	45
861	93536	93541	93546									
862	93586	93591	93596									
863	93636	93641	93646									
864	93686	93692	93697									
865	93737	93742	93747	5	10	15	20	25	30	35	40	45
866	93787	93792	93797									
867	93837	93842	93847									
868	93887	93892	93897									
869	93937	93492	93947									
870	93987	93992	93997	5	10	15	20	25	30	35	40	45
871	94037	94042	94047									
872	94086	94091	94096									
873	94136	94141	94146									
874	94186	94191	94196									
875	94235	94240	94245	5	10	15	20	25	30	35	40	45
876	94285	94290	94295									
877	94335	94340	94344									
878	94384	94389	94394									
879	94433	94438	94443									
880	94483	94488	94493	5	10	15	20	25	30	35	39	44
881	94532	94537	94542									
882	94581	94586	94591									
883	94630	94635	94640									
884	94680	94684	94689									
885	94729	94734	94738	5	10	15	20	25	29	34	39	44
886	94778	94783	94787									
887	94827	94831	94836									
888	94875	94880	94885									
889	94924	94929	94934									
890	94973	94978	94983	5	10	15	20	24	29	34	39	44
891	95022	95027	95032									
892	95070	95075	95080									
893	95119	95124	95129									
894	95168	95173	95177									
895	95216	95221	95226	5	10	15	19	24	29	34	39	44
896	95265	95270	95274									
897	95313	95318	95323									
898	95361	95366	95371									
899	95410	95415	95419									
900	95458	95463	95468	5	10	14	19	24	29	34	39	43

	0	1	2	3	4	5	6
900	95424	95429	95434	95439	95443	95448	95453
901	95472	95477	95482	95487	95492	95497	95501
902	95520	95525	95530	95535	95540	95545	95549
903	95569	95574	95578	95583	95588	95593	95598
904	95617	95622	95626	95631	95636	95641	95646
905	95665	95670	95674	95679	95684	95689	95694
906	95713	95718	95722	95727	95732	95737	95742
907	95761	95765	95770	95775	95780	95785	95789
908	95809	95813	95818	95823	95828	95832	95837
909	95856	95861	95866	95871	95875	95880	95885
910	95904	95909	95914	95918	95923	95928	95933
911	95952	95957	95961	95966	95971	95976	95980
912	95999	96004	96009	96014	96018	96023	96028
913	96047	96052	96057	96061	96066	96071	96076
914	96095	96099	96104	96109	96114	96118	96123
915	96142	96147	96152	96156	96161	96166	96171
916	96189	96194	96199	96204	96208	96213	96218
917	96237	96242	96246	96251	96256	96261	96265
918	96284	96289	96294	96298	96303	96308	96312
919	96332	96336	96341	96346	96350	96355	96360
920	96379	96383	96388	96393	96398	96402	96407
921	96426	96431	96435	96440	96445	96449	96454
922	96473	96478	96482	96487	96492	96497	96501
923	96520	96525	96530	96534	96539	96544	96548
924	96567	96572	96577	96581	96586	96591	96595
925	96614	96619	96624	96628	96633	96638	96642
926	96661	96666	96670	96675	96680	96684	96689
927	96708	96713	96717	96722	96727	96731	96736
928	96755	96759	96764	96769	96773	96778	96783
929	96802	96806	96811	96816	96820	96825	96830
930	96848	96853	96858	96862	96867	96872	96876
931	96895	96900	96904	96909	96914	96918	96923
932	96942	96946	96951	96956	96960	96965	96969
933	96988	96993	96997	97002	97007	97011	97016
934	97035	97039	97044	97049	97053	97058	97063
935	97081	97086	97090	97095	97100	97104	97109
936	97128	97132	97137	97141	97146	97151	97155
937	97174	97178	97183	97188	97192	97197	97202
938	97220	97225	97229	97234	97239	97243	97248
939	97267	97271	97276	97280	97285	97290	97294
940	97313	97317	97322	97327	97331	97336	97340
941	97359	97363	97368	97373	97377	97382	97387
942	97405	97410	97414	97419	97423	97428	97433
943	97451	97456	97460	97465	97470	97474	97479
944	97497	97502	97506	97511	97516	97520	97525
945	97543	97548	97552	97557	97562	97566	97577
946	97589	97594	97598	97603	97607	97612	97617
947	97635	97640	97644	97649	97653	97658	97662
948	97681	97685	97690	97695	97699	97704	97708
949	97727	97731	97736	97740	97745	97749	97754
950	97772	97777	97781	97786	97791	97795	97800

Logarithms (*contd.*)

	7	8	9	Mean Log. Differences								
				1	2	3	4	5	6	7	8	9
900	95458	95463	95468	5	10	14	19	24	29	34	39	43
901	95506	95511	95516									
902	95554	95559	95564									
903	95602	95607	95612									
904	95650	95655	95660									
905	95698	95703	95708	5	10	14	19	24	29	34	38	43
906	95746	95751	95756									
907	95794	95799	95804									
908	95842	95847	95852									
909	95890	95895	95899									
910	95937	95942	95947	5	10	14	19	24	29	33	38	43
911	95985	95990	95995									
912	96033	96038	96042									
913	96080	96085	96090									
914	96128	96133	96137									
915	96175	96180	96185	5	9	14	19	24	28	33	38	43
916	96223	96227	96232									
917	96270	96275	96279									
918	96317	96322	96327									
919	96365	96369	96374									
920	96412	96416	96421	5	9	14	19	24	28	33	38	42
921	96459	96464	96468									
922	96506	96511	96515									
923	96553	96558	96562									
924	96600	96605	96609									
925	96647	96652	96656	5	9	14	19	23	28	33	38	42
926	96694	96699	96703									
927	96741	96745	96750									
928	96787	96792	96797									
929	96834	96839	96844									
930	96881	96886	96890	5	9	14	19	23	28	33	37	42
931	96928	96932	96937									
932	96974	96979	96983									
933	97021	97025	97030									
934	97067	97072	97076									
935	97114	97118	97123	5	9	14	19	23	28	32	37	42
936	97160	97165	97169									
937	97206	97211	97216									
938	97253	97257	97262									
939	97299	97303	97308									
940	97345	97350	97354	5	9	14	18	23	28	32	37	42
941	97391	97396	97400									
942	97437	97442	97447									
943	97483	97488	97493									
944	97529	97534	97539									
945	97575	97580	97584	5	9	14	18	23	28	32	37	41
946	97621	97626	97630									
947	97667	97672	97676									
948	97713	97717	97722									
949	97759	97763	97768									
950	97804	97809	97813	5	9	14	18	23	27	32	37	41

	0	1	2	3	4	5	6
950	97772	97777	97781	97786	97791	97795	97800
951	97818	97823	97827	97832	97836	97841	97845
952	97864	97868	97873	97877	97882	97886	97891
953	97909	97914	97918	97923	97927	97932	97937
954	97955	97959	97964	97968	97973	97978	97982
955	98000	98005	98009	98014	98018	98023	98028
956	98046	98050	98055	98059	98064	98068	98073
957	98091	98096	98100	98105	98109	98114	98118
958	98137	98141	98146	98150	98155	98159	98164
959	98182	98186	98191	98195	98200	98204	98209
960	98227	98232	98236	98241	98245	98250	98254
961	98272	98277	98281	98286	98290	98295	98299
962	98317	98322	98326	98331	98336	98340	98345
963	98363	98367	98372	98376	98381	98385	98390
964	98408	98412	98417	98421	98426	98430	98435
965	98453	98457	98462	98466	98471	98475	98480
966	98498	98502	98507	98511	98516	98520	98525
967	98543	98547	98552	98556	98561	98565	98570
968	98587	98592	98596	98601	98605	98610	98614
969	98632	98637	98641	98646	98650	98655	98659
970	98677	98682	98686	98691	98695	98700	98704
971	98722	98726	98731	98735	98740	98744	98749
972	98767	98771	98776	98780	98784	98789	98793
973	98811	98816	98820	98825	98829	98834	98838
974	98856	98860	98865	98869	98874	98878	98883
975	98900	98905	98909	98914	98918	98923	98927
976	98945	98949	98954	98958	98963	98967	98972
977	98989	98993	98998	99003	99007	99012	99016
978	99034	99038	99043	99047	99052	99056	99060
979	99078	99083	99087	99092	99096	99100	99105
980	99123	99127	99131	99136	99140	99145	99149
981	99167	99171	99176	99180	99185	99189	99193
982	99211	99216	99220	99224	99229	99233	99238
983	99255	99260	99264	99269	99273	99277	99282
984	99299	99304	99308	99313	99317	99322	99326
985	99344	99348	99352	99357	99361	99366	99370
986	99388	99392	99396	99401	99405	99410	99414
987	99432	99436	99440	99445	99449	99454	99458
988	99476	99480	99484	99489	99493	99498	99502
989	99520	99524	99528	99533	99537	99542	99546
990	99563	99568	99572	99577	99581	99585	99590
991	99607	99612	99616	99620	99625	99629	99634
992	99651	99655	99660	99664	99669	99673	99677
993	99695	99699	99704	99708	99712	99717	99721
994	99739	99743	99747	99752	99756	99760	99765
995	99782	99787	99791	99795	99800	99804	99808
996	99826	99830	99835	99839	99843	99848	99852
997	99869	99873	99878	99883	99887	99891	99896
998	99913	99917	99922	99926	99930	99935	99939
999	99956	99961	99965	99970	99974	99978	99983
1000	00000	00043	00087	00130	00173	00217	00260

Logarithms (*contd.*)

	7	8	9	Mean Log. Differences								
				1	2	3	4	5	6	7	8	9
950	97804	97809	97813	5	9	14	18	23	27	32	37	41
951	97850	97855	97859									
952	97896	97900	97905									
953	97941	97946	97950									
954	97987	97991	97996									
955	98032	98037	98041	5	9	14	18	23	27	32	36	41
956	98078	98082	98087									
957	98123	98127	98132									
958	98168	98173	98177									
959	98213	98218	98223									
960	98259	98263	98268	5	9	14	18	23	27	32	36	41
961	98304	98308	98313									
962	98349	98354	98358									
963	98394	98399	98403									
964	98439	98444	98448									
965	98484	98489	98493	4	9	13	18	22	27	31	36	40
966	98529	98534	98538									
967	98574	98579	98583									
968	98619	98623	98628									
969	98664	98668	98673									
970	98708	98713	98717	4	9	13	18	22	27	31	36	40
971	98753	98758	98762									
972	98798	98802	98807									
973	98842	98847	98851									
974	98887	98892	98896									
975	98932	98936	98940	4	9	13	18	22	27	31	36	40
976	98976	98981	98985									
977	99021	99025	99029									
978	99065	99069	99074									
979	99109	99114	99118									
980	99154	99158	99162	4	9	13	18	22	27	31	35	40
981	99198	99202	99207									
982	99242	99246	99251									
983	99286	99291	99295									
984	99330	99335	99339									
985	99374	99379	99383	4	9	13	18	22	26	31	35	40
986	99418	99423	99427									
987	99462	99467	99471									
988	99506	99511	99515									
989	99550	99555	99559									
990	99594	99599	99603	4	9	13	18	22	26	31	35	39
991	99638	99642	99647									
992	99682	99686	99691									
993	99725	99730	99734									
994	99769	99774	99778									
995	99813	99817	99822	4	9	13	17	22	26	31	35	39
996	99856	99861	99865									
997	99900	99904	99909									
998	99943	99948	99952									
999	99987	99991	99996									
1000	00303	00346	00389	43	86	130	173	216	259	303	346	389

TABLE OF

	0	1	2	3	4	5	6
·000	10000	10002	10005	10007	10009	10011	10014
·001	10023	10025	10028	10030	10032	10035	10037
·002	10046	10048	10051	10053	10055	10058	10060
·003	10069	10072	10074	10076	10079	10081	10083
·004	10092	10095	10097	10099	10102	10104	10106
·005	10116	10118	10120	10123	10125	10127	10130
·006	10139	10141	10144	10146	10148	10151	10153
·007	10162	10165	10167	10169	10172	10174	10176
·008	10186	10188	10191	10193	10195	10198	10200
·009	10209	10212	10214	10216	10219	10221	10223
·010	10233	10235	10238	10240	10242	10245	10247
·011	10256	10259	10261	10264	10266	10268	10271
·012	10280	10282	10285	10287	10290	10292	10294
·013	10304	10306	10309	10311	10313	10316	10318
·014	10328	10330	10332	10335	10337	10339	10342
·015	10351	10354	10356	10359	10361	10363	10366
·016	10375	10378	10380	10382	10385	10387	10390
·017	10399	10402	10404	10406	10409	10411	10414
·018	10423	10426	10428	10430	10433	10435	10438
·019	10447	10450	10452	10454	10457	10459	10462
·020	10471	10474	10476	10478	10481	10483	10486
·021	10495	10498	10500	10503	10505	10507	10510
·022	10520	10522	10524	10527	10529	10532	10534
·023	10544	10546	10549	10551	10554	10556	10558
·024	10568	10571	10573	10575	10578	10580	10583
·025	10592	10595	10597	10600	10602	10605	10607
·026	10617	10619	10622	10624	10627	10629	10632
·027	10641	10644	10646	10649	10651	10654	10656
·028	10666	10668	10671	10673	10676	10678	10681
·029	10690	10693	10695	10698	10700	10703	10705
·030	10715	10718	10720	10723	10725	10727	10730
·031	10740	10742	10745	10747	10750	10752	10755
·032	10765	10767	10770	10772	10775	10777	10779
·033	10789	10792	10794	10797	10799	10802	10804
·034	10814	10817	10819	10822	10824	10827	10829
·035	10839	10842	10844	10847	10849	10852	10854
·036	10864	10867	10869	10872	10874	10877	10879
·037	10889	10892	10894	10897	10899	10902	10904
·038	10914	10917	10919	10922	10924	10927	10929
·039	10940	10942	10945	10947	10950	10952	10955
·040	10965	10967	10970	10972	10975	10977	10980
·041	10990	10993	10995	10998	11000	11002	11005
·042	11015	11018	11020	11023	11025	11028	11031
·043	11041	11043	11046	11048	11051	11053	11056
·044	11066	11069	11071	11074	11076	11079	11081
·045	11092	11094	11097	11099	11102	11104	11107
·046	11117	11120	11122	11125	11128	11130	11133
·047	11143	11145	11148	11151	11153	11156	11158
·048	11169	11171	11174	11176	11179	11181	11184
·049	11194	11197	11199	11202	11205	11207	11210

ANTILOGARITHMS

	7	8	9	Mean Log. Differences								
				1	2	3	4	5	6	7	8	9
·000	10016	10018	10020	2	5	7	9	12	14	16	18	21
·001	10039	10041	10044	2	5	7	9	12	14	16	18	21
·002	10062	10065	10067	2	5	7	9	12	14	16	18	21
·003	10086	10088	10090	2	5	7	9	12	14	16	19	21
·004	10109	10111	10113	2	5	7	9	12	14	16	19	21
·005	10132	10134	10137	2	5	7	9	12	14	16	19	21
·006	10155	10158	10160	2	5	7	9	12	14	16	19	21
·007	10179	10181	10184	2	5	7	9	12	14	16	19	21
·008	10202	10205	10207	2	5	7	9	12	14	16	19	21
·009	10226	10228	10231	2	5	7	9	12	14	16	19	21
·010	10249	10252	10254	2	5	7	9	12	14	17	19	21
·011	10273	10275	10278	2	5	7	9	12	14	17	19	21
·012	10297	10299	10301	2	5	7	9	12	14	17	19	21
·013	10320	10323	10325	2	5	7	9	12	14	17	19	21
·014	10344	10347	10349	2	5	7	10	12	14	17	19	21
·015	10368	10370	10373	2	5	7	10	12	14	17	19	21
·016	10392	10394	10397	2	5	7	10	12	14	17	19	22
·017	10416	10418	10421	2	5	7	10	12	14	17	19	22
·018	10440	10442	10445	2	5	7	10	12	14	17	19	22
·019	10464	10466	10469	2	5	7	10	12	14	17	19	22
·020	10488	10491	10493	2	5	7	10	12	14	17	19	22
·021	10512	10515	10517	2	5	7	10	12	15	17	19	22
·022	10537	10539	10541	2	5	7	10	12	15	17	19	22
·023	10561	10563	10566	2	5	7	10	12	15	17	19	22
·024	10585	10588	10590	2	5	7	10	12	15	17	19	22
·025	10607	10612	10614	2	5	7	10	12	15	17	20	22
·026	10634	10636	10639	2	5	7	10	12	15	17	20	22
·027	10659	10661	10663	2	5	7	10	12	15	17	20	22
·028	10683	10686	10688	2	5	7	10	12	15	17	20	22
·029	10708	10710	10713	2	5	7	10	12	15	17	20	22
·030	10732	10735	10737	2	5	7	10	12	15	17	20	22
·031	10757	10760	10762	2	5	7	10	12	15	17	20	22
·032	10782	10784	10787	2	5	7	10	12	15	17	20	22
·033	10807	10809	10812	2	5	7	10	12	15	17	20	22
·034	10832	10834	10837	2	5	7	10	12	15	17	20	22
·035	10857	10859	10862	2	5	7	10	12	15	17	20	22
·036	10882	10884	10887	3	5	8	10	13	15	18	20	23
·037	10907	10909	10912	3	5	8	10	13	15	18	20	23
·038	10932	10934	10937	3	5	8	10	13	15	18	20	23
·039	10957	10960	10962	3	5	8	10	13	15	18	20	23
·040	10982	10985	10987	3	5	8	10	13	15	18	20	23
·041	11008	11010	11013	3	5	8	10	13	15	18	20	23
·042	11033	11036	11038	3	5	8	10	13	15	18	20	23
·043	11059	11061	11064	3	5	8	10	13	15	18	20	23
·044	11084	11087	11089	3	5	8	10	13	15	18	20	23
·045	11110	11112	11115	3	5	8	10	13	15	18	20	23
·046	11135	11138	11140	3	5	8	10	13	15	18	20	23
·047	11161	11163	11166	3	5	8	10	13	15	18	21	23
·048	11187	11189	11192	3	5	8	10	13	15	18	21	23
·049	11212	11215	11218	3	5	8	10	13	15	18	21	23

	0	1	2	3	4	5	6
·050	11220	11223	11225	11228	11230	11233	11236
·051	11246	11249	11251	11254	11256	11259	11262
·052	11272	11275	11277	11280	11282	11285	11288
·053	11298	11301	11303	11306	11308	11311	11314
·054	11324	11327	11329	11332	11334	11337	11340
·055	11350	11353	11355	11358	11367	11363	11366
·056	11376	11379	11381	11384	11387	11389	11392
·057	11402	11405	11408	11410	11413	11416	11418
·058	11429	11431	11434	11437	11439	11442	11445
·059	11455	11458	11460	11463	11466	11468	11471
·060	11481	11484	11487	11489	11492	11495	11497
·061	11508	11511	11513	11516	11519	11521	11524
·062	11534	11537	11540	11542	11545	11548	11550
·063	11561	11564	11566	11569	11572	11574	11577
·064	11588	11590	11593	11596	11598	11601	11604
·065	11614	11617	11620	11622	11625	11628	11630
·066	11641	11644	11647	11649	11652	11655	11657
·067	11668	11671	11673	11676	11679	11681	11684
·068	11695	11698	11700	11703	11706	11708	11711
·069	11722	11725	11727	11730	11733	11735	11738
·070	11749	11752	11754	11757	11760	11762	11765
·071	11776	11779	11781	11784	11787	11790	11792
·072	11803	11806	11809	11811	11814	11817	11819
·073	11830	11833	11836	11839	11841	11844	11847
·074	11858	11860	11863	11866	11869	11871	11874
·075	11885	11888	11890	11893	11896	11899	11901
·076	11912	11915	11918	11921	11923	11926	11929
·077	11940	11943	11945	11948	11951	11954	11956
·078	11967	11970	11973	11976	11978	11981	11984
·079	11995	11998	12000	12003	12006	12009	12012
·080	12023	12025	12028	12031	12034	12036	12039
·081	12050	12053	12056	12059	12061	12064	12067
·082	12078	12081	12084	12086	12089	12092	12095
·083	12106	12109	12112	12114	12117	12120	12123
·084	12134	12137	12139	12142	12145	12148	12151
·085	12162	12165	12167	12170	12173	12176	12179
·086	12190	12193	12195	12198	12201	12204	12207
·087	12218	12221	12224	12226	12229	12232	12235
·088	12246	12249	12252	12254	12257	12260	12263
·089	12274	12277	12280	12283	12286	12288	12291
·090	12303	12305	12308	12311	12314	12317	12320
·091	12331	12334	12337	12340	12342	12345	12348
·092	12359	12362	12365	12368	12371	12374	12377
·093	12388	12391	12394	12396	12399	12402	12405
·094	12416	12419	12422	12425	12428	12431	12434
·095	12445	12448	12451	12454	12457	12459	12462
·096	12474	12477	12480	12482	12485	12488	12491
·097	12503	12505	12508	12511	12514	12517	12520
·098	12531	12534	12537	12540	12543	12546	12549
·099	12560	12563	12566	12569	12572	12575	12578

Antilogarithms *(contd.)*

	7	8	9	Mean Log. Differences								
				1	2	3	4	5	6	7	8	9
·050	11238	11241	11243	3	5	8	10	13	16	18	21	23
·051	11264	11267	11269	3	5	8	10	13	16	18	21	23
·052	11290	11293	11295	3	5	8	10	13	16	18	21	23
·053	11316	11312	11321	3	5	8	10	13	16	18	21	23
·054	11342	11345	11347	3	5	8	10	13	16	18	21	23
·055	11368	11371	11374	3	5	8	10	13	16	18	21	24
·056	11395	11397	11400	3	5	8	10	13	16	18	21	24
·057	11421	11423	11426	3	5	8	11	13	16	18	21	24
·058	11447	11450	11452	3	5	8	11	13	16	18	21	24
·059	11474	11476	11479	3	5	8	11	13	16	18	21	24
·060	11500	11503	11505	3	5	8	11	13	16	19	21	24
·061	11527	11529	11532	3	5	8	11	13	16	19	21	24
·062	11553	11556	11558	3	5	8	11	13	16	19	21	24
·063	11560	11582	11585	3	5	8	11	13	16	19	21	24
·064	11606	11609	11612	3	5	8	11	13	16	19	21	24
·065	11633	11636	11639	3	5	8	11	13	16	19	21	24
·066	11660	11663	11665	3	5	8	11	13	16	19	21	24
·067	11687	11690	11692	3	5	8	11	13	16	19	22	24
·068	11714	11717	11719	3	5	8	11	13	16	19	22	24
·069	11741	11744	11746	3	5	8	11	14	16	19	22	24
·070	11768	11771	11773	3	5	8	11	14	16	19	22	24
·071	11795	11798	11800	3	5	8	11	14	16	19	22	24
·072	11822	11825	11828	3	5	8	11	14	16	19	22	24
·073	11849	11852	11855	3	5	8	11	14	16	19	22	25
·074	11877	11880	11882	3	5	8	11	14	16	19	22	25
·075	11904	11907	11910	3	5	8	11	14	16	19	22	25
·076	11932	11934	11937	3	5	8	11	14	16	19	22	25
·077	11959	11962	11965	3	6	8	11	14	17	19	22	25
·078	11987	11989	11992	3	6	8	11	14	17	19	22	25
·079	12014	12017	12020	3	6	8	11	14	17	19	22	25
·080	12042	12045	12048	3	6	8	11	14	17	19	22	25
·081	12070	12073	12075	3	6	8	11	14	17	19	22	25
·082	12098	12100	12103	3	6	8	11	14	17	20	22	25
·083	12125	12128	12131	3	6	8	11	14	17	20	22	25
·084	12153	12156	12159	3	6	8	11	14	17	20	22	25
·085	12181	12184	12187	3	6	8	11	14	17	20	22	25
·086	12210	12212	12215	3	6	8	11	14	17	20	22	25
·087	12238	12240	12243	3	6	8	11	14	17	20	23	25
·088	12266	12269	12272	3	6	8	11	14	17	20	23	25
·089	12294	12297	12300	3	6	8	11	14	17	20	23	25
·090	12322	12325	12328	3	6	9	11	14	17	20	23	26
·091	12351	12354	12357	3	6	9	11	14	17	20	23	26
·092	12379	12382	12385	3	6	9	11	14	17	20	23	26
·093	12408	12411	12414	3	6	9	11	14	17	20	23	26
·094	12437	12439	12442	3	6	9	11	14	17	20	23	26
·095	12465	12468	12471	3	6	9	11	14	17	20	23	26
·096	12494	12497	12500	3	6	9	12	14	17	20	23	26
·097	12523	12526	12528	3	6	9	12	14	17	20	23	26
·098	12552	12555	12557	3	6	9	12	14	17	20	23	26
·099	12581	12584	12586	3	6	9	12	14	17	20	23	26

Table of

	0	1	2	3	4	5	6
·100	12589	12592	12595	12598	12601	12604	12607
·101	12618	12621	12624	12627	12630	12633	12636
·102	12647	12650	12653	12656	12659	12662	12665
·103	12676	12679	12682	12685	12688	12691	12694
·104	12706	12709	12712	12714	12717	12720	12723
·105	12735	12738	12741	12744	12747	12751	12753
·106	12764	12767	12770	12773	12776	12779	12782
·107	12794	12797	12800	12803	12806	12809	12811
·108	12823	12826	12829	12832	12835	12838	12841
·109	12853	12856	12859	12862	12865	12868	12871
·110	12882	12885	12888	12891	12894	12897	12900
·111	12912	12915	12918	12921	12924	12927	12930
·112	12942	12945	12948	12951	12954	12957	12960
·113	12972	12975	12978	12981	12984	12987	12990
·114	13002	13005	13008	13011	13014	13017	13020
·115	13032	13035	13038	13041	13044	13047	13050
·116	13062	13065	13068	13071	13074	13077	13080
·117	13092	13095	13098	13101	13104	13107	13110
·118	13122	13125	13128	13131	13134	13137	13140
·119	13152	13155	13158	13161	13164	13167	13170
·120	13183	13186	13189	13192	13195	13198	13201
·121	13213	13216	13219	13222	13225	13228	13230
·122	13243	13246	13249	13253	13256	13259	13262
·123	13274	13277	13280	13283	13286	13289	13292
·124	13304	13308	13311	13314	13317	13320	13323
·125	13335	13338	13341	13344	13347	13351	13354
·126	13366	13369	13372	13375	13378	13381	13384
·127	13397	13400	13403	13406	13409	13412	13415
·128	13428	13431	13434	13437	13440	13443	13446
·129	13459	13462	13465	13468	13471	13474	13477
·130	13490	13493	13496	13499	13502	13505	13508
·131	13521	13524	13527	13530	13533	13536	13539
·132	13552	13555	13558	13561	13564	13567	13571
·133	13583	13586	13589	13592	13596	13599	13602
·134	13614	13618	13621	13624	13627	13630	13633
·135	13646	13649	13652	13655	13658	13662	13665
·136	13677	13680	13684	13687	13690	13693	13696
·137	13709	13712	13715	13718	13721	13725	13728
·138	13740	13744	13747	13750	13753	13756	13759
·139	13772	13775	13778	13782	13785	13788	13791
·140	13804	13807	13810	13813	13817	13820	13823
·141	13836	13834	13842	13845	13848	13852	13855
·142	13867	13871	13874	13877	13880	13883	13887
·143	13899	13903	13906	13909	13912	13915	13919
·144	13932	13935	13938	13941	13944	13948	13951
·145	13964	13967	13970	13973	13977	13980	13983
·146	13990	13999	14002	14005	14009	14012	14015
·147	14028	14031	14035	14038	14041	14044	14047
·148	14060	14064	14067	14070	14073	14077	14080
·149	14093	14096	14099	14103	14106	14109	14112

Antilogarithms (contd.)

	7	8	9	Mean Log. Differences								
				1	2	3	4	5	6	7	8	9
·100	12610	12612	12615	3	6	9	12	15	17	20	23	26
·101	12639	12641	12644	3	6	9	12	15	17	20	23	26
·102	12668	12671	12674	3	6	9	12	15	17	20	23	26
·103	12697	12700	12703	3	6	9	12	15	18	20	23	26
·104	12726	12729	12732	3	6	9	12	15	18	21	23	26
·105	12756	12758	12761	3	6	9	12	15	18	21	24	26
·106	12785	12788	12791	3	6	9	12	15	18	21	24	26
·107	12814	12817	12820	3	6	9	12	15	18	21	24	27
·108	12844	12847	12850	3	6	9	12	15	18	21	24	27
·109	12874	12877	12879	3	6	9	12	15	18	21	24	27
·110	12903	12906	12909	3	6	9	12	15	18	21	24	27
·111	12933	12936	12939	3	6	9	12	15	18	21	24	27
·112	12963	12966	12969	3	6	9	12	15	18	21	24	27
·113	12993	12996	12999	3	6	9	12	15	18	21	24	27
·114	13023	13026	13029	3	6	9	12	15	18	21	24	27
·115	13053	13056	13059	3	6	9	12	15	18	21	24	27
·116	13083	13086	13089	3	6	9	12	15	18	21	24	27
·117	13113	13116	13119	3	6	9	12	15	18	21	24	27
·118	13143	13146	13149	3	6	9	12	15	18	21	24	27
·119	13173	13176	13179	3	6	9	12	15	18	21	24	27
·120	13204	13207	13210	3	6	9	12	15	18	21	24	27
·121	13234	13237	13240	3	6	9	12	15	18	21	24	27
·122	13265	13268	13271	3	6	9	12	15	18	21	24	27
·123	13295	13298	13301	3	6	9	12	15	18	21	24	28
·124	13326	13329	13332	3	6	9	12	15	18	21	25	28
·125	13357	13360	13363	3	6	9	12	15	18	22	25	28
·126	13387	13391	13394	3	6	9	12	15	18	22	25	28
·127	13418	13421	13425	3	6	9	12	15	19	22	25	28
·128	13449	13452	13455	3	6	9	12	15	19	22	25	28
·129	13480	13483	13486	3	6	9	12	16	19	22	25	28
·130	13511	13514	13518	3	6	9	12	16	19	22	25	28
·131	13542	13548	13549	3	6	9	12	16	19	22	25	28
·132	13574	13577	13580	3	6	9	12	16	19	22	25	28
·133	13605	13608	13611	3	6	9	13	16	19	22	25	28
·134	13636	13639	13643	3	6	9	13	16	19	22	25	28
·135	13668	13671	13674	3	6	9	13	16	19	22	25	28
·136	13700	13702	13706	3	6	9	13	16	19	22	25	28
·137	13731	13734	13737	3	6	9	13	16	19	22	25	28
·138	13762	13766	13769	3	6	10	13	16	19	22	25	29
·139	13794	13797	13801	3	6	10	13	16	19	22	25	29
·140	13826	13829	13832	3	6	10	13	16	19	22	25	29
·141	13858	13861	13864	3	6	10	13	16	19	22	26	29
·142	13889	13893	13896	3	6	10	13	16	19	22	26	29
·143	13922	13925	13928	3	6	10	13	16	19	22	26	29
·144	13954	13957	13960	3	6	10	13	16	19	22	26	29
·145	13986	13989	13993	3	6	10	13	16	19	23	26	29
·146	14018	14022	14025	3	6	10	13	16	19	23	26	29
·147	14051	14054	14057	3	6	10	13	16	19	23	26	29
·148	14083	14086	14089	3	6	10	13	16	19	23	26	29
·149	14116	14119	14122	3	6	10	13	16	19	23	26	29

	0	1	2	3	4	5	6
·150	14125	14129	14132	14135	14138	14142	14145
·151	14158	14161	14164	14168	14171	14174	14177
·152	14197	14194	14197	14200	14204	14207	14210
·153	14223	14227	14230	14233	14236	14240	14243
·154	14256	14259	14263	14266	14269	14272	14276
·155	14289	14292	14295	14300	14302	14305	14309
·156	14322	14325	14328	14332	14335	14338	14342
·157	14355	14358	14361	14365	14368	14371	14375
·158	14388	14391	14395	14398	14401	14405	14408
·159	14421	14424	14428	14431	14434	14438	14441
·160	14454	14458	14461	14464	14468	14471	14474
·161	14488	14491	14494	14498	14501	14504	14508
·162	14521	14524	14528	14531	14534	14538	14541
·163	14555	14558	14561	14564	14568	14571	14575
·164	14588	14591	14595	14598	14602	14605	14608
·165	14622	14625	14628	14632	14635	14639	14642
·166	14655	14659	14662	14666	14669	14672	14676
·167	14689	14693	14696	14699	14703	14706	14701
·168	14723	14726	14730	14733	14737	14740	14743
·169	14757	14760	14764	14767	14771	14774	14777
·170	14791	14794	14798	14801	14805	14808	14811
·171	14825	14829	14832	14835	14839	14842	14846
·172	14859	14863	14866	14870	14873	14876	14880
·173	14894	14897	14900	14904	14907	14911	14914
·174	14928	14931	14935	14938	14942	14945	14949
·175	14962	14966	14969	14973	14976	14980	14983
·176	14997	15000	15004	15007	15011	15014	15018
·177	15031	15035	15038	15042	15045	15049	15052
·178	15066	15069	15073	15076	15080	15083	15087
·179	15101	15104	15108	15111	15115	15118	15122
·180	15136	15139	15143	15146	15150	15153	15156
·181	15170	15174	15177	15181	15184	15188	15191
·182	15205	15209	15212	15216	15219	15223	15226
·183	15240	15244	15247	15251	15255	15258	15262
·184	15276	15279	15283	15286	15290	15293	15297
·185	15311	15314	15318	15321	15325	15328	15332
·186	15346	15350	15353	15357	15360	15364	15367
·187	15381	15385	15389	15392	15396	15399	15403
·188	15417	15421	15424	15428	15431	15435	15438
·189	15452	15456	15460	15463	15467	15470	15474
·190	15488	15492	15495	15500	15502	15506	15510
·191	15524	15527	15531	15535	15538	15542	15545
·192	15560	15563	15567	15570	15574	15578	15581
·193	15595	15599	15603	15606	15610	15613	15617
·194	15631	15635	15639	15642	15646	15649	15653
·195	15667	15671	15675	15678	15682	15686	15689
·196	15704	15707	15711	15714	15718	15722	15725
·197	15740	15743	15747	15751	15754	15758	15762
·198	15776	15780	15783	15787	15791	15794	15798
·199	15812	15816	15820	15823	15827	15831	15834

Antilogarithms (contd.)

	7	8	9	Mean Log. Differences								
				1	2	3	4	5	6	7	8	9
·150	14148	14151	14155	3	7	10	13	16	20	23	26	29
·151	14181	14184	14187	3	7	10	13	16	20	23	26	29
·152	14213	14217	14220	3	7	10	13	16	20	23	26	29
·153	14246	14249	14253	3	7	10	13	16	20	23	26	30
·154	14279	14282	14286	3	7	10	13	16	20	23	26	30
·155	14312	14315	14319	3	7	10	13	16	20	23	26	30
·156	14345	14348	14352	3	7	10	13	17	20	23	26	30
·157	14378	14381	14385	3	7	10	13	17	20	23	26	30
·158	14411	14414	14418	3	7	10	13	17	20	23	27	30
·159	14444	14448	14451	3	7	10	13	17	20	23	27	30
·160	14478	14481	14484	3	7	10	13	17	20	23	27	30
·161	14511	14514	14518	3	7	10	13	17	20	23	27	30
·162	14544	14548	14551	3	7	10	13	17	20	23	27	30
·163	14578	14581	14585	3	7	10	13	17	20	23	27	30
·164	14618	14615	14618	3	7	10	13	17	20	24	27	30
·165	14645	14649	14652	3	7	10	13	17	20	24	27	30
·166	14679	14682	14686	3	7	10	14	17	20	24	27	30
·167	14713	14716	14720	3	7	10	14	17	20	24	27	30
·168	14747	14750	14754	3	7	10	14	17	20	24	27	31
·169	14781	14784	14788	3	7	10	14	17	20	24	27	31
·170	14815	14818	14822	3	7	10	14	17	20	24	27	31
·171	14849	14852	14856	3	7	10	14	17	21	24	27	31
·172	14883	14887	14890	3	7	10	14	17	21	24	27	31
·173	14918	14921	14924	3	7	10	14	17	21	24	27	31
·174	14952	14955	14959	3	7	10	14	17	21	24	28	31
·175	14986	14990	14993	3	7	10	14	17	21	24	28	31
·176	15021	15024	15028	3	7	10	14	17	21	24	28	31
·177	15056	15059	15063	3	7	10	14	17	21	24	28	31
·178	15090	15094	15097	3	7	10	14	17	21	24	28	31
·179	15125	15129	15132	3	7	10	14	17	21	24	28	31
·180	15160	15163	15167	3	7	10	14	17	21	24	28	31
·181	15195	15198	15202	3	7	10	14	17	21	24	28	31
·182	15230	15233	15237	4	7	11	14	18	21	25	28	32
·183	15265	15269	15272	4	7	11	14	18	21	25	28	32
·184	15300	15304	15307	4	7	11	14	18	21	25	28	32
·185	15336	15339	15343	4	7	11	14	18	21	25	28	32
·186	15371	15374	15378	4	7	11	14	18	21	25	28	32
·187	15406	15410	15413	4	7	11	14	18	21	25	28	32
·188	15442	15445	15449	4	7	11	14	18	21	25	28	32
·189	15477	15481	15485	4	7	11	14	18	21	25	28	32
·190	15513	15517	15520	4	7	11	14	18	21	25	29	32
·191	15549	15552	15556	4	7	11	14	18	21	25	29	32
·192	15585	15588	15592	4	7	11	14	18	22	25	29	32
·193	15621	15624	15628	4	7	11	14	18	22	25	29	32
·194	15657	15660	15664	4	7	11	14	18	22	25	29	32
·195	15693	15696	15700	4	7	11	14	18	22	25	29	33
·196	15729	15733	15736	4	7	11	14	18	22	25	29	33
·197	15765	15769	15772	4	7	11	15	18	22	25	29	33
·198	15802	15805	15809	4	7	11	15	18	22	25	29	33
·199	15838	15842	15845	4	7	11	15	18	22	25	29	33

Table of

	0	1	2	3	4	5	6
·200	15849	15853	15856	15860	15863	15867	15871
·201	15885	15889	15893	15896	15900	15904	15907
·202	15922	15926	15929	15933	15937	15940	15944
·203	15959	15962	15966	15970	15973	15977	15981
·204	15996	15999	16003	16007	16010	16014	16018
·205	16032	16036	16040	16043	16047	16051	16055
·206	16069	16073	16077	16080	16084	16088	16092
·207	16106	16110	16114	16118	16121	16125	16129
·208	16144	16147	16151	16155	16158	16162	16166
·209	16181	16184	16188	16192	16196	16199	16203
·210	16218	16222	16226	16229	16233	16237	16240
·211	16255	16259	16263	16267	16270	16274	16278
·212	16293	16297	16300	16304	16308	16312	16315
·213	16330	16334	16338	16342	16346	16349	16353
·214	16368	16372	16376	16379	16383	16387	16391
·215	16406	16410	16413	16417	16421	16425	16429
·216	16444	16447	16451	16455	16459	16463	16466
·217	16482	16485	16489	16493	16497	16501	16504
·218	16520	16523	16527	16531	16535	16539	16542
·219	16558	16561	16565	16569	16573	16577	16581
·220	16596	16600	16603	16607	16611	16615	16619
·221	16634	16638	16642	16646	16649	16653	16657
·222	16672	16676	16680	16684	16688	16692	16695
·223	16711	16715	16719	16722	16726	16730	16734
·224	16749	16753	16757	16761	16764	16769	16773
·225	16788	16792	16796	16780	16803	16807	16811
·226	16827	16831	16834	16838	16842	16846	16850
·227	16865	16869	16873	16877	16881	16885	16889
·228	16904	16908	16912	16916	16920	16924	16928
·229	16943	16947	16951	16955	16959	16963	16967
·230	16982	16986	16990	16994	16998	17002	17006
·231	17022	17025	17029	17033	17037	17041	17045
·232	17061	17065	17069	17073	17076	17080	17084
·233	17100	17104	17108	17112	17116	17120	17123
·234	17140	17143	17147	17151	17155	17159	17163
·235	17179	17183	17187	17191	17195	17199	17203
·236	17219	17223	17227	17231	17235	17238	17242
·237	17258	17262	17266	17270	17274	17278	17282
·238	17298	17302	17306	17310	17314	17318	17322
·239	17338	17342	17346	17350	17354	17358	17362
·240	17378	17382	17386	17390	17394	17398	17402
·241	17418	17422	17426	17430	17434	17438	17442
·242	17458	17462	17466	17470	17474	17478	17482
·243	17498	17502	17506	17511	17515	17519	17523
·244	17539	17543	17547	17551	17555	17559	17563
·245	17579	17583	17587	17591	17595	17600	17603
·246	17620	17624	17628	17632	17636	17640	17644
·247	17660	17664	17668	17673	17677	17681	17685
·248	17701	17705	17709	17713	17717	17721	17726
·249	17742	17746	17750	17754	17758	17762	17766

Antilogarithms *(contd.)*

	7	8	9	Mean Log. Differences								
				1	2	3	4	5	6	7	8	9
·200	15874	15878	15882	4	7	11	15	18	22	26	29	33
·201	15911	15915	15918	4	7	11	15	18	22	26	29	33
·202	15948	15951	15955	4	7	11	15	18	22	26	29	33
·203	15984	15988	15992	4	7	11	15	18	22	26	29	33
·204	16021	16025	16029	4	7	11	15	18	22	26	29	33
·205	16058	16062	16066	4	7	11	15	18	22	26	30	33
·206	16095	16099	16103	4	7	11	15	19	22	26	30	33
·207	16132	16136	16140	4	7	11	15	19	22	26	30	33
·208	16170	16173	16177	4	7	11	15	19	22	26	30	34
·209	16207	16211	16214	4	7	11	15	19	22	26	30	34
·210	16244	16248	16252	4	7	11	15	19	22	26	30	34
·211	16282	16285	16289	4	7	11	15	19	22	26	30	34
·212	16319	16323	16327	4	8	11	15	19	23	26	30	34
·213	16357	16361	16364	4	8	11	15	19	23	26	30	34
·214	16395	16398	16402	4	8	11	15	19	23	26	30	34
·215	16432	16436	16440	4	8	11	15	19	23	26	30	34
·216	16470	16474	16478	4	8	11	15	19	23	27	30	34
·217	16508	16512	16516	4	8	11	15	19	23	27	30	34
·218	16545	16550	16554	4	8	11	15	19	23	27	30	34
·219	16584	16588	16592	4	8	11	15	19	23	27	31	34
·220	16623	16626	16630	4	8	11	15	19	23	27	31	34
·221	16661	16665	16669	4	8	12	15	19	23	27	31	35
·222	16699	16703	16707	4	8	12	15	19	23	27	31	35
·223	16738	16742	16746	4	8	12	15	19	23	27	31	35
·224	16776	16780	16784	4	8	12	15	19	23	27	31	35
·225	16815	16819	16823	4	8	12	15	19	23	27	31	35
·226	16854	16858	16862	4	8	12	16	19	23	27	31	35
·227	16893	16896	16900	4	8	12	16	19	23	27	31	35
·228	16932	16936	16939	4	8	12	16	19	23	27	31	35
·229	16971	16975	16978	4	8	12	16	20	23	27	31	35
·230	17010	17014	17018	4	8	12	16	20	23	27	31	35
·231	17049	17053	17057	4	8	12	16	20	24	27	31	35
·232	17088	17092	17096	4	8	12	16	20	24	28	31	35
·233	17128	17132	17136	4	8	12	16	20	24	28	32	35
·234	17167	17171	17175	4	8	12	16	20	24	28	32	36
·235	17207	17211	17215	4	8	12	16	20	24	28	32	36
·236	17246	17250	17254	4	8	12	16	20	24	28	32	36
·237	17286	17290	17294	4	8	12	16	20	24	28	32	36
·238	17326	17330	17334	4	8	12	16	20	24	28	32	36
·239	17366	17370	17374	4	8	12	16	20	24	28	32	36
·240	17406	17410	17414	4	8	12	16	20	24	28	32	36
·241	17446	17450	17454	4	8	12	16	20	24	28	32	36
·242	17486	17490	17494	4	8	12	16	20	24	28	32	36
·243	17527	17531	17535	4	8	12	16	20	24	28	32	36
·244	17567	17571	17575	4	8	12	16	20	24	28	32	36
·245	17608	17612	17616	4	8	12	16	20	24	28	32	37
·246	17648	17652	17656	4	8	12	16	20	24	28	32	37
·247	17689	17693	17697	4	8	12	16	20	24	28	33	37
·248	17729	17734	17738	4	8	12	16	20	24	29	33	37
·249	17770	17775	17779	4	8	12	16	20	25	29	33	37

	0	1	2	3	4	5	6
·250	17783	17787	17791	17795	17799	17803	17807
·251	17824	17828	17832	17836	17840	17844	17848
·252	17865	17869	17873	17877	17881	17885	17890
·253	17906	17910	17914	17918	17923	17927	17931
·254	17947	17951	17956	17960	17964	17968	17972
·255	17989	17993	17997	18001	18005	18009	18014
·256	18030	18034	18038	18043	18047	18051	18055
·257	18072	18076	18080	18084	18088	18093	18097
·258	18113	18118	18122	18126	18130	18134	18138
·259	18155	18159	18163	18168	18172	18176	18180
·260	18197	18201	18205	18210	18214	18218	18222
·261	18239	18243	18247	18252	18256	18260	18264
·262	18281	18285	18289	18294	18298	18302	18306
·263	18323	18327	18332	18336	18340	18344	18348
·264	18365	18370	18374	18378	18382	18386	18391
·265	18408	18412	18416	18420	18425	18429	18433
·266	18450	18454	18459	18463	18467	18471	18476
·267	18493	18497	18501	18505	18510	18514	18518
·268	18535	18540	18544	18548	18552	18557	18561
·269	18578	18582	18587	18591	18595	18599	18604
·270	18621	18625	18629	18634	18638	18642	18647
·271	18664	18668	18672	18677	18681	18685	18690
·272	18707	18711	18715	18720	18724	18728	18733
·273	18750	18754	18759	18763	18767	18771	18776
·274	18793	18797	18802	18806	18810	18815	18819
·275	18836	18841	18845	18849	18854	18858	18862
·276	18880	18884	18889	18893	18897	18902	18906
·277	18923	18928	18932	18936	18941	18945	18950
·278	18967	18971	18976	18980	18984	18989	18993
·279	19011	19015	19019	19024	19028	19033	19037
·280	19055	19059	19063	19068	19072	19077	19081
·281	19098	19103	19107	19112	19116	19120	19125
·282	19143	19147	19151	19156	19160	19165	19169
·283	19187	19191	19195	19200	19204	19209	19213
·284	19231	19235	19240	19244	19249	19253	19257
·285	19275	19280	19284	19289	19293	19297	19302
·286	19320	19324	19329	19333	19337	19342	19346
·287	19364	19369	19373	19378	19382	19386	19391
·288	19409	19413	19418	19422	19427	19431	19436
·289	19454	19458	19463	19467	19471	19476	19480
·290	19498	19503	19507	19512	19516	19521	19525
·291	19543	19548	19552	19557	19561	19566	19570
·292	19588	19593	19597	19602	19606	19611	19615
·293	19634	19638	19643	19647	19652	19656	19661
·294	19679	19683	19688	19692	19697	19701	19706
·295	19724	19729	19733	19738	19742	19747	19751
·296	19770	19774	19779	19783	19788	19792	19797
·297	19815	19820	19824	19829	19833	19838	19843
·298	19861	19865	19870	19875	19879	19884	19888
·299	19907	19911	19916	19920	19925	19930	19934

Antilogarithms (*contd.*)

	7	8	9	Mean Log. Differences								
				1	2	3	4	5	6	7	8	9
·250	17811	17816	17820	4	8	12	16	20	25	29	33	37
·251	17852	17857	17861	4	8	12	16	21	25	29	33	37
·252	17894	17898	17902	4	8	12	16	21	25	29	33	37
·253	17935	17939	17943	4	8	12	17	21	25	29	33	37
·254	17976	17980	17985	4	8	12	17	21	25	29	33	37
·255	18018	18022	18026	4	8	12	17	21	25	29	33	37
·256	18059	18063	18068	4	8	12	17	21	25	29	33	37
·257	18101	18105	18109	4	8	13	17	21	25	29	33	38
·258	18143	18147	18151	4	8	13	17	21	25	29	33	38
·259	18184	18189	18193	4	8	13	17	21	25	29	33	38
·260	18226	18231	18235	4	8	13	17	21	25	29	34	38
·261	18268	18273	18277	4	8	13	17	21	25	29	34	38
·262	18310	18314	18319	4	8	13	17	21	25	29	34	38
·263	18353	18357	18361	4	8	13	17	21	25	30	34	38
·264	18395	18399	18403	4	8	13	17	21	25	30	34	38
·265	18437	18442	18446	4	8	13	17	21	25	30	34	38
·266	18480	18484	18488	4	9	13	17	21	26	30	34	38
·267	18522	18527	18531	4	9	13	17	21	26	30	34	38
·268	18565	18569	18574	4	9	13	17	21	26	30	34	38
·269	18608	18612	18617	4	9	13	17	21	26	30	34	39
·270	18651	18655	18659	4	9	13	17	21	26	30	34	39
·271	18694	18698	18702	4	9	13	17	22	26	30	34	39
·272	18737	18741	18746	4	9	13	17	22	26	30	34	39
·273	18780	18784	18789	4	9	13	17	22	26	30	35	39
·274	18823	18828	18832	4	9	13	17	22	26	30	35	39
·275	18867	18871	18876	4	9	13	17	22	26	30	35	39
·276	18910	18915	18919	4	9	13	17	22	26	30	35	39
·277	18954	18958	18963	4	9	13	17	22	26	31	35	39
·278	18998	19002	19006	4	9	13	17	22	26	31	35	39
·279	19041	19046	19050	4	9	13	18	22	26	31	35	39
·280	19085	19090	19094	4	9	13	18	22	26	31	35	40
·281	19129	19134	19138	4	9	13	18	22	26	31	35	40
·282	19173	19178	19182	4	9	13	18	22	26	31	35	40
·283	19218	19222	19226	4	9	13	18	22	27	31	35	40
·284	19262	19266	19271	4	9	13	18	22	27	31	35	40
·285	19306	19310	19315	4	9	13	18	22	27	31	36	40
·286	19351	19355	19360	4	9	13	18	22	27	31	36	40
·287	19395	19400	19404	4	9	13	18	22	27	31	36	40
·288	19440	19445	19449	4	9	13	18	22	27	31	36	40
·289	19485	19489	19494	4	9	13	18	22	27	31	36	40
·290	19530	19534	19539	4	9	13	18	22	27	31	36	40
·291	19575	19579	19584	5	9	14	18	23	27	32	36	41
·292	19620	19625	19629	5	9	14	18	23	27	32	36	41
·293	19665	19670	19674	5	9	14	18	23	27	32	36	41
·294	19711	19715	19720	5	9	14	18	23	27	32	36	41
·295	19756	19761	19765	5	9	14	18	23	27	32	36	41
·296	19802	19806	19811	5	9	14	18	23	27	32	36	41
·297	19847	19852	19856	5	9	14	18	23	27	32	36	41
·298	19893	19898	19902	5	9	14	18	23	27	32	37	41
·299	19939	19943	19948	5	9	14	18	23	28	32	37	41

·300—·349

	0	1	2	3	4	5	6
·300	19953	19957	19962	19966	19971	19976	19980
·301	19999	20003	20008	20012	20017	20022	20026
·302	20045	20049	20054	20059	20063	20068	20072
·303	20091	20096	20100	20105	20109	20114	20119
·304	20137	20142	20146	20151	20156	20160	20165
·305	20184	20188	20193	20198	20202	20207	20212
·306	20230	20235	20239	20244	20249	20253	20258
·307	20277	20281	20286	20291	20295	20300	20305
·308	20324	20328	20333	20337	20342	20347	20352
·309	20370	20375	20380	20385	20389	20394	20399
·310	20417	20422	20427	20431	20436	20441	20246
·311	20464	20469	20474	20479	20483	20488	20493
·312	20512	20516	20521	20526	20530	20535	20540
·313	20559	20564	20568	20573	20578	20583	20587
·314	20606	20611	20616	20620	20625	20630	20635
·315	20654	20659	20663	20668	20673	20677	20682
·316	20701	20706	20711	20716	20720	20725	20730
·317	20749	20754	20759	20763	20768	20773	20778
·318	20797	20802	20806	20811	20816	20821	20826
·319	20845	20850	20854	20859	20864	20869	20874
·320	20893	20898	20903	20907	20912	20917	20922
·321	20941	20946	20951	20956	20960	20965	20970
·322	20989	20994	20999	21004	21009	21014	21018
·323	21038	21043	21047	21052	21057	21062	21067
·324	21086	21091	21096	21101	21106	21111	21115
·325	21135	21140	21145	21149	21154	21159	21164
·326	21184	21188	21193	21198	21203	21208	21213
·327	21232	21237	21242	21247	21252	21257	21262
·328	21281	21286	21291	21296	21301	21306	21310
·329	21330	21335	21340	21345	21350	21355	21360
·330	21380	21384	21389	21394	21399	21404	21409
·331	21429	21434	21439	21444	21449	21454	21458
·332	21478	21483	21488	21493	21498	21503	21508
·333	21528	21533	21538	21543	21548	21553	21558
·334	21577	21582	21587	21592	21597	21602	21607
·335	21627	21632	21637	21642	21647	21652	21657
·336	21677	21682	21687	21692	21697	21702	21707
·337	21727	21732	21737	21742	21747	21752	21757
·338	21777	21782	21787	21792	21797	21802	21807
·339	21827	21832	21837	21842	21847	21852	21857
·340	21878	21883	21888	21893	21898	21903	21908
·341	21928	21933	21938	21943	21948	21953	21958
·342	21979	21984	21989	21994	21999	22004	22009
·343	22029	22034	22039	22044	22050	22055	22060
·344	22080	22085	22090	22095	22100	22105	22111
·345	22131	22136	22141	22146	22151	22156	22161
·346	22182	22187	22192	22197	22202	22207	22213
·347	22233	22238	22243	22248	22254	22259	22264
·348	22284	22289	22295	22300	22305	22310	22315
·349	22336	22341	22346	22351	22356	22361	22367

Antilogarithms *(contd.)*

	7	8	9	Mean Log. Differences								
				1	2	3	4	5	6	7	8	9
·300	19985	19989	19994	5	9	14	18	23	28	32	37	41
·301	20031	20035	20040	5	9	14	18	23	28	32	37	41
·302	20077	20082	20086	5	9	14	18	23	28	32	37	42
·303	20123	20128	20133	5	9	14	19	23	28	32	37	42
·304	20170	20174	20179	5	9	14	19	23	28	33	37	42
·305	20216	20221	20225	5	9	14	19	23	28	33	37	42
·306	20263	20267	20272	5	9	14	19	23	28	33	37	42
·307	20309	20314	20319	5	9	14	19	23	28	33	37	42
·308	20356	20361	20366	5	9	14	19	23	28	33	37	42
·309	20403	20408	20413	5	9	14	19	23	28	33	38	42
·310	20450	20455	20460	5	9	14	19	24	28	33	38	42
·311	20497	20502	20507	5	9	14	19	24	28	33	38	42
·312	20545	20549	20554	5	9	14	19	24	28	33	38	43
·313	20592	20597	20602	5	9	14	19	24	28	33	38	43
·314	20639	20644	20649	5	10	14	19	24	29	33	38	43
·315	20687	20692	20697	5	10	14	19	24	29	33	38	43
·316	20735	20740	20744	5	10	14	19	24	29	33	38	43
·317	20783	20787	20792	5	10	14	19	24	29	33	38	43
·318	20830	20835	20840	5	10	14	19	24	29	34	38	43
·319	20878	20883	20888	5	10	14	19	24	29	34	38	43
·320	20927	20931	20936	5	10	14	19	24	29	34	39	43
·321	20975	20980	20985	5	10	14	19	24	29	34	39	43
·322	21023	21028	21033	5	10	15	19	24	29	34	39	44
·323	21072	21077	21081	5	10	15	19	24	29	34	39	44
·324	21120	21125	21130	5	10	15	19	24	29	34	39	44
·325	21169	21174	21179	5	10	15	19	24	29	34	39	44
·326	21218	21223	21228	5	10	15	20	24	29	34	39	44
·327	21267	21272	21276	5	10	15	20	24	29	34	39	44
·328	21316	21321	21325	5	10	15	20	25	29	34	39	44
·329	21365	21370	21375	5	10	15	20	25	30	34	39	44
·330	21414	21419	21424	5	10	15	20	25	30	34	39	44
·331	21463	21468	21473	5	10	15	20	25	30	35	40	44
·332	21513	21518	21523	5	10	15	20	25	30	35	40	45
·333	21562	21567	21572	5	10	15	20	25	30	35	40	45
·334	21612	21617	21622	5	10	15	20	25	30	35	40	45
·335	21662	21667	21672	5	10	15	20	25	30	35	40	45
·336	21712	21717	21722	5	10	15	20	25	30	35	40	45
·337	21762	21767	21772	5	10	15	20	25	30	35	40	45
·338	21812	21817	21822	5	10	15	20	25	30	35	40	45
·339	21862	21867	21873	5	10	15	20	25	30	35	40	45
·340	21913	21918	21923	5	10	15	20	25	30	35	40	45
·341	21963	21968	21973	5	10	15	20	25	30	35	40	46
·342	22014	22019	22024	5	10	15	20	25	30	35	41	46
·343	22065	22070	22075	5	10	15	20	25	30	36	41	46
·344	22116	22121	22126	5	10	15	20	25	31	36	41	46
·345	22167	22172	22177	5	10	15	20	26	31	36	41	46
·346	22218	22223	22228	5	10	15	20	26	31	36	41	46
·347	22269	22274	22279	5	10	15	21	26	31	36	41	46
·348	22320	22325	22331	5	10	15	21	26	31	36	41	46
·349	22372	22377	22382	5	10	15	21	26	31	36	41	46

Table of

	0	1	2	3	4	5	6
·350	22387	22392	22397	22403	22408	22413	22418
·351	22439	22444	22449	22454	22460	22465	22470
·352	22490	22496	22501	22506	22511	22516	22523
·353	22542	22548	22553	22558	22563	22568	22574
·354	22594	22600	22605	22610	22615	22620	22626
·355	22646	22652	22657	22662	22667	22672	22678
·356	22699	22704	22709	22714	22720	22725	22730
·357	22751	22756	22761	22767	22772	22777	22782
·358	22803	22809	22814	22819	22824	22830	22835
·359	22856	22861	22866	22872	22877	22882	22888
·360	22909	22914	22919	22924	22930	22935	22940
·361	22961	22967	22972	22977	22983	22988	22993
·362	23014	23020	23025	23030	23036	23041	23046
·363	23067	23073	23078	23083	23089	23094	23099
·364	23121	23126	23131	23137	23142	23147	23153
·365	23174	23179	23185	23190	23195	23201	23206
·366	23227	23233	23238	23243	23249	23254	23259
·367	23281	23286	23292	23297	23302	23308	23313
·368	23335	23340	23345	23351	23356	23361	23367
·369	23388	23394	23399	23404	23410	23415	23421
·370	23442	23448	23453	23458	23464	23469	23475
·371	23496	23502	23507	23513	23518	23523	23529
·372	23550	23556	23561	23567	23572	23578	23583
·373	23605	23610	23616	23621	23626	23632	23637
·374	23659	23665	23670	23675	23681	23686	23692
·375	23714	23719	23725	23730	23736	23741	23746
·376	23768	23774	23779	23785	23790	23796	23801
·377	23823	23829	23834	23840	23845	23851	23856
·378	23878	23884	23889	23895	23900	23906	23911
·379	23933	23939	23944	23950	23955	23961	23966
·380	23988	23994	23999	24005	24010	24016	24021
·381	24044	24049	24055	24060	24066	24071	24077
·382	24099	24105	24110	24116	24121	24127	24132
·383	24155	24160	24166	24171	24177	24182	24188
·384	24210	24216	24221	24227	24233	24238	24244
·385	24266	24272	24277	24283	24288	24294	24300
·386	24322	24328	24333	24339	24344	24350	24356
·387	24378	24384	24389	24395	24401	24406	24412
·388	24434	24440	24446	24451	24457	24462	24468
·389	24491	24496	24502	24508	24513	24519	24524
·390	24547	24553	24558	24564	24570	24575	24581
·391	24604	24609	24615	24621	24626	24632	24638
·392	24660	24666	24672	24677	24683	24689	24694
·393	24717	24723	24729	24734	24740	24746	24751
·394	24774	24780	24786	24791	24797	24803	24808
·395	24831	24837	24843	24848	24854	24860	24866
·396	24889	24894	24900	24906	24911	24917	24923
·397	24946	24952	24957	24963	24969	24975	24980
·398	25003	25009	25015	25021	25026	25032	25038
·399	25061	25067	25073	25078	25084	25090	25096

Antilogarithms (*contd.*)

	7	8	9	Mean Log. Differences								
				1	2	3	4	5	6	7	8	9
·350	22423	22428	22434	5	10	15	21	26	31	36	41	46
·351	22475	22480	22485	5	10	16	21	26	31	36	41	47
·352	22527	22532	22537	5	10	16	21	26	31	36	41	47
·353	22579	22584	22589	5	10	16	21	26	31	36	42	47
·354	22631	22636	22641	5	10	16	21	26	31	36	42	47
·355	22683	22688	22693	5	10	16	21	26	31	37	42	47
·356	22735	22740	22746	5	10	16	21	26	31	37	42	47
·357	22788	22793	22798	5	10	16	21	26	31	37	42	47
·358	22840	22845	22851	5	11	16	21	26	32	37	42	47
·359	22893	22898	22903	5	11	16	21	26	32	37	42	47
·360	22946	22951	22956	5	11	16	21	26	32	37	42	48
·361	22998	23004	23009	5	11	16	21	26	32	37	42	48
·362	23051	23057	23062	5	11	16	21	27	32	37	42	48
·363	23105	23110	23115	5	11	16	21	27	32	37	43	48
·364	23158	23163	23169	5	11	16	21	27	32	37	43	48
·365	23211	23217	23222	5	11	16	21	27	32	37	43	48
·366	23265	23270	23276	5	11	16	21	27	32	37	43	48
·367	23318	23324	23329	5	11	16	21	27	32	38	43	48
·368	23372	23378	23383	5	11	16	22	27	32	38	43	48
·369	23426	23431	23437	5	11	16	22	27	32	38	43	49
·370	23480	23485	23491	5	11	16	22	27	32	38	43	49
·371	23534	23540	23545	5	11	16	22	27	32	38	43	49
·372	23588	23594	23599	5	11	16	22	27	33	38	43	49
·373	23643	23648	23654	5	11	16	22	27	33	38	44	49
·374	23697	23703	23708	5	11	16	22	27	33	38	44	49
·375	23752	23757	23763	5	11	16	22	27	33	38	44	49
·376	23807	23812	23818	5	11	16	22	27	33	38	44	49
·377	23862	23867	23873	5	11	16	22	27	33	38	44	49
·378	23917	23922	23928	6	11	17	22	28	33	39	44	50
·379	23972	23977	23983	6	11	17	22	28	33	39	44	50
·380	24027	24033	24038	6	11	17	22	28	33	39	44	50
·381	24082	24088	24093	6	11	17	22	28	33	39	44	50
·382	24138	24143	24149	6	11	17	22	28	33	39	44	50
·383	24194	24199	24205	6	11	17	22	28	33	39	45	50
·384	24249	24255	24260	6	11	17	22	28	33	39	45	50
·385	24305	24311	24316	6	11	17	22	28	34	39	45	50
·386	24361	24367	24372	6	11	17	22	28	34	39	45	50
·387	24417	24423	24429	6	11	17	22	28	34	39	45	51
·388	24474	24479	24485	6	11	17	23	28	34	39	45	51
·389	24530	24536	24541	6	11	17	23	28	34	40	45	51
·390	24587	24592	24598	6	11	17	23	28	34	40	45	51
·391	24643	24649	24655	6	11	17	23	28	34	40	45	51
·392	24700	24706	24712	6	11	17	23	28	34	40	45	51
·393	24757	24763	24768	6	11	17	23	28	34	40	46	51
·394	24814	24820	24826	6	11	17	23	29	34	40	46	51
·395	24871	24877	24883	6	11	17	23	29	34	40	46	52
·396	24929	24934	24940	6	11	17	23	29	34	40	46	52
·397	24986	24992	24998	6	12	17	23	29	35	40	46	52
·398	25044	25050	25055	6	12	17	23	29	35	40	46	52
·399	25101	25107	25113	6	12	17	23	29	35	40	46	52

Table of

	0	1	2	3	4	5	6
·400	25119	25124	25130	25136	25142	25148	25153
·401	25177	25182	25188	25194	25200	25206	25211
·402	25235	25240	25246	25252	25258	25264	25270
·403	25293	25299	25304	25310	25316	25322	25328
·404	25351	25357	25363	25369	25374	25380	25386
·405	25410	25415	25421	25427	25433	25439	25445
·406	25468	25474	25480	25486	25492	25497	25503
·407	25527	25532	25539	25545	25550	25556	25562
·408	25586	25592	25597	25603	25609	25615	25621
·409	25645	25651	25657	25662	25668	25674	25680
·410	25704	25710	25716	25722	25727	25733	25739
·411	25763	25769	25775	25781	25787	25793	25800
·412	25822	25828	25834	25840	25846	25852	25858
·413	25882	25888	25894	25900	25906	25911	25918
·414	25942	25948	25954	25960	25966	25972	25978
·415	26001	26008	26013	26020	26025	26031	26037
·416	26061	26067	26073	26078	26085	26091	26097
·417	26121	26127	26133	26140	26146	26152	26158
·418	26182	26188	26194	26200	26206	26212	26218
·419	26242	26248	26254	26260	26266	26272	26278
·420	26303	26309	26315	26321	26327	26333	26339
·421	26363	26369	26375	26381	26387	26394	26400
·422	26424	26430	26436	26442	26448	26454	26460
·423	26485	26491	26497	26503	26509	26515	26521
·424	26546	26552	26558	26564	26570	26576	26583
·425	26607	26613	26619	26625	26632	26638	26644
·426	26669	26675	26681	26687	26693	26699	26705
·427	26730	26736	26742	26748	26755	26761	26767
·428	26792	26798	26804	26810	26816	26822	26829
·429	26853	26859	26866	26872	26878	26884	26890
·430	26915	26921	26928	26934	26940	26946	26952
·431	26977	26983	26990	26996	27002	27008	27015
·432	27040	27046	27052	27058	27064	27071	27077
·433	27102	27108	27114	27120	27127	27133	27139
·434	27164	27171	27177	27183	27189	27196	27202
·435	27227	27233	27239	27246	27252	27258	27265
·436	27290	27296	27302	27308	27315	27321	27327
·437	27353	27359	27365	27371	27378	27384	27390
·438	27416	27422	27428	27435	27441	27447	27454
·439	27479	27485	27491	27498	27504	27510	27517
·440	27542	27548	27555	27561	27568	27574	27580
·441	27606	27612	27618	27625	27631	27637	27644
·442	27669	27676	27682	27688	27695	27701	27708
·443	27733	27739	27746	27752	27759	27765	27771
·444	27797	27803	27810	27816	27823	27829	27836
·445	27861	27867	27874	27880	27887	27893	27900
·446	27925	27932	27938	27945	27951	27957	27964
·447	27990	27996	28003	28009	28015	28022	28028
·448	28054	28061	28067	28074	28080	28087	28093
·449	28119	28125	28132	28138	28145	28151	28158

Antilogarithms *(contd.)*

	7	8	9	Mean Log. Differences								
				1	2	3	4	5	6	7	8	9
·400	25159	25165	25171	6	12	17	23	29	35	41	46	52
·401	25217	25223	25229	6	12	17	23	29	35	41	46	52
·402	25275	25281	25287	6	12	17	23	29	35	41	47	52
·403	25334	25340	25345	6	12	17	23	29	35	41	47	53
·404	25392	25398	25404	6	12	18	23	29	35	41	47	53
·405	25451	25456	25462	6	12	18	23	29	35	41	47	53
·406	25509	25515	25521	6	12	18	23	29	35	41	47	53
·407	25568	25574	25580	6	12	18	24	29	35	41	47	53
·408	25627	25633	25639	6	12	18	24	29	35	41	47	53
·409	25686	25692	25698	6	12	18	24	30	35	41	47	53
·410	25745	25751	25757	6	12	18	24	30	36	41	47	53
·411	25805	25811	25817	6	12	18	24	30	36	42	48	53
·412	25864	25870	25876	6	12	18	24	30	36	42	48	54
·413	25924	25930	25936	6	12	18	24	30	36	42	48	54
·414	25983	25989	25995	6	12	18	24	30	36	42	48	54
·415	26043	26049	26055	6	12	18	24	30	36	42	48	54
·416	26103	26109	26115	6	12	18	24	30	36	42	48	54
·417	26164	26170	26176	6	12	18	24	30	36	42	48	54
·418	26224	26230	26236	6	12	18	24	30	36	42	48	54
·419	26284	26290	26296	6	12	18	24	30	36	42	48	54
·420	26345	26351	26357	6	12	18	24	30	36	42	49	55
·421	26406	26412	26418	6	12	18	24	30	36	43	49	55
·422	26467	26473	26479	6	12	18	24	30	37	43	49	55
·423	26528	26534	26540	6	12	18	24	31	37	43	49	55
·424	26589	26595	26601	6	12	18	24	31	37	43	49	55
·425	26650	26656	26662	6	12	18	25	31	37	43	49	55
·426	26711	26718	26724	6	12	18	25	31	37	43	49	55
·427	26773	26779	26785	6	12	18	25	31	37	43	49	55
·428	26835	26841	26847	6	12	19	25	31	37	43	49	56
·429	26897	26903	26909	6	12	19	25	31	37	43	50	56
·430	26959	26965	26971	6	12	19	25	31	37	43	50	56
·431	27021	27027	27033	6	12	19	25	31	37	44	50	56
·432	27083	27089	27096	6	12	19	25	31	37	44	50	56
·433	27145	27152	27158	6	12	19	25	31	37	44	50	56
·434	27208	27214	27221	6	13	19	25	31	38	44	50	56
·435	27271	27277	27283	6	13	19	25	31	38	44	50	56
·436	27334	27340	27346	6	13	19	25	31	38	44	50	57
·437	27397	27403	27409	6	13	19	25	32	38	44	50	57
·438	27460	27466	27472	6	13	19	25	32	38	44	51	57
·439	27523	27529	27536	6	13	19	25	32	38	44	51	57
·440	27587	27593	27599	6	13	19	25	32	38	44	51	57
·441	27650	27657	27663	6	13	19	25	32	38	45	51	57
·442	27714	27720	27727	6	13	19	26	32	38	45	51	57
·443	27778	27784	27791	6	13	19	26	32	38	45	51	58
·444	27842	27848	27855	6	13	19	26	32	38	45	51	58
·445	27906	27912	27919	6	13	19	26	32	39	45	51	58
·446	27970	27977	27983	6	13	19	26	32	39	45	51	58
·447	28035	28041	28048	6	13	19	26	32	39	45	52	58
·448	28099	28106	28112	6	13	19	26	32	39	45	52	58
·449	28164	28171	28177	6	13	19	26	32	39	45	52	58

	0	1	2	3	4	5	6
·450	28184	28190	28197	28203	28210	28216	28223
·451	28249	28255	28262	28268	28275	28281	28288
·452	28313	28320	28327	28333	28340	28346	28353
·453	28379	28386	28392	28399	28405	28412	28418
·454	28444	28451	28458	28464	28471	28477	28484
·455	28510	28517	28523	28530	28536	28543	28550
·456	28576	28582	28589	28596	28602	28609	28615
·457	28642	28648	28655	28661	28668	28675	28681
·458	28708	28714	28721	28727	28734	28741	28747
·459	28774	28780	28787	28794	28800	28807	28814
·460	28840	28847	28853	28860	28867	28873	28880
·461	28907	28913	28920	28927	28933	28940	28947
·462	28973	28980	28987	28993	29000	29007	29013
·463	29040	29047	29053	29060	29067	29074	29080
·464	29107	29114	29120	29127	29134	29141	29147
·465	29174	29181	29188	29194	29201	29208	29214
·466	29241	29248	29255	29262	29268	29275	29282
·467	29309	29316	29322	29329	29336	29343	29349
·468	29376	29383	29390	29397	29403	29410	29417
·469	29444	29451	29458	29464	29471	29478	29485
·470	29512	29519	29526	29532	29539	29546	29553
·471	29580	29587	29594	29600	29607	29614	29621
·472	29648	29655	29662	29669	29675	29682	29689
·473	29717	29723	29730	29737	29744	29751	29758
·474	29785	29792	29799	29806	29812	29819	29826
·475	29854	29861	29867	29874	29881	29888	29895
·476	29922	29929	29936	29943	29950	29957	29964
·477	29991	29998	30005	30012	30019	30026	30033
·478	30061	30068	30074	30081	30088	30095	30102
·479	30130	30137	30144	30151	30158	30165	30172
·480	30199	30206	30213	30220	30227	30234	30241
·481	30269	30276	30283	30290	30297	30304	30311
·482	30339	30346	30353	30360	30367	30374	30381
·483	30409	30416	30423	30430	30437	30444	30451
·484	30479	30486	30493	30500	30507	30514	30521
·485	30549	30556	30563	30570	30577	30584	30591
·486	30619	30627	30634	30641	30648	30655	30662
·487	30690	30697	30704	30711	30718	30725	30732
·488	30761	30768	30775	30782	30789	30796	30803
·489	30832	30839	30846	30853	30860	30867	30874
·490	30903	30910	30917	30924	30931	30938	30946
·491	30974	30981	30988	30995	31003	31010	31017
·492	31045	31053	31060	31067	31074	31081	31088
·493	31117	31124	31131	31139	31146	31153	31160
·494	31189	31196	31203	31210	31217	31225	31232
·495	31261	31268	31275	31282	31289	31297	31304
·496	31333	31340	31347	31354	31362	31369	31376
·497	31405	31412	31420	31427	31434	31441	31448
·498	31477	31485	31492	31499	31506	31514	31521
·499	31550	31557	31564	31572	31579	31586	31594

Antilogarithms (*contd.*)

	7	8	9	Mean Log. Differences								
				1	2	3	4	5	6	7	8	9
·450	28229	28236	28242	6	13	19	26	32	39	45	52	58
·451	28294	28301	28307	7	13	20	26	33	39	46	52	59
·452	28359	28366	28373	7	13	20	26	33	39	46	52	59
·453	28425	28431	28438	7	13	20	26	33	39	46	52	59
·454	28490	28497	28503	7	13	20	26	33	39	46	52	59
·455	28556	28563	28569	7	13	20	26	33	39	46	53	59
·456	28622	28628	28635	7	13	20	26	33	40	46	53	59
·457	28688	28694	28701	7	13	20	26	33	40	46	53	59
·458	28754	28761	28767	7	13	20	26	33	40	46	53	60
·459	28820	28827	28834	7	13	20	27	33	40	46	53	60
·460	28887	28893	28900	7	13	20	27	33	40	47	53	60
·461	28953	28960	28967	7	13	20	27	33	40	47	53	60
·462	29020	29027	29033	7	13	20	27	33	40	47	53	60
·463	29087	29094	29100	7	13	20	27	33	40	47	54	60
·464	29154	29161	29167	7	13	20	27	34	40	47	54	60
·465	29221	29228	29235	7	13	20	27	34	40	47	54	61
·466	29289	29295	29302	7	13	20	27	34	40	47	54	61
·467	29356	29363	29370	7	14	20	27	34	41	47	54	61
·468	29424	29431	29437	7	14	20	27	34	41	47	54	61
·469	29492	29498	29505	7	14	20	27	34	41	48	54	61
·470	29560	29566	29573	7	14	20	27	34	41	48	54	61
·471	29628	29635	29641	7	14	20	27	34	41	48	55	61
·472	29696	29703	29710	7	14	21	27	34	41	48	55	62
·473	29764	29771	29778	7	14	21	27	34	41	48	55	62
·474	29833	29840	29847	7	14	21	27	34	41	48	55	62
·475	29902	29909	29916	7	14	21	28	34	41	48	55	62
·476	29971	29978	29985	7	14	21	28	34	41	48	55	62
·477	30040	30047	30054	7	14	21	28	35	41	48	55	62
·478	30109	30116	30123	7	14	21	28	35	42	49	55	62
·479	30179	30185	30193	7	14	21	28	35	42	49	56	62
·480	30248	30255	30262	7	14	21	28	35	42	49	56	63
·481	30318	30325	30332	7	14	21	28	35	42	49	56	63
·482	30388	30395	30402	7	14	21	28	35	42	49	56	63
·483	30458	30465	30472	7	14	21	28	35	42	49	56	63
·484	30528	30535	30542	7	14	21	28	35	42	49	56	63
·485	30598	30605	30612	7	14	21	28	35	42	49	56	63
·486	30669	30676	30683	7	14	21	28	35	42	49	56	64
·487	30740	30747	30754	7	14	21	28	35	42	50	57	64
·488	30810	30818	30825	7	14	21	28	35	43	50	57	64
·489	30881	30889	30896	7	14	21	28	36	43	50	57	64
·490	30953	30960	30967	7	14	21	28	36	43	50	57	64
·491	31024	31031	31038	7	14	21	29	36	43	50	57	64
·492	31096	31103	31110	7	14	21	29	36	43	50	57	64
·493	31167	31174	31182	7	14	22	29	36	43	50	57	65
·494	31239	31246	31253	7	14	22	29	36	43	50	58	65
·495	31311	31318	31325	7	14	22	29	36	43	50	58	65
·496	31383	31390	31398	7	14	22	29	36	43	51	58	65
·497	31456	31463	31470	7	14	22	29	36	44	51	58	65
·498	31528	31535	31543	7	15	22	29	36	44	51	58	65
·499	31601	31608	31615	7	15	22	29	36	44	51	58	65

Table of

	0	1	2	3	4	5	6
·500	31623	31630	31637	31644	31652	31659	31666
·501	31696	31703	31710	31717	31725	31732	31739
·502	31769	31776	31783	31791	31798	31805	31813
·503	31842	31849	31856	31864	31871	31879	31886
·504	31915	31923	31930	31937	31945	31952	31959
·505	31989	31996	32004	32011	32018	32026	32033
·506	32063	32070	32077	32085	32092	32099	32107
·507	32136	32144	32151	32159	32166	32173	32181
·508	32211	32218	32225	32233	32240	32248	32255
·509	32285	32292	32300	32307	32315	32322	32329
·510	32359	32367	32374	32382	32389	32396	32404
·511	32434	32441	32449	32456	32464	32471	32479
·512	32509	32516	32524	32531	32539	32546	32554
·513	32584	32591	32599	32606	32614	32621	32629
·514	32659	32666	32674	32681	32689	32696	32704
·515	32734	32741	32749	32757	32764	32772	32779
·516	32809	32817	32824	32832	32840	32847	32855
·517	32885	32893	32900	32908	32915	32923	32930
·518	32961	32968	32976	32984	32991	32999	33006
·519	33037	33044	33052	33060	33067	33075	33082
·520	33113	33121	33128	33136	33143	33151	33159
·521	33189	33197	33205	33212	33220	33228	33235
·522	33266	33273	33281	33290	33296	33304	33312
·523	33342	33350	33358	33366	33373	33381	33389
·524	33419	33427	33435	33442	33450	33458	33466
·525	33496	33504	33512	33520	33527	33535	33543
·526	33574	33581	33589	33597	33605	33612	33620
·527	33651	33659	33667	33674	33682	33690	33698
·528	33729	33736	33744	33752	33760	33767	33775
·529	33806	33814	33822	33830	33837	33845	33853
·530	33884	33892	33900	33908	33915	33923	33931
·531	33962	33970	33978	33986	33994	34002	34009
·532	34041	34049	34056	34064	34072	34080	34088
·533	34119	34127	34135	34143	34157	34158	34166
·534	34198	34206	34214	34221	34229	34237	34245
·535	34277	34285	34292	34300	34308	34316	34324
·536	34356	34364	34371	34379	34387	34395	34403
·537	34435	34443	34451	34459	34467	34475	34482
·538	34514	34522	34530	34538	34546	34554	34562
·539	34594	34602	34610	34618	34626	34634	34642
·540	34674	34682	34690	34697	34705	34713	34721
·541	34753	34761	34770	34777	34785	34794	34802
·542	34834	34842	34850	34858	34866	34874	34882
·543	34914	34922	34930	34938	34946	34954	34962
·544	34994	35002	35010	35019	35027	35035	35043
·545	35075	35083	35091	35099	35107	35115	35124
·546	35156	35164	35172	35180	35188	35196	35204
·547	35237	35245	35253	35261	35269	35278	35286
·548	35318	35326	35334	35343	35351	35359	35367
·549	35400	35408	35416	35424	35432	35440	35449

Antilogarithms (*contd.*)

	7	8	9	Mean Log. Differences								
				1	2	3	4	5	6	7	8	9
·500	31674	31681	31688	7	15	22	29	36	44	51	58	66
·501	31747	31754	31761	7	15	22	29	37	44	51	58	66
·502	31820	31827	31834	7	15	22	29	37	44	51	59	66
·503	31893	31901	31908	7	15	22	29	37	44	51	59	66
·504	31967	31974	31981	7	15	22	29	37	44	52	59	66
·505	32040	32048	32055	7	15	22	29	37	44	52	59	66
·506	32114	32122	32129	7	15	22	30	37	44	52	59	67
·507	32188	32196	32203	7	15	22	30	37	44	52	59	67
·508	32262	32270	32277	7	15	22	30	37	45	52	59	67
·509	32337	32344	32352	7	15	22	30	37	45	52	60	67
·510	32411	32419	32426	7	15	22	30	37	45	52	60	67
·511	32486	32494	32501	7	15	22	30	37	45	52	60	67
·512	32561	32569	32576	7	15	22	30	37	45	52	60	67
·513	32636	32644	32651	8	15	23	30	38	45	53	60	68
·514	32711	32719	32726	8	15	23	30	38	45	53	60	68
·515	32787	32794	32802	8	15	23	30	38	45	53	60	68
·516	32862	32870	32877	8	15	23	30	38	45	53	61	68
·517	32938	32946	32953	8	15	23	30	38	45	53	61	68
·518	33014	33022	33029	8	15	23	30	38	46	53	61	68
·519	33090	33098	33105	8	15	23	30	38	46	53	61	69
·520	33166	33174	33182	8	15	23	31	38	46	53	61	69
·521	33243	33250	33258	8	15	23	31	38	46	54	61	69
·522	33319	33327	33335	8	15	23	31	38	46	54	61	69
·523	33396	33404	33412	8	15	23	31	38	46	54	62	69
·524	33473	33481	33489	8	15	23	31	39	46	54	62	69
·525	33550	33558	33566	8	15	23	31	39	46	54	62	70
·526	33628	33636	33643	8	15	23	31	39	46	54	62	70
·527	33705	33713	33721	8	16	23	31	39	47	54	62	70
·528	33783	33791	33799	8	16	23	31	39	47	54	62	70
·529	33861	33869	33876	8	16	23	31	39	47	55	62	70
·530	33939	33947	33955	8	16	23	31	39	47	55	63	70
·531	34017	34025	34033	8	16	23	31	39	47	55	63	70
·532	34096	34103	34111	8	16	24	31	39	47	55	63	71
·533	34174	34182	34190	8	16	24	31	39	47	55	63	71
·534	34253	34261	34269	8	16	24	32	39	47	55	63	71
·535	34332	34340	34348	8	16	24	32	40	47	55	63	71
·536	34411	34419	34427	8	16	24	32	40	48	55	63	71
·537	34490	34498	34506	8	16	24	32	40	48	56	64	71
·538	34570	34578	34586	8	16	24	32	40	48	56	64	72
·539	34650	34658	34666	8	16	24	32	40	48	56	64	72
·540	34729	34737	34745	8	16	24	32	40	48	56	64	72
·541	34810	34818	34826	8	16	24	32	40	48	56	64	72
·542	34890	34898	34906	8	16	24	32	40	48	56	64	72
·543	34970	34978	34986	8	16	24	32	40	48	56	64	72
·544	35051	35059	35067	8	16	24	32	40	48	56	65	73
·545	35132	35140	35148	8	16	24	32	40	48	57	65	73
·546	35213	35221	35229	8	16	24	32	41	49	57	65	73
·547	35294	35302	35310	8	16	24	32	41	49	57	65	73
·548	35375	35383	35391	8	16	24	33	41	49	57	65	73
·549	35457	35465	35473	8	16	24	33	41	49	57	65	73

E.W.D.—18*

Table of

	0	**1**	**2**	**3**	**4**	**5**	**6**
·550	35481	35489	35498	35506	35514	35522	35530
·551	35563	35571	35579	35588	35596	35604	35612
·552	35645	35653	35661	35670	35678	35686	35694
·553	35727	35735	35744	35752	35760	35768	35777
·554	35810	35818	35826	35834	35842	35851	35859
·555	35892	35900	35909	35917	35925	35933	35942
·556	35975	35983	35991	36000	36008	36016	36025
·557	36058	36066	36074	36083	36091	36099	36108
·558	36141	36149	36157	36166	36174	36182	36191
·559	36224	36232	36241	36249	36258	36266	36274
·560	36308	36316	36324	36333	36341	36350	36358
·561	36391	36400	36408	36417	36425	36433	36442
·562	36475	36484	36492	36501	36509	36517	36526
·563	36560	36568	36576	36585	36593	36601	36610
·564	36644	36652	36660	36669	36677	36686	36694
·565	36728	36737	36745	36753	36762	36770	36779
·566	36813	36821	36830	36838	36847	36855	36864
·567	36898	36906	36915	36923	36932	36940	36949
·568	36983	36991	37000	37008	37017	37025	37034
·569	37068	37076	37085	37094	37102	37110	37119
·570	37153	37162	37170	37179	37188	37196	37205
·571	37239	37248	37256	37265	37273	37282	37291
·572	37325	37333	37342	37351	37359	37368	37377
·573	37411	37420	37428	37437	37445	37454	37463
·574	37497	37506	37514	37523	37532	37540	37549
·575	37584	37592	37601	37610	37618	37627	37636
·576	37670	37679	37688	37696	37705	37714	37722
·577	37757	37766	37775	37783	37792	37801	37809
·578	37844	37853	37862	37870	37879	37888	37897
·579	37931	37940	37949	37958	37966	37975	37984
·580	38019	38028	38036	33045	38054	38063	38071
·581	38106	38115	38124	38133	38142	38150	38159
·582	38194	38203	38212	38221	38230	38238	38247
·583	38282	38291	38300	38309	38318	38327	38335
·584	38371	38380	38388	38397	38406	38415	38424
·585	38459	38468	38477	38486	38494	38503	38512
·586	38548	38557	38565	38574	38583	38592	38601
·587	38637	38646	38654	38663	38672	38681	38690
·588	38726	38735	38743	38752	38761	38770	38779
·589	38815	38824	38833	38842	38851	38860	38869
·590	38904	38913	38922	38931	38940	38949	38958
·591	38994	39003	39012	39021	39030	39039	39048
·592	39084	39093	39102	39111	39120	39129	39138
·593	39174	39183	39192	39201	39210	39219	39228
·594	39264	39273	39282	39291	39301	39310	39319
·595	39355	39364	39373	39382	39391	39400	39409
·596	39446	39455	39464	39473	39482	39491	39500
·597	39537	39546	39555	39564	39573	39582	39591
·598	39628	39637	39646	39655	39664	39673	39682
·599	39719	39728	39737	39747	39756	39765	39774

Antilogarithms *(contd.)*

	7	8	9	Mean Log. Differences								
				1	2	3	4	5	6	7	8	9
·550	35538	35547	35555	8	16	25	33	41	49	57	65	74
·551	35620	35629	35637	8	16	25	33	41	49	57	66	74
·552	35702	35711	35719	8	16	25	33	41	49	58	66	74
·553	35785	35793	35801	8	16	25	33	41	49	58	66	74
·554	35867	35876	35884	8	17	25	33	41	50	58	66	74
·555	35950	35958	35967	8	17	25	33	41	50	58	66	74
·556	36033	36041	36045	8	17	25	33	41	50	58	66	75
·557	36116	36124	36133	8	17	25	33	42	50	58	66	75
·558	36199	36208	36216	8	17	25	33	42	50	58	67	75
·559	36283	36291	36299	8	17	25	33	42	50	58	67	75
·560	36366	36375	36383	8	17	25	33	42	50	59	67	75
·561	36450	36458	36467	8	17	25	34	42	50	59	67	76
·562	36534	36542	36551	8	17	25	34	42	50	59	67	76
·563	36618	36627	36635	8	17	25	34	42	51	59	67	76
·564	36703	36711	36720	8	17	25	34	42	51	59	68	76
·565	36787	36796	36804	8	17	25	34	42	51	59	68	76
·566	36872	36881	36889	8	17	25	34	42	51	59	68	76
·567	36957	36966	36974	9	17	26	34	43	51	60	68	77
·568	37042	37051	37059	9	17	26	34	43	51	60	68	77
·569	37128	37136	37145	9	17	26	34	43	51	60	68	77
·570	37213	37222	37230	9	17	26	34	43	51	60	69	77
·571	37299	37308	37316	9	17	26	34	43	52	60	69	77
·572	37385	37394	37402	9	17	26	34	43	52	60	69	77
·573	37471	37480	37489	9	17	26	34	43	52	60	69	78
·574	37558	37566	37575	9	17	26	35	43	52	60	69	78
·575	37644	37653	37662	9	17	26	35	43	52	61	69	78
·576	37731	37740	37748	9	17	26	35	43	52	61	69	78
·577	37818	37827	37835	9	17	26	35	44	52	61	70	78
·578	37905	37914	37923	9	17	26	35	44	52	61	70	79
·579	37993	38001	38010	9	17	26	35	44	52	61	70	79
·580	38080	38089	38098	9	18	26	35	44	53	61	70	79
·581	38168	38177	38186	9	18	26	35	44	53	61	70	79
·582	38256	38265	38274	9	18	26	35	44	53	62	70	79
·583	38344	38353	38362	9	18	26	35	44	53	62	71	79
·584	38432	38441	38450	9	18	27	35	44	53	62	71	80
·585	38521	38530	38539	9	18	27	35	44	53	62	71	80
·586	38610	38619	38628	9	18	27	36	44	53	62	71	80
·587	38699	38708	38717	9	18	27	36	45	53	62	71	80
·588	38788	38797	38806	9	18	27	36	45	54	62	71	80
·589	38877	38887	38896	9	18	27	36	45	54	63	72	81
·590	38967	38976	38985	9	18	27	36	45	54	63	72	81
·591	39057	39066	39075	9	18	27	36	45	54	63	72	81
·592	39147	39156	39165	9	18	27	36	45	54	63	72	81
·593	39237	39246	39255	9	18	27	36	45	54	63	72	81
·594	39328	39337	39346	9	18	27	36	45	54	63	72	81
·595	39418	39427	39437	9	18	27	36	45	54	64	73	82
·596	39509	39518	39528	9	18	27	36	45	55	64	73	82
·597	39600	39610	39619	9	18	27	36	46	55	64	73	82
·598	39692	39701	39710	9	18	27	37	46	55	64	73	82
·599	39783	39792	39802	9	18	27	37	46	55	64	73	82

	0	1	2	3	4	5	6
·600	39811	39820	39829	39838	39847	39856	39866
·601	39902	39912	39921	39930	39939	39948	39958
·602	39994	40004	40013	40022	40031	40040	40045
·603	40087	40096	40105	40114	40123	40133	40142
·604	40179	40188	40197	40207	40216	40225	40234
·605	40272	40281	40290	40299	40309	40318	40327
·606	40364	40374	40383	40392	40402	40411	40420
·607	40457	40467	40476	40485	40495	40504	40513
·608	40551	40560	40569	40579	40588	40597	40607
·609	40644	40654	40663	40672	40682	40691	40700
·610	40738	40747	40757	40766	40775	40785	40794
·611	40832	40841	40851	40860	40869	40879	40888
·612	40926	40935	40945	40954	40964	40973	40982
·613	41020	41030	41039	41049	41058	41068	41077
·614	41115	41124	41134	41143	41153	41162	41171
·615	41210	41219	41229	41238	41248	41257	41267
·616	41305	41314	41324	41333	41343	41352	41362
·617	41400	41409	41419	41428	41438	41448	41457
·618	41495	41505	41514	41524	41533	41543	41553
·619	41591	41600	41610	41620	41629	41639	41644
·620	41687	41696	41706	41716	41725	41735	41745
·621	41783	41793	41802	41812	41821	41831	41841
·622	41879	41889	41899	41908	41918	41927	41937
·623	41976	41985	41995	42005	42014	42024	42034
·624	42073	42082	42092	42102	42111	42121	42131
·625	42170	42179	42189	42200	42208	42218	42228
·626	42267	42276	42286	42296	42306	42315	42325
·627	42364	42374	42384	42393	42403	42413	42423
·628	42462	42472	42481	42491	42501	42511	42521
·629	42560	42570	42579	42589	42599	42608	42619
·630	42658	42668	42677	42687	42697	42707	42717
·631	42756	42766	42776	42786	42796	42805	42815
·632	42855	42865	42874	42884	42894	42904	42914
·633	42953	42963	42973	42983	42993	43003	43013
·634	43053	43062	43072	43082	43092	43102	43112
·635	43152	43162	43172	43182	43192	43201	43211
·636	43251	43261	43271	43281	43291	43301	43311
·637	43351	43361	43371	43381	43391	43401	43411
·638	43451	43461	43471	43481	43491	43501	43511
·639	43551	43561	43571	43581	43591	43601	43611
·640	43651	43661	43672	43682	43692	43702	43712
·641	43752	43762	43772	43782	43792	43802	43813
·642	43853	43863	43873	43883	43893	43903	43914
·643	43954	43964	43974	43984	43995	44005	44015
·644	44055	44065	44076	44086	44096	44106	44116
·645	44157	44167	44177	44187	44198	44208	44218
·646	44259	44269	44279	44289	44299	44310	44320
·647	44361	44371	44381	44391	44402	44412	44422
·648	44463	44473	44483	44494	44504	44514	44524
·649	44565	44576	44586	44596	44607	44617	44627

Antilogarithms *(contd.)*

	7	8	9	Mean Log. Differences								
				1	2	3	4	5	6	7	8	9
·600	39875	39884	39893	9	18	28	37	46	55	64	73	83
·601	39967	39976	39985	9	18	28	37	46	55	64	74	83
·602	40059	40068	40077	9	18	28	37	46	55	65	74	83
·603	40151	40160	40170	9	18	28	37	46	55	65	74	83
·604	40244	40253	40262	9	19	28	37	46	56	65	74	83
·605	40337	40346	40355	9	19	28	37	46	56	65	74	84
·606	40423	40439	40448	9	19	28	37	47	56	65	74	84
·607	40523	40532	40541	9	19	28	37	47	56	65	75	84
·608	40616	40625	40635	9	19	28	37	47	56	65	75	84
·609	40710	40719	40728	9	19	28	37	47	56	66	75	84
·610	40804	40813	40822	9	19	28	38	47	56	66	75	85
·611	40898	40907	40916	9	19	28	38	47	56	66	75	85
·612	40992	41001	41011	9	19	28	38	47	57	66	75	85
·613	41086	41096	41105	9	19	28	38	47	57	66	76	85
·614	41181	41191	41200	9	19	28	38	47	57	66	76	85
·615	41276	41286	41295	10	19	29	38	47	57	66	76	86
·616	41371	41381	41390	10	19	29	38	48	57	67	76	86
·617	41467	41476	41486	10	19	29	38	48	57	67	76	86
·618	41562	41572	41381	10	19	29	38	48	57	67	77	86
·619	41658	41668	41677	10	19	29	38	48	57	67	77	86
·620	41754	41764	41773	10	19	29	38	48	58	67	77	87
·621	41850	41860	41870	10	19	29	39	48	58	67	77	87
·622	41947	41956	41966	10	19	29	39	48	58	68	77	87
·623	42043	42053	42063	10	19	29	39	48	58	68	77	87
·624	42140	42150	42160	10	19	29	39	48	58	68	78	87
·625	42238	42247	42257	10	19	29	39	49	58	68	78	88
·626	42335	42345	42354	10	19	29	39	49	58	68	78	88
·627	42432	42442	42452	10	20	29	39	49	59	68	78	88
·628	42530	42540	42550	10	20	29	39	49	59	69	78	88
·629	42628	42638	42648	10	20	29	39	49	59	69	78	88
·630	42727	42736	42746	10	20	30	39	49	59	69	79	88
·631	42825	42835	42845	10	20	30	39	49	59	69	79	89
·632	42924	42934	42944	10	20	30	40	49	59	69	79	89
·633	43023	43033	43043	10	20	30	40	50	59	69	79	89
·634	43122	43132	43142	10	20	30	40	50	60	69	79	89
·635	43221	43231	43241	10	20	30	40	50	60	70	80	90
·636	43321	43331	43341	10	20	30	40	50	60	70	80	90
·637	43421	43431	43441	10	20	30	40	50	60	70	80	90
·638	43521	43531	43541	10	20	30	40	50	60	70	80	90
·639	43621	43631	43641	10	20	30	40	50	60	70	80	90
·640	43722	43732	43742	10	20	30	40	50	60	70	80	91
·641	43823	43833	43843	10	20	30	40	50	61	71	81	91
·642	43924	43934	43944	10	20	30	40	51	61	71	81	91
·643	44025	44035	44045	10	20	30	41	51	61	71	81	91
·644	44126	44137	44147	10	20	30	41	51	61	71	81	91
·645	44228	44238	44249	10	20	31	41	51	61	71	81	92
·646	44330	44340	44351	10	20	31	41	51	61	71	82	92
·647	44432	44443	44453	10	20	31	41	51	61	72	82	92
·648	44535	44545	44555	10	20	31	41	51	62	72	82	92
·649	44637	44648	44658	10	21	31	41	51	62	72	82	92

	0	1	2	3	4	5	6
·650	44668	44679	44689	44699	44709	44720	44730
·651	44771	44782	44792	44802	44812	44823	44833
·652	44874	44885	44895	44905	44916	44926	44936
·653	44978	44988	44999	45009	45019	45030	45040
·654	45082	45092	45102	45113	45123	45133	45144
·655	45185	45196	45206	45217	45227	45237	45248
·656	45289	45300	45310	45321	45331	45342	45352
·657	45394	45404	45415	45425	45436	45446	45457
·658	45499	45509	45520	45530	45541	45551	45562
·659	45604	45614	45625	45635	45646	45656	45667
·660	45709	45719	45730	45740	45751	45761	45772
·661	45814	45825	45835	45846	45856	45867	45877
·662	45920	45930	45941	45951	45962	45973	45983
·663	46026	46036	46047	46057	46068	46079	46089
·664	46132	46142	46153	46163	46174	46185	46195
·665	46238	46249	46259	46270	46281	46291	46302
·666	46345	46355	46366	46377	46387	46398	46409
·667	46451	46462	46473	46483	46494	46505	46515
·668	46559	46569	46580	46591	46601	46612	46623
·669	46666	46677	46687	46698	46709	46720	46730
·670	46773	46784	46795	46806	46816	46827	46838
·671	46881	46892	46903	46914	46924	46935	46946
·672	46989	47000	47011	47022	47033	47043	47054
·673	47098	47108	47119	47130	47141	47152	47163
·674	47206	47217	47228	47239	47250	47261	47271
·675	47315	47326	47337	47348	47359	47370	47380
·676	47424	47345	47446	47457	47468	47479	47490
·677	47533	47544	47555	47566	47577	47588	47599
·678	47643	47654	47665	47676	47687	47698	47709
·679	47753	47764	47775	47786	47797	47808	47819
·680	47863	47874	47885	47896	47907	47918	47929
·681	47973	47984	47995	48006	48017	48028	48040
·682	48084	48095	48106	48117	48128	48139	48150
·683	48195	48206	48217	48228	48239	48250	48261
·684	48306	48317	48328	48339	48350	48361	48373
·685	48417	48428	48439	48451	48462	48473	48484
·686	48529	48540	48551	48562	48573	48585	48596
·687	48641	48652	48663	48674	48685	48697	48708
·688	48753	48764	48775	48786	48798	48809	48820
·689	48865	48876	48888	48899	48910	48921	48933
·690	48978	48989	49000	49012	49023	49034	49045
·691	49091	49102	49113	49125	49136	49147	49159
·692	49204	49215	49226	49238	49249	49260	49272
·693	49317	49329	49340	49351	49363	49374	49385
·694	49431	49442	49454	49465	49476	49488	49499
·695	49545	49556	49568	49579	49591	49602	49613
·696	49659	49671	49682	49693	49705	49716	49728
·697	49774	49785	49796	49808	49819	49831	49842
·698	49888	49900	49911	49923	49934	49946	49957
·699	50003	50015	50026	50038	50049	50061	50072

Antilogarithms (contd.)

	7	8	9	Mean Log. Differences								
				1	2	3	4	5	6	7	8	9
·650	44740	44751	44761	10	21	31	41	51	62	72	82	93
·651	44843	44854	44864	10	21	31	41	52	62	72	83	93
·652	44947	44957	44967	10	21	31	41	52	62	72	83	93
·653	45050	45061	45071	10	21	31	41	52	62	73	83	93
·654	45154	45165	45175	10	21	31	42	52	62	73	83	93
·655	45258	45269	45279	10	21	31	42	52	63	73	83	94
·656	45363	45373	45384	10	21	31	42	52	63	73	84	94
·657	45467	45478	45888	10	21	31	42	52	63	73	84	94
·658	45572	45583	45593	10	21	31	42	52	63	73	84	94
·659	45677	45688	45698	11	21	32	42	53	63	74	84	95
·660	45782	45793	45803	11	21	32	42	53	63	74	84	95
·661	45888	45899	45909	11	21	32	42	53	63	74	84	95
·662	45994	46004	46015	11	21	32	42	53	64	74	85	95
·663	46100	46110	46121	11	21	32	42	53	64	74	85	95
·664	46206	46217	46227	11	21	32	43	53	64	74	85	96
·665	46313	46323	46334	11	21	32	43	53	64	75	85	96
·666	46419	46430	46441	11	21	32	43	53	64	75	85	96
·667	46526	46537	46548	11	21	32	43	54	64	75	86	96
·668	46634	46644	46655	11	21	32	43	54	64	75	86	97
·669	46741	46752	46763	11	22	32	43	54	65	75	86	97
·670	46849	46860	46870	11	22	32	43	54	65	75	86	97
·671	46957	46968	46978	11	22	32	43	54	65	76	86	97
·672	47065	47076	47087	11	22	32	43	54	65	76	87	97
·673	47174	47184	47195	11	22	33	43	54	65	76	87	98
·674	47282	47293	47304	11	22	33	44	54	65	76	87	98
·675	47391	47402	47413	11	22	33	44	55	65	76	87	98
·676	47501	47511	47522	11	22	33	44	55	66	77	87	98
·677	47610	47621	47632	11	22	33	44	55	66	77	88	99
·678	47720	47731	47742	11	22	33	44	55	66	77	88	99
·679	47830	47841	47852	11	22	33	44	55	66	77	88	99
·680	47940	47951	47962	11	22	33	44	55	66	77	88	99
·681	48051	48062	48073	11	22	33	44	55	66	77	88	100
·682	48161	48173	48184	11	22	33	44	55	67	78	89	100
·683	48272	48284	48295	11	22	33	44	56	67	78	89	100
·684	48384	48395	48406	11	22	33	45	56	67	78	89	100
·685	48495	48506	48518	11	22	34	45	56	67	78	89	101
·686	48607	48618	48629	11	22	34	45	56	67	78	89	101
·687	48719	48730	48742	11	22	34	45	56	67	78	90	101
·688	48831	48843	48854	11	22	34	45	56	67	79	90	101
·689	48944	48955	48967	11	23	34	45	56	68	79	90	101
·690	49057	49068	49079	11	23	34	45	56	68	79	90	102
·691	49170	49181	49192	11	23	34	45	57	68	79	91	102
·692	49283	49295	49306	11	23	34	45	57	68	79	91	102
·693	49397	49408	49420	11	23	34	45	57	68	80	91	102
·694	49511	49522	49533	11	23	34	46	57	68	80	91	103
·695	49625	49636	49648	11	23	34	46	57	69	80	91	103
·696	49739	49751	49762	11	23	34	46	57	69	80	92	103
·697	49854	49865	49877	11	23	34	46	57	69	80	92	103
·698	49969	49980	49992	12	23	35	46	58	69	81	92	104
·699	50084	50096	50107	12	23	35	46	58	69	81	92	104

	0	1	2	3	4	5	6
·700	50119	50130	50142	50153	50165	50176	50188
·701	50234	50246	50257	50269	50280	50292	50304
·702	50350	50362	50373	50385	50396	50408	50420
·703	50466	50478	50489	50501	50512	50524	50536
·704	50582	50594	50606	50617	50629	50641	50652
·705	50699	50711	50722	50734	50746	50757	50769
·706	50816	50828	50839	50851	50863	50874	50886
·707	50933	50945	50956	50968	50980	50992	51003
·708	51050	51062	51074	51096	51097	51109	51121
·709	51168	51180	51192	51203	51215	51227	51239
·710	51286	51298	51310	51321	51333	51345	51357
·711	51404	51416	51428	51440	51452	51463	51475
·712	51523	51535	51546	51558	51570	51582	51594
·713	51641	51653	51665	51677	51689	51701	51713
·714	51761	51772	51784	51796	51808	51820	51832
·715	51880	51892	51904	51916	51928	51940	51952
·716	51999	52011	52023	52035	52047	52059	52071
·717	52119	52131	52143	52155	52167	52179	52191
·718	52239	52251	52264	52276	52288	52300	52312
·719	52360	52372	52384	52396	52408	52420	52432
·720	52481	52493	52505	52517	52529	52541	52553
·721	52602	52614	52626	52638	52650	52662	52674
·722	52723	52735	52747	52759	52771	52784	52796
·723	52844	52857	52869	52881	52893	52905	52917
·724	52966	52978	52991	53003	53015	53027	53039
·725	53088	53101	53113	53125	53137	53149	53162
·726	53211	53223	53235	53247	53260	53272	53824
·727	53333	53346	53358	53370	53382	53395	53407
·728	53456	53469	53481	53493	53506	53518	53530
·729	53580	53592	53604	53617	53629	53641	53654
·730	53703	53715	53728	53740	53753	53765	53777
·731	53827	53839	53852	53864	53876	53889	53901
·732	53951	53963	53976	53988	54001	54013	54025
·733	54075	54088	54100	54113	54125	54138	54150
·734	54200	54212	54225	54237	54250	54262	54275
·735	54325	54337	54350	54362	54375	54387	54400
·736	54450	54463	54475	54488	54500	54513	54525
·737	54576	54588	54601	54613	54626	54639	54651
·738	54701	54714	54727	54739	54752	54764	54777
·739	54828	54840	54853	54865	54878	54891	54903
·740	54954	54967	54979	54992	55005	55017	55030
·741	55081	55093	55106	55119	55131	55144	55157
·742	55208	55220	55233	55246	55259	55271	55284
·743	55335	55348	55360	55373	55386	55399	55411
·744	55462	55475	55488	55501	55514	55526	55539
·745	55590	55603	55616	55629	55641	55654	55667
·746	55718	55731	55744	55757	55770	55783	55795
·747	55847	55860	55873	55885	55898	55911	55924
·748	55976	55989	56001	56014	56027	56040	56053
·749	56105	56118	56130	56143	56156	56169	56182

Antilogarithms *(contd.)*

	7	8	9	Mean Log. Differences								
				1	2	3	4	5	6	7	8	9
·700	50200	50211	50223	12	23	35	46	58	69	81	92	104
·701	50315	50327	50338	12	23	35	46	58	69	81	93	104
·702	50431	50443	50454	12	23	35	46	58	70	81	93	104
·703	50547	50559	50571	12	23	35	47	58	70	81	93	105
·704	50664	50676	50687	12	23	35	47	58	70	82	93	105
·705	50781	50792	50804	12	23	35	47	58	70	82	93	105
·706	50898	50910	50921	12	23	35	47	59	70	82	94	105
·707	51015	51027	51039	12	23	35	47	59	70	82	94	106
·708	51133	51144	51156	12	24	35	47	59	71	82	94	106
·709	51251	51262	51274	12	24	35	47	59	71	83	94	106
·710	51369	51381	51392	12	24	35	47	59	71	83	95	106
·711	51487	51499	51511	12	24	36	48	59	71	83	95	107
·712	51606	51618	51630	12	24	36	48	59	71	83	95	107
·713	51725	51737	51749	12	24	36	48	60	71	83	95	107
·714	51844	51856	51868	12	24	36	48	60	72	84	95	107
·715	51964	51976	51987	12	24	36	48	60	72	84	96	108
·716	52083	52095	52107	12	24	36	48	60	72	84	96	108
·717	52203	52215	52227	12	24	36	48	60	72	84	96	108
·718	52324	52336	52348	12	24	36	48	60	72	84	96	108
·719	52444	52456	52469	12	24	36	48	60	72	84	97	109
·720	52565	52577	52589	12	24	36	48	60	73	85	97	109
·721	52686	52699	52711	12	24	36	49	61	73	85	97	109
·722	52808	52820	52832	12	24	36	49	61	73	85	97	109
·723	52930	52942	52954	12	24	37	49	61	73	85	97	110
·724	53052	53064	53076	12	24	37	49	61	73	85	98	110
·725	53174	53186	53198	12	24	37	49	61	73	86	98	110
·726	53297	53309	53321	12	25	37	49	61	74	86	98	110
·727	53419	53432	53444	12	25	37	49	61	74	86	98	111
·728	53543	53555	53567	12	25	37	49	62	74	86	99	111
·729	53666	53678	53691	12	25	37	49	62	74	86	99	111
·730	53790	53802	53814	12	25	37	50	62	74	87	99	111
·731	53914	53926	53938	12	25	37	50	62	74	87	99	112
·732	54038	54050	54063	12	25	37	50	62	75	87	99	112
·733	54163	54175	54187	12	25	37	50	62	75	87	100	112
·734	54287	54300	54312	12	25	37	50	62	75	87	100	112
·735	54413	54425	54438	13	25	38	50	63	75	88	100	113
·736	54538	54551	54563	13	25	38	50	63	75	88	100	113
·737	54664	54676	54689	13	25	38	50	63	75	88	101	113
·738	54790	54802	54815	13	25	38	50	63	76	88	101	113
·739	54916	54929	54941	13	25	38	51	63	76	88	101	114
·740	55043	55055	55068	13	25	38	51	63	76	89	101	114
·741	55169	55182	55195	13	25	38	51	63	76	89	102	114
·742	55297	55309	55322	13	25	38	51	64	76	89	102	115
·743	55424	55437	55450	13	26	38	51	64	77	89	102	115
·744	55552	55565	55577	13	26	38	51	64	77	89	102	115
·745	55680	55693	55706	13	26	38	51	64	77	90	103	115
·746	55808	55821	55834	13	26	39	51	64	77	90	103	116
·747	55937	55950	55963	13	26	39	51	64	77	90	103	116
·748	56066	56079	56092	13	26	39	52	65	77	90	103	116
·749	56195	56208	56221	13	26	39	52	65	78	91	103	116

	0	1	2	3	4	5	6
·750	56234	56247	56260	56273	56286	56299	56312
·751	56364	56377	56390	56403	56416	56429	56442
·752	56494	56507	56520	56533	56546	56559	56572
·753	56624	56637	56650	56663	56676	56689	56702
·754	56754	56767	56780	56794	56807	56820	56833
·755	56885	56898	56911	56925	56938	56951	56964
·756	57016	57029	57043	57056	57069	57082	57095
·757	57148	57161	57174	57187	57200	57214	57227
·758	57280	57293	57306	57319	57332	57345	57359
·759	57411	57425	57438	57451	57464	57478	57491
·760	57544	57557	57570	57584	57597	57610	57623
·761	57676	57690	57703	57716	57730	57743	57756
·762	57809	57823	57836	57850	57863	57876	57890
·763	57943	57956	57970	57983	57996	58010	58023
·764	58076	58090	58103	58116	58130	58143	58157
·765	58210	58224	58337	58250	58264	58277	58291
·766	58344	58358	58371	58385	58398	58412	58425
·767	58479	58492	58506	58519	58533	58546	58560
·768	58614	58627	58641	58654	58668	58681	58695
·769	58749	58762	58776	58789	58803	58816	58830
·770	58884	58898	58911	58925	58939	58952	58966
·771	59020	59034	59047	59061	59074	59088	59102
·772	59156	59170	59183	59197	59211	59224	59238
·773	59292	59306	59320	59333	59347	59361	59374
·774	59429	59443	59456	59470	59484	59498	59511
·775	59566	59580	59594	59607	59621	59635	59649
·776	59703	59717	59731	59745	59758	59772	59786
·777	59841	59855	59869	59882	59896	59910	59924
·778	59979	59993	60007	60020	60034	60048	60062
·779	60117	60131	60145	60159	60173	60187	60200
·780	60256	60270	60284	60297	60311	60325	60339
·781	60395	60409	60423	60436	60450	60464	60478
·782	60534	60548	60562	60576	60590	60604	60618
·783	60673	60687	60701	60715	60729	60743	60757
·784	60813	60827	60841	60855	60869	60883	60897
·785	60954	60968	60982	60996	61010	61024	61038
·786	61094	61108	61122	61136	61150	61164	61179
·787	61235	61249	61263	61277	61291	61305	61320
·788	61376	61390	61404	61419	61433	61447	61461
·789	61518	61532	61546	61560	61574	61588	61603
·790	61659	61674	61688	61702	61716	61730	61745
·791	61801	61816	61830	61844	61859	61873	61887
·792	61944	61958	61972	61987	62001	62015	62030
·793	62087	62101	62115	62130	62144	62158	62173
·794	62230	62244	62259	62273	62287	62302	62316
·795	62373	62388	62402	62416	62431	62445	62460
·796	62517	62532	62546	62560	62575	62589	62604
·797	62661	62676	62690	62705	62719	62733	62748
·798	62806	62820	62835	62849	62864	62878	62893
·799	62950	62965	62980	62994	63009	63023	63038

Antilogarithms *(contd.)*

	7	8	9	Mean Log. Differences								
				1	2	3	4	5	6	7	8	9
·750	56325	56338	56351	13	26	39	52	65	78	91	104	117
·751	56455	56468	56481	13	26	39	52	65	78	91	104	117
·752	56585	56598	56611	13	26	39	52	65	78	91	104	117
·753	56715	56728	56741	13	26	39	52	65	78	91	104	117
·754	56846	56859	56872	13	26	39	52	65	78	92	105	118
·755	56977	56990	57003	13	26	39	52	66	79	92	105	118
·756	57108	57121	57135	13	26	39	53	66	79	92	105	118
·757	57240	57253	57266	13	26	40	53	66	79	92	105	119
·758	57372	57385	57398	13	26	40	53	66	79	92	106	119
·759	57504	57517	57531	13	26	40	53	66	79	93	106	119
·760	57637	57650	57663	13	27	40	53	66	80	93	106	119
·761	57770	57783	57796	13	27	40	53	66	80	93	106	120
·762	57903	57916	57929	13	27	40	53	67	80	93	107	120
·763	58036	58050	58063	13	27	40	53	67	80	93	107	120
·764	58170	58183	58197	13	27	40	54	67	80	94	107	121
·765	58304	58317	58331	13	27	40	54	67	81	94	107	121
·766	58438	58452	58465	13	27	40	54	67	81	94	108	121
·767	58573	58587	58600	13	27	40	54	67	81	94	108	121
·768	58708	58722	58735	14	27	41	54	68	81	95	108	122
·769	58844	58857	58871	14	27	41	54	68	81	95	108	122
·770	58979	58993	59006	14	27	41	54	68	81	95	109	122
·771	59115	59129	59142	14	27	41	54	68	82	95	109	122
·772	59251	59265	59279	14	27	41	55	68	82	95	109	123
·773	59388	59402	59415	14	27	41	55	68	82	96	109	123
·774	59525	59539	59552	14	27	41	55	68	82	96	110	123
·775	59662	59676	59690	14	27	41	55	69	82	96	110	124
·776	59800	59813	59827	14	28	41	55	69	83	96	110	124
·777	59938	59951	59965	14	28	41	55	69	83	97	110	124
·778	60076	60090	60103	14	28	41	55	69	83	97	111	124
·779	60214	60228	60242	14	28	42	55	69	83	97	111	125
·780	60353	60367	60381	14	28	42	56	69	83	97	111	125
·781	60492	60506	60520	14	28	42	56	70	84	97	111	125
·782	60632	60646	60660	14	28	42	56	70	84	98	112	126
·783	60771	60785	60799	14	28	42	56	70	84	98	112	126
·784	60911	60925	60939	14	28	42	56	70	84	98	112	126
·785	61052	61066	61080	14	28	42	56	70	84	98	112	126
·786	61193	61207	61221	14	28	42	56	70	84	99	113	127
·787	61334	61348	61362	14	28	42	56	71	85	99	113	127
·788	61475	61489	61503	14	28	42	57	71	85	99	113	127
·789	61617	61631	61645	14	28	43	57	71	85	99	113	128
·790	61759	61773	61787	14	28	43	57	71	85	99	114	128
·791	61901	61915	61930	14	28	43	57	71	85	100	114	128
·792	62044	62058	62072	14	29	43	57	71	86	100	114	129
·793	62187	62201	62216	14	29	43	57	72	86	100	114	129
·794	62330	62345	62359	14	29	43	57	72	86	100	115	129
·795	62474	62488	62503	14	29	43	58	72	86	101	115	129
·796	62618	62632	62647	14	29	43	58	72	86	101	115	130
·797	62762	62777	62791	14	29	43	58	72	87	101	116	130
·798	62907	62921	62936	14	29	43	58	72	87	101	116	130
·799	63052	63067	63081	15	29	44	58	73	87	102	116	131

	0	1	2	3	4	5	6
·800	63096	63110	63125	63139	63154	63168	63183
·801	63241	63256	63270	63285	63299	63314	63328
·802	63387	63401	63416	63431	63445	63460	63474
·803	63533	63548	63562	63577	63591	63606	63621
·804	63680	63694	63709	63723	63738	63753	63767
·805	63826	63841	63856	63870	63885	63900	63914
·806	63973	63988	64003	64018	64032	64047	64062
·807	64121	64136	64150	64165	64180	64195	64209
·808	64269	64283	64298	64313	64328	64343	64357
·809	64417	64432	64446	64461	64476	64491	64506
·810	64565	64580	64595	64610	64625	64640	64655
·811	64714	64729	64744	64759	64774	64789	64804
·812	64863	64878	64893	64908	64923	64938	64953
·813	65013	65028	65043	65058	65073	65088	65103
·814	65163	65178	65193	65208	65223	65238	65253
·815	65313	65328	65343	65358	65373	65388	65403
·816	65463	65479	65494	65509	65524	65539	65554
·817	65614	65630	65644	65660	65675	65690	65705
·818	65766	65781	65796	65811	65826	65841	65857
·819	65917	65932	65948	65963	65978	65993	66008
·820	66069	66084	66100	66115	66130	66145	66161
·821	66222	66237	66252	66267	66283	66298	66313
·822	66374	66389	66405	66420	66435	66451	66466
·823	66527	66542	66558	66573	66589	66604	66619
·824	66681	66696	66711	66727	66742	66757	66773
·825	66834	66850	66865	66880	66896	66911	66927
·826	66988	67004	67019	67035	67050	67065	67081
·827	67143	67158	67170	67189	67205	67220	67236
·828	67298	67313	67329	67344	67360	67375	67391
·829	67453	67468	67484	67499	67515	67530	67546
·830	67608	67624	67639	67655	67670	67686	67702
·831	67764	67780	67795	67811	67826	67842	67858
·832	67920	67936	67951	67967	67983	67998	68014
·833	68077	68092	68108	68124	68140	68155	68171
·834	68234	68249	68265	68281	68297	68312	68328
·835	68391	68407	68423	68438	68454	68470	68486
·836	68549	68564	68580	68596	68612	68628	68643
·837	68707	68723	68738	68754	68770	68786	68802
·838	68865	68881	68897	68913	68929	68944	68960
·839	69024	69040	69056	69072	69087	69103	69119
·840	69183	69199	69215	69231	69247	69263	69279
·841	69342	69358	69374	69390	69406	69422	69438
·842	69502	69518	69534	69550	69566	69582	69598
·843	69663	69679	69695	69711	69727	69743	69759
·844	69823	69839	69855	69871	69887	69904	69920
·845	69984	70000	70016	70032	70049	70065	70081
·846	70145	70162	70178	70194	70210	70226	70242
·847	70307	70323	70339	70356	70372	70388	70404
·848	70469	70485	70502	70518	70534	70550	70567
·849	70632	70648	70664	70680	70697	70713	70729

Antilogarithms (*contd.*)

	7	8	9	Mean Log. Differences								
				1	2	3	4	5	6	7	8	9
·800	63197	63212	63226	15	29	44	58	73	87	102	116	131
·801	63343	63358	63372	15	29	44	58	73	87	102	117	131
·802	63489	63504	63518	15	29	44	58	73	88	102	117	132
·803	63635	63650	63665	15	29	44	59	73	88	103	117	132
·804	63782	63797	63812	15	29	44	59	73	88	103	117	132
·805	63929	63944	63959	15	29	44	59	74	88	103	118	132
·806	64077	64091	64106	15	29	44	59	74	88	103	118	133
·807	64224	64239	64254	15	30	44	59	74	89	103	118	133
·808	64372	64387	64402	15	30	44	59	74	89	104	119	133
·809	64521	64536	64550	15	30	45	59	74	89	104	119	134
·810	64669	64684	64699	15	30	45	60	74	89	104	119	134
·811	64819	64833	64848	15	30	45	60	75	89	104	119	134
·812	64968	64983	64998	15	30	45	60	75	90	105	120	135
·813	65118	65133	65148	15	30	45	60	75	90	105	120	135
·814	65268	65283	65298	15	30	45	60	75	90	105	120	135
·815	65418	65433	65448	15	30	45	60	75	90	105	120	135
·816	65569	65584	65599	15	30	45	60	75	91	106	121	136
·817	65720	65735	65750	15	30	45	61	76	91	106	121	136
·818	65872	65887	65902	15	30	45	61	76	91	106	121	136
·819	66024	66039	66054	15	30	46	61	76	91	106	122	137
·820	66176	66191	66206	15	30	46	61	76	91	107	122	137
·821	66328	66344	66359	15	31	46	61	76	92	107	122	137
·822	66481	66497	66512	15	31	46	61	77	92	107	122	138
·823	66634	66650	66665	15	31	46	61	77	92	107	123	138
·824	66788	66803	66819	15	31	46	61	77	92	108	123	138
·825	66942	66957	66973	15	31	46	62	77	92	108	123	139
·826	67096	67112	67127	15	31	46	62	77	93	108	124	139
·827	67251	67267	67282	15	31	46	62	77	93	108	124	139
·828	67406	67422	67437	16	31	47	62	78	93	109	124	140
·829	67561	67577	67593	16	31	47	62	78	93	109	124	140
·830	67717	67733	67748	16	31	47	62	78	94	109	125	140
·831	67873	67889	67905	16	31	47	62	78	94	109	125	141
·832	68030	68045	68061	16	31	47	63	78	94	110	125	141
·833	68187	68202	68218	16	31	47	63	78	94	110	126	141
·834	68344	68360	68375	16	31	47	63	79	94	110	126	142
·835	68501	68517	68533	16	32	47	63	79	95	110	126	142
·836	68659	68675	68691	16	32	47	63	79	95	111	126	142
·837	68818	68833	68849	16	32	48	63	79	95	111	127	143
·838	68976	68992	69008	16	32	48	64	79	95	111	127	143
·839	69135	69151	69167	16	32	48	64	80	95	111	127	143
·840	69295	69311	69326	16	32	48	64	80	96	112	128	144
·841	69454	69470	69486	16	32	48	64	80	96	112	128	144
·842	69614	69630	69646	16	32	48	64	80	96	112	128	144
·843	69775	69791	69807	16	32	48	64	80	96	112	128	144
·844	69936	69952	69968	16	32	48	64	80	97	113	129	145
·845	70097	70113	70129	16	32	48	65	81	97	113	129	145
·846	70259	70275	70291	16	32	49	65	81	97	113	129	146
·847	70420	70437	70453	16	32	49	65	81	97	113	130	146
·848	70583	70599	70615	16	32	49	65	81	97	114	130	146
·849	70746	70762	70778	16	33	49	65	81	98	114	130	147

Table of

	0	1	2	3	4	5	6
·850	70794	70811	70827	70843	70860	70876	70892
·851	70958	70974	70990	71007	71023	71039	71056
·852	71121	71138	71154	71170	71187	71203	71220
·853	71285	71308	71318	71334	71351	71367	71384
·854	71450	71466	71482	71499	71515	71532	71548
·855	71614	71631	71647	71664	71680	71697	71713
·856	71779	71796	71812	71829	71845	71862	71879
·857	71945	71961	71978	71994	72011	72028	72044
·858	72111	72127	72144	72160	72177	72194	72210
·859	72277	72293	72310	72327	72343	72360	72377
·860	72443	72460	72477	72494	72510	72527	72544
·861	72610	72627	72644	72661	72677	72694	72711
·862	72778	72795	72811	72828	72845	72862	72879
·863	72946	72962	72979	72996	73013	73030	73046
·864	73114	73131	73147	73164	73181	73198	73215
·865	73282	73299	73316	73333	73350	73367	73384
·866	73451	73468	73485	73502	73519	73536	73553
·867	73621	73638	73654	73671	73688	73705	73722
·868	73790	73807	73894	73841	73858	73875	73892
·869	73960	73977	73994	74011	74029	74046	74063
·870	74131	74148	74165	74182	74199	74216	74233
·871	74302	74319	74336	74353	74370	74387	74404
·872	74473	74490	74507	74525	74542	74559	74576
·873	74645	74662	74679	74696	74714	74731	74748
·874	74817	74834	74851	74868	74886	74903	74920
·875	74989	75007	75024	75041	75058	75076	75093
·876	75162	75179	75197	75214	75231	75249	75266
·877	75335	75353	75370	75387	75405	75422	75440
·878	75509	75526	75544	75561	75579	75596	75613
·879	75683	75701	75718	75735	75753	75770	75788
·880	75858	75875	75893	75910	75928	75945	75962
·881	76032	76050	76068	76085	76103	76120	76138
·882	76208	76225	76243	76260	76278	76296	76313
·883	76384	76401	76419	76436	76454	76471	76489
·884	76560	76577	76595	76612	76630	76648	76665
·885	76736	76754	76771	76789	76807	76824	76842
·886	76913	76931	76948	76966	76984	77001	77019
·887	77090	77108	77126	77143	77161	77179	77197
·888	77268	77286	77303	77321	77339	77357	77375
·889	77446	77464	77482	77500	77517	77535	77553
·890	77625	77642	77660	77678	77696	77714	77732
·891	77804	77821	77839	77857	77875	77893	77911
·892	77983	78001	78019	78037	78055	78073	78091
·893	78163	78181	78199	78217	78235	78253	78271
·894	78343	78361	78379	78397	78415	78433	78451
·895	78523	78541	78560	78578	78596	78614	78632
·896	78704	78723	78741	78759	78777	78795	78813
·897	78886	78904	78922	78940	78959	78977	78995
·898	79068	79086	79104	79122	79141	79159	79177
·899	79250	79268	79286	79305	79323	79341	79360

Antilogarithms (*contd.*)

	7	8	9	Mean Log. Differences								
				1	2	3	4	5	6	7	8	9
·850	70909	70925	70941	16	33	49	65	82	98	114	131	147
·851	71072	71088	71105	16	33	49	65	82	98	115	131	147
·852	71236	71252	71269	16	33	49	66	82	98	115	131	148
·853	71400	71417	71433	16	33	49	66	82	99	115	131	148
·854	71565	71581	71598	16	33	49	66	82	99	115	132	148
·855	71730	71746	71763	17	33	50	66	83	99	116	132	149
·856	71895	71912	71928	17	33	50	66	83	99	116	132	149
·857	72061	72077	72094	17	33	50	66	83	100	116	133	149
·858	72227	72244	72260	17	33	50	67	83	100	116	133	150
·859	72394	72410	72427	17	33	50	67	83	100	117	133	150
·860	72560	72577	72594	17	33	50	67	83	100	117	134	150
·861	72728	72744	72761	17	33	50	67	84	100	117	134	151
·862	72895	72912	72929	17	34	50	67	84	101	117	134	151
·863	73063	73080	73097	17	34	50	67	84	101	118	134	151
·864	73232	73249	73265	17	34	51	67	84	101	118	135	152
·865	73401	73417	73434	17	34	51	68	84	101	118	135	152
·866	73570	73587	73604	17	34	51	68	85	102	119	135	152
·867	73739	73756	73773	17	34	51	68	85	102	119	136	153
·868	73909	73926	73943	17	34	51	68	85	102	119	136	153
·869	74080	74097	74114	17	34	51	68	85	102	119	136	153
·870	74250	74268	74285	17	34	51	68	85	103	120	137	154
·871	74422	74439	74456	17	34	51	69	86	103	120	137	154
·872	74593	74610	74628	17	34	52	69	86	103	120	137	155
·873	74765	74782	74800	17	34	52	69	86	103	120	138	155
·874	74937	74955	74972	17	34	52	69	86	103	121	138	155
·875	75110	75128	75145	17	35	52	69	86	104	121	138	156
·876	75283	75301	75318	17	35	52	69	87	104	121	139	156
·877	75457	75474	75492	17	35	52	69	87	104	122	139	156
·878	75631	75648	75666	17	35	52	70	87	104	122	139	157
·879	75805	75823	75840	17	35	52	70	87	105	122	140	157
·880	75980	75997	76015	17	35	52	70	87	105	122	140	157
·881	76155	76173	76190	18	35	53	70	88	105	123	140	158
·882	76331	76348	76366	18	35	53	70	88	105	123	141	158
·883	76507	76524	76542	18	35	53	70	88	106	123	141	158
·884	76683	76701	76718	18	35	53	71	88	106	123	141	159
·885	76860	76877	76895	18	35	53	71	88	106	124	142	159
·886	77037	77055	77072	18	35	53	71	89	106	124	142	160
·887	77215	77232	77250	18	36	53	71	89	107	124	142	160
·888	77393	77410	77428	18	36	53	71	89	107	125	142	160
·889	77571	77589	77607	18	36	54	71	89	107	125	143	161
·890	77750	77768	77786	18	36	54	72	89	107	125	143	161
·891	77929	77947	77965	18	36	54	72	90	108	126	143	161
·892	78109	78127	78145	18	36	54	72	90	108	126	144	162
·893	78289	78307	78325	18	36	54	72	90	108	126	144	162
·894	78469	78487	78505	18	36	54	72	90	108	126	144	163
·895	78650	78668	78686	18	36	54	72	91	109	127	145	163
·896	78831	78850	78868	18	36	54	73	91	109	127	145	163
·897	79013	79031	79050	18	36	55	73	91	109	127	145	164
·898	79195	79213	79232	18	36	55	73	91	109	128	146	164
·899	79378	79396	79414	18	37	55	73	91	110	128	146	164

	0	1	2	3	4	5	6
·900	79433	79451	79469	79488	79506	79524	79542
·901	79616	79634	79652	79671	79689	79707	79726
·902	79799	79818	79836	79854	79873	79891	79910
·903	79983	80002	80020	80039	80057	80075	80094
·904	80168	80186	80205	80223	80242	80260	80278
·905	80352	80371	80389	80408	80427	80445	80464
·906	80538	80556	80575	80593	80612	80630	80649
·907	80723	80742	80761	80779	80798	80816	80835
·908	80909	80928	80947	80965	80984	81003	81021
·909	81096	81115	81133	81152	81171	81189	81208
·910	81283	81302	81320	81339	81358	81377	81395
·911	81470	81489	81508	81527	81545	81564	81583
·912	81658	81677	81696	81715	81733	81752	81771
·913	81846	81865	81884	81903	81922	81941	81959
·914	82035	82054	82073	82092	82111	82130	82148
·915	82224	82243	82262	82281	82300	82319	82338
·916	82414	82433	82452	82471	82490	82508	82528
·917	82604	82623	82642	82661	82680	82699	82718
·918	82794	82813	82832	82851	82870	82890	82909
·919	82985	83004	83023	83042	83061	83081	83100
·920	83176	83195	83215	83234	83253	83272	83291
·921	83368	83387	83406	83426	83445	83464	83483
·922	83560	83579	83599	83618	83637	83656	83676
·923	83753	83772	83791	83812	83830	83849	83869
·924	83946	83965	83985	84004	84023	84043	84062
·925	84139	84159	84178	84198	84217	84236	84256
·926	84333	84353	84372	84392	84411	84430	84450
·927	84528	84547	84567	84586	84606	84625	84645
·928	84723	84742	84762	84781	84801	84820	84840
·929	84918	84937	84957	84977	84996	85016	85035
·930	85114	85133	85153	85172	85192	85212	85231
·931	85310	85330	85349	85369	85389	85408	85428
·932	85507	85526	85546	85566	85585	85605	85625
·933	85704	85723	85743	85763	85783	85802	85822
·934	85901	85921	85941	85961	85980	86000	86020
·935	86099	86119	86139	86159	86179	86198	86218
·936	86298	86318	86337	86357	86377	86397	86417
·937	86497	86517	86536	86556	86576	86596	86616
·938	86696	86716	86736	86756	86776	86796	86816
·939	86896	86916	86936	86956	86976	86996	87016
·940	87096	87116	87136	87156	87176	87197	87217
·941	87297	87317	87337	87357	87377	87398	87418
·942	87498	87518	87539	87559	87579	87599	87619
·943	87700	87720	87740	87760	87781	87801	87821
·944	87902	87922	87943	87963	87983	88003	88024
·945	88105	88125	88145	88166	88186	88206	88227
·946	88308	88328	88349	88369	88389	88410	88430
·947	88511	88532	88552	88573	88593	88613	88634
·948	88715	88736	88756	88777	88797	88818	88838
·949	88920	88940	88961	88981	89002	89022	89043

Antilogarithms (contd.)

	7	8	9	Mean Log. Differences								
				1	2	3	4	5	6	7	8	9
·900	79561	79579	79597	18	37	55	73	92	110	128	146	165
·901	79744	79763	79781	18	37	55	73	92	110	128	147	165
·902	79928	79946	79965	18	37	55	74	92	110	129	147	166
·903	80112	80131	80149	18	37	55	74	92	111	129	148	166
·904	80297	80315	80334	18	37	55	74	92	111	129	148	166
·905	80482	80501	80519	19	37	56	74	93	111	130	148	167
·906	80668	80686	80705	19	37	56	74	93	111	130	149	167
·907	80854	80872	80891	19	37	56	74	93	112	130	149	167
·908	81040	81059	81077	19	37	56	75	93	112	131	149	168
·909	81227	81245	81264	19	37	56	75	93	112	131	150	168
·910	81414	81433	81452	19	37	56	75	94	112	131	150	169
·911	81602	81620	81639	19	38	56	75	94	113	131	150	169
·912	81790	81809	81827	19	38	56	75	94	113	132	151	169
·913	81978	81997	82016	19	38	57	75	94	113	132	151	170
·914	82167	82186	82205	19	38	57	76	95	113	132	151	170
·915	82357	82376	82395	19	38	57	76	95	114	133	152	171
·916	82547	82566	82585	19	38	57	76	95	114	133	152	171
·917	82737	82756	82775	19	38	57	76	95	114	133	152	171
·918	82928	82947	82966	19	38	57	76	95	115	134	153	172
·919	83119	83138	83157	19	38	57	77	96	115	134	153	172
·920	83310	83330	83349	19	38	58	77	96	115	134	153	173
·921	83502	83522	83541	19	38	58	77	96	115	135	154	173
·922	83695	83714	83733	19	39	58	77	96	116	135	154	173
·923	83888	83907	83927	19	39	58	77	97	116	135	154	174
·924	84081	84101	84120	19	39	58	77	97	116	135	155	174
·925	84275	84294	84314	19	39	58	78	97	116	136	155	175
·926	84469	84489	84508	19	39	58	78	97	117	136	156	175
·927	84664	84684	84703	19	39	58	78	97	117	136	156	175
·928	84859	84879	84898	20	39	59	78	98	117	137	156	176
·929	85055	85074	85094	20	39	59	78	98	117	137	157	176
·930	85251	85271	85290	20	39	59	78	98	118	137	157	177
·931	85447	85467	85486	20	39	59	79	98	118	138	157	177
·932	85644	85664	85684	20	39	59	79	99	118	138	158	177
·933	85842	85862	85881	20	40	59	79	99	119	138	158	178
·934	86040	86060	86079	20	40	59	79	99	119	139	158	178
·935	86238	86258	86278	20	40	60	79	99	119	139	159	179
·936	86437	86457	86477	20	40	60	80	99	119	139	159	179
·937	86636	86656	86676	20	40	60	80	100	120	140	160	179
·938	86836	86856	86876	20	40	60	80	100	120	140	160	180
·939	87036	87056	87076	20	40	60	80	100	120	140	160	180
·940	87237	87257	87277	20	40	60	80	100	120	140	161	181
·941	87438	87458	87478	20	40	60	80	101	121	141	161	181
·942	87639	87660	87680	20	40	61	81	101	121	141	161	182
·943	87841	87862	87882	20	40	61	81	101	121	142	162	182
·944	88044	88064	88084	20	41	61	81	101	122	142	162	182
·945	88247	88267	88288	20	41	61	81	102	122	142	162	183
·946	88450	88471	88491	20	41	61	81	102	122	143	163	183
·947	88654	88675	88695	20	41	61	82	102	122	143	163	184
·948	88859	88879	88900	20	41	61	82	102	123	143	164	184
·949	89063	89084	89104	20	41	61	82	102	123	143	164	184

	0	1	2	3	4	5	6
·950	89125	89145	89166	89187	89207	89228	89248
·951	89330	89351	89372	89392	89413	89433	89454
·952	89536	89557	89578	89598	89619	89639	89660
·953	89743	89763	89784	89805	89825	89846	89867
·954	89950	89970	89991	90012	90032	90053	90074
·955	90157	90178	90199	90219	90240	90261	90282
·956	90365	90386	90406	90427	90448	90469	90490
·957	90573	90594	90615	90636	90657	90677	90698
·958	90782	90803	90824	90845	90866	90886	90907
·959	90991	91012	91033	91054	91075	91096	91117
·960	91201	91222	91243	91264	91285	91306	91327
·961	91411	91432	91453	91474	91495	91516	91538
·962	91622	91643	91664	91685	91706	91727	91749
·963	91833	91854	91875	91897	91918	91939	91960
·964	92045	92066	92087	92108	92130	92151	92172
·965	92257	92278	92299	92321	92342	92363	92385
·966	92470	92491	92512	92534	92555	92576	92598
·967	92683	92704	92726	92747	92768	92790	92811
·968	92896	92918	92939	92961	92982	93004	93025
·969	93111	93132	93154	93175	93196	93218	93239
·970	93325	93347	93368	93390	93411	93433	93454
·971	93540	93562	93584	93605	93627	93648	93670
·972	93756	93778	93799	93821	93842	93864	93886
·973	93972	93994	94015	94037	94059	94080	94102
·974	94189	94210	94232	94254	94276	94297	94319
·975	94406	94428	94449	94471	94493	94515	94536
·976	94624	94645	94667	94689	94711	94733	94754
·977	94842	94864	94885	94907	94929	94951	94973
·978	95060	95082	95104	95126	95148	95170	95192
·979	95280	95301	95323	95345	95367	95389	95411
·980	95499	95521	95543	95565	95587	95609	95631
·981	95719	95741	95763	95785	95807	95830	95852
·982	95940	95962	95984	96006	96028	96050	96073
·983	96161	96183	96205	96228	96250	96272	96294
·984	96383	96405	96427	96449	96472	96494	96516
·985	96605	96627	96649	96672	96694	96716	96738
·986	96828	96850	96872	96895	96917	96939	96962
·987	97051	97073	97096	97118	97140	97163	97185
·988	97275	97297	97319	97342	97364	97387	97409
·989	97499	97521	97544	97566	97589	97611	97634
·990	97724	97746	97769	97791	97814	97836	97859
·991	97949	97971	97994	98017	98039	98062	98084
·992	98175	98197	98220	98242	98265	98288	98310
·993	98401	98424	98446	98469	98492	98514	98537
·994	98628	98651	98673	98696	98719	98741	98764
·995	98855	98878	98901	98923	98946	98969	98992
·996	99083	99106	99129	99152	99174	99197	99220
·997	99311	99334	99357	99380	99403	99426	99449
·998	99540	99563	99586	99609	99632	99655	99678
·999	99770	99793	99816	99839	99862	99885	99908

Antilogarithms (contd.)

	7	8	9	Mean Log. Differences								
				1	2	3	4	5	6	7	8	9
·950	89269	89289	89310	21	41	62	82	103	123	144	164	185
·951	89474	89495	89516	21	41	62	82	103	124	144	165	185
·952	89681	89701	89722	21	41	62	83	103	124	144	165	186
·953	89887	89908	89929	21	41	62	83	103	124	145	166	186
·954	90095	90115	90136	21	41	62	83	104	124	145	166	187
955	90302	90323	90344	21	42	62	83	104	125	145	166	187
·956	90511	90531	90552	21	42	63	83	104	125	146	167	187
·957	90719	90740	90761	21	42	63	84	104	125	146	167	188
·958	90928	90949	90970	21	42	63	84	105	126	146	167	188
·959	91138	91159	91180	21	42	63	84	105	126	147	168	189
·960	91348	91369	91390	21	42	63	84	105	126	147	168	189
·961	91559	91580	91601	21	42	63	84	105	126	147	169	190
·962	91770	91791	91812	21	42	63	85	106	127	148	169	190
·963	91981	92002	92024	21	42	64	85	106	127	148	169	191
·964	92193	92215	92236	21	42	64	85	106	127	148	170	191
·965	92406	92427	92448	21	43	64	85	106	128	149	170	191
·966	92619	92640	92661	21	43	64	85	107	128	149	171	192
·967	92832	92854	92875	21	43	64	85	107	128	150	171	192
·968	93046	93068	93089	21	43	64	86	107	129	150	171	193
·969	93261	93282	93304	21	43	64	86	107	129	150	172	193
·970	93476	93497	93519	22	43	65	86	108	129	151	172	194
·971	93691	93713	93734	22	43	65	86	108	129	151	172	194
·972	93907	93929	93951	22	43	65	86	108	130	151	173	195
·973	94124	94145	94167	22	43	65	87	108	130	152	173	195
·974	94341	94362	94384	22	43	65	87	109	130	152	174	195
·975	94558	94580	94602	22	44	65	87	109	131	152	174	196
·976	94776	94798	94820	22	44	65	87	109	131	153	175	196
·977	94995	95017	95038	22	44	66	87	109	131	153	175	197
·978	95214	95236	95258	22	44	66	88	110	131	153	175	197
·979	95433	95455	95477	22	44	66	88	110	132	154	176	198
·980	95653	95675	95697	22	44	66	88	110	132	154	176	198
·981	95874	95896	95918	22	44	66	88	110	132	154	177	199
·982	96095	96117	96139	22	44	66	88	111	133	155	177	199
·983	96316	96338	96361	22	44	67	89	111	133	155	177	200
·984	96538	96560	96583	22	44	67	89	111	133	156	178	200
·985	96761	96783	96805	22	45	67	89	111	134	156	178	200
·986	96984	97006	97029	22	45	67	89	112	134	156	179	201
·987	97207	97230	97252	22	45	67	89	112	134	157	179	201
·988	97431	97454	97476	22	45	67	90	112	135	157	179	202
·989	97656	97679	97701	22	45	67	90	112	135	157	180	202
·990	97881	97904	97926	23	45	68	90	113	135	158	180	203
·991	98107	98129	98152	23	45	68	90	113	135	158	181	203
·992	98333	98356	98378	23	45	68	91	113	136	158	181	204
·993	98560	98582	98605	23	45	68	91	113	136	159	181	204
·994	98787	98810	98832	23	45	68	91	114	136	159	182	205
·995	99015	99037	99060	23	46	68	91	114	137	159	182	205
·996	99243	99266	99289	23	46	69	91	114	137	160	183	206
·997	99472	99495	99517	23	46	69	92	114	137	160	183	206
·998	99701	99724	99747	23	46	69	92	115	138	161	184	207
·999	99931	99954	99977	23	46	69	92	115	138	161	184	207

INDEX

Abrasives, grinding wheels, 334
Acme thread, 161
Acme thread, checking, 172
Addendum angle, bevel gear, definition, 251
Addendum, bevel gear, definition, 250
  spur gear, 225
  worm gear, definition, 263
Adhesive, *see* Cements and adhesives
Agate, grinding wheel for, 342
Air bags, rubber, cleaning, grinding-wheel selection, 342
Aircraft, materials and components, British Standards for, 223
  spline shaft for aircraft purposes (B.S. A20–1942), 223
Alloy steels, hardening and tempering, 404
Alloys, brazing, 403
  Brinell hardness, 395
  light, annealing and normalising, 410
  magnesium, annealing and normalising, 413
  magnesium (Elektron), tapping lubricant recipes, 325
Aloxite grinding-wheel abrasive, 334
Aluminium, 428
  Alunize, solder, 429
  annealing, 410
  anodise, to, 428
  blacken, to, 428
  cutting lubricants, 323
  drilling, 279
  etching, 438
  frost, to, 429
  Fryal solder, 429
  Fry's L.M. solder, 429
  grinding-wheel selection, 342
  polishing, 429
  power constants for, 319
  soldering, 429
  solders, special, with no fluxes, 429
  workshop methods and recipes, 428
Aluminium alloys, cutting-tool angles, 308
  drill-point angle, 277
  grinding-wheel selection, 342

Aluminium bronze, drill data, 280
Aluminium-nickel-iron bronze, drill data, 280
Aluminium oxide grinding-wheel abrasive, 334
Aluminium tubes, sizes and weights, 61–9
Alundum and Crystolon Norton grinding wheels, 336
Alundum grinding-wheel abrasive, 334
Alunize, solder, 429
American National (Sellers) threads, 134
American National Standard taper pipe thread (N.P.T.), 139
American National Thread System (60°), 165
American S.A.E. plain washers, 208
American S.A.E. split-pins (cotter-pins), 207
American sparking-plugs (S.A.E. standard), 164
  sparking-plug threads, 164
  tapped hole threads, 164
American Standard tapers, 305
Angle of obliquity, gears, definition, 226
Angles, cutting-tool, table of, 308
Anglo-American-Canadian Conferences on Unified Screw Threads (1943–5), 158
Annealing and normalising of metals, 410
  aluminium and light alloys, 412
  brass, 412
  cast iron, 410
  copper, 412
  definition of, 410
  magnesium alloys, 413
  manganese steel, 411
  monel metal, 412
  nickel, 412
  stainless steels, 411
  steel, 411
  steel, articles, 410
  steel, local annealing of, 411
  tool steels, temperatures, 411
Anodise, aluminium, to, 428

Antilogarithms, 494
  examples, 494
  tables, 532
Antique finish on copper, 436
Apothecaries weights, 2
Arc of approach (gears), definition, 226
Arc of recess (gears), definition, 226
Ardoloy (tool-cutting alloy), 306
  grinding-wheel selection, 342
  tools, shank size, nomogram for determining, 322
  turning tools, cutting speeds, power constants and angles, 320
  turning tools (tungsten-carbide), 312
Areas, and circumferences of circles, tables, 16–19
  plane figures, see Plane figures, areas of
Armatures, grinding-wheel selection, 342
Armour plate, grinding-wheel selection, 342
Atmospheric pressure, definition, 4
Automobile, spline shafts for, 223
Automobile gears, 274
Avoirdupois (weight), 2
Axial pitch, worm gear, definition, 262
Axial pressure angle, worm gear, definition, 263
Axles, grinding-wheel selection, 342

B.A. bolts and screws (British Standard), cheese-head, 196
  countersunk-head, 194
  hexagon head, alternative forms of head, 192
  round-head, 195
B.A. (47½°) screw threads, 165
B.A. nuts, ordinary and thin, 193
B.A. washers, 203
  British Standard (abstract B.S. 57–1944), 203
  large, 204
  small, 204
Babbitt cutting lubricants, 323
Back cone angle, bevel gear, definition, 251
Back cones, bevel gear, definition, 248

Bakelite and other plastics, drill-point angle, 277
Bakelite laminated, drill-point angle, 277
Ball bearings, grinding-wheel selection, 342
Base circle (gears), definition, 224
Bath tubs, grinding-wheel selection, 343
Bearings (cam-shaft), grinding-wheel selection, 345
Belt pulleys, train of, 426
Belts, length of, 427
  cross belt, 427
  open belt, 427
  speeds of belts and pulleys, 426
Belts, to prevent slipping, 430
  belt dressings, 429
  flexibility and pulley-gripping qualities, 429
  recipe for preventing slip, 429
Bevel-gear teeth, proportions of, 257
Bevel gears, British Standards, 251, 254
  commercial cut, 251
  curved spiral, 254
  definitions, see Bevel gears, definitions
  formulæ, 252
  helical, 254
  high-class cut, 251
  spiraloid, 254
  straight, British Standard tooth for, 251
  types of, 254
Bevel gears, definitions, 248
  addendum, 250
  addendum angle, 251
  back cone angle, 251
  back cones, 248
  bottom clearance, 250
  British Standard bevel gear, 249
  British Standard involute tooth terms, 249
  cone distance, definition, 248
  constant chord, 250
  dedendum, 250
  dedendum angle, 251
  diametral pitch, 249
  face angle, 251
  face width, 250
  fillet, 251
  module, 250

Bevel gears, definition—*continued*
  normal pitch, 249
  outside diameter, 250
  pitch circles, 248
  pitch cones, 248
  pitch diameter, 248
  pitch point, 248
  pressure angle, 249
  ratio of bevel gears, 248
  root diameter, 250
  shaft angle, 251
  tooth thickness, 250
  working depth of tooth, 250
Billets, grinding-wheel selection, 343
Birmingham Wire Gauge (B.W.G.), 44
Bits, auger, grinding-wheel selection,
  344
Blank, determination of size of, 415
  equal-volume method, 416
  equal-weight method, 416
  mean-height method, 417
  surface-area method, 416
Bolts, *see* Screw-thread data
Bonds, grinding wheel, 335
  ceramics, 335
  "Redmanol" cut-off wheels, 335
  rubber-bonded wheels, 335
  shellac-bonded wheels, 335
  silicate-bonded wheels, 335
  synthetic-resin wheels, 335
Bottom clearance, bevel gears, definition, 250
Bower-Barff rust-prevention process,
  445
Brake, drums, linings, shoes, grinding-wheel selection, 344
Brass, cutting lubricant, 323
  cutting-tool angles, 308
  drill-point angle, 277
  grinding-wheel selection, 344
  power constants for, 319
  stepped flat drills for, 279
Brass, workshop methods and
  recipes, 430
  annealing, 412
  blackening, 430
  blue colouring, 431
  bronzing, 430
  cementing to wood, 435
  cleaning, 430
  etching, 435
  green colouring, 431
  lacquering, 431, 443

Brass workshop methods and
  recipes—*continued*
  oxidised finish on, 432
  steel-blue colour, 432
  tin coating of, 432
Brasswork, cementing to glass tubes,
  recipe, 434
Brazing alloys, 403
  notes on, 403
Brick (vitrified), grinding-wheel
  selection, 344
Brinell hardness, and tensile strength,
  392
  metals and alloys, 394
  tensile strength equivalents, 393
  testing hardness, method of, 390
  Vickers' hardness numbers, relation between, 395
Brinell numbers and minimum thicknesses, 394
British Association Threads (B.A.),
  132, 133
British Governmental Inter-Services
  Engineering Standards Co-ordinating Committee, and screw
  threads, 165
British Motor Tyre Valve Thread
  (S.M.M.T.), 163
British Specification for Limits and
  Fits, 80
British Standards, B.A. cheese-head
  bolts and screws, 196
  B.A. countersunk-head bolts and
  screws, 194
  B.A. hexagon-head bolts and screws
  (alternate forms of head), 192
  B.A. ordinary and thin nuts, 193
  B.A. round-head bolts and screws,
  195
  B.A. washers (abstract B.S. 57–
  1944), 203
  bevel gears, 249, 251, 254
  bright screws (cheese-head, countersunk, round), 199, 200
  cotter-pins, split, 206
  cycle threads (B.S.C.), 151
  cycle threads, bolts, nuts and
  similar applications, basic dimensions, 152
  cycle threads, special applications,
  basic dimensions, 153
  cycle threads, spokes and nipples,
  basic dimensions, 152

British Standards—_continued_
drill specification (B.S. No. 328–1928), 282
drilling-jig bushes, 299
fine bolts (B.S.F.), limits and tolerances, close fit, 110
fine bolts (B.S.F.), limits and tolerances, free fit, 114
fine bolts (B.S.F.), limits and tolerances, medium fit, 112
fine (B.S.F.) open-ended spanners, 201
fine (B.S.F.) screw threads, 109
fine nuts (B.S.F.), limits and tolerances, close fit, 111
fine nuts (B.S.F.), limits and tolerances, free fit, 115
fine nuts (B.S.F.), limits and tolerances, medium fit, 113
form, buttress thread, 158, 159
form, buttress thread, numerical data, 160
gear terms, 226
gears, machine-cut, 272
gears, 20° pressure angle high-class or commercial cut gears, 229
gears, 20° pressure angle (precision-machined), 229
hardness of metals, 391
hexagon-head bolts and screws, 186
hexagon ordinary and lock nuts, 188
hexagon slotted nuts and castle nuts, 190
involute tooth terms, bevel gears, 249
keys, keyways and coned shaft ends (B.S. No. 46, Part I–1929), 217
limits and fits, 80
limits and fits for engineering, 90
limits for shafts, 87, 89
limits for unilateral, bilateral and oversize holes, 86, 88
materials and components (aircraft), list of, 223
metric thread dimensions, 142
metric thread tolerances, metric bolts, limits and tolerances, close fit, 143
pan-head rivets (ferrous and non-ferrous), 214
pipe threads (B.S.P.), bolts, limits and tolerances, close fit, 117

British Standards—_continued_
pipe threads (B.S.P.), bolts, limits and tolerances, free fit, 121
pipe threads (B.S.P.), bolts, limits and tolerances, medium fit, 119
pipe threads (B.S.P.), nuts, limits and tolerances, close fit, 118
pipe threads (B.S.P.), nuts, limits and tolerances, free fit, 122
pipe threads (B.S.P.), nuts, limits and tolerances, medium fit, 120
pipe threads (B.S.P.), parallel, general engineering purposes, 116
plain washers, 205
precision hexagon bolts, screws, nuts and plain washers, 185
rivet proportions, 212, 214
screw threads, specifications, 132
spanners (open-ended), 201
sparking plug dimensions, 164
specification 436–1940, 272
specification 84–1940, 97
system of fits, 84
taper pipe threads, 126
tolerance zones for limit gauges, 96
tooth for straight bevel gears, 251
truncated Whitworth thread, 124
unified screw threads, numerical data for standard pitches, 168
Whitworth bolts (B.S.W.), limits and tolerances, close fit, 103
Whitworth bolts (B.S.W.), limits and tolerances, free fit, 107
Whitworth bolts (B.S.W.), limits and tolerances, medium fit, 105
Whitworth (B.S.W.) spanners, open-ended, 201
Whitworth nuts (B.S.W.), limits and tolerances, close fit, 104
Whitworth nuts (B.S.W.), limits and tolerances, free fit, 108
Whitworth nuts (B.S.W.), limits and tolerances, medium fit, 106
Whitworth screw threads (B.S.W.), 101, 102
wing nuts, 197
Woodruff keys and keyways, 222
Broaches, sharpening, grinding-wheel selection, 345
Bronze, cutting-tool angles, 308
hard, grinding-wheel selection, 345
power constants for, 319

Bronzing, recipe, 430
Brown and Sharpe gears, Lewis formulae, 270
spur, 237
spur gear teeth, 239–43
worm, 260, 267
worm, 29°, 265
Brown and Sharpe tables, grinding limits, 94
Brown and Sharpe tapers, 303
B.S. 641–1935, rivets, reference to, 213
B.S. 1083–1951, 185
See also British Standards
B.S.F., B.S.P., B.S.W., see British Standards
Bushes, press-fit (B.S.), headless and headed types, 300
renewable (B.S.), slip and fixed sizes, 301
Bushings, grinding-wheel selection, 345

Calipers, vernier, reading, 73
Cam rollers, grinding-wheel selection, 345
Cam wheels, grinding-wheel selection, 345
Cams, grinding-wheel selection, 345
Cam-shaft bearings, grinding-wheel selection, 345
Canada, screw-thread systems used in, 165
Carbide-tipped negative-rake cutters, production data for, 333
Carboloy tool-cutting alloy, 306
Carbon tetrachloride liquid fire extinguisher, 441
Carbon-steel drills, drill-performance data, 282
Carbons, various, grinding-wheel selection, 346
Carborundum grinding-wheel abrasive, 334
Carborundum grinding-wheels, selection for various operations, 341
Card clothing grinding-wheel selection, 346
Cast iron, annealing, 410
cutting-tool angles, 308
drill performance with, 282
grinding-wheel selection, 346

Cast iron—continued
lathe machining data, 315
material, drill performance data, 282
softer grades, drill-point angle, 277
tapping lubricant recipes, 325
turning tool data (Ardoloy), 320
turning tool data (Escaloy), 311
Castings, workshop methods and recipes, 432
filling holes in, 432
porous aluminium casting, 433
sand removal, 433
Cellulose cement (universal) recipe, 434
Cements and adhesives, workshop methods and recipes, 433
brass to wood, cement for, 435
cellulose, cement (universal) for, recipe, 434
cloth to metal, 434
fire cement, 436
fireproof and waterproof glue, 435
fireproof cement for fixing tiles, 436
fireproof cement for stonework, 435
glass and porcelain cement, 436
glass tubes in brasswork, for, recipe, 434
glue, waterproof and fireproof, 435
grinder discs, for, recipe, 435
heat-resistant cement, 436
hydraulic pipe joints, for, recipe, 433
iron to concrete, recipe, 435
iron to iron, recipe, 434
knife- and tool-handle cement, 435
leather belting, for, recipe, 433
leather to steel, recipe, 433
metal to glass, for, recipe, 434
rubber cement, recipe, 434
waterglass (sodium silicate) cement, 435
waterproof and fireproof glue, recipe, 435
Ceramics grinding-wheel bonds, 335
Chain links, grinding-wheel selection, 346, 347
Chasers, grinding-wheel selection, 347
Chemical etching, 438
Chilled iron, grinding-wheel selection, 347
Chip-breaker drill, 279
Chisels, grinding-wheel selection, 347
Chordal pitch, gears, definition, 225

Chordal thickness, gears, definition, 225, 250
Chords, tables of circle division method, 46, 47
Chrome nickel, cutting speeds, clearance and rake angle, 310
Chrome nickel, turning-tool data, Escaloy, 310
Chrome nickel steel, drill performance with, 282
Circle division, methods of, 45
Circles, properties of, 458
Circular pitch, gears, definition, 224
Circular pitch, worm wheel, 263
Circumference, ratio to diameter, of circle, 457
Circumference and areas of circles, table, 16–19
Clearance, gears, definition, 225
Clearance diagram, bolts and nuts, 203
Cleveland system of tapers, 304
Cleveland Twist Drill Co., drill performance data table, 282
recommendations, 275
Cloth to metal cement, recipe, 434
Clutch plates, grinding-wheel selection, 347
Commutators, grinding-wheel selection, 347
Concrete, grinding-wheel selection, 347
recipe, concrete to iron, 435
Cone distance, bevel gear, definition, 248
Constant chord, bevel gear, 250
Conversion, feet into metres, 11
kilograms per square centimetre to pounds per square inch, 13
kilograms to pounds and pounds to kilograms, 13
litres to pints, 14
metres to feet, 11
metres to yards, 12
pints to litres, 14
pounds per square inch to kilograms per square centimetre, 13
yards into metres, 12
Conversion factors, some useful, 14
Copper, annealing, 412
cutting lubricant, 323
cutting-tool angles, 308
drill data, copper alloys, 280

Copper—continued
drilling copper and alloys, 279
etching, 438
grinding-wheel selection, 348
physical and mechanical properties of copper and copper alloys (sheet or strip), 386
Copper, workshop methods and recipes, 436
antique finish on, 436
black finish on, 436
blue finish on, 436
copper-plating steel, iron or cast iron, 437
green finish, 436
grey finish, 436
oxidising copper, 436
Copper alloys (sheet or strip), physical and mechanical properties, 386
Copper Development Association drill data table, copper alloys, 280
Copper-plating steel, iron or cast iron, 437
Coslettising rust-prevention process, recipe, 445
Cotter-pins, American S.A.E. (split-pins), 207
B.S., split cotter-pins, 206
Couplers and draw bars, grinding-wheel selection, 348
Cranked knife tools (Ardoloy), 314
Cranked round-nose turning tool (Ardoloy), 313
Crankshafts, various, grinding-wheel selection, 348
Crystalline finish on metal surfaces, 437
Crystolon and Alundum Norton grinding-wheels, 336
Crystolon grinding-wheel abrasive, 334
Cubes and cube roots, tables, 20–39
worked examples, 495
Cubic inch–cubic centimetre equivalents, 9
Cupro-nickel drill data, 280, 321
Cup-wheel cutter clearance, grinding, 370
Cutanit grinding-wheel selection, 348
Cutters, epicycloidal or double-curve gear cutters, 245
involute-gear cutters, 249

Cutting angles of tools, 306
aluminium, cutting lubricants, 323
aluminium, power constants for, 319
aluminium alloys, cutting-tool angles, 308
angle, end cutting edge, definition, 307
angle, end relief, definition, 307
angle, tool, 306
angle, top rake, 306
angles, cutting-tool, table of, 308
Ardoloy, tool-cutting alloy, 306
Ardoloy tools, shank size, determining, 322
Ardoloy tungsten-carbide turning tools, 312
Babbitt, cutting lubricants, 323
brass, cutting lubricant, 323
brass, cutting-tool angles, 308
brass, power constants for, 319
bronze, cutting-tool angles, 308
bronze, power constants for, 319
carbide-tipped negative-rake cutters, production data for, 333
Carboloy, tool-cutting alloy, 306
cast iron, cutting-tool angles, 308
cemented or sintered carbide tool materials, 307
chrome nickel, cutting speeds, clearance and rake angle, 310, 321
clearance angle, definition, 306, 307
copper, cutting lubricant, 323
copper, cutting-tool angles, 308
cutting edge, definition, 307
cutting lubricants, or fluids, 323
cutting-power, lathes, 319
cutting speeds, angles and power constants, Ardoloy turning tools, see Cutting speeds, angles, etc.
cutting speeds, clearance and rake angles, Escaloy sintered-carbide turning tools, see Cutting speeds, clearance and rake angles, etc.
cutting speeds, milling-cutter, 327
diamond-tipped tools, see Diamond-tipped tools
ebonite, cutting speeds, clearance and rake angles, 311, 321
end cutting edge angle, definition, 307
end relief angle, definition, 307

Cutting angles of tools—continued
Engineering Workshop Practice (Caxton), reference to, 325
Erinoid, cutting speeds, clearance and rake angles, 311, 321
Escaloy, tool-cutting alloy, 306
face, definition, 307
feeds, carbon-steel cutters, 329
feeds, milling-cutter, 328, 329
flank, definition, 307
glass, cutting speeds, clearance and rake angles, 311, 321
glass, cutting lubricant, 323
hard rubber, cutting speeds, clearance and rake angles, 311, 321
heel, definition, 307
high-speed steel, cutting speeds, clearance and rake angle, 310, 321
high-speed tools, heat treatment of, 307
high-speed tools, materials, 306
horse-power, machining metals, 317
horse-power (motor) for multi-tool machines, 318
iron, cast and wrought, cutting lubricant, 323
iron, cast and wrought, cutting speeds, clearance and rake angle, 311, 321
knife (cranked) tool, lathe machining data for, 316
lathe machining data, cranked knife tool, 316
lathe machining data, parting tool, 316
lathe machining data, turning and facing data, 316
lathe machining data, tungsten-carbon tools, see Lathe machining data, tungsten-carbon tools
lathe machining data, turning tools, 316
lathes, cutting power, 319
lubricants, cutting, various materials, 323
lubricants, recipes, see Tapping lubricant, recipes
lubricants or fluids, cutting, 323
machining materials, special, 309
machining speeds, materials and tools, various, 309

Cutting angles of tools—*continued*
magnesium alloys, cutting-tool angles, 308
manganese steel, cutting speeds, clearance and rake angles, 310, 321
marble, cutting speeds, clearance and rake angles, 311, 321
materials, tool, 306
miller-cutter, cutting speeds, 327
milling, negative-rake, 331
milling, "Up" and "Down" milling, 328
milling cutters, negative-rake, 330
milling cutters, teeth, numbers of, 329
milling cutters and reamers, British Standard, 330
milling cutting feeds, 328
monel metal cutting-tool angles, 308
negative-rake, cemented-carbide-tipped milling cutters, approximate cutting speeds and rates of metal removed with, 333
negative-rake cutters, carbide-tipped, production data, 333
negative-rake milling, aluminium alloy machining, 332
negative-rake milling, cutting performances, 332
negative-rake milling, notes on, 331
negative-rake slotting cutters, 331
nomenclature, cutting tool, 306
nomogram, shank size of Ardoloy and similar sintered-carbide tools, determining, 322
non-ferrous alloys or sintered carbides for tool materials, 306
non-ferrous metals, cutting speeds, clearance and rake angles, 311, 321
non-ferrous metals, power constants for, 319
non-metallic materials, cutting speeds, clearance and rake angles, 311
nose angle, definition, 307
nose radius, definition, 307
parting tool lathe machining data, 316
plastics, cutting speeds, clearance and rake angles, 311, 321

Cutting angles of tools—*continued*
porcelain, cutting speeds, clearance and rake angles, 311, 321
power constant values for steels etc., 318
power constants, angles, cutting speeds, Ardoloy turning tools, 320
power constants for non-ferrous metals, 319
power constants, various metals, 319
reamers, milling, and cutters, British Standard, 330
shank, definition, 307
shoe relief angle, 307
side cutting-edge angle, definition, 307
side rake angle, 306
side relief angle, definition, 307
sintered-carbide tools, 317
sintered-carbide tool materials, 307
sintered-carbide turning tools, cutting speeds, clearance and rake angles, 310
slate, cutting speeds, clearance and rake angles, 311, 321
slotting cutters, negative-rake, 331
stainless steel, cutting speeds, clearance and rake angles, 310, 321
steel, cutting speeds, clearance and rake angles, 310, 321
steels, cutting lubricants for, 323
steels, cutting-tool angles, 308
steels, etc., power-constant values for, 318
steel-turning, cutting lubricant recipe, 323
Stellite, tool-cutting alloy, 306
tapping lubricants, recipes, *see* Tapping lubricant, recipes
terms employed, 306, 307
tool angle, 306
tool-cutting alloy, Ardoloy, 306
tool-cutting alloy, Carboloy, 306
tool-cutting alloy, Escaloy, 306
tool-cutting alloy, Stellite, 306
tool-cutting alloy, Wimet, 306
tool-cutting alloys and metals, 306
tool materials, 306
tools, diamond-tipped, 325

Cutting angles of tools—*continued*
  tools, sintered-carbide, 317
  tools, sintered-carbide Ardoloy, shank size, nomogram, 322
  tools, tungsten-carbon, lathe machining data, 313
  top-rake angle, definition, 306
  tungsten-carbide turning tools (Ardoloy), *see* Tungsten-carbide turning tools (Ardoloy)
  turning and facing-tools, lathe machining data, 316
  Wimet, tool-cutting alloy, 306
Cutting lubricants or fluids, 323
  steel lubricant recipe, 323
Cutting-power, lathes, 319
Cutting speeds, angles and power constants, Ardoloy turning tools, 320
  cast iron, 320
  non-ferrous metals, 321
  non-metallic materials, 321
  steels, 320
  wrought iron, 320
Cutting speeds, clearance and rake angles, Escaloy sintered-carbide turning tools, 310
  cast iron, 311
  chrome nickel, 310
  high-speed steel, 310
  manganese steel, 310
  non-ferrous metals, 311
  non-metallic materials, 311
  stainless steel, 310
  steels, 310
  wrought iron, 311
Cutting speeds, milling-cutter, 327
Cutting speeds (drill) and equivalent revolutions per minute, 284
Cycle Engineers Institute (C.E.I.) threads, 149
  table, 150
Cycloid curve diagram (gears), 230
Cycloidal teeth (gears), 230
Cylinder liners, grinding-wheel selection, 349
Cylinders, various, grinding-wheel selection, 348

Data, general, 1
  apothecaries (weights), 2
  areas, and circumferences of circles, table, 16–19

Data, general—*continued*
  atmospheric pressure, definition, 4
  avoirdupois (weight), 2
  Birmingham Wire Gauge (B.W.G.), 44
  chords, table of, circle division method, 46, 47
  circle division, methods of, 45
  circumference and areas, of circles, table, 16–19
  conversion, feet into metres, 11
  conversion, kilograms per square centimetre to pounds per square inch, 13
  conversion, kilograms to pounds and pounds to kilograms, 13
  conversion, litres to pints, 14
  conversion, metres into feet, 11
  conversion, metres into yards, 12
  conversion, pints to litres, 14
  conversion, pounds per square inch to kilograms per square centimetre, 13
  conversion, yards into metres, 12
  conversion factors, some useful, 14
  cube roots, tables, 20–40
  cubes and cube roots, tables, 20–40
  cubic inch–cubic centimetre equivalents, 9
  English and Metric equivalents, 3
  English weights, 2
  English weights and measures, 1
  equivalents, English and Metric, 3
  equivalents, Imperial gallons in cubic feet, 15
  fractions and decimals of inch and millimetres, 6
  gallons, Imperial, in cubic feet, equivalents, 15
  heat, definition, 5
  Imperial Wire Gauge (S.W.G.), 42
  inch–millimetre equivalents, 8
  length, data, 1
  length (metric), data, 2
  linear measure, English and metric equivalents, 3
  litres to pints, conversion, 14
  metals, physical properties of, 49
  metrical weights and measures, data, 2
  millimetre–inch equivalents, 7
  miscellaneous useful information, 4
  physical properties of metals, 49

Data, general—*continued*
  pints to litres, conversion table, 14
  power and work, definition, 4
  pressure, atmospheric, definition, 4
  pressure, definition, 5
  square centimetres into square inches, 10
  square feet–square metre equivalents, 9
  square inches into square centimetres, 10
  square roots, tables, 20–40
  squares, square roots, cubes and cube roots, table of, 20–40
  steel wire gauge, Stubs', 43
  Stubs' steel wire gauge, 43
  surface, measurement data, 1
  surface measure, English and metric equivalents, 3
  surface (metric) data, 2
  Troy (weight), 2
  velocity, definition, 5
  volume, data, 1
  volume (measure), English and metric equivalents, 3
  volume (metric), data, 2
  Warrington wire gauge, 41
  weight, English and metric equivalents, 3
  weights, materials, various, 48
  Whitworth's wire gauge, 44
  wire, steel, gauge, Stubs', 43
  wire gauge, Birmingham (B.W.G.), 44
  wire gauge, Imperial (S.W.G.), 42
  wire gauge, Warrington, 41
  wire gauge, Whitworth, 44
  wire gauges used in United States, 41
  work and power, definition, 4
D.B.S. gears and gearing, 260, 267
Dedendum, bevel gear, definition, 250
  worm gear, definition, 263
Dedendum angle, bevel gear, definition, 251
Degreasing metal parts, 437
Diametral pitch, bevel gear, definition, 249
  spur gears, definition, 224
Diamond hardness of typical hard steels, 396

Diamond-tipped tools, 325
  dimensions, boring tools (diagram), 327
  tables, 326
Dies, and punches, materials, 413
  various, grinding-wheel selection, 349
Drawings, lacquer for, 443
Drill performance data, 282
  carbon-steel drills, 282
  cast iron, 282
  chrome-nickel steel, 282
  machinery steel, 282
Drills and drilling data, 275
  aluminium alloys, drill-point angle, 277
  aluminium bronze, drill data, 280
  aluminium drilling, chip-breaker drill for, 279
  aluminium-nickel-iron bronze, drill data, 280
  American standard tapers, 305
  Bakelite and other plastics, drill-point angle, 277
  Bakelite laminated drill-point angle, 277
  body clearance, definition, 276
  brass, stepped flat drills for, 279
  brass and soft bronze, drill-point angle, 277
  British Standard Drill Specification (B.S. No. 328–1928), 282
  British Standard drilling-jig bushes, 299
  Brown and Sharpe tapers, 303
  carbon-steel drills, drill performance data, 282
  cast iron, material drill performance data, 282
  cast iron (softer grades), drill-point angle, 277
  chip-breaker drill, 279
  chrome nickel steel, material drill performance data, 282
  Cleveland system of tapers, 304
  Cleveland Twist Drill Co., drill-performance data table, 282
  Cleveland Twist Drill Co.'s recommendations, twist drills, 275
  copper, drill data, 280
  copper alloys, drill data, 280
  copper and alloys, drilling, 279

Drills and drilling data—*continued*
Copper Development Association's drill-data table, copper alloys, 280
cupro-nickel drill data, 280
cutting lips or edges, definition, 275
cutting speeds (drill) and equivalent revolutions per minute, 284
dead centre, definition, 275
drill diameters, definition, 275
drill letters and numbers, 286
drill-performance data, *see* Drill-performance data
drilling deep holes, special drills with spiral lubricant holes, 279
flat drills, 279
flute length, definition, 275
formula, drill speeds, 285
glass, 441
gunmetal (cast), drill data, 280
gunmetal (leaded), drill data, 280
hard rubber, fibre drill-point angle, 277
hard steels, manganese steel, drill-point angle, 277
heat-treated steel—drop forgings, connecting rods, drill-point angles, 277
heel, definition, 275
high-speed screwing and turning brass, drill data, 280
hot stamping brass, drill data, 280
Jarno taper, 305
land, definition, 276
lead bronze (cast), drilling data, 280
liners, headless and headed, 299
lip clearance, definition, 275
lubricant recipes, 323
machinery steel, material, drill-performance data, 282
magnesium alloys, 277
manganese bronzes, drill data, 280
manganese steel, drill speeds and feeds for, 278
margin, definition, 275
mild and medium steels, drill-point angle, 277
morse taper shanks, 302
nickel brass (leaded), drilling data, 280
nickel silver, drill data, 280

Drills and drilling data—*continued*
nickel silver (leaded), drilling data, 280
notes on drills and drilling, 277
overall length, definition, 275
performance test, British Standard, for twist drills No. 60–2 in. diameter, 283
phosphor bronze (cast), drill data, 280
phosphor bronze (wrought), drill data, 280
point angle, definition, 275
point of drill, definition, 275
press-fit bushes (B.S.), headless and headed types, 300
rake angles, definition, 276
renewable bushes (B.S.), slip and fixed sizes, 301
S.A.E. screw threads, drills for tapped holes, 296
selenium copper, drilling data, 280
sheet metal, drilling, diagram, 278
silicon bronze, drill data, 280
Slocomb centre drills, and sizes, 299
speeds, cutting, 284
speeds, drill, formula, 285
"Stag Major" manganese steel, drill speeds and feeds, 278
stainless steel, drilling speeds and feeds, 278
stainless steels, drills used, 277
Standard Tool Co., tapers, 305
"Staybrite" stainless steel, drilling speeds and feeds, 278
"Staybrite" stainless steel, drills, 278
steel drilling, chip breaker drill, 279
steel sheet, drilling relatively thin sheet, 278
stepped drill, diagram, 280
taper systems, 305
tapping drills for British Association (B.A.) threads, 293
tapping drills for British Standard Fine (B.S.F.) threads, 290
tapping drills for British Standard Pipe threads (parallel), 292
tapping drills for British Standard Whitworth threads, 288

Drills and drilling data—*continued*
tapping drills for metric screw
threads (Système Internationale), 294
tapping drills for S.A.E. screw
threads, 296
Tellurium copper drilling data, 280
troubles, twist drill, causes and
remedies, 281
twist drill nomenclature, 275
twist drill troubles, causes and
remedies, 281
various drills, grinding-wheel selection, 349
web, definition, 276
wood, ebonite, vulcanite, drill-
point angle, 277
yellow brass, drill data, 280
Dryseal American (National) Standard taper pipe thread, 139
Ductility and malleability of common metals, 390

Ebonite, cutting speeds, clearance
and rake angles, 311, 321
grinding-wheel selection, ebonite
and erinoid, 350
Elasticity for timbers, moduli for, 385
Electro-induction heating, 408
Elektron, magnesium alloy tapping
lubricant recipes, 325
weights, 55
Ellipse, the, 469
circle projection method, 470
construction of, 469
mechanical method of drawing, 469
mechanical trammel method, 470
Engineering, limits and fits in, *see*
Limits and fits in engineering
Engineering Workshop Practice (Cax-
ton), reference to, 325
English and metric equivalents, 3
English weights, 2
English weights and measures, 1
Epicyclic-gear trains, 259
Epicycloid curve, gears, definition,
231
Epicycloidal or double-curve gear
cutters, 245
Equivalents, English and metric, 3
Imperial gallons in cubic feet, 15
Erinoid, cutting speeds, clearances
and rake angles, 311, 321

Escaloy, grinding-wheel selection,
350
tool-cutting alloy, 306
turning tools, cutting speeds,
clearance and rake angle, data,
310
Etching metals, workshop methods
and recipes, 438
aluminium, 438
brass, 438
chemical etching, 438
copper, 438
glass, 438
lead, 439
magnesium alloys, 439
resist, 439
steel, 439
zinc, 439

Face angle, definition, 251
Face width, bevel gears, definition,
250
Feeds, carbon-steel cutters, 329
milling-cutters (table), 329
milling-cutting, 328
Fibre rods, grinding-wheel selection,
350
File cleaning and resharpening,
workshop methods and recipes,
439
cleaning, 439
resharpening, 440
Files, grinding-wheel selection, 350
Fillet, bevel gear, definition, 251
Finish turning tool (Ardoloy), 312
Fire cement, 436
Fire extinguisher, carbon-tetra-
chloride as, 441
recipes, 440
Fireproof (and waterproof) glue,
recipe, 435
Fireproof cement, for fixing tiles, 436
for stonework, 435
Firth Brown carbide, grinding-wheel
selection, 350
Fits and limits in engineering, *see*
Limits and fits in engineer-
ing
Flat irons, grinding-wheel selection,
350
Flexible metallic tubing, weight, 60
Fluxes, soft-soldering, 401
soldering, 401

Forgings, grinding-wheel selection, 350
Fork tines, grinding-wheel selection, 350
Formulæ, gears, general, 230
  gears, strength-calculation, 268
  rivet proportions, 213
  trigonometrical, *see* Trigonometrical formulæ
Fractions and decimals of inch and millimetres, 6
Frosting glass, 441
Fryal aluminium solder, 429
Fry's L.M. solder, 429

Gallons, Imperial, in cubic feet equivalents, 15
Gas and steam pipe, weight, 60
Gauges, Vernier height, 76
  various, grinding-wheel selection, 350
Gears, machine-cut, 224
  addendum, definition, 225
  allowable tangential load, 273
  angle of obliquity, definition, 226
  arc of approach, definition, 226
  arc of recess, definition, 226
  automobile gears, 274
  base circle, definition, 224
  bevel- and spiral-gear teeth, proportions of, 257
  bevel-gear formulæ, 252
  bevel gears, British Standard, 251
  bevel gears, definitions, *see* Bevel gears, definitions
  British Standard 20° pressure angle—high-class or commercial cut gears, 229
  British Standard 20° pressure angle (precision-machined) gears, 229
  British Standard gear terms, 226
  British Standard machine-cut gears, 272
  British Standard specification B.S. 436 : 1940, 272
  British Standard tooth for straight bevel gears, 251
  British Standard types of bevel gears, 254
  Brown and Sharpe 29° worm, 265
  Brown and Sharpe spur gears, 237
  chordal pitch, definition, 225

Gears, machine-cut—*continued*
  chordal thickness, definition, 225
  circular pitch, definition, 224
  clearance, definition, 225
  commercial cut bevel gears, 251
  curved spiral bevel gear, 254
  cutters, epicycloidal or double-curve gear cutters, 245
  cutters, involute-gear cutters for more accurate teeth, 245
  cycloid curve diagram, 230
  cycloidal teeth, 230
  David Brown and Sharpe or D.B.S. worm gears, 260
  David Brown and Sharpe Ltd. (D.B.S.) worm gearing, 267
  D.B.S. worm gear (diagram), 261
  definitions, bevel gears, 255
  definitions, spur gears, 224
  diametral pitch, definition, 224
  efficiency, worm gear, 261
  efficiency of worm gearing, 267
  epicyclic-gear trains, 259
  epicycloid curve, definition, 231
  factor of safety, gearing, 274
  formula, general, 230
  formula, strength-calculation, 268
  gear-strength formulæ, British Standard, 272
  gear-tooth forms, construction, 230
  Guest worm gear, 261
  helical bevel gear, 254
  high-class cut gears, 251
  Hindley or Hour-glass type worm gear, 260, 261
  horse power, transmitted, 274
  hypocycloid curve, definition, 231
  interference, definition, 227
  involute curve, 232
  involute rack gear, diagram, 233
  involute teeth, 231
  involute-gear cutters, 244
  involute-gear teeth shapes, to construct, 232
  Lanchester worm gear, 261
  Lewis formula, Brown and Sharpe gears, 270
  Lewis formula (strength), 268
  Lewis formula, values of f, 270
  Lewis formula, values of y, 269
  line of action, definition, 225
  Maag-Sulzer gear-generation principle (diagram), 234

Gears, machine-cut—*continued*
module (M), definition, 224
parallel on straight worm type, 260
pitch circle, definition, 224
pitch diameter, definition, 224
pitches, table of equivalent diametral and circular pitches, 235
planing gear principle (diagram), 234
pressure angle, definition, 226
rack and pinion, 233
safe working stresses, zero speed, 272
Sellers (Wm.) Company, U.S.A., 268
speed, effect of gear-teeth speed on stress f, 271
speed, effect of on gear strength, 270
speed allowance, Brown and Sharpe standard gears, 272
spiral angle of work, 262
spiraloid bevel gear, 254
spur gear teeth formulæ, 229
spur gears, 224
spur gears, Brown and Sharpe, 237
straight bevel gear, 254
strength, Brown and Sharpe spur gears, 271
strength, gear teeth, 268
strength, gears, 273
stub-gear tooth proportions, 244
table, gear teeth, Brown and Sharpe spur gears, 242
table, gear teeth, standard depths, 239
table, gear teeth, stub-tooth standard, 243
teeth, chordal thickness, 247
teeth, chordal thickness and height, 246
terms used, 226
tooth, fillet, definition, 226
tooth, flank, definition, 226
tooth, whole depth of, definition, 225
tooth, working depth of, definition, 225
tooth face, definition, 226
tooth face, width, definition, 226
tooth sizes, comparison of, 227
tooth thickness, definition, 226
types of, 254

Gears, machine-cut—*continued*
Vernier gear caliper (illustration), 246
worm-gear calculations, 266
worm-gear formulæ, 263
worm gears, 260, *see also* Worm gears
Gears, various, grinding-wheel selection, 351
Glass, cutting lubricant, 323
cutting speeds, clearance and rake angles, 311, 321
etching, 438
lamp shades, grinding-wheel selection, 352
lenses, grinding-wheel selection, 352
metal, glass to, cement, recipe, 434
porcelain, glass to, cement, 436
special brands, grinding-wheel selection, 352
tubes, glass, in brasswork, recipe, 434
tubing, grinding-wheel selection, 352
tumblers, grinding-wheel selection, 352
various class of work upon, grinding-wheel selection, 351
workshop methods and recipes, *see* Glass, workshop methods and recipes
writing on, ink for, 442
Glass, workshop methods and recipes, 441
anti-dimming solutions, 442
cleaning, 441
drilling glass, 441
frosting glass, 441
ink for writing on glass, 442
Gold lacquer, tinplate, 443
Granite, grinding-wheel selection, 352
Great Britain, screw threads used in, 165
Grinding, faults, causes and cures, 381
roughness, 381
surface flaws on work, 381
wavy surfaces, 382
work out-of-round, 381
work tapered, 381
Grinding limit shafts table, 94

Grinding metals, sparks generated by, 425
Grinding (wet) lubricant recipes, 323
Grinding wheels, 334
  abrasive grain size, selection, 340
  abrasive selection, 339
  abrasives, Norton, 338
  abrasives, types of, 334
  Aloxite abrasive, 334
  aluminium oxide abrasive, 334
  Alundum abrasive, 334
  Alundum and Crystolon Norton wheels, 336
  bond, Norton wheels, 338
  bond, selection of, 341
  bonds, 335
  Carborundum abrasive, 334
  Carborundum key symbols, 337
  Carborundum wheels, selection for various operations, 341
  cemented carbide grinding and lapping tools, 366
  circumferences of grinding wheels of given diameters, 374
  Crystolon abrasive, 334
  Crystolon and Alundum Norton wheels, 336
  cup-wheel clearance table, 371
  cup-wheel cutter clearance grinding, 370
  designations and identifications of, 337
  diamond layer grinding and lapping wheels, 367
  diamond-impregnated abrasive, 334
  diamond-impregnated wheels, 366
  faults, grinding, causes and cures, see Grinding, faults, causes and cures
  grade, selection of, 340
  grade scale of Carborundum and Aloxite brand wheels, 336
  grade scale of Norton Alundum and Crystolon wheels, 336
  grades of wheels, 336
  grain size or grit, 335
  grinding and lapping cemented carbide tools, 366
  grinding cemented-carbide tools, 379
  grinding milling cutters, 368

Grinding wheels—continued
  Grinding-wheel Selection Table (class of work, etc.), 342–65
  lapping and grinding cemented-carbide tools, 366
  methods of grinding, 368
  milling-cutter clearance, 368
  Norton abrasive designations, 338
  Norton grain-size designations, 338
  Norton Grinding Wheel Co. Ltd., recommendations regarding choice of wheel, 339
  Norton key symbols, 338
  Norton wheel-structure numbers, 337
  Norton wheels, 338
  plain-wheel clearance table, 370
  plain-wheel cutter clearance grinding, 370
  primary and secondary clearances (diagram), 368
  sections, standard grinding wheels, 379
  selection of grinding wheels, 339
  selection table, grinding wheels, (class of work), etc., 342–6
  setting tooth rest, tables, 370
  shapes, standard grinding wheel, 375, 376, 377, 378
  silicon carbide abrasive, 334
  sizes, surface speeds and R.P.M., 372
  speeds, 371, 374
  speeds, work, 375
  standard abrasive grain sizes, 334
  structure, or grain spacing, 337
  structure, selection of, 340
  surface speed of polishing mops, feet per minute, 365
  types of abrasive, 334
  work speed, 375
Guest worm gear, 261
Guide bars, grinding-wheel selection, 353
Gunmetal (cast), drill data, 280
  (leaded), drill data, 280

Hammers, grinding-wheel selection, 353
Hard rubber, cutting speeds, clearance and rake angles, 311, 321
  fibre, drill-point angle, 277

Hard steels, manganese steel, drill-point angle, 277
Hardening, alloy steels, hardening and tempering, 404
    edge, 406
    steel, hardening and tempering, 404
    surface, 406
Hardness, materials, 390
    metals, British Standards, 391
    Mohs' scale of, 400
    Rockwell method, 396
    Vickers diamond-pyramid, 395
Hardness scales, approximate comparison of, 398
Hardness values of metals on Shore scale, 397
Heat, definition, 5
Heat-resistant cement, 436
Heat-treated steel, drop forgings, connecting rods, drill-point angles, 277
Heating, electric-induction, 408
Helix angles of screw threads, 179
Helix angles of thread, definition of, 100
Hexagon bolts, screws, nuts and plain washers, precision, British Standard, 185
    bolts and screws, lengths, 185
    British Standard B.A. cheese-head bolts and screws, 196
    British Standard B.A. countersunk-head bolts and screws, 194
    B.S. 1083 : 1952, abstracts from, 185
    B.S. hexagon ordinary and lock-nuts, 188
    B.S. hexagon slotted nuts and castle nuts, 190
    B.S. hexagon-head B.A. bolts and screws (alternate forms of head), 192
    B.S. hexagon-head bolts and screws, 186
    clearance diagram, bolts and nuts, 203
    length of bolts and screws, 185
    length of screwed thread, 185
    screw threads, 185
    screws and bolts, lengths, 185
High-speed screwing and turning brass, drill data, 280

High-speed tools, materials, 306
Hindley or Hour-glass type worm gear, 260, 261
Hobs, high-speed steel sharpening, grinding wheel, 353
Holes, hard metals, 442
Hooke's Law, 383
Horse power, machining metals, 317
    motor, for multi-tool machines, 318
    transmitted, gears, 274
Hot-stamping brass drill data, 280
Hour-glass (or Hindley) type worm gear, 260, 261
Housings (auto axle), grinding-wheel selection, 353
Hydraulic pipe joints, recipe, 433
Hypocyloid curve, gears, definition, 231

Imperial Wire Gauge (S.W.G.), 42
Inch–millimetre equivalents, 8
Inertia, moments of, see Moments of inertia
Ink, for writing on glass, 442
Inspection grade, slip block, 78
Interference, gears, definition, 227
International Metric Threads, 141
    diameter of rod or wire, 171
Involute-gear cutters, 244
Involute-gear teeth, 231
Involute-gear teeth cutters, 249
Iron, cast and wrought, cutting lubricant, 323
    cast and wrought, cutting speeds, clearance and rake angle, 311, 321
Iron and cast iron, copper-plating, 437
Iron and steel, tapping-lubricant recipes, 325
Iron to concrete, cement recipe, 435
Iron to iron, cement recipe, 434
Irregular figures, areas, 462

Jarno taper, 305
Johansson or slip gauges, 77

Keys and keyways and keybars, 217–22
    British Standard for keys, keyways and cone shaft ends, B.S. No. 46, Part I : 1929, 217

Keys and keyways and keybars—*continued*
   plain rectangular taper keys, keyways and key bars, 218
   rectangular parallel keys, keyways and key bars, 220
   Woodruff keys and keyways, British Standard, 222
Knife- and tool-handle cement, 435
Knife (cranked) tool, lathe machining data, 316
Knives, various, sharpening, surfacing, etc., grinding-wheel selection, 353–5
Knuckle thread, 161

Lacquer, gold, for tinplate, recipe, 443
Lacquering, brass, recipe, 431
Lacquers, workshop methods and recipes, 443
   brass lacquers, 443
   drawings, lacquers for, 443
   steel, black lacquer for, 443
   tinplate, gold lacquer, 443
Lanchester worm gear, 261
Lathe centres, grinding-wheel selection, 355
Lathe machining data, tungsten-carbide tools, 315
   cast-iron, 315
   non-ferrous, 315
   steel, 315
Lathes, cutting-power, 319
   gear train, simple, 174
   gear trains, to prove or check, 176
   machining data, 315
   screw-cutting gear trains, 173
Lawn-mower blades, sharpening, grinding-wheel selection, 355
Lead, etching, 439
Lead bronze (cast) drilling data, 280
Lead of worm (gears), definition, 263
Leather belting, adhesive for, recipe, 433
Leather to steel, cement recipe, 433
Length, data, 1
Length, metric, data, 2
Lewis formulæ, Brown and Sharpe gears, 270
   strength, 268
Limestone, work on, grinding-wheel selection, 355

Limits, definition, 81
Limits and fits in engineering, 79
   basic size, definition, 81
   bilateral and unilateral systems, 81
   British specifications for limits and fits, 80
   British Standards for limits and fits for engineering, 90
   British Standards limits and fits, 80
   British Standards limits for shafts, 87, 89
   British Standards limits for unilateral, bilateral and oversize holes, 86, 88
   British Standards system of fits, 84
   Brown and Sharpe tables, grinding limit, 94
   B.S. 164—1924, 80
   B.S. lateral fits, 83
   B.S. unilateral fits, table, 83
   B.S.I. tolerance zones for limit gauges, 96
   definitions, 80
   dimensions, definition, 80
   Formula B tolerances, 85
   grinding limits shafts table, 94
   interference fits, 80
   limit gauge, 96
   limits, definition, 81
   multipliers for B.S. tolerances (table), 85
   Newall standards, 80, 91, 92, 93
   nominal size, definition, 80
   shafts, limit gauge dimensions, 95
   tolerance, definition, 81
   tolerances, formulæ, 85
   transition fits, 80
   unilateral and bilateral systems, 81
Line of action gears, definition, 225
Linear measure, English and Metric equivalents, 3
Links, various, snagging, etc., grinding-wheel selection, 355
Litres to pints, conversion, 14
Lock-washers, spring, S.A.E. standard, 209
Logarithms, tables of, 492
   antilogarithms, and examples, 494
   calculation by, 492
   cube roots, 495
   division of numbers, 495
   examples, 492

Logarithms, tables of—*continued*
  multiplication of numbers, 494
  powers of numbers, 495
  square roots, 495
  tables, antilogarithm, 532–71
  tables, logarithm, 496–531
  tables, using the, 493
Löwenherz thread (German instrument thread), 154
Lubricant, tapping (metals), recipes, *see* Tapping lubricant, recipes
Lubricants, cutting, 323
  aluminium, 323
  drawing dies for brass, 323
  drilling hard steel or glass, 323
  iron, cast and wrought, 323
  screw cutting and tapping, 323
  steel-turning, 323
  tapping, 325, *see also* Tapping lubricant, recipes
  turning, machine screw cutting and drilling steel, 323
  various materials, 323
  wet grinding, 323

Maag-Sulzer gear-generation principle (diagram), 234
Machine-cut gears, *see* Gears, machine-cut
Machine-shop grinding, grinding-wheel selection, 355
Machining, materials, special, 309
  speeds, materials and tools, various, 309
  steel, material, drill-performance data, 282
Magnesium alloys, annealing and normalising, 413
  cutting-tool angles, 308
  drill data, 277
  Elektron, tapping lubricant recipes, 325
  etching, 439
  wrought (Elektron) weight, 55
Malleability and ductility, common metals, 390
Malleable iron, grinding-wheel selections, 355
Manganese bronzes, drill data, 280
Manganese steel, annealing, 411
Manganese steel, cutting speeds, clearance and rake angle, 311, 321

Manganese steel, drill speeds and feeds for, 278
  turning tool data (Escaloy), 310
Marble, cutting speeds, clearances and rake angles, 311, 321
Marking mediums for steel, 443
Materials, physical properties and weights of, 51
  tool, 306
Materials, properties of, 383
  alloy steels, hardening and tempering, 404
  alloys, brazing, 403
  alloys, Brinell hardness, 395
  annealing and normalising of metals, *see* Annealing and normalising of metals
  belt pulleys, train of, 426
  belts, lengths of, 427
  belts and pulleys, speeds of, 426
  blank, determination of size of, *see* Blank, determination of size of
  blanking pressures, 415
  brazing alloys, and notes on, 403
  Brinell and Vickers hardness numbers, relation between, 395
  Brinell hardness, metals and alloys, 394
  Brinell hardness and tensile strength, 392
  Brinell hardness and tensile strength equivalents, 393
  Brinell hardness method of testing hardness, 390
  Brinell numbers and minimum thicknesses, 394
  British Standard and hardness of metals, 391
  Bulk Modulus K, values of, 385
  colours and temperature of heated steel, 408
  copper and copper alloys (sheet or strip), physical and mechanical properties, 386
  diamond hardness, typical hard steels, 396
  dies and punches, 413
  drawing pressures, shells, 418
  ductility and malleability of common metals, 390
  edge hardening, 406
  elastic strain, work done in, 384

Materials, properties of—*continued*
elasticity for timbers, moduli of, 385
electric-induction heating, 408
fluxes, soft-soldering, 401
fluxes, soldering, 401
grinding metals, sparks generated by, 425
hardening, edge, 406
hardening, surface, 406
hardening and tempering, alloy steels, 404
hardening and tempering, steel, 404
hardness, metals, 390
hardness, metals, British Standards, 391
hardness, Mohs' scale of, 400
hardness, Rockwell method, 396
hardness, Vickers diamond-pyramid, 395
hardness scales, approximate comparison of, 398
hardness values of metals on Shore scale, 397
heating, electric-induction, 408
Hooke's Law, 383
length of belts, cross and open, 427
malleability, and ductility, common metals, 390
metal thinning in drawing shells, 417
metals and alloys, Brinell hardness, 395
minimum thickness and Brinell numbers, 394
moduli of elasticity and rigidity, 384
Mohs' scale of hardness, 400
nickel-chromium-molybdenum steel tempering curves, 405
Poisson's ratio, 384
Poisson's ratio, values for, 385
punch and die clearances, 413, 414
punches and dies, 413
recipes, solder flux, 402
relation between elastic moduli, 383
resiliences of different materials (Perry), 388
rigidity, moduli of elasticity and, 384
Rockwell hardness method, 396

Materials, properties of—*continued*
self-fluxing solders, 402
shear on punches and dies, 414
shear strengths of materials, 415
shear stress within elastic limit, 383
sheet-metal bending allowances, 419
sheet-metal bending allowances, chart, 422
shells, drawing pressures, 418
Shore scale, hardness values of metals on, 397
Shore scleroscope method, 397
silver (hard) solders, and fluxes for, 403
silver solder, notes on, 402
soft solders, 400
solder flux recipes, 402
soldering, soft, fluxes, 401
soldering fluxes, 401
soldering fluxes, acid-free, recipe, 402
soldering fluxes, general-purpose, recipe, 402
solders, British Standard, 401
solders, self-fluxing, 402
solders, silver, 402
solders, soft, 400
sparks generated by grinding of metals, characteristics of, 425
speeds of belts and pulleys, 426
steel, hard, diamond hardness of, 396
steel, heated, colours and temperatures, 408
steel tempering oxide, colours and temperatures, 409
steels, alloy, hardening and tempering, 404
steels, alloy, tensile strength factors, 392
steels, hardening and tempering, 404
strength, tensile, Brinell hardness and, 392
strength properties of timbers, 389
stress, volumetric, within elastic limit, 383
Stress Conversion Table, English to Metric, 387
surface hardening, *see* Surface hardening (metals)
tap, nomenclature (diagram), 423

Materials, properties of—*continued*
  temperature colours of heated steel, 408
  tempering and hardening, alloy steels, 404
  tempering curves, nickel-chromium-molybdenum steel, 405
  tensile strength, Brinell hardness and, 392
  tensile strength factors, alloy steels, 392
  thinning of metal in drawing operations, 417
  timbers, elasticity moduli, 385
  timbers, strength properties of, 389
  train of belt pulleys, 426
  Vickers diamond-pyramid hardness, 395
  Vickers hardness numbers, 395
  volumetric stress within elastic limit, 383
  weights of various (table), 50
  work done in elastic strain, 384
Measurements, precision, *see* Precision measurements
Mensuration and trigonometry, 457
  circles, properties of, 458
  circumference, ratio to diameter of circle, 457
  ellipse, the, *see* Ellipse, the
  plane figures, areas of, *see* Plane figures, areas of
  squares and circles, inscribed, 459
  surfaces and volumes of solids, *see* Surfaces and volumes of solids
  taper angles, measurement or setting of, *see* Taper angles, measurement or setting of
  trigonometrical formulæ, *see* Trigonometrical formulæ
  volumes, plane solids, *see* Volumes, plane solids
Metal parts, degreasing, 437
Metal sheets, dimensions and weights, 52
Metal surfaces, crystalline finish on, recipe, 437
Metal thinning in drawing shells, 417
  aluminium cylindrical shells, drawing operations, 418
  circular shells, number of operations, 418

Metal to cloth, cement recipe, 434
  to glass, cement recipe, 434
Metallic tubing, flexible, weight, 60
Metals, annealing and normalising of, 410
  Brinell hardness, metals and alloys, 394
  etching, *see* Etching metals, workshop methods and recipes
  physical properties of, 48
Metric and English equivalents, 3
Metric bolts, tolerances, close fit, 143
  free fit, 147
  medium fit, 145
Metric nuts, tolerances, close fit, 144
  free fit, 148
  medium fit, 146
Metrical weights and measures, data, 2
Micrometers, grinding-wheel selection, 356
  reading, 72
  thread, 165, 167
Millimetre–inch equivalents, 7
Milling, negative-rake, 331
  "Up" and "Down," 328
Milling-cutters, British Standard (cutters and reamers), 330
  cutting speeds, 327
  feeds, 328
  negative-rake, 330
  teeth, numbers of, 329
Minor diameter or core diameter, definition, 97
Module, bevel gear, definition, 250
  spur gears, definition, 224
Mohs' scale of hardness, 400
Moments of inertia, 451
  area, any, 451
  area about a parallel axis, 452
  Polar moment of, 452
  radius of gyration, 451
  solids, 451
  various sections, also Radius of Gyration, 453–6
Monel metal, annealing, 412
  cutting-tool angles, 308
  grinding-wheel selection, 356
Morse taper shanks, 302
Mottled finish, steel tools, 449
  rainbow mottled finish, 449

Needles, gramophone and sewing, grinding-wheel selection, 356
Negative-rake milling, 331
Newall Standards of limits and fits, 80, 91, 92, 93
Nickel, annealing, 412
Nickel brass (leaded), drilling data, 280
Nickel-chromium-molybdenum steel, tempering temperature curves, 405
Nickel-plating (without electricity) compound, 448
Nickel silver, drill and drilling data, 280
Nitralloy steel grinding-wheel selection, 356
Nomenclature, worm gears, 262
Non-ferrous alloys or sintered carbides for tool materials, 306
Non-ferrous metals, cutting speeds clearance and rake angles, 311, 321
  machining data, 315
  turning-tool data (Ardoloy), 321
  turning-tool data (Escaloy), 311
Non-metallic materials, cutting speeds, clearance and rake angles, 311
  turning-tool data (Ardoloy), 321
  turning-tool data (Escaloy), 311
Normal circular pitch, worm gear, definition, 262
Normal pitch, bevel gear, definition, 249
Normal pressure angle, worm gear, definition, 263
Normalising and annealing metals, 410
Norton Grinding Wheel Co. Ltd., abrasive designations, 339
  wheel recommendations, 339
Numbers, division, multiplication and powers of, tables, 495
Nuts, see Screw thread data

Oxidised finish, brass, recipe, 432
Oxidising copper, 436

Paraboloid of revolution, solid, surfaces and volumes of, 468
Parallelogram areas, 460

Parker rust-prevention process, recipe, 446
Parting tool (Ardoloy), lathe machining data, 314, 316
Pearl buttons and novelties, grinding-wheel selection, 356
Phosphor bronze, (cast), drill data, 280
  (wrought), drill data, 280
Physical properties and weights of materials, 51
aluminium tubes, sizes and weights, 61–9
bars, round and square section, weights, 58
dimensions and weights, hard steel wire, 56
dimensions and weights, metal sheets, 52
Elektron, weight of, sheet and strip, 55
flexible metallic tubing, weight, 60
gas and steam pipe, weight, 60
magnesium alloy, sheet and strip, (Elektron) weight, 55
materials, physical properties and weights of, 51
metal sheets, weights and dimensions, 52
metallic tubing, flexible, weight, 60
metals, 48
sizes and weights, aluminium tubes, 61–9
steam and gas pipe weight, 60
steel bars, angle and tee, weights per foot length, 54
steel wire (hard), weights and dimensions, 56
tubes, aluminium, sizes and weights, 61–9
weight, angle and tee steel bars (per foot length), 54
weight, flexible metallic tubing, 60
weight, gas and steam pipe, 60
weight, wrought magnesium alloy (Elektron), 55
weights and sizes, aluminium tubes, 61–9
weights, materials, miscellaneous, 51
weights, round- and square-section bars, 58

Physical properties and weights of materials—*continued*
weights and dimensions, hard steel wire, 56
weights and dimensions, metal sheets, 52
Pins, pointing, grinding-wheel selection, 357
Pints to litres, conversion table, 14
Pipe balls, manganese steel, grinding-wheel selection, 357
Piston pins, grinding-wheel selection, 357
Piston rings, various, grinding-wheel selection, 357
Pistons, various, grinding wheel selection, 357
Pitch circles, gears, definition, 224, 248
Pitch cones, bevel gear, definition, 248
Pitch diameter, gears, definition, 224, 248
Pitch point, bevel gear, definition, 248
Pitches, gears, table of equivalents, diametral and circular pitches, 235
Pitting and scaling, steel parts, prevention, 450
Plane figures, areas of, 459
irregular figure, 462
parallelogram, 460
rectangle, 460
Simpson rule for irregular figures, 463
square, 459
trapezium, 462
trapezoid, 461
triangle, acute-angled, 461
triangle, obtuse-angled, 461
triangle, right-angled, 460
Planing gear principle (diagram), 234
Plastics, cutting speeds, clearance and rake angles, 311, 321
Plating metals, without electricity, 446
Ploughs, steel and chilled iron, grinding-wheel selection, 358
Points and crossings (manganese steel), grinding-wheel selection, 358

Poisson's ratio, 384
values for, 385
Porcelain, cement, 436
Porcelain, cutting speeds, clearance and rake angles, 311, 321
Porcelain work, grinding-wheel selection, 358
Power and work, definition, 4
Power constants, various metals, 319
Precision-machined gears, British Standard 20° pressure angle, 229
Precision measurements, 70
calipers, Vernier, reading, 73
fits and limits in engineering, *see* Limits and fits in engineering
gauges, slip (or block), 78
gauges, Vernier height, 76
grades, slip block, 78
inspection grade, slip block, 78
Johansson or slip gauges, 77
limits and fits in engineering, *see* Limits and fits in engineering
micrometers, reading, 72
protractor, Vernier, 77
reading metric micrometer, 72
reading micrometer calipers, 70
reading ten-thousandth micrometer, 71
reading Vernier calipers, 73
reading Vernier protractor, 77
slip blocks, grades of accuracy of, 78
slip blocks, inspection grade, 78
slip blocks, reference grade, 78
slip blocks, workshop grade, 78
slip gauges, English measurement, 77
slip gauges, Johansson, 77
slip gauges, metric measurement, 78
slip (or block) gauge British Standards No. 888–1940, 78
Vernier caliper, 72
reading, 73
Vernier height gauge, 76
Vernier protractor, reading, 77
Pressure, definition, 5
atmospheric, definition, 4
Pressure angle, bevel gear, definition, 226, 249
Properties of materials, *see* Materials, properties of

Protractor, Vernier, 77
Pulleys, grinding-wheel selection, 358
Punches and dies, 413

Rack-and-pinion gears, 233
Rails, welds, 358
Ratio (gears), bevel, definition, 248
  worm, definition, 262
Razor blades, grinding-wheel selection, 359
Razors, grinding-wheel selection, 359
Reamers, grinding-wheel selection, 359
Reamers and milling-cutters, British Standard, 330
Recipes, see Workshop methods and recipes
Rectangle, area, 460
"Redmanol" cut-off grinding wheels, 335
Resiliences, different materials (Perry), 388
Rigidity, moduli of elasticity and, 384
Rims, automobile, grinding-wheel selection, 359
Rivets, British Standard, proportions, 212
  B.S. No. 641–1953, reference to, 213
  B.S. tabular proportions of rivets, 214
  countersunk-head 60° (non-ferrous), 216
  countersunk-head 90° (ferrous and non-ferrous), 216
  countersunk-head 120° (ferrous), 216
  countersunk-head 140° (non-ferrous), 217
  ferrous and non-ferrous, 213
  flat-head (ferrous and non-ferrous), 215
  formulæ for rivet proportions, 213
  mushroom-head rivets (ferrous and non-ferrous), 215
  pan-head (B.S.) (ferrous and non-ferrous), 214
  proportions, British Standards, 214
  snap- or round-head (ferrous and non-ferrous), 214
  types, 213

Rockwell hardness method, 396
Roll scouring (bricks), grinding-wheel selection, 360
Rollers, for bearings, grinding-wheel selection, 359
Rolls, various metals, and rubber, grinding-wheel selection, 359
Root diameter, bevel gears, definition, 250
Rough turning tool (Ardoloy), 312
Rubber (hard), cutting-off, grinding-wheel selection, 360
Rubber cement, recipe, 434
Rubber-bonded grinding wheels, 335
Rust prevention, workshop methods and recipes, 445
  Bower-Barff process, 445
  commercial rust-prevention processes, 445
  coslettising, 445
  metallisation process, 446
  Parker process, 446
  sherardising, 445
Rust removal, from steel and iron, recipes, 444

S.A.E., American plain washers, 208
  coarse (N.C.), series thread, 135
  coarse series thread, 134
  Dryseal Taper Pipe Thread (N.P.T.F.), (table), 140
  Extra Fine (E.F.) series thread, 135
  fine series thread, 134
  Handbook, reference to, 135
  screw standard thread, 134
  screw threads, drills for tapered holes, 296
  split-pins, 207
  spring lock washers, 209
  standard extra fine series threads, 135
  standard pipe threads, 138
  standard spring lock washers, 209, 211
  thread, length of engagement, 135
  tolerance and allowance, 135
  uniform tap drill sizes, threads, 135
Sandstone, grinding-wheel selection, 360
Saws, grinding-wheel selection, 360
Scaling and pitting of steel parts, prevention, 450

Scissors and shears (steel), grinding-wheel selection, 361
Screw cutting, lubricant recipes, 323
Screw-cutting Whitworth thread, 178
Screw micrometer readings for standard pitches, 169
Screw-thread data, 97
Acme thread, 161
Acme thread checking, 172
American National (Sellers) threads, diameter of rod or wire, 171
American National Standard (Sellers) thread, 134
American National Standard taper pipe thread (N.P.T.F.), 139
American National Thread System (60°), 165
American sparking plugs (S.A.E. Standard), 164
American sparking plugs, sparking-plug threads, 164
American sparking plugs, tapped hole threads, 164
angle of thread, definition of, 99
Anglo-American-Canadian Conference on unified screw threads (1943–5), 158
B.A. (47½°) screw threads, 165
basic sizes for B.S. pipe threads, 129
bolts and nuts, classes of, 167
British Association Threads (B.A.), 132, 133
British Association Threads (B.A.), diameter of rod or wire, 171
British Government Inter-Services Engineering Standards Co-ordinating Committee, and screw threads, 165
British Motor Tyre Valve Thread (S.M.M.T.), 163
British Standard 811—1950 cycle threads, 151
British Standard B.A. cheese-head bolts and screws, 196
British Standard B.A. countersunk-head bolts and screws, 194
British Standard B.A. ordinary and thin nuts, 193
British Standard B.A. round-head bolts and screws, 195

Screw-thread data—*continued*
British Standard bright screws (cheese-head, countersunk and round), 199, 200
British Standard Cycle (B.S.C.) threads, 151
British Standard Cycle Threads, bolts, nuts and similar applications, basic dimensions, 152
British Standard Cycle Threads, special applications, basic dimensions, 153
British Standard Cycle Threads, spokes and nipples, basic dimensions, 152
British Standard Fine (B.S.F.) screw threads, 109
British Standard form, buttress thread, 158, 159
British Standard form buttress thread, numerical data, 160
British Standard metric thread dimensions, 142
British Standard metric thread tolerances, metric bolts, limits and tolerances, close fit, 143
British Standard screw thread, specifications, 132
British Standard sparking-plug dimensions, 164
British Standard Specification No. 84—1940, definitions, 97
British Standard taper pipe threads, 126
British Standard truncated Whitworth thread, 124
British Standard Whitworth (B.S.W.) threads, 101
British Standard Whitworth screw threads (B.S.W.), limits and tolerances, 102
British Standard unified screw threads, numerical data for standard pitches, 168
British Standard wing nuts, *see* Wing nuts, British Standard
B.S. fine bolts (B.S.F.), limits and tolerances, close fit, 110
B.S. fine bolts (B.S.F.), limits and tolerances, free fit, 114
B.S. fine bolts (B.S.F.), limits and tolerances, medium fit, 112

Screw-thread data—*continued*
  B.S. fine nuts (B.S.F.), limits and tolerances, close fit, 111
  B.S. fine nuts (B.S.F.), limits and tolerances, free fit, 115
  B.S. fine nuts (B.S.F.), limits and tolerances, medium fit, 112, 113
  B.S. hexagon-head B.A. bolts and screws (alternative forms of head), 192
  B.S. hexagon-head bolts and screws, 186
  B.S. hexagon ordinary and lock nuts, 188
  B.S. hexagon slotted nuts and castle nuts, 190
  B.S. pipe threads (B.S.P.), bolts, limits and tolerances, close fit, B.S.P., 117
  B.S. pipe threads, bolts, limits and tolerances, free fit, 121
  B.S. pipe threads (B.S.P.) bolts, limits and tolerances, medium fit, 119
  B.S. pipe threads (B.S.P.), nuts, limits and tolerances, close fit, 118
  B.S. pipe threads (B.S.P.), nuts, limits and tolerances, medium fit, 120
  B.S. pipe threads (B.S.P.), (Parallel), general engineering purposes, 116
  B.S. pipe threads, nuts, limits and tolerances, free fit, 122
  B.S. Whitworth bolts (B.S.W.), limits and tolerances, close fit, 103
  B.S. Whitworth bolts (B.S.W.), limits and tolerances, free fit, 107
  B.S. Whitworth bolts (B.S.W.), limits and tolerances, medium fit, 105
  B.S. Whitworth nuts (B.S.W.), limits and tolerances, close fit, 104
  B.S. Whitworth nuts (B.S.W.), limits and tolerances, free fit, 108
  B.S. Whitworth nuts (B.S.W.), limits and tolerances, medium fit, 106
  buttress threads, 157
  Canada, screw-thread systems used in, 165

Screw-thread data—*continued*
  complete thread, definition of, 128
  compound gear trains, lathe, 175
  crest, definition, of, 98
  cutting English threads on metric lathe, 177
  cutting fractional pitches on lathe, 175
  cutting metric pitch threads on English lathes, 176
  Cycle Engineers Institute (C.E.I.) threads, 149
  Cycle Engineers Institute (C.E.I.) threads, table, 150
  definitions, Vee section screw threads, 97
  depth of engagement, definition, 99
  depth of thread, definition, 99
  diameter and length of thread, S.A.E. Standard pipe thread, 139
  diameter of rod or wire, 171
  double-start threads, lead of, 98
  Dryseal American (National) Standard taper pipe thread, 139
  effective diameter, parallel thread, definition, 97
  Engineering Precision Measurements, by A. W. Judge, reference to, 172
  fitting allowance, definition, 128
  flank angles, definition, 99
  flanks of thread, definition, 99
  form of thread, definition, 99
  form of unified screw thread, 166
  formula for best diameter, 171
  full diameter, definition, 97
  gauge diameter, definition, 127
  gauge length, definition, 127
  gauge plan, definition, 127
  general information, 97
  general purpose, Acme thread, 163
  Great Britain, screw threads used in, 165
  Helix angle of thread, definition, 100
  Helix angles for screw threads, English diameter and pitches, 181
  Helix angles for screw threads, Metric diameter and pitches, 183
  Helix angles of screw threads, 179
  imperfect thread, definition, 128
  International metric threads, 141

Screw-thread data—*continued*
International metric threads, diameter of rod or wire, 171
knuckle thread, 161
lathe, gear train, simple, 174
lathe gear trains, to prove or check, 176
lathe screw-cutting gear trains, 173
lead, definition of, 98
limits of size for B.S. pipe threads, linear measure, 131
limits of size for B.S. pipe threads (turns of thread), 130
Löwenherz thread (German instrument thread), 154
measurement of core and outside diameter, 172
metric bolts, tolerances, free fit, 147
metric bolts, tolerances, medium fit, 145
metric nuts, tolerances, close fit, 144
metric nuts, tolerances, free fit, 148
metric nuts, tolerances, medium fit, 146
micrometer, thread micrometer, 167
micrometer method of gauging screw threads, 167
minor diameter or core diameter, definition, 97
multiple-start threads, lead of, 98
nomenclature, threads, 127
Notes on Screw Gauges, National Physical Laboratory Publication, reference to, 172
pitch, lead of, 98
pitch line, definition, 98
prime numbers, English lathes, 177
principal screw-thread systems, 165
root of thread, definition, 99
S.A.E. coarse series thread, 134
S.A.E. coarse (N.C.) series thread, 135
S.A.E. Dryseal taper pipe thread (N.P.T.F.) (table), 140
S.A.E. extra fine (E.F.) series thread, 135
S.A.E. fine series thread, 134
S.A.E. handbook, reference to, 135
S.A.E. screw standard thread, 134

Screw-thread data—*continued*
S.A.E. standard extra fine series threads, 135
S.A.E. standard pipe threads, 138
S.A.E. thread, length of engagement, 135
S.A.E. thread, tolerance and allowance, 135
S.A.E. threads, uniform tap drill sizes, 135
screw cutting, method of setting slide rest of lathe at angle for screw-cutting, 178
screw-cutting Whitworth thread, 178
screw micrometer readings for Whitworth thread pitches, 169
screw thread, basic form of unified, diagram, 166
screw thread, nomenclature, 97
single-start threads, lead of, 98
Society of Automotive Engineers, 135
Society of Automotive Engineers (S.A.E.) threads (table), 136
Society of Automotive Engineers standard threads, 134
sparking-plug screw threads, 164
square threads, 157
Steinlen thread (Switzerland), 154
standard length of engagement (N.P.T.F.), 139
standard screw thread, depths in inches, 162
Swiss or Thury screw threads, 154
taper and form of pipe thread, 138
thread form checking, 173
thread micrometer, 165
thread profile checking, diagram, 173
three-wire method of gauging screw threads, 170
treble-start threads, lead of, 98
truncated Whitworth threads with flat crests, 125
truncation, definition, 99
two-wire method of gauging screw threads, 170
types of threads, 97
Unified Coarse thread series (U.N.C.), 165
Unified Fine thread series (U.N.F.), 165

Screw-thread data—*continued*
  Unified screw threads, 165
  Unified screw threads, designation of, 167
  Unified Special thread (U.N.S.), 165
  United States, screw-thread system used in, 165
  U.S. National pipe threads, Sellars or 60° thread, 128
  Vee section screw threads, 97
  Vee threads, types of, 100
  wash-out thread, definition of, 128
  Whitworth (55°) screw threads, 165
  Whitworth screw threads, special diameters, pitches, and lengths of engagement, series of pitches, 123
  Whitworth screw threads, watches and instruments, 156
  Whitworth thread, diameter of rod or wire, 171
  Whitworth thread, prism angle of, 173
  wrenching allowance, definition of, 128
Screws, *see* Screw-thread data
Selenium copper, drilling data, 280
Sellers (Wm.) Company, U.S.A., 268
Shaft angle, bevel gears, definition, 251
Shafts, grinding limit, gauge dimensions, 95
Shear on punches and dies, 414
Shear strength, materials, 415
Shear stress within elastic limit, 383
Sheet-metal, bending allowance, chart, 422
  drilling, diagram, 278
Shellac-bonded grinding wheels, 335
Shells, drawing pressures, 418
Sherardising, rust-prevention process, recipe, 445
Shore scale, hardness values of metals on, 397
Shore scleroscope method, hardness, 397
Shovels, grinding-wheel, selection, 361
Silicate-bonded grinding wheels, 335
Silicon bronze, drill data, 280
Silicon-carbide grinding-wheel abrasive, 334

Silver (hard) solders, 403
  fluxes for, 403
Silver-plating (without electricity) compounds, 447
Silver solder, notes on, 402
Simpson's rule for areas of irregular figures, 463
Sintered-carbide tool materials, 307
Sintered-carbide tools, 317
Sintered-carbide turning tools, cutting speeds, clearance and rake angle, 310
Sizes and weights, aluminium tubes, 61–9
Slate, cutting speeds, clearance and rake angles, 311, 321
  grinding-wheel selection, 361
Slip blocks, grades of accuracy of, 78
  inspection, 78
  reference, 78
  workshop, 78
Slip gauges (or blocks), British Standard No. 800–1940, 78
  English measurement, 77
  Johansson, 77
  Metric measurement, 78
Slocomb centre drills, 299
  sizes (tables), 299
Society of Automotive Engineers, 135
  Standard threads, 134
  threads (S.A.E.), table, 136
Sodium-silicate cement, 435
Soldering fluxes, 401
  acid-free, recipe, 402
  general-purpose, recipe, 402
  recipes, 402
  soft, 401
Solders, aluminium, recipes, 429
  Alunize, 429
  British Standard, 401
  flux recipes, 402
  Fryal aluminium, 429
  Fry's L.M., 429
  self-fluxing, 402
  silver, 402
  soft, 400
Spanners, British Standard set (open-ended), 201
  B.S.F., open-ended, 201
  B.S.W., open-ended, 201
  dimensions and proof test moments, 202
Sparking-plug screw threads, 164

Sparks generated by grinding of metals, characteristics, 425

Speed, allowance, Brown and Sharpe standard gears, 272

effect of gear teeth speed on stress f., 271

effect on gear strength, 270

Speeds, cutting, drilling, 284

drill, formula, 285

grinding-wheel speeds, 371

Sphere, solid, surfaces and volumes of, 467

Spherical sector and segment, solids, surfaces and volumes of, 467

Spiral- and bevel-gear teeth, proportion of, 257

Spiraloid bevel gear, 254

Spline shafts, for aircraft purposes (B.S. A20–1942), 223

for automobile purposes (B.S. 5015–1927), 223

grinding-wheel selection, 361

Split-pins, see Cotter-pins

Springs (coil), grinding-wheel selection, 361

(leaf), grinding-wheel selection, 361

Spur-gear teeth formulæ, 229

Spur gears, 224

Brown and Sharpe, 237

Square, areas, 459

Square centimetres into square inches, conversion, 10

Square feet–square metre equivalents, 9

Square inches into square centimetres conversion, 10

Square roots, tables, 20–40

Squares, and circles, inscribed, 459

Squares, square roots, cubes and cube roots, table of, 20–40

"Stag Allenite," grinding-wheel selection, 361

"Stag Major" manganese steel, drill speeds and feeds, 278

Stainless steel, cutting speeds, clearance and rake angle, 310, 321

drilling speeds and feeds for, 278

drills used for, 277

tapping lubricant recipes, 325

turning tool data (Escaloy), 310

Standard length of engagement (N.P.T.F.), 139

Standard screw-thread depths in inches, 162

Standard Tool Company, tapers, 305

"Staybrite" stainless steel, drilling speeds and feeds for, 278

drills for, 278

Steam and gas pipe weights, 60

Steel, bars, angle and tee, weights per foot length, 54

black lacquer for, 443

castings (low carbon), grinding-wheel selection, 362

castings (manganese), grinding-wheel selection, 362

copper-plating, recipe, 437

cutting speeds, clearance and rake angle, 310, 321

drilling, chip-breaker drill for, 279

etching, 439

hard, Diamond hardness of typical, 396

hardened, grinding-wheel selection, 362

heated, colours and temperatures of, 408

high-speed, cutting speeds, clearance and rake angles, 310, 321

high-speed, grinding-wheel selection, 363

lathe machinery data, 315

leather, cementing to, recipe, 433

marking medium for, 443

parts, scaling and pitting, precautions, 450

sheet, drilling relatively thin sheet, 278

soft, grinding-wheel selection, 363

stainless, grinding-wheel selection, 363

See also Steels

Steel, workshop methods and recipes, 448

black coating, 448

blue and gunmetal coating on, 448

brown finish, 448

copper-plating, 448

oxidised finish, 449

Steel tempering oxide, colours and temperatures, 409

Steel tools, mottled finish, 449

Steel-turning, cutting lubricant recipe, 323

Steel wire, hard, dimensions and weights, 56

Steel wire gauge, Stubs', 43

Steels, annealing and normalising steels and steel articles, 410, 411
cutting lubricants for, 323
cutting-tool angles, 308
drill performance data, 282
hardening and tempering, 404
power-constant values for, 318
tapping lubricant recipes, 325
turning-tool data (Ardoloy), 320
turning-tool data (Escaloy), 310

Steels (alloy), hardening and tempering, 404
tensile strength factors, 392

Steinlen thread (Switzerland), 154

Stellite, grinding-wheel selection, 363

Stonework, fireproof cement for, 435

Stove parts (cast iron), grinding-wheel selection, 364

Straight bevel gear, 254

Straight round-nose turning tool (Ardoloy), 313

Stratite tubes, grinding-wheel selection, 361

Strength, Brown and Sharpe spur gears, 271
gears, 273
tensile, Brinell hardness and, 392
timbers, strength properties of, 389

Stress, within elastic limit, 383

Stress Conversion Table, English to Metric, 387

Stub-gear tooth (gear) proportions, 244

Stubs' steel wire gauge, 43

Surface, English measures data, 1

Surface hardening (metals), 406
case hardening, 407
flame hardening method, 408
induction hardening method, 408
nitrogen hardening process, 407

Surface measure, English and Metric equivalents, 3

Surface (Metric), data, 2

Surfaces and volumes of solids, 465
cone, 466
cone, frustum of, 466
cylinder, 465, 466
paraboloid of revolution, 468
parallel-sided link of circular section, 468

Surfaces and volumes of solids—continued
sphere, 467
spherical sector, 467
spherical segment, 467
torus, or circular section ring, 468

Swiss or Thury screw threads, 154

Synthetic-resin grinding wheels, 335

Taper angles, measurement or setting of, 471
external taper gauge, 471
external tapers, 471
internal taper gauge, 472
internal tapers, 472

Taper systems, 305

Tapping drills, British Association (B.A.) threads, 293
British Standard fine threads, 290
British Standard pipe threads (Parallel), 292
British Standard Whitworth threads, 288
Metric screw threads (Système Internationale), 294
S.A.E. screw threads, 296

Tapping lubricant, recipes, 325
aluminium, 325
cast iron, 325
copper, 325
Elektron magnesium alloys, 325
iron and steel, 325
stainless steel, 325

Taps, grinding-wheel selection, 364

Tellurium copper drilling data, 280

Temperatures, colours and, heated steel, 408

Tempering and hardening, alloy steels, 404

Tempering curves, nickel-chromium-molybdenum steel, 405

Tensile strength, Brinell hardness and, 392
factors, alloy steels, 392

Threads, screw, see Screw-thread data

Tiles, cutting off, grinding-wheel selection, 364
fixing, fireproof cement for, 436

Timbers, elasticity moduli, 385
strength properties of, 389

Tin coating of brass, recipe, 432

Tinplate, gold lacquer, 443

Tolerance, definition, 81
Tool-cutting angles and metals, 306
Tools, British Standard for straight
    bevel gears, 251
  diamond-tipped, data, 324, 325,
    326
  high-speed, heat treatment of, 307
  lathe and planer, grinding-wheel
    selection, 364
  materials, 306
  sintered-carbide, 317
  sintered-carbide turning (Escaloy),
    cutting speeds, clearance and
    rake angles, data, 310
  steel, mottled finish, 449
  tungsten-carbide lathe machinery
    data, 315
  turning, tungsten-carbide (Ardo-
    loy), see Tungsten-carbide turn-
    ing tools (Ardoloy)
  turning (Ardoloy), cutting speeds,
    angles, power constants, 320
Tooth (gear), face, 226
  face, width, 226
  fillet, 226
  flank, 226
  sizes, comparative, 227
  thickness, 226, 250
  whole depth of, 225
  working depth of, 225
Torus, or circular section ring, solid,
    surface and volume of, 468
Train, belt pulleys, 426
Trapezium, area, 462
Trapezoid, area, 461
Triangles, areas, 460, 461
Trigonometrical formulæ, 473
  abbreviations, 473
  acute-angled triangle, 474
  angles, 473
  angles, 90°–180°, 474
  angular measurement, 476
  compound angles, 476
  length of sides, 473
  right-angled triangles, 473
  tables (trigonometrical), 477–91
  value of special angles, 474
Troy (weight), 2
Truncated Whitworth threads with
    flat crests, 125
Tubes, aluminium, sizes and weights,
    61–9
  grinding-wheel selection, 364

Tungsten-carbide tools, lathe machin-
    ing data, 315
Tungsten-carbide   turning   tools
    (Ardoloy), 312
  cranked knife tool, 314
  cranked round-nose turning tool,
    313
  finish turning tool, 312
  parting tool, 314
  rough turning tool, 312
  straight round-nose turning tool,
    313
Tungsten rods, grinding-wheel selec-
    tion, 364
Turning and facing tools, lathe
    machining data, 316
Turning tools (Ardoloy), 312
  lathe machining data, 315
Twist drill nomenclature, 275
Twist drill troubles, causes and
    remedies, 281

Unified Coarse thread series (U.N.C.),
    165
Unified Fine thread series (U.N.F.),
    165
Unified screw threads, 165
  designation of, 167
Unified Special thread (U.N.S.), 165
United States, national pipe threads,
    Sellers or 60° thread, 128
  screw-thread system used in, 165

Valve tappets, grinding-wheel selec-
    tion, 364
Valves (automobile), grinding-wheel
    selection, 364
Vee threads, types of, 100
Velocity, definition, 5
Vernier calipers, 72
  gear calipers (illustration), 246
Vernier height gauge, 76
Vernier protractor, reading, 77
Vickers, diamond-pyramid hardness,
    395
  hardness numbers, 395
Vitreous ware, grinding-wheel selec-
    tion, 364
Volume, data, 1
  (measure), English and Metric
    equivalents, 3
  Metric, data, 2

Volumes, plane solids, 463
 cube, 463
 parallelopiped or square prism, 464
 pyramid, 464
 pyramid, frustum, 464
 wedge, 465
Volumetric stress within elastic
  limit, 383

Warrington wire gauge, 41
Washers, American S.A.E., plain, 208
 B.A., 203
 B.A., large, 204
 B.A., small, 204
 British Standard B.A. (Abstract
  B.S. 57–1944), 203
 B.S., plain, 205
 coiling, 209
 designations and specifications, 210
 finish, 209
 lock spring, S.A.E. standard, 209
 material and hardness, 209
 plain, B.S., 205
 quality of finish, 209
 requirements of, 209
 spring lock, S.A.E. standard, 209
 spring lock, S.A.E. standard
  (table), 211
 temper test, 210
 toughness test, 210
 use of, 209
 washer section, 209.
 See also Screw-thread data
Waterglass (sodium-silicate) cement,
  435
Waterproof and fireproof glue, recipe,
  435
Weight, angle and tee steel bars (per
  foot length), 54
 English and Metric equivalents, 3
 flexible metallic tubing, 60
 gas and steam pipe, 60
 wrought magnesium alloy (Elektron), 55
Weights, materials, various, 50, 51
 round and square section bars,
  58
Weights and dimensions, hard steel
  wire, 56
 metal sheets, 52
Weights and sizes, aluminium tubes,
  61–9
Welds, grinding-wheel selection, 365

Wheels, car, grinding-wheel selection, 345
 grinding-wheels, see Grinding
  wheels
Whitworth (55°) screw threads, 165
Whitworth screw threads, special
  diameters, pitches and lengths of
  engagement, series of pitches,
  123
 watches and instruments, 156
Whitworth threads, diameter of rod
  or wire, 171
 prism angle of, 173
Whitworth wire gauge, 44
Widia or Wimet, grinding-wheel
  selection, 365
Wimet, tool-cutting alloy, 306
Wing nuts, British Standard, 197
 brass, cold-forged, 198
 hot-brass or non-ferrous stampings,
  197
 hot-steel stampings, 197
 malleable-iron castings, 197
 mild steel, cold-forged, 198
Wire gauges, Birmingham (B.W.G.),
  44
 Imperial (S.W.G.), 42
 Stubs', 43
 United States, used in, 41
 Warrington, 41
 Whitworth, 44
Wood, cement recipe, wood to brass,
  435
 ebonite, vulcanite, drill-point
  angle, 277
Woodruff keys and keyways, British
  Standard, 222
Work and power, definition, 4
Working depth of tooth, bevel gear,
  definition, 250
Workshop methods and recipes, 428
 aluminium, 428
 belts, to prevent slipping, 430
 brass, 430
 carbon tetrachloride as fire extinguisher, 441
 castings, 432
 cements and adhesives, 433
 copper, 436
 crystalline finish on metal surfaces,
  437
 degreasing metal parts, 437
 etching metals, 438

Workshop methods and recipes—*continued*
  etching resist, 439
  file cleaning and re-sharpening, 439
  fire extinguisher recipes, 440
  glass, 441
  holes, hard metals, 442
  lacquers, 443
  marking mediums for steel, 443
  mottled finish, rainbow, 449
  mottled finish, steel tools, 449
  nickel-plating (without electricity) compound, 448
  plating metals without electricity, 446
  rust-prevention recipes, 445
  rust removal from steel and iron, recipes, 444
  scaling and pitting of steel parts, prevention, 450
  silver-plating (without electricity) compounds, 447
  solder flux recipe, 402
  steel, 448
  zinc and zinc die castings, 450
Worm gears, 260
  addendum, 263
  axial pitch, 262
  axial pressure angle, 263
  calculations, 266
  centre distance, 262
  circular pitch of worm wheel, 263
  D.B.S., 260, 267
  dedendum, 263
  definitions, 263
  efficiency of, 267

Worm gears—*continued*
  formulæ, 263
  Guest, 261
  Hindley or Hour-glass type, 260, 261
  Lanchester, 261
  lead of worm, 263
  nomenclature, 262
  normal circular pitch, 262
  normal pressure angle, 263
  overall diameter of worm wheel, 263
  ratio of gears, 262
  types, 260
  worm crest diameter, 263
  worm grinding threads, wheel selection, 365
  worm lead angle, 262
  worm pitch cylinder, 262
  worm root diameter, 263
  worm spiral angle, 262
  worm-wheel pitch circle, 262
  worm-wheel root diameter, 263
  worm-wheel throat diameter, 263
Wrenches, grinding-wheel selection, 365
Wrought iron, snagging, grinding-wheel selection, 365
  turning tool data, 320
  turning tool data (Escaloy), 311

Yellow brass, drill data, 280

Zinc, etching, 439
Zinc and zinc die castings, 450
  black finish on, 450